Reader's Digest

BRAIN STRETCHERS

FOR READER'S DIGEST CANADA

Project editor
Pamela Johnson

Assistant editor
Jim Hynes

Copy editor
Judy Yelon

Designer
Andrée Payette

Vice-president, book editorial
Robert Goyette

Production manager
Gordon Howlett

Production coordinator
Gillian Sylvain

FOR READER'S DIGEST U.K.

Project editor
Lol Henderson

Art editor
Heather Dunleavy

Copy editors
Caroline Saltissi, Gordon Torbet,
Andy Durrant, Laura Ward

Designers
Mike Cornwell,
Terry Sambridge, Peter Byrne

Art director and lead illustrator
Paul Southcombe

Illustrators
Mike Cornwell, Matt Drew

Picture research
Susannah Jayes

CONTRIBUTORS

Consultant
Ruth Binney

Puzzles Consultant
Philip Carter

FOR THE READER'S DIGEST ASSOCIATION, INC.

President and chief executive officer
Eric W. Schrier

Brain Stretchers
was published by
The Reader's Digest Association (Canada) Ltd.
1100 René-Lévesque Blvd. West
Montreal, Quebec H3B 5H5

First Canadian edition copyright © 2007

Library and Archives Canada Cataloguing in Publication

Brain stretchers: over 1000 ingenious crosswords, cryptograms, rebuses, logic puzzles-- / editors of Reader's Digest. -- 1st Canadian ed.

ISBN 0-88850-892-1

1. Puzzles. I. Reader's Digest Association (Canada)
GV1493.B715 2007 793.73 C2006-905626-9

We are committed to both the quality of our products and the service we provide to our customers. We value your comments, so please feel free to contact the editors at the address above. For further information about our products, visit our website at **rd.ca**.

All rights reserved

No part of this book may be reproduced, stored in a retrieval system, or transmitted in any form or by any means, electronic, electrostatic, magnetic tape, mechanical, photocopying, recording or otherwise, without permission in writing from the publishers.

® Reader's Digest, The Digest and the Pegasus logo are registered trademarks of The Reader's Digest Association, Inc., of Pleasantville, New York, USA.

Created by Planet 3 Publishing Network Ltd, Northburgh House, 10 Northburgh Street, London EC1V 0AT

Printed in China

Reader's Digest

BRAIN STRETCHERS

Published by The Reader's Digest Association Limited
London • New York • Montreal

CONT

KNOW YOUR STRENGTHS

6-16

Learn how your brain works and test your skills. Check out the puzzles and tricks that will help stretch your brain to the maximum.

A WORD A DAY

21-102

Test your word power with hundreds of puzzles from Acrostics to Enigmagrams, and from Oxymorons to Verbosities.

THE MIND'S EYE

103-146

Train your eye and brain to spot the difference, rearrange shapes, turn two dimensions into three and pick out a face in the crowd.

THINK OF A NUMBER

147-194

Make math fun and be brilliant c budgets with number tests including Sudoku, Kakuro, Magic Squares, Mazes and Connections.

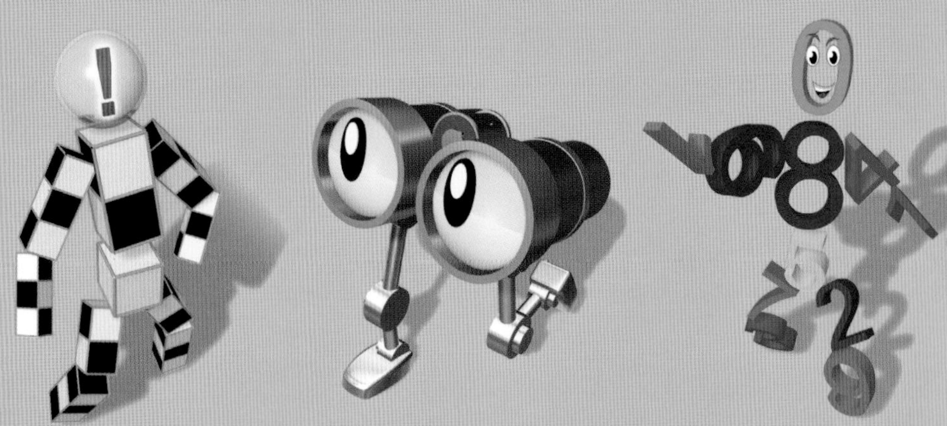

ENTS

SMART THINKING
195-250

Are you a logic master? You soon will be with a host of puzzles that test to the limit your powers of analysis, reasoning and lateral thinking.

WORD CHALLENGES
251-308

More word puzzles to really push your verbal skills. Try out a Language Equation or some Palindromic Anagrams.

MEMORY PUZZLES
309-340

Improve your memory in every sense. Recall numerical and visual detail at will. Even play chess and crack codes using just your memory.

ANSWERS & CREDITS
341-400

Don't cheat. Use this section as your last resort. You'll find solutions and explanations for every puzzle.

INTRODUCTION

If you relish solving a really good puzzle, then this is the book for you. There are brainteasers for all ages and in all grades of difficulty – from simple to utterly fiendish. Tantalizing word games will test your powers of verbal association and recall, and number puzzles will quiz your mathematical dexterity. You can hone deductive skills with baffling logic problems, and improve your perception with intricate mazes and illusion puzzles. As well as being fun, these puzzles will give your brain a thorough workout to help you in all aspects of life.

WHY CHALLENGE YOUR BRAIN WITH PUZZLES? It's a fact that puzzling will help to increase your vocabulary, communication and numerical skills and perceptiveness. Puzzles teach you new ways of dealing with everyday problems, for instance with lateral thinking. They also help to ward off the problems of ageing, such as poor memory and limited mental agility.

HOW DOING PUZZLES IS GOOD FOR YOU When you complete a puzzle you feel like a winner. Frequent mental stimulation gives the brain a workout in the same way as physical exercise does for the body, and it helps to strengthen different areas of ability, such as spatial awareness and creativity. It will also improve your performance in a range of situations, from understanding difficult vocabulary to adding up a supermarket bill, to hitting winning shots on the tennis court or golf course.

USING THE ACETATE AND PEN To save you from having to write on the book, we've supplied you with an acetate sheet. Simply place the acetate sheet over the page you want to use and fill in the puzzle using the pen supplied. The acetate can then be wiped clean when you've finished.

USING THE BOOK The puzzles are organized into five categories: words (in two sections: A Word a Day and the more difficult Word Challenges), numbers, visual teasers, logic problems and memory tests. Each section features a range of puzzles, graded from one star (Standard) through to four stars (Fiendish). You may choose to work your way through the easier puzzles first, or dive in to the more difficult examples of your favourites.

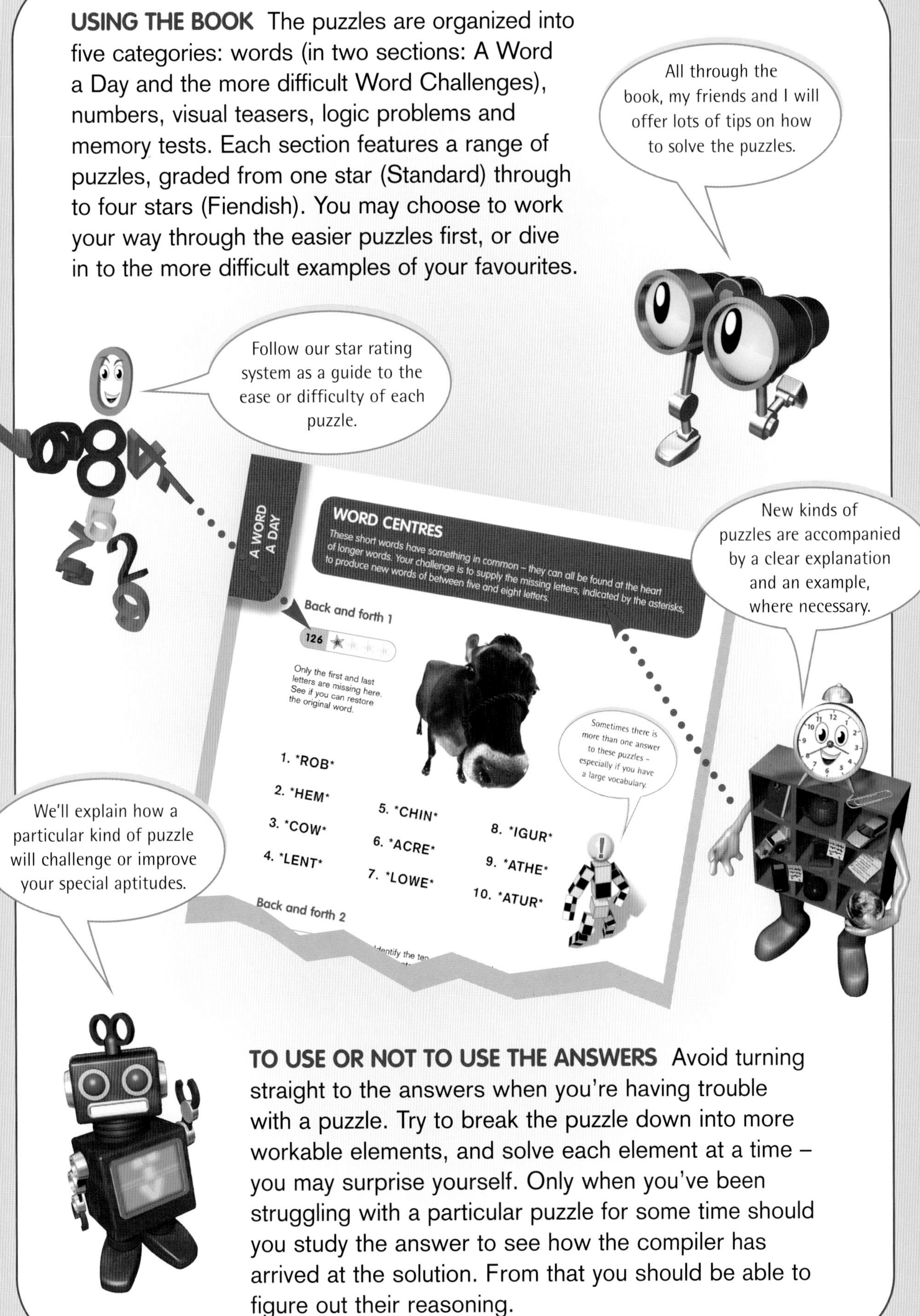

All through the book, my friends and I will offer lots of tips on how to solve the puzzles.
Follow our star rating system as a guide to the ease or difficulty of each puzzle.
New kinds of puzzles are accompanied by a clear explanation and an example, where necessary.
We'll explain how a particular kind of puzzle will challenge or improve your special aptitudes.
A WORD A DAY
WORD CENTRES
These short words have something in common – they can all be found at the heart of longer words. Your challenge is to supply the missing letters, indicated by the asterisks, to produce new words of between five and eight letters.
Back and forth 1
126
Only the first and last letters are missing here. See if you can restore the original word.
1. *ROB*
2. *HEM*
3. *COW*
4. *LENT*
5. *CHIN*
6. *ACRE*
7. *LOWE*
8. *IGUR*
9. *ATHE*
10. *ATUR*
Sometimes there is more than one answer to these puzzles – especially if you have a large vocabulary.
Back and forth 2

TO USE OR NOT TO USE THE ANSWERS Avoid turning straight to the answers when you're having trouble with a puzzle. Try to break the puzzle down into more workable elements, and solve each element at a time – you may surprise yourself. Only when you've been struggling with a particular puzzle for some time should you study the answer to see how the compiler has arrived at the solution. From that you should be able to figure out their reasoning.

HOW THE BRAIN WORKS

Your aptitudes or talents are governed by the individual way that your brain works and its special balance of 'left brain' to 'right brain' activity. This is what gives you, for example, mathematical brilliance, an artistic bent or a superb grasp of logic.

LEFT BRAIN, RIGHT BRAIN

The largest part of the brain, the cerebrum, is divided into two halves or hemispheres. They are almost mirror images, each controlling and responding to messages from the opposite side of the body. Signals from each hemisphere cross over to control the other side of the body – when you raise your right hand, it is the left hemisphere that controls it. Equally, sensory input from one side of the body will be sent to the opposite side of the brain. Each hemisphere is capable of doing nearly everything the other can do, but they also have individual strengths – when faced with a task, the side of the brain that is more adept at that specific task automatically takes control.

EMOTION
NUMBER
R
MEMORY
L
INTUITION
LOGIC
EMPATHY
LANGUAGE

DIFFERENT SKILLS

In practice, nearly everything in our minds is the result of combined right- and left-hemisphere processing. While the right hemisphere is good at grasping concepts, such as comprehending patterns or emotions, the left hemisphere is better at analysing things, for example tackling math problems. In nearly all right-handed people, language is processed entirely by the left hemisphere. Language is crucial because most of our thinking is done in the form of words. If you look at a picture, the right hemisphere will tend to interpret the content in an intuitive way – the colours may provoke a feeling of pleasure or sadness. In contrast, the left hemisphere will recognise the colours as 'red', 'blue' and so on, but will not be as moved by them emotionally. Normally the right hemisphere will transmit its feelings about the picture to the left hemisphere through the corpus callosum – a complex network of nerves joining the two halves. This information is then incorporated into the left hemisphere's own view, before turning the overall perception into words.

ARE YOU LEFT OR RIGHT BRAINED?

Try answering these questions to see which half of your brain plays the stronger role in determining your behaviour.

1 Do you often have 'hunches'?

2 Do you use your hands a lot when you talk?

3 Can you tell how much time has passed without using a watch?

4 When you have hunches do you often follow them?

5 Would you prefer to learn a new dance step by following the sequence in your head rather than by following a demonstration?

6 Do you find algebra easier than geometry?

7 Are you good at getting the gist of what people mean when they talk in a language you can't speak?

8 When you see a picture in a book do you look at the caption before the image?

9 Are you better at faces than names?

10 Do you like to complete one task before going on to the next?

For questions 1, 2, 4, 7 and 9:
If you answered 'Yes', give yourself an 'R'.
If you answered 'No', give yourself an 'L'.

For questions 3, 5, 6, 8 and 10:
If you answered 'Yes', give yourself an 'L'.
If you answered 'No', give yourself an 'R'.

Add up your total number of Ls and Rs. More Rs than Ls overall suggests that you tend towards right-hemisphere thinking. More Ls than Rs suggests left-hemisphere dominance. Most people have a mixture of both left and right styles of thinking.

WHAT ARE YOUR SPECIAL APTITUDES?

These will almost certainly be obvious to you if you're a fluent speaker or writer, or a math wiz who can make detailed calculations in your head. But you can train yourself to improve mental skills that don't come naturally. Like making progress in sport, they all benefit from being worked harder – so challenge yourself and the rewards will follow.

NUMERICAL SKILLS

33 Numerical ability is controlled by the right side of the brain. Mathematical skills are important in all aspects of our lives, from calculating the weekly shopping bill to drawing up a monthly budget or working out your tax bill. Mathematical puzzles explore both your ability to perform basic arithmetic functions and a more abstract ability to reason. 84 42

People with a high level of numerical skill may be drawn to, and often excel in, jobs such as: accountant or auditor, business consultant, financial analyst, mathematics or physics teacher or researcher, quantity surveyor, tax adviser, or stockbroker. 68 99

MEMORY

We are all defined by our remembrance of ourselves, other people and of specific events. That is why amnesia – the loss of memory – is such a catastrophe. The sufferer loses all sense of who they are. Although memory gets less sharp as we get older (the short-term particularly at risk), with regular exercise you'll be amazed at what you can recall.

LOGIC

Superlative logical skill, largely the province of the left brain, is an ability used by people such as computer programmers. It can help you in the most surprising areas of your life by developing the 'intuitive leaps' that will help you to solve all kinds of problems quickly and successfully – from taking short cuts to avoid traffic jams to thinking up new ideas for local fund-raising.

VERBAL SKILLS

Verbal ability is controlled by the left side of the brain. Your verbal intelligence is a measure of how you use language to express yourself and understand written text and what others say.
People with good verbal skills often excel in fields such as writing (author, journalist, editing, critic), teaching (language, drama), the legal profession (judge, barrister, lawyer), personnel work (advocate, human resources, counsellor) and as actors, psychologists, interpreters and interviewers.

SPATIAL SKILLS

Spatial ability is controlled by the right side of the brain, which is responsible for creative and intuitive thinking. Ideas for drawing diagrams, and for the visual and musical arts will be generated in this part of the brain. Your spatial aptitude is based on your ability to identify patterns and meaning from what might initially appear to be abstract, random or very complex information.

People with strong spatial aptitude often excel in artistic and technical fields, such as architecture, photography, engineering design, decorating, and as artists, graphic designers, carpenters, garden landscapers, cartoon animators, fashion designers and civil engineers.

FIND YOUR STRENGTHS

The following questions are not a formal intelligence (IQ) test, but your results will help you to understand where your mental skills are strongest and, by contrast, those areas that you could improve. Enjoy it and don't take the results too seriously.

HOW IT WORKS

This test will help you to assess your aptitude in verbal, numerical and diagrammatic or spatial reasoning. The questions will also test your logical thought processes and lateral thinking ability.

The results will help you to identify your particular strengths and point you in the direction of puzzles you will especially enjoy. It will also show you where a 'Brain-stretching' workout could help you to improve your skill in another area.

INSTRUCTIONS

Give yourself a time limit of 90 minutes to complete the 30 questions. Don't use a calculator for the numerical questions.

HOW YOU SHAPE UP

As well as testing yourself, and discovering your strengths, it is interesting to see how you match up against your partner and other family members. Do your abilities complement each other, or are your skills similar? Which parent do your children take after? Are there left-handers in the family, and do they have notable right-brain abilities?

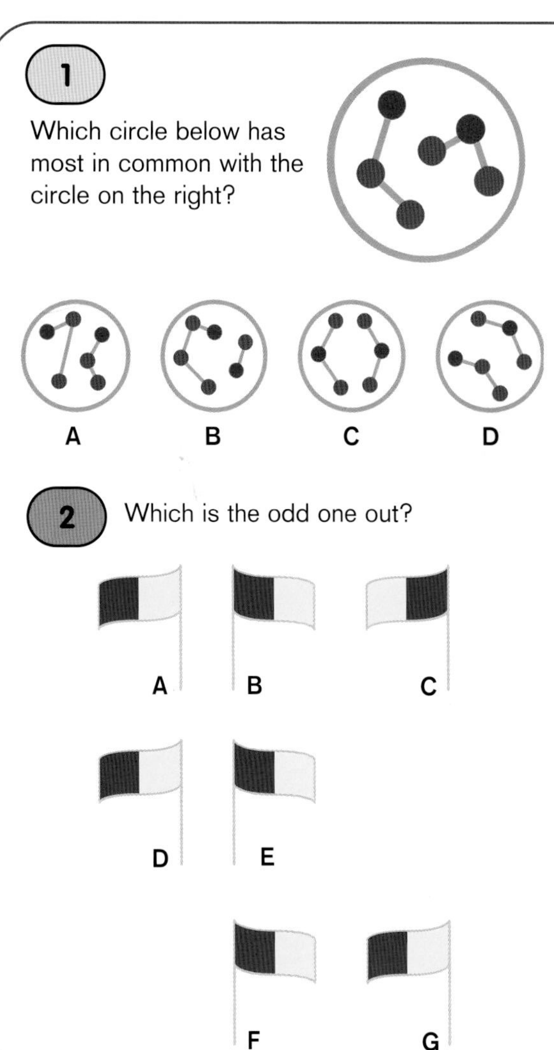

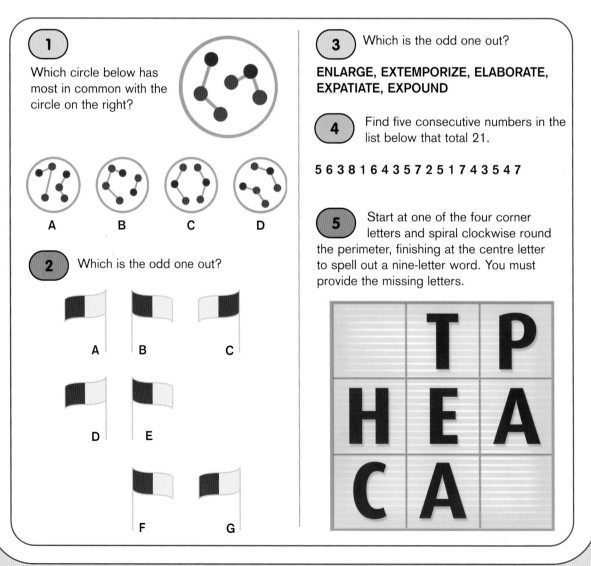

1 Which circle below has most in common with the circle on the right?

A B C D

2 Which is the odd one out?

A B C D E F G

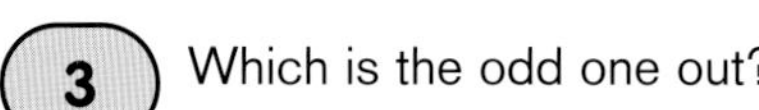

3 Which is the odd one out?

ENLARGE, EXTEMPORIZE, ELABORATE, EXPATIATE, EXPOUND

4 Find five consecutive numbers in the list below that total 21.

5 6 3 8 1 6 4 3 5 7 2 5 1 7 4 3 5 4 7

5 Start at one of the four corner letters and spiral clockwise round the perimeter, finishing at the centre letter to spell out a nine-letter word. You must provide the missing letters.

	T	P
H	E	A
C	A	

6 Moving in a straight line either horizontally, vertically or diagonally, what number is: three places away from itself multiplied by 3, two places away from itself plus 2, three places away from itself less 2 and three places away from itself plus 8.

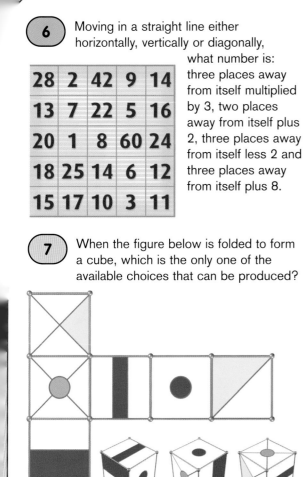

28	2	42	9	14
13	7	22	5	16
20	1	8	60	24
18	25	14	6	12
15	17	10	3	11

7 When the figure below is folded to form a cube, which is the only one of the available choices that can be produced?

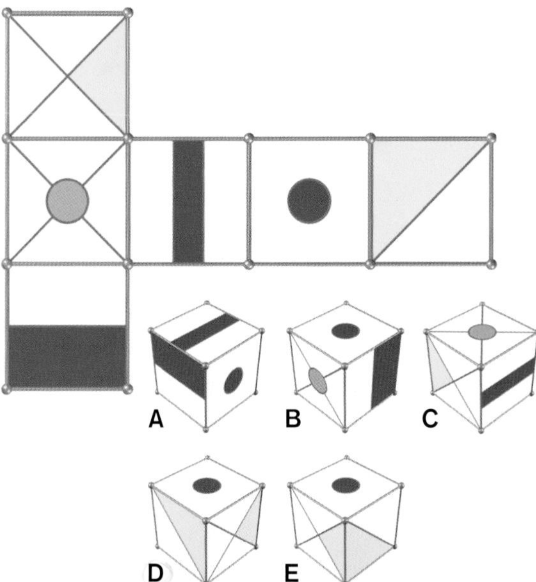

8 Peter, Paul and Mary wish to share out a certain sum of money between them. Peter receives 2/5, Paul receives 0.45 and Mary receives $21.00.

How much is the original amount of money?

9 Which of the following is not an anagram of an occupation?

CAN CHIME

SCARY TREE

OPEN CLAIM

LURE LAMB

CAN COAT NUT

10 What number should replace the question mark?

3	5	8	13
1	6	7	?
4	11	15	26
5	17	22	39

11 Arrange the six sets of three letters into two groups of three to produce two words that are similar in meaning.

TED, IED, TEN, GRA, CON, TIF

12 Which shield below has most in common with the shield on the right?

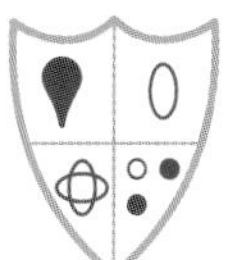

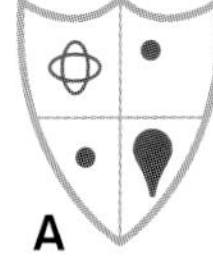
A

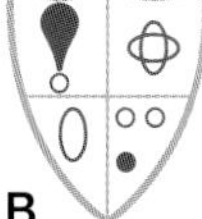
B

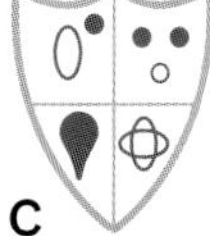
C

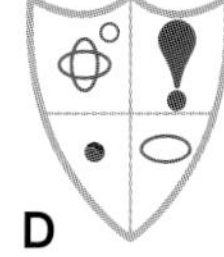
D

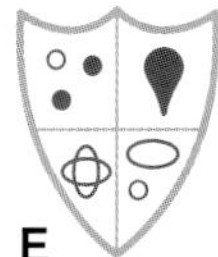
E

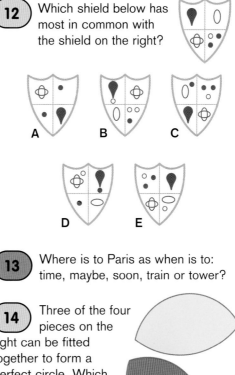

13 Where is to Paris as when is to: time, maybe, soon, train or tower?

14 Three of the four pieces on the right can be fitted together to form a perfect circle. Which piece is the odd one out?

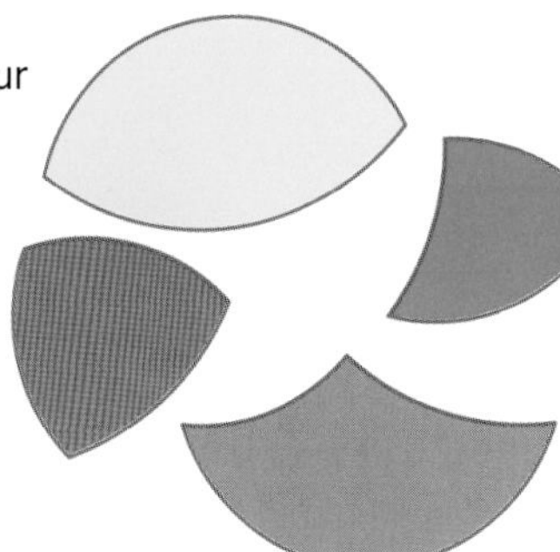

15

376 : 27   581 : 41   739 : 30

Which one set of numbers below has the same relationship to one another as all the sets of numbers above?

a. 629 : 24   **c.** 438 : 20

b. 592 : 49   **d.** 387 : 33

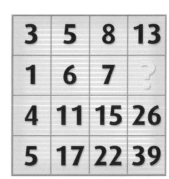

16

Which word in brackets is most opposite in meaning to the word in capitals?

REPEAL
(recall, validate, renovate, submit, abound)

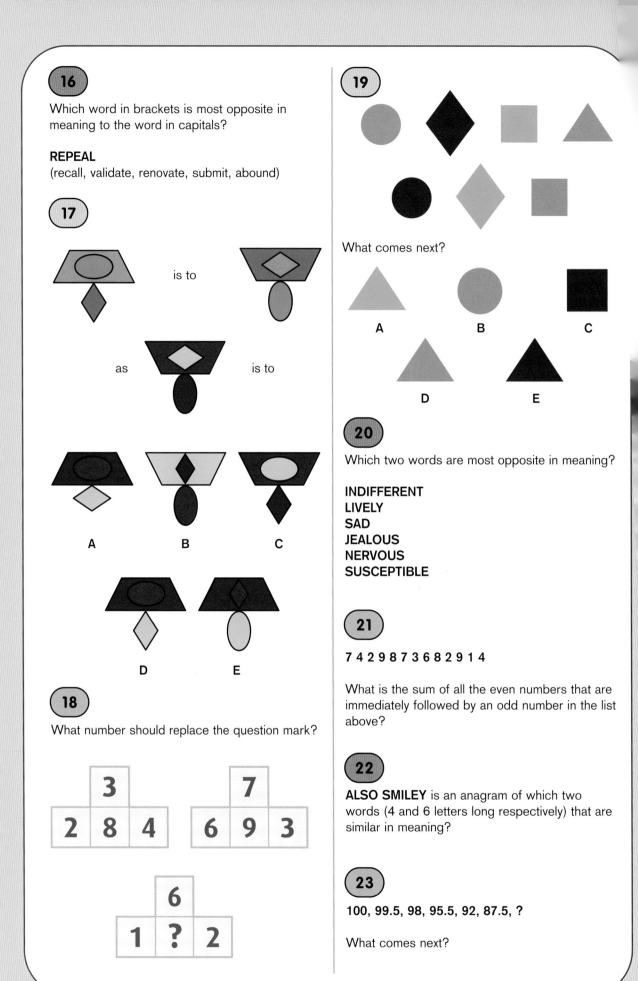

17

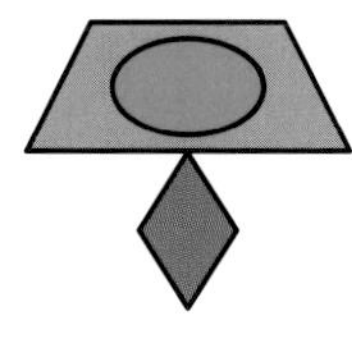 is to 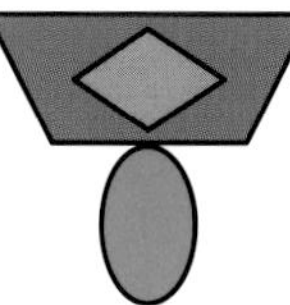

as 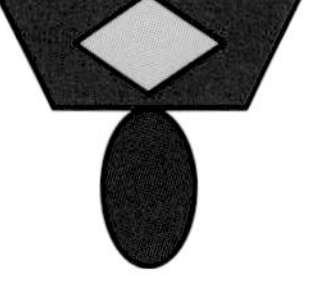 is to

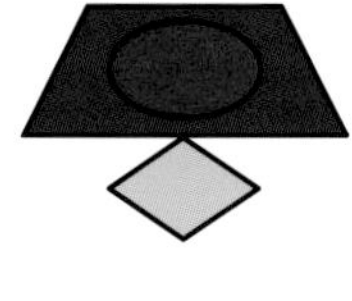

A

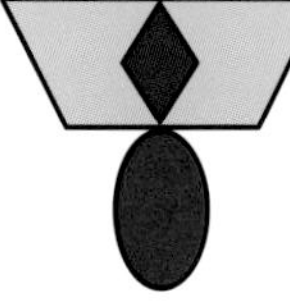

B

C

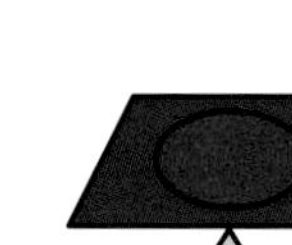

D

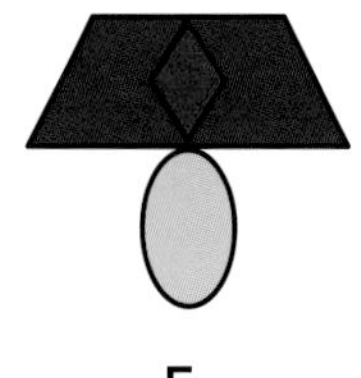

E

18

What number should replace the question mark?

	3	
2	8	4

	7	
6	9	3

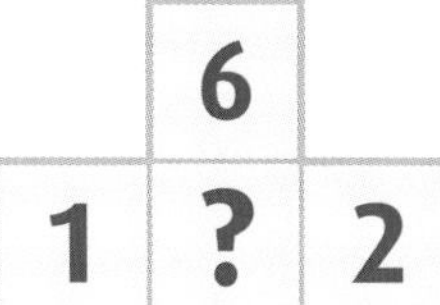

19

What comes next?

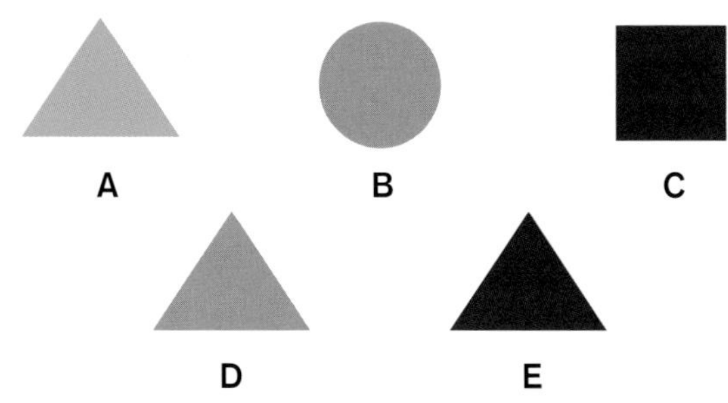

20

Which two words are most opposite in meaning?

INDIFFERENT
LIVELY
SAD
JEALOUS
NERVOUS
SUSCEPTIBLE

21

7 4 2 9 8 7 3 6 8 2 9 1 4

What is the sum of all the even numbers that are immediately followed by an odd number in the list above?

22

ALSO SMILEY is an anagram of which two words (4 and 6 letters long respectively) that are similar in meaning?

23

100, 99.5, 98, 95.5, 92, 87.5, ?

What comes next?

24

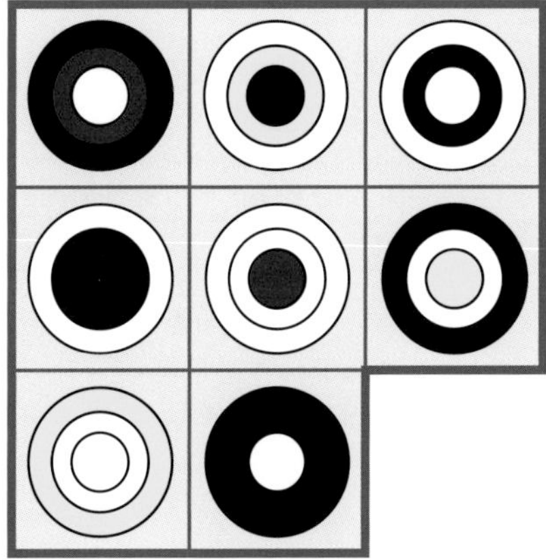

Which is the missing tile?

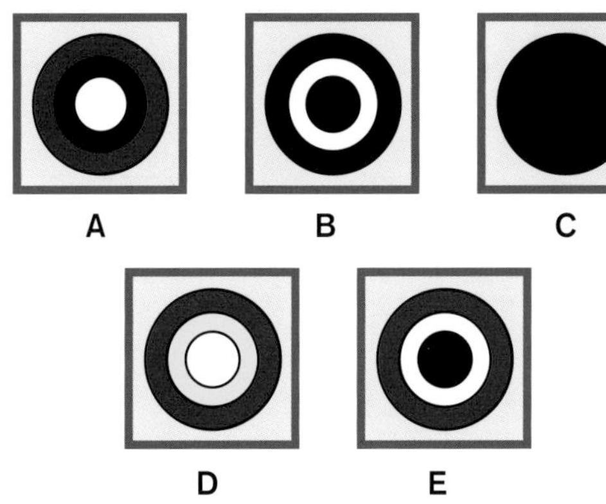

25

Divide 320 by 0.25 and add 5.

What is the answer?

26

Which shield below has most in common with the shield above?

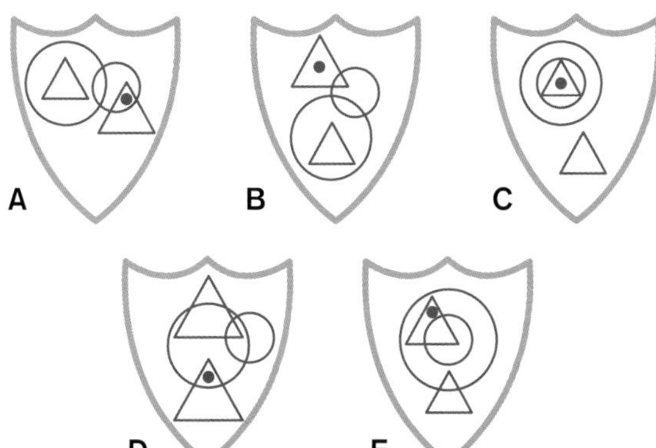

27

If you were given the words MAR, AM and FAR and asked to find the shortest word in the English language that contained all the letters in these words, you would almost certainly come up with the word FARM.

Now look at the following list of words:

STUN COUNT STAIR SLOT

What is the shortest word in the English language from which all four of these words can be produced?

28

How many minutes is it before 12 noon if 9 minutes ago it was twice as many minutes past 10am?

29

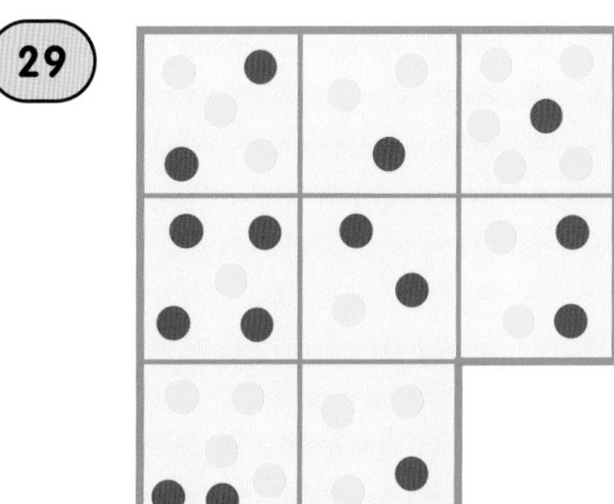

Which is the missing tile?

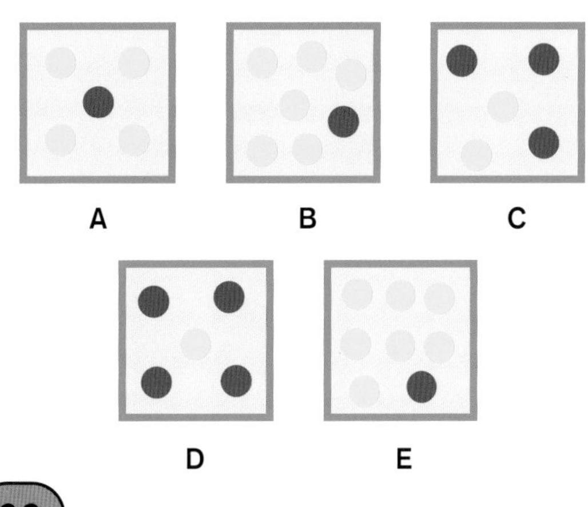

30

Which word in brackets is closest in meaning to the word in capitals?

DIFFIDENCE
(dispersion, modesty, tribulation, diversity, boldness)

ANSWERS

01 **D:** it contains the same two strings – red/blue/blue and blue/red/blue

02 **C:** all the remaining left-facing flags have the blue section furthest away from the mast. All the right-facing flags have the yellow section furthest away from the mast.

03 **Extemporize:** it means to improvise. The rest mean to increase, expand or build on.

04 43572

05 Parachute

---

06 5

07 D

08 **$140.00**
Peter $56.00
Paul $63.00
Mary $21.00
= $140.00

09 **LURE LAMB = umbrella.**
The occupations are:
mechanic (can chime),
secretary (scary tree),
policeman (open claim)
accountant (can coat nut).

10 **13:** In each line across and down add the first and second numbers to obtain the third number, and the second and third to obtain the fourth.

11 Gratified, contented

12 **D:** It contains all the same symbols as the top shield, albeit that they may be in different positions and segments.

13 soon

14 B

---

15 **C:** 438 : 20 (4 x 3) + 8

16 Validate

17 **D:** The four-sided figure rotates 180° and changes from red to blue (the same colour as the ellipse), the diamond rotates 90° and goes to the bottom, and the ellipse rotates 90°, changes from blue to red and goes inside the four-sided figure.

18 **2:** 6 x 2 = 12. Similarly 3 x 8 = 24 and 7 x 9 = 63

19 **E:** The figures alternate circle/diamond/square/triangle and the colour alternates orange/blue/green

20 Indifferent, jealous

21 12

22 lose, mislay

---

23 **82:** Deduct 0.5, 1.5, 2.5, 3.5, 4.5, 5.5

24 **E:** There are three rings. In each row and column one of the three rings is shaded black. Also in each row and column, one of the rings only is shaded red and one is shaded yellow.

25 **1,285**
There are four quarters in 1, therefore 1,280 (320 x 4) quarters in 320.

26 **D:** One dot is in a triangle and one circle. The other dot is in a triangle and two circles.

27 Ultrasonic

28 **37 minutes**
12 noon less 37 minutes = 11.23
11.23 less 9 minutes = 11.14
10 a.m. plus 74 minutes (37 x 2) = 11.14

29 **E:** When looking across and down, the number of green dots in the final square is the difference between the numbers of green dots in the first two squares. The number of yellow dots in the final square is the total of the number of yellow dots in the first two squares.

30 Modesty

SELF ANALYSIS

SCORING

Score 1 point for each correct answer. Then assess your performance using the following guidelines.

SCORE	RATING	PERCENTAGE OF POPULATION
28 – 30	Genius level	Top 5%
25 – 27	High expert	Top 10%
22 – 24	Expert	Top 30%
19 – 21	High average	Top 40%
15 – 18	Average	Top 60%
12 – 14	Low average	Bottom 40%
9 – 11	Borderline low	Bottom 30%
6 – 8	Low	Bottom 10%
0 – 5	Very low	Bottom 5%

APTITUDES

SCORING

You can also analyze your performance within each of the three types of questions in the test (see below). This will give a clear indication of your current strengths and weaknesses.

SCORE	RATING	PERCENTAGE OF POPULATION
9 – 10	Genius level	Top 5%
8	High expert	Top 10%
7	Expert	Top 30%
6	High average	Top 40%
5	Average	Top 60%
4	Low average	Bottom 40%
3	Borderline low	Bottom 30%
2	Low	Bottom 10%
0 – 1	Very low	Bottom 5%

WHAT YOUR RESULTS MEAN

Your results are a personal profile of your ability to solve these particular sorts of puzzles – and they are only a profile, not the whole 'you'.

The grading used in these tests is similar to that used in general IQ tests (in which the average score is 100 and the results are graded above and below this norm). The percentages above are calculated from the test results of large numbers of people of all ages and both sexes, and with diverse educational and ethnic backgrounds.

SPECIFIC APTITUDE RATINGS

RED answers measure verbal aptitude

GREEN answers measure numerical skill

YELLOW answers measure spatial skill

Verbal intelligence measures use of language, comprehension of written text and understanding of the spoken word.

Mathematical intelligence tests explore your ability to reason and to perform basic arithmetic functions.

Spatial aptitude tests measure the ability to identify pattern and meaning from apparently random or complex information. If you score less well on spatial tests, after excelling in verbal and numerical aptitude tests, there is no great cause for concern. Take the opportunity to practise these types of spatial aptitude exercises and to develop your 'right-brain' thinking.

PERSONALIZE YOUR MENTAL FITNESS WORKOUT

One of the best ways to keep your mind active is do a puzzle of some kind every day. As well as puzzling, there are many other types of activities that will sharpen your skills, as outlined in the suggestions below.

IF YOU WANT TO WORK ON YOUR VERBAL SKILLS Join a discussion group or book group. Write letters, short stories or poems. Buy a dictionary and use it to look up new words or check the meanings of words you are unsure of. Read literature by early writers, such as Geoffrey Chaucer, to tune in your brain to a different way of looking at language. Learn another language. Make up your own word puzzles, including anagrams and crosswords.

IF YOU WANT TO WORK ON YOUR SPATIAL SKILLS Join a sketching or life-drawing class and learn how to represent three dimensions in real life as two dimensions on the page. Offer to do the map reading on long or complicated journeys. Try to paint pictures in your mind's eye when reading a book or listening to music. Redesign your kitchen or garden.

IF YOU WANT TO WORK ON YOUR NUMBER SKILLS Keep a running tally of your purchases when supermarket shopping. Try to convert currency mentally when abroad. Always try to work out sums in your head before reaching for a calculator.

IF YOU WANT TO WORK ON YOUR MEMORY Regularly use code puzzles to help you remember dates, telephone numbers, PIN numbers and computer passwords. Construct visual links to help implant facts in your mind. Make a shopping list, memorize it, then deliberately leave it at home.

IF YOU WANT TO WORK ON YOUR LOGIC SKILLS Try lateral thinking – for example use random, unconnected ideas to see if they lead you to a new line of thought. Be unconventional – try looking at a problem from an entirely different angle to the one you would normally use. When reading a detective novel, ignore the ending; instead line up the clues and see if you can figure out 'who did it' on your own.

A WORD A DAY

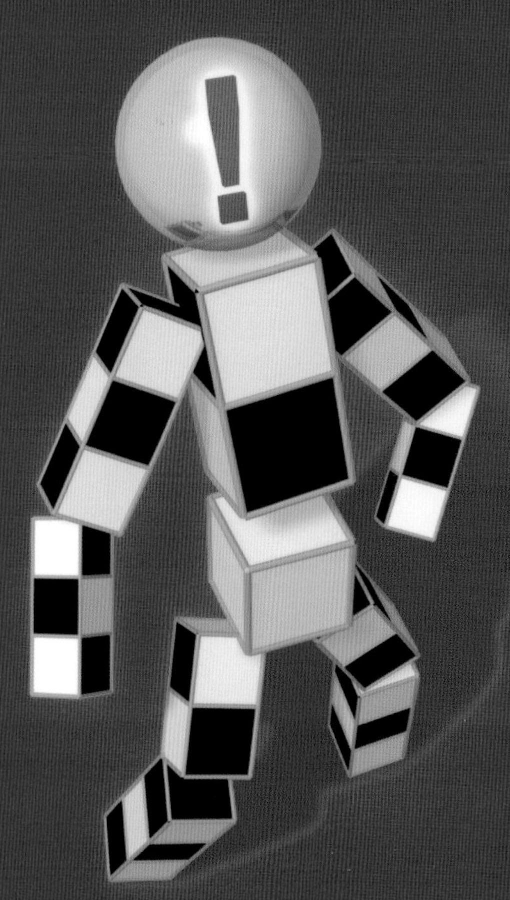

A WORD A DAY

A WORD A DAY

Of all the ways we communicate, language is the most powerful. And the stronger your word power, the easier it will be to get your message across. Learning and using new words is also great fun and can be the key to discovering a host of new facts.

MORE THAN ANY OTHER LANGUAGE, English has synonyms and subtleties in abundance – another reason why learning new ones can add flavour and accuracy to your expression. Take shades of red. Being able to choose between crimson, carmine, scarlet, maroon, pink, rose, plum, ruby, cerise or burgundy, gives you the chance to create exactly the right impression.

It is a reasonable aim to try to add one word to your vocabulary every day. The trick is to find words whose meaning you find interesting or useful and to put them into practice. Reading – with a dictionary to hand to check meanings – is a great way to start, but you may also want to look up and memorize words you hear in conversation, or on the radio or television.

PLAYING WITH WORDS by using puns or nicknames is something we do every day, but the easiest way to have word fun – and learn more – is with word puzzles like the ones you'll find in this section. Many of these puzzles test and tease out your general knowledge and powers of deduction as well as your vocabulary. They are also a great aid to correct spelling!

THE PUZZLES IN THIS SECTION are at Standard and Challenging levels. Once you have mastered the basics of each puzzle type, you can then move on to the more advanced Difficult and Fiendish examples in the Word Challenges section on pages 253-308.

Of all word games, the ones with most enduring appeal are crossword puzzles and their variations.

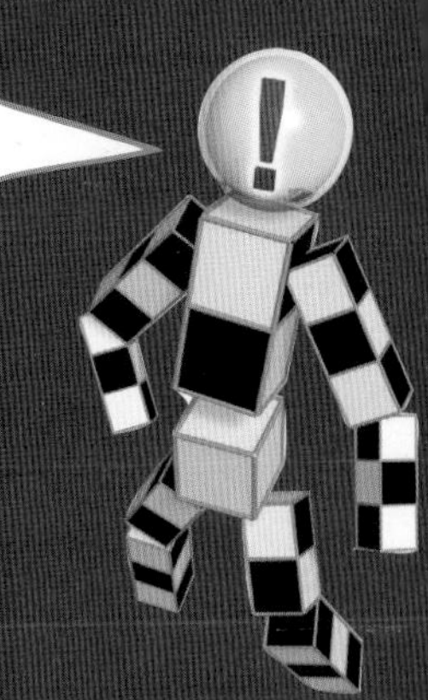

I'm Mr Spellman, and my job is to give you hints, tips and fun information that will help you to hone your word-puzzling skills. You may find it helpful to have paper and a pencil handy while you are completing the puzzles in this section. A good dictionary is also a great asset. Happy puzzling!

THERE ARE TWO BASIC TYPES of crossword puzzle – one with straight-forward synonym or general knowledge clues, the other with cryptic clues.

TO SOLVE SYNONYM CLUES you need to find words with similar, though not necessarily exact meanings. The synonym for 'ginger' for instance might be 'fiery' or 'redhead'. Cryptic clues demand more lateral thinking. An example of a hidden word is the clue 'Red is inside to begin German (6)'. A double-definition type is 'Spice girl added to curry (6)'. In both cases the answer is, of course, 'ginger'.

ANAGRAMS ARE ANOTHER FUN WAY to expand your vocabulary, and are staples of cryptic puzzles. 'Innovate new leaf markings (8)', for instance gives you the answer 'venation'. Or you may be required to combine letters from more than one word, as in the clue: 'Red-headed George first entered Niger confused (6)'. The answer 'ginger' is an anagram of 'Niger' and 'G'. You can also add to your word power by making many words from just one. The word 'innovation' has at least 19 words with four or more letters in, all containing the letter 'n'. These include 'invent', 'naïve', 'native', 'vote', 'vine', 'enovi'. Can you find the rest – and do you know their meanings? To help, rearrange the letters of the anagram into a circle.

I
N N
O V
A T
I O
N

CROSSWORD COMPILERS use several words to signal anagrams, such as 'confused', 'jumbled', 'mixed' and 'varied'. They also use other conventions. For instance, 'The French' usually means you need the letters 'le', 'la' or 'les', while the word 'church' will get you thinking of 'CE' or 'CH'.

SOLVING THESE KINDS OF CLUES may need the help of a dictionary of synonyms and antonyms, or a conventional dictionary. An atlas is also helpful, or you can invest in a special crossword dictionary.

IN WORD LADDERS, one word is transformed into another by changing a letter at a time. So to transform 'ginger' to 'longed' you need the missing links 'linger' and 'longer'. By contrast, Word Searches supply all the words in the puzzle, and it's your job to locate them. With these, instead of exercising vocabulary, you need to be able to recognise patterns in letters (both backwards and forwards).

SOLVING CRYPTIC CROSSWORDS

Cryptic crosswords are one of the hardest, but most rewarding challenges for puzzle fans. To solve them it is essential to know how to interpret the clues and to get into the same 'mindset' as the compiler. If you regularly do the same cryptic crossword, take time to check the answers you didn't get so you learn the compiler's tricks.

- In cryptic clues the answer is always defined within the clue, sometimes more than once, but not always blatantly. The defining word often appears at the beginning, less often at the end, and rarely in the middle. The rest of the clue helps clarify the meaning; how it works depends on the type of clue.

- One of the best ways into a cryptic crossword is through double-definition clues or through anagrams or hidden words. Words such as 'unusually,' 'mixed up' and 'odd' are anagram markers. 'Hidden', 'within' and 'inside' commonly indicate hidden words. Keep an eye out for these when you read the clues.

- Punctuation is used by compilers to signal interpretation, but also to confuse or conceal. Exclamation marks may indicate that meanings are to be taken literally, while commas and question marks are more likely to indicate tricks or puns of some kind. Try reading clues without the punctuation to see if they can be interpreted another way.

- Watch out for keywords that clearly signal the compiler's intentions as to how other words in the clue are used. For instance, 'endless' and 'headless' alert you to words that lose their last or first letters, while 'headed' may offer a clue to a word's first letters. 'Included', 'entered' or 'centred' can mean that one word sits inside another while 'around', 'grasping' or 'clutches' may imply a word that is split around another.

- The letter count at the end of the clue is a vital hint when you are looking for hidden words or anagrams. It will alert you to which groups of successive letters and words you need to look at, though the compiler may still try tricks in order to confuse you.

- Days of the week and compass points often appear as single letters in the answer, such as 'T' for Tuesday or 'E' for East.

- Single letters are indicated in many ways. When they write about a number, for instance, compilers may well mean a Roman numeral, such as 'L' for 50, 'C' for 100, and 'M' for a thousand. Compass points also often appear as single letters in the answer. Other common single letters are 'C' for 'about' (circa), and 'X' or 'Y' for unknown (as in algebra), though 'Y' can also stand for yard.

- Standard abbreviations and slang terms are used by the dozen in cryptic clues. Common ones include 'GI' and 'OR' for soldier; 'AB' or 'tar' for sailor; 'MO' or 'DR' for doctor; 'C' 'RC' or 'CE' for church, 'US' for America and so on.

EXAMPLE:

This simple cryptic crossword, complete with answers and explanations, provides some useful hints about the compiler's techniques and how to arrive at the correct solutions.

Across

1. Dirty mark is tan mixture. (5)
6. Little mischief-making one jumps in front of Redcap. (3)
7. French veto anyway you look at it. (3)
8. Thousand left inside a tree. (3)
10. Mistake! The gold fell off. (3)
11. Westminster landmark sounds like a social insect. (5)

Down

2. First to play the best. (3)
3. Watch out for this particle! (3)
4. Eternal city's flower? (5)
5. Doorway record. (5)
9. Gang crowds around. (3)
10. Bottom's up! Get the last drop. (3)

Solving Cryptic Crosswords continued from page 19

1. Across
A simple anagram, indicated by the word 'mixture'.

6. Across
'One' translates into the letter 'I', 'MP' is a standard abbreviation for Military Police, also known as 'Redcaps'.

7. Across
'Any way you look at it' is the clue to a word that reads the same back and front. Added to this is the general knowledge of the French for 'no'.

8. Across
Placing a letter (in this case 'L' for left) inside another word or group of letters is signalled by 'inside'.

10. Across
A literal clue has been added to one that tells you letters need to be deleted. 'Or' (as well as 'au', its chemical symbol) is an abbreviation for gold used in heraldry.

11. Across
'Sounds like' (or 'we hear') tells you to think about how a word is pronounced, so 'a bee' translates to 'abbey'.

2. Down
'First' tells you to look at the initial letters of the words in the clue. The answer will then become obvious.

3. Down
A typical 'sounds like' pun which requires you to find another phrase meaning 'Watch out for'. You need to spot that 'particle' is the definition word.

4. Down
'Flower' is not necessarily referring to a budding plant. It's a popular choice to indicate a river, which flows. (A more likely word for flower will be 'bloomer'.)

5. Down
A typical double definition that requires only a good vocabulary.

9. Down
Another double definition in which the solution is used as both a noun and a verb.

10. Down
Another variation on a word that reads the same both ways.

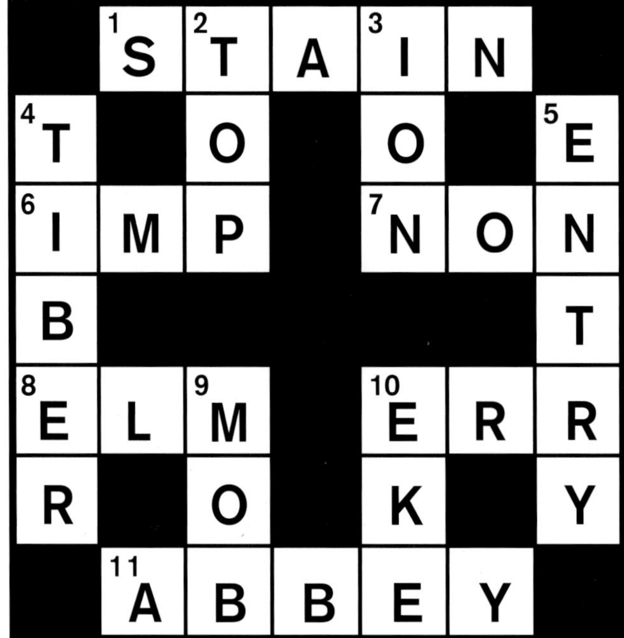

WORD SEARCHES

The aim of word searches is to find words hidden in the grid. They may run up, down, forward, backwards, diagonally – and in any direction.

!KCUL DOOG

1 No picnic?

```
  Z O                                             U C
Q Y I V D                                     W B O B N
Y G Y O G I   N X A D V E D Q Y G L V V     J B T Q L D
M G R D G   R B S K D A C U B J G Z P M G     Q A V A J
  F S V   S B E Z M Q U B P B Y D G L S E Q     K C C
  M G   J Y Z V B H I J J M T D H G U R Y F I     P K
      S S P X N     U J T O W R S     H B M B B
      P H O Z M     W Z K R U R Z     G A S A R
      G A K A R F M U G J E R O B S N X Z X K I
      Y R N U Z I K I R H T V P R W A V W K L N
      J C J D Z K V K I O K S M L Y X J V F U X
      R D T I A E P O Z G M A R U P E R T V G U
      Q A H J V H M T Z       U N X S S M O A M
      E E M I A G F A L       R G Z G W T U F B
      F K Z L P A Q Z Y I   P S L I Y D P G P C
      R C Q E K A D S F V B P Z C J S I A P O P
      I T H W V M D J J U B A X U D P L O G L F
      K X B N Y A K D O K   L E Z S O M I R A P
      P S A B K K I O I   V   I K Y O V V T R S
      B I L   E L R H   N K G   M H H L   A M M
      Y L O Q         R F G R B         C W T W
      L A O T C X I B B R P T E Z X K G F L G L
      X K C I B B K M R C Z V O I K U T Y J V N
        H F V E A P G O K I Q A N V B W B K L
            E A X B V W T X Z C R X G J C
              H G P Y N M Q K I M B R F
                    S V E T C G A E G
```

Go down to the woods to see if you can find all these well-known bears.

BALOO
BLACK
BROWN
GRIZZLY
HUGGY
PADDINGTON
PANDA
POLAR
POOH
RUPERT
YOGI

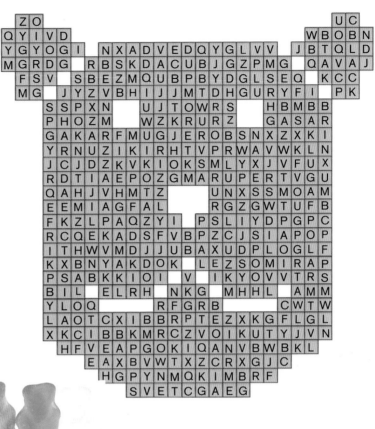

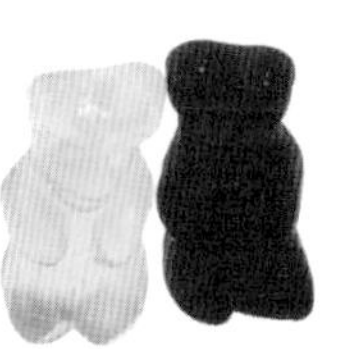

2 An appetite for more?

V	W	E	G	S	S	A	A	U	A	D	I	R	M	B	V
E	X	N	K	I	S	R	E	P	P	E	P	O	U	U	O
V	G	Y	N	Z	S	N	B	F	S	W	S	C	I	G	B
M	G	A	A	M	U	S	H	R	O	O	M	S	N	A	J
G	W	T	S	S	G	P	K	L	T	E	A	I	B	P	T
P	J	O	S	U	C	B	E	A	N	S	D	D	M	E	L
J	D	M	H	A	A	B	T	O	W	D	W	R	T	D	A
S	D	A	P	A	O	S	K	S	U	J	E	M	Q	D	S
B	G	T	G	H	C	T	Y	P	M	N	C	N	Q	P	C
V	U	O	Y	T	R	D	K	K	X	Y	I	J	S	Z	J
M	S	U	Y	I	Z	C	N	F	U	T	Q	G	E	R	U
V	W	T	B	L	A	S	A	B	G	V	G	E	G	X	I
C	B	K	O	L	Y	R	O	A	A	E	M	R	I	R	V
L	L	Q	B	H	U	X	W	N	Z	C	N	P	L	G	J
V	S	Y	W	J	S	H	L	G	Q	Y	O	I	Q	V	P
E	C	I	U	J	E	G	N	A	R	O	B	N	R	Z	B

These dozen items can all be found on the breakfast table. Find them before you leave the house.

BACON
BEANS
BLACK PUDDING
EGGS
MUSHROOMS
ORANGE JUICE
PEPPER
SALT
SAUSAGE
TEA
TOAST
TOMATO

Pet hates?

Nine domestic animals are concealed in this grid. If you find them all, try and pick out a more exotic creature lurking in the undergrowth.

CAT
DOG
GUINEA PIG
HAMSTER
MOUSE
PARROT
PONY
RABBIT
STICK INSECT

L	Y	H	U	A	G	I	N	H	G	L	V	N	W	F	F	Q
D	P	B	D	W	N	E	D	J	P	Q	G	I	U	M	Z	D
T	R	T	O	S	P	D	D	K	F	Q	P	A	R	R	O	T
C	B	C	G	I	T	V	V	L	F	T	M	Y	X	B	K	D
E	Z	D	X	X	B	N	Z	E	G	N	W	G	R	D	V	C
S	M	C	R	C	J	W	S	M	I	K	K	I	X	D	D	M
N	U	P	Q	I	U	U	L	W	P	M	R	G	I	F	X	W
I	Y	Q	V	J	O	Y	K	T	A	K	N	V	R	O	K	K
K	A	V	X	M	C	X	G	W	E	O	H	P	A	P	V	G
C	F	Q	U	R	H	S	O	S	N	T	G	G	N	M	S	N
I	B	W	N	Z	A	L	W	Q	I	G	E	T	L	Q	V	S
T	O	Q	W	I	M	N	C	B	U	W	I	E	G	D	I	T
S	U	T	U	D	S	Z	L	K	G	G	N	C	W	Y	M	A
Y	M	Y	M	H	T	D	F	A	E	I	K	L	N	Z	B	C
O	V	F	V	S	E	J	G	R	Y	O	T	O	Y	X	R	R
I	W	J	D	B	R	B	N	J	N	D	P	P	F	X	K	A
A	R	A	B	B	I	T	O	V	M	K	V	F	W	D	Q	H

T	R	K	K	M	U	R	C	F	L	P	X	G	Y	S	P	R	U	F	K
M	H	U	J	Z	B	O	B	L	G	O	W	Q	D	P	K	C	R	E	C
O	T	S	O	R	R	Q	H	M	S	I	Q	A	K	L	K	E	C	D	X
T	E	R	F	A	Y	R	R	E	F	T	Y	E	R	T	N	S	R	H	P
J	P	I	C	Q	G	K	Y	A	C	V	C	E	G	I	I	F	D	D	Q
P	E	L	N	W	E	Z	O	K	F	B	P	Y	L	R	R	X	E	E	W
O	E	L	S	W	R	Z	Y	A	E	C	M	E	I	I	A	Q	Y	K	Y
O	I	K	Q	E	F	T	D	P	I	H	S	L	L	A	T	B	C	R	H
L	H	H	A	V	A	T	Y	P	X	I	B	C	S	E	C	L	E	A	D
S	M	X	B	F	Q	J	Z	J	U	Z	T	R	C	R	B	N	J	Z	T
Y	Q	P	S	X	G	J	T	R	J	S	A	A	G	M	O	C	A	O	D
A	K	S	D	H	F	G	C	Y	P	Z	F	X	O	O	J	M	M	P	N
A	M	T	J	F	C	A	G	G	T	Q	P	A	H	B	R	O	U	S	S
T	C	C	R	J	E	L	R	H	G	G	U	C	U	C	D	C	F	B	D
Z	Z	M	K	O	F	L	Y	V	Z	Q	S	G	A	C	C	E	V	A	O
Y	A	C	H	T	T	E	I	A	U	Q	B	L	B	R	U	J	E	U	I
Q	H	D	T	N	L	O	P	W	C	U	H	V	I	K	I	T	B	P	L
S	A	H	U	Y	F	N	C	A	T	A	M	A	R	A	N	C	I	F	S
I	A	P	X	W	O	J	O	Z	P	H	O	A	Y	Z	I	K	O	F	B
F	S	F	O	A	J	S	Q	E	B	H	I	O	C	K	I	H	R	G	S

Water water, everywhere

Ahoy puzzlers! See if you can locate 12 water-going vessels here.

BARGE
CATAMARAN
CORACLE
CRUISE LINER
FERRY
GALLEON
PUNT
SCHOONER
SLOOP
SPEEDBOAT
TALL SHIP
YACHT

5

A gem of a puzzle

A host of precious stones lie buried in this wordsearch. See how quickly you can dig them up.

X	R	C	H	J	H	G	I	L	U	Z	A	L	S	I	P	A	L	T	O
E	I	A	W	O	O	X	R	P	Z	C	W	L	M	Y	K	V	L	U	G
L	G	M	Q	A	H	T	O	P	A	Z	B	K	I	D	K	S	O	R	Y
F	Y	E	Q	B	K	W	V	F	X	H	T	J	A	J	M	A	V	Q	B
U	Y	T	A	X	V	O	V	G	F	I	Y	S	Q	Z	B	P	M	U	U
U	T	H	A	W	A	G	I	Z	H	O	X	P	H	S	Z	P	G	O	R
V	X	Y	A	U	G	G	Z	C	D	L	A	R	E	M	E	H	E	I	E
W	Y	S	Z	X	K	F	C	P	G	Z	A	L	G	N	L	I	E	S	E
P	P	T	U	I	Z	O	E	E	N	X	T	P	R	Z	Q	R	Y	E	Q
S	O	P	X	C	M	M	I	A	R	Q	I	S	J	U	Y	E	W	B	A
S	D	O	Y	T	F	F	R	R	M	Y	V	L	Y	R	E	B	P	H	J
H	I	B	E	V	N	L	P	L	W	O	J	M	Z	E	U	F	X	R	I
S	A	U	N	G	B	F	J	J	D	E	C	D	U	P	K	U	L	Q	P
Z	M	L	O	N	D	F	G	A	R	N	E	T	W	S	G	W	M	M	Q
P	O	G	T	K	X	S	U	V	G	V	Y	A	S	A	D	U	T	E	H
F	N	F	S	Y	U	M	N	D	A	C	V	L	I	J	Z	S	F	E	O
E	D	I	N	Q	F	Z	X	H	Y	L	N	A	M	B	E	R	O	B	K
Q	A	O	O	K	E	U	J	U	V	X	T	G	R	C	S	P	D	M	A
C	D	F	O	Y	T	K	T	K	K	A	E	T	R	G	A	V	N	B	I
J	K	W	M	L	O	Y	X	G	C	O	N	C	A	L	E	Z	X	X	F

AMBER
AMETHYST
BERYL
DIAMOND
EMERALD
GARNET
JASPER
LAPIS LAZULI
MOONSTONE
ONYX
OPAL
PEARL
RUBY
SAPPHIRE
TOPAZ
TURQUOISE

6

Orchestrate wildly

The Brain Stretchers orchestra has lost some vital components – see if you can track all of them down.

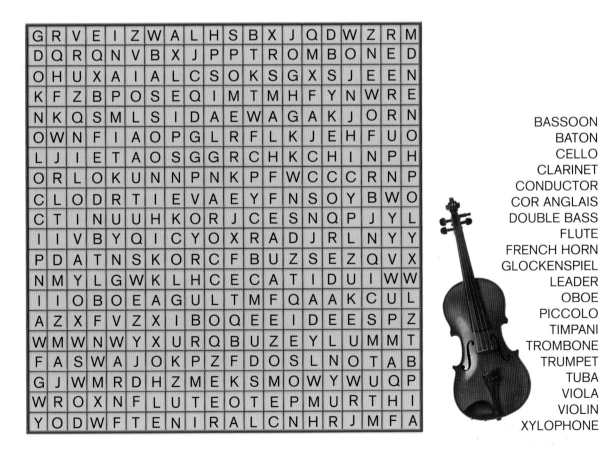

G	R	V	E	I	Z	W	A	L	H	S	B	X	J	Q	D	W	Z	R	M
D	Q	R	Q	N	V	B	X	J	P	P	T	R	O	M	B	O	N	E	D
O	H	U	X	A	I	A	L	C	S	O	K	S	G	X	S	J	E	E	N
K	F	Z	B	P	O	S	E	Q	I	M	T	M	H	F	Y	N	W	R	E
N	K	Q	S	M	L	S	I	D	A	E	W	A	G	A	K	J	O	R	N
O	W	N	F	I	A	O	P	G	L	R	F	L	K	J	E	H	F	U	O
L	J	I	E	T	A	O	S	G	G	R	C	H	K	C	H	I	N	P	H
O	R	L	O	K	U	N	N	P	N	K	P	F	W	C	C	C	R	N	P
C	L	O	D	R	T	I	E	V	A	E	Y	F	N	S	O	Y	B	W	O
C	T	I	N	U	U	H	K	O	R	J	C	E	S	N	Q	P	J	Y	L
I	I	V	B	Y	Q	I	C	Y	O	X	R	A	D	J	R	L	N	Y	Y
P	D	A	T	N	S	K	O	R	C	F	B	U	Z	S	E	Z	Q	V	X
N	M	Y	L	G	W	K	L	H	C	E	C	A	T	I	D	U	I	W	W
I	I	O	B	O	E	A	G	U	L	T	M	F	Q	A	A	K	C	U	L
A	Z	X	F	V	Z	X	I	B	O	Q	E	E	I	D	E	E	S	P	Z
W	M	W	N	W	Y	X	U	R	Q	B	U	Z	E	Y	L	U	M	M	T
F	A	S	W	A	J	O	K	P	Z	F	D	O	S	L	N	O	T	A	B
G	J	W	M	R	D	H	Z	M	E	K	S	M	O	W	Y	W	U	Q	P
W	R	O	X	N	F	L	U	T	E	O	T	E	P	M	U	R	T	H	I
Y	O	D	W	F	T	E	N	I	R	A	L	C	N	H	R	J	M	F	A

BASSOON
BATON
CELLO
CLARINET
CONDUCTOR
COR ANGLAIS
DOUBLE BASS
FLUTE
FRENCH HORN
GLOCKENSPIEL
LEADER
OBOE
PICCOLO
TIMPANI
TROMBONE
TRUMPET
TUBA
VIOLA
VIOLIN
XYLOPHONE

For more advanced Wordsearches, go to page 254

Colours

The artist's palette contains 14 colours – can you spot them all? They may read across or down in any direction. Some may overlap.

BLACK
BLUE
BROWN
CRIMSON
EMERALD
GOLD
GREEN
ORANGE
PINK
PURPLE
RED
SILVER
WHITE
YELLOW

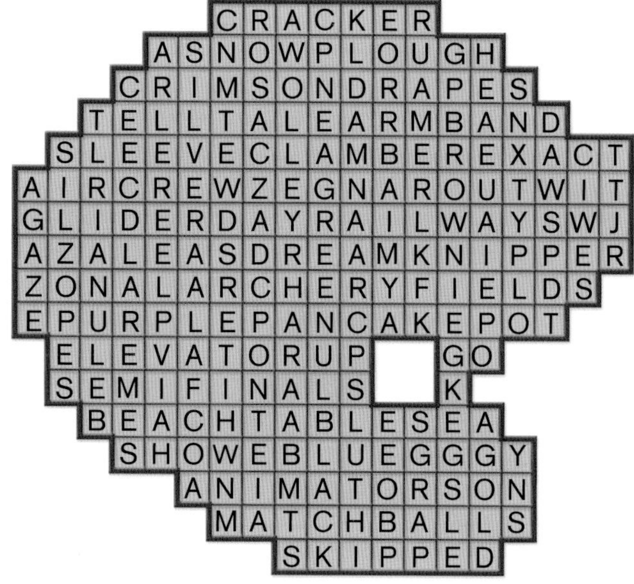

Found in the forest

The items and creatures listed below are normally concealed amongst trees in a forest. Can you uncover them all from the tree grid opposite?

BADGER
BIRCH
BLUEBELL
CEDAR
DEER
FOX
FUNGI
HEDGEHOG
JAY
LICHEN
MOSS
NUTHATCH
PINE
PRIMROSE
SQUIRREL
WOODPECKER

Bones of the body

'The hip bone's connected to the thigh bone...' Find out if this is true by locating the sixteen human bones hidden in this grid.

ANVIL
CLAVICLE
FEMUR
HAMMER
HIP
JAW
KNEECAP
PALATE
PELVIS
RIB
SCAPULA
SKULL
STERNUM
STIRRUP
ULNA
VERTEBRA

10 Garments

A whole wardrobe of clothes and accessories are immersed in this grid. Can you spot them all? One word appears twice. Which is it?

BELT	HAT	SWEATER
BOOTS	JEANS	TIE
CAP	PANTS	T-SHIRT
COAT	SCARF	VEST
DRESS	SHOES	
GLOVES	SOCKS	

		C	A	T						O	B	O		
	M	A	T	H						V	E	S	G	
O	S	L	I	N	K				S	H	C	C	F	G
J	E	K	L	A	T	R	I	H	S	T	O	R	S	A
B	A	T	C	R	O	I	F	S	T	N	A	P	A	N
A	R	R	A	O	L	D	E	H	J	C	T	A	N	K
			P	O	S	E	O	H	S	H	O			
			M	V	E	G	I	A	S	R	T			
			J	K	V	L	O	V	E	S	T			
			A	B	L	O	N	T	R	Y	S			
			F	O	Y	V	A	S	D	O	E			
			L	O	N	E	L	Y	C	A	T			
			A	T	W	S	G	L	O	V	V			
			H	S	G	R	I	H	A	T	O			
			S	N	A	E	J	A	T	P	I			

E	F	R	O	M	Y	R	U	T	N	E	C
Q	U	A	R	T	R	O	Y	C	A	R	S
U	R	T	E	P	O	U	N	D	L	A	G
U	L	T	A	M	I	B	T	E	R	T	E
G	O	E	M	E	A	N	I	N	O	C	H
Y	N	R	R	I	H	T	T	L	I	E	T
A	G	T	O	R	T	C	I	N	C	H	O
E	G	I	M	P	A	K	A	Q	E	B	N
R	E	L	M	W	E	B	O	R	D	E	R
T	H	A	T	G	A	S	M	Y	E	G	G
E	L	E	P	H	A	N	T	H	R	A	S
M	O	H	T	A	F	I	Q	U	R	E	M

11 Weights and measures

Prove that you are a heavyweight puzzler by revealing all the listed weights and measures in the grid opposite. Can you spot which word appears twice?

BARREL	KEG	QUART
CENTURY	KILO	REAM
FATHOM	LITRE	THERM
FURLONG	METRE	TON
HECTARE	PINT	
INCH	POUND	

12 Olympic venues

These venues have all hosted the Olympic Games – can you find them all in the grid? They may read across or down in any direction. Some may overlap.

Are you familiar with which countries these cities are in? If not, you could look them up in an atlas.

ATHENS	MOSCOW	SARAJEVO
BARCELONA	MUNICH	SEOUL
CALGARY	NAGANO	SYDNEY
GRENOBLE	OSLO	TOKYO
HELSINKI	PARIS	
MELBOURNE	ROME	

O	B	L	I	G	A	S	H	E	L	S	I	M	N
S	A	R	A	J	E	V	O	N	A	S	U	H	A
O	R	L	A	O	C	E	L	B	O	N	E	R	G
A	C	G	U	Y	A	P	S	Y	I	E	M	P	A
G	E	L	L	A	L	H	O	C	K	H	E	Y	N
O	L	D	A	R	G	A	H	O	R	T	J	E	O
G	O	S	I	R	A	P	A	N	T	A	H	N	O
F	N	I	C	O	R	A	C	K	E	T	S	R	Y
F	A	F	X	S	Y	D	N	Y	E	R	G	U	R
M	E	A	D	E	G	K	A	M	O	S	C	O	W
O	G	G	N	E	V	E	O	R	L	A	N	B	O
S	G	D	I	O	R	R	S	T	H	I	S	L	H
C	Y	S	P	A	N	I	K	N	I	S	L	E	H
S	I	N	K	I	M	A	Y	P	L	E	A	M	P

WORD SCRAMBLES

These puzzles are word searches with a twist. In conventional word search puzzles, the hidden words are all found in straight lines. In word scrambles, the words are found by moving from square to adjacent square horizontally, vertically and diagonally in any direction, providing an added level of difficulty.

13 Look and listen

With the aid of the two clues provided, find a three-word phrase (4,2,4 letters long) that does not repeat a letter.

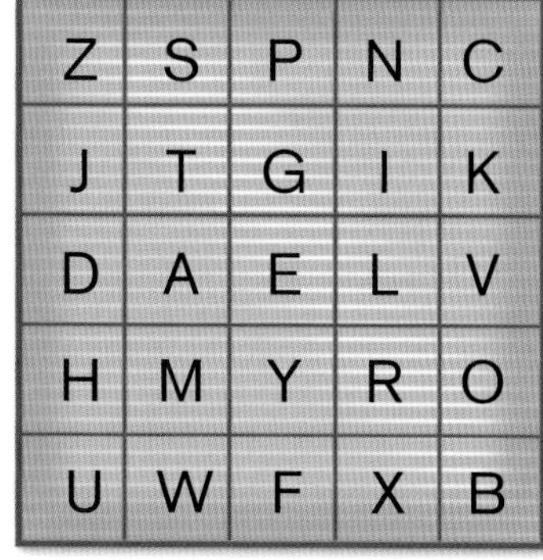

Z	S	P	N	C
J	T	G	I	K
D	A	E	L	V
H	M	Y	R	O
U	W	F	X	B

Clue 1: SIMPLY DEAR is an anagram of the phrase you are looking for.

Clue 2: Look and listen.

14 Optimistic?

Starting at the centre square, work from letter to letter to find six optimistic words. Each letter in the grid is used only once.

Clue: The first word starts with 'P'.

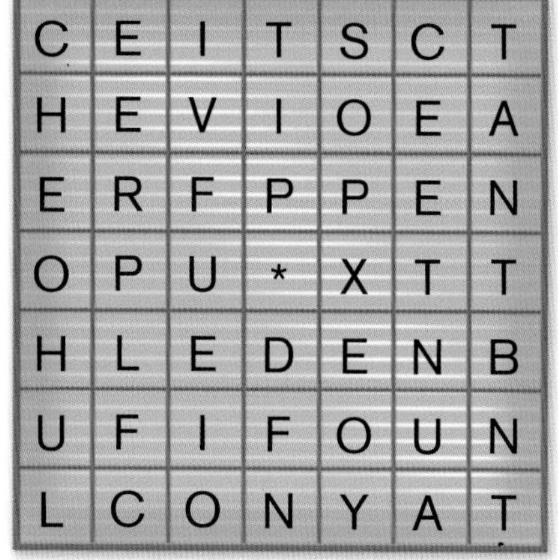

C	E	I	T	S	C	T
H	E	V	I	O	E	A
E	R	F	P	P	E	N
O	P	U	*	X	T	T
H	L	E	D	E	N	B
U	F	I	F	O	U	N
L	C	O	N	Y	A	T

15 Colours

In this puzzle, by moving from square to square, you should be able to find to find 14 colours. Squares may be used more than once, but not in the same word.

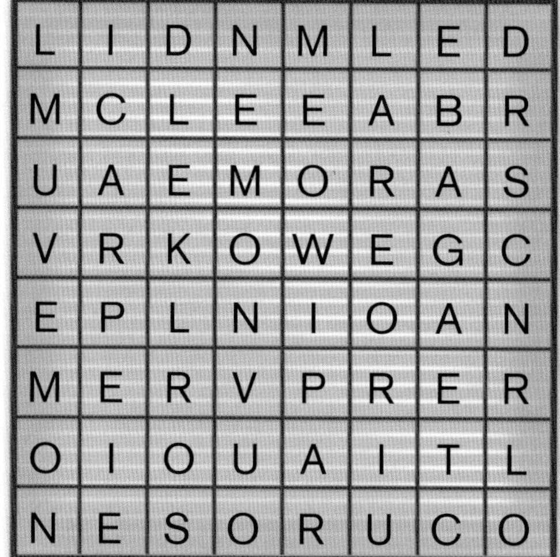

L	I	D	N	M	L	E	D
M	C	L	E	E	A	B	R
U	A	E	M	O	R	A	S
V	R	K	O	W	E	G	C
E	P	L	N	I	O	A	N
M	E	R	V	P	R	E	R
O	I	O	U	A	I	T	L
N	E	S	O	R	U	C	O

16 One word

What is the longest word that can be found in this grid by working from square to square in any direction? You may start anywhere you like, but each letter can be used only once.

B	W	L	G	S
V	E	X	O	D
J	Y	R	H	I
P	K	A	M	Q
C	F	T	U	N

Clue:
A place of burial.

17 One word 2

What is the longest word that can be found in this grid by working from square to square in any direction? You may start anywhere you like, but each letter can be used only once.

W	Y	D	T	X
H	K	V	E	Z
S	C	M	B	G
A	R	O	N	U
P	J	I	F	L

Clue: Bore out

20 Find the phrase

Starting at the top left-hand corner letter and finishing at the bottom right-hand corner, work from square to square to find a well-known phrase. Use each letter once.

F	A	T	S	S
N	R	C	I	C
G	A	T	I	T
E	T	H	F	I
R	A	N	O	N

Clue: You had better believe it!

18 Error message

Starting wherever you wish, find four words meaning 'error'. Letters may be used more than once, but not in the same word.

L	B	R	D	K
T	U	N	E	A
I	Y	G	H	T
X	L	I	S	O
A	M	R	E	V

21 US states

This grid contains the names of 16 US states. How many can you find? Squares may be used more than once, but not in the same name.

L	Y	K	S	A	R	E	C
A	R	A	L	W	D	I	O
D	N	A	B	A	L	E	X
T	O	M	F	L	A	E	M
A	N	A	E	O	N	W	Y
T	U	T	X	H	R	O	G
N	R	E	A	D	I	E	R
O	M	S	V	M	A	N	K

19 All-embracing

With the aid of the two clues provided, find a three word phrase (4,4,4 letters long) that does not repeat a letter.

Y	J	A	R	U
V	N	G	B	M
D	E	I	T	S
L	W	P	H	F
Z	K	C	O	X

Clue 1:
THIS MANPOWER is an anagram of the phrase you are looking for.

Clue 2:
All-embracing welcome.

!
With these puzzles you are simultaneously exercising your vocabulary and your powers of observation and logic – making them particularly effective Brain Stretchers.

WORD LADDERS

Transform one word into another by altering a single letter at each step, creating a new word on each rung of the ladder along the way.

Turn PALE into DARK
1. Peel
2. Public space

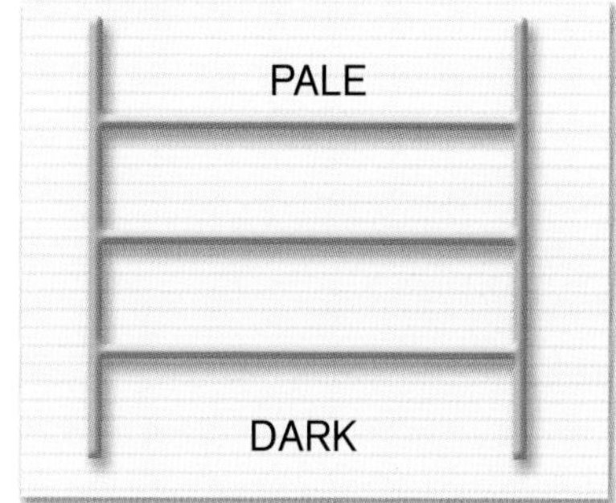

Turn DOG into CAT
1. Small gear wheel
2. Baby's bed

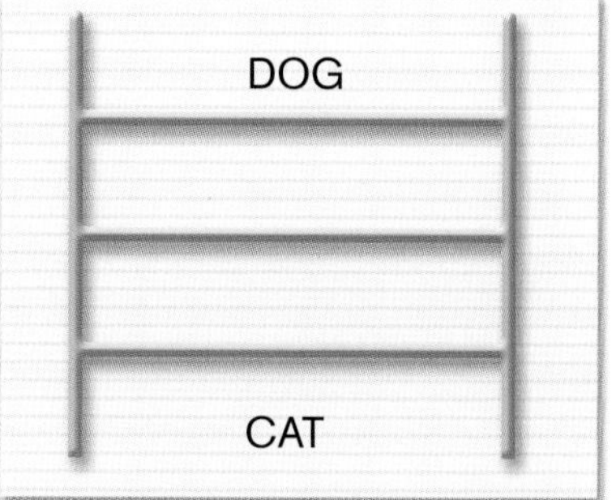

Turn BALL into FOOT
1. Seed capsule
2. Arrow
3. Young horse
4. Aquatic bird

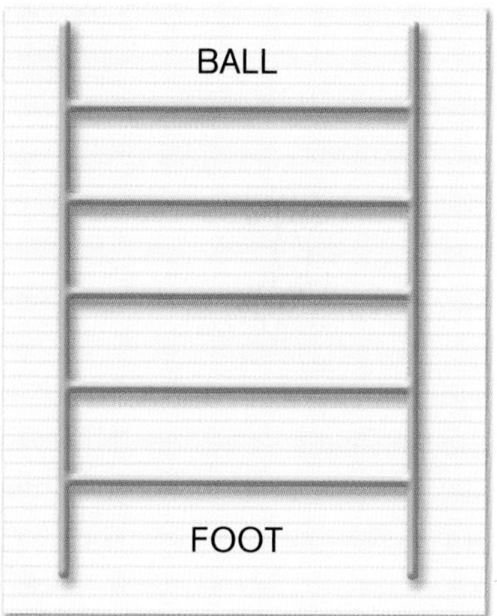

Turn GAEL into CELT

1. Impudence or cheek
2. Strong wind
3. Light in colour
4. Legendary soccer player
5. Animal's skin

Turn BURN into CURE

1. 'To the Manor......'
2. On-the-cob
3. Pull-string
4. Coagulated milk
5. Ringlet

In this puzzle, we've taken out the clues to make it a little more difficult.

Turn BASS into SOLE

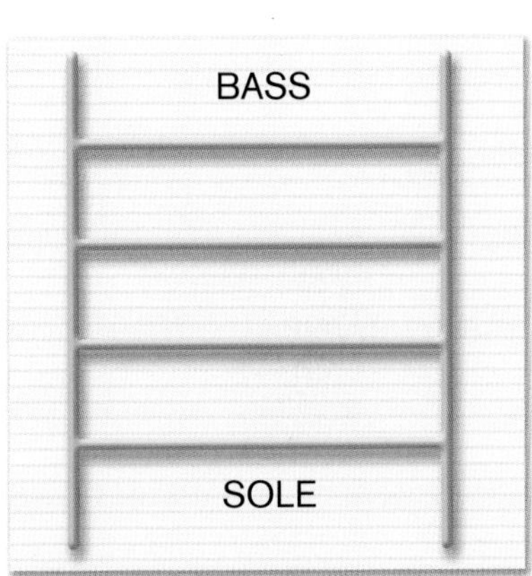

Invented in 1878 by Lewis Carroll, the author of *Alice in Wonderland*, these puzzles test both your vocabulary and deduction skills.

For more advanced Word Ladders, go to page **253**

WORD PYRAMIDS

In each of these puzzles you are given a number of clues. The first answer has two letters, the second three letters, the third four, and so on. Each answer consists of the same letters as the previous word plus one additional letter which you have to find.

28

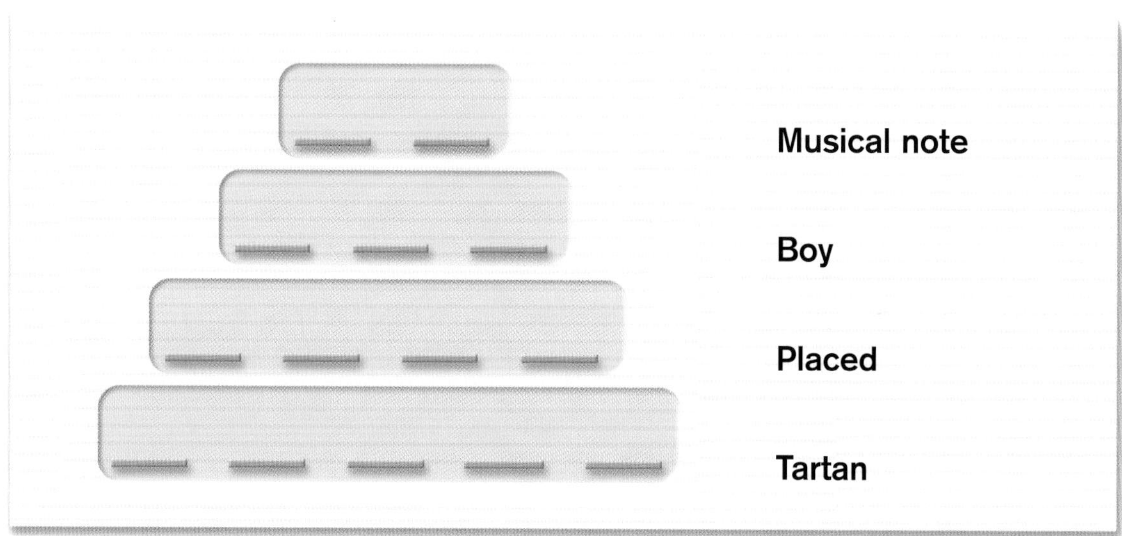

29

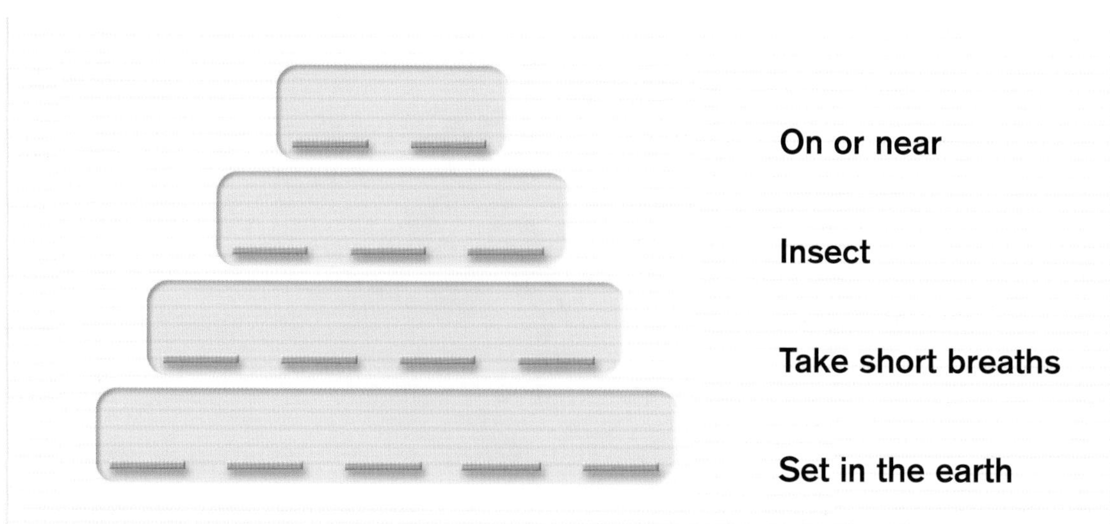

30

At home

Can

One of a pair

Yarn

Sudden ache

If you can't answer the clues at the top of the pyramid try to solve later clues. By taking letters away from words you do know, you can work backwards and fill in the gaps.

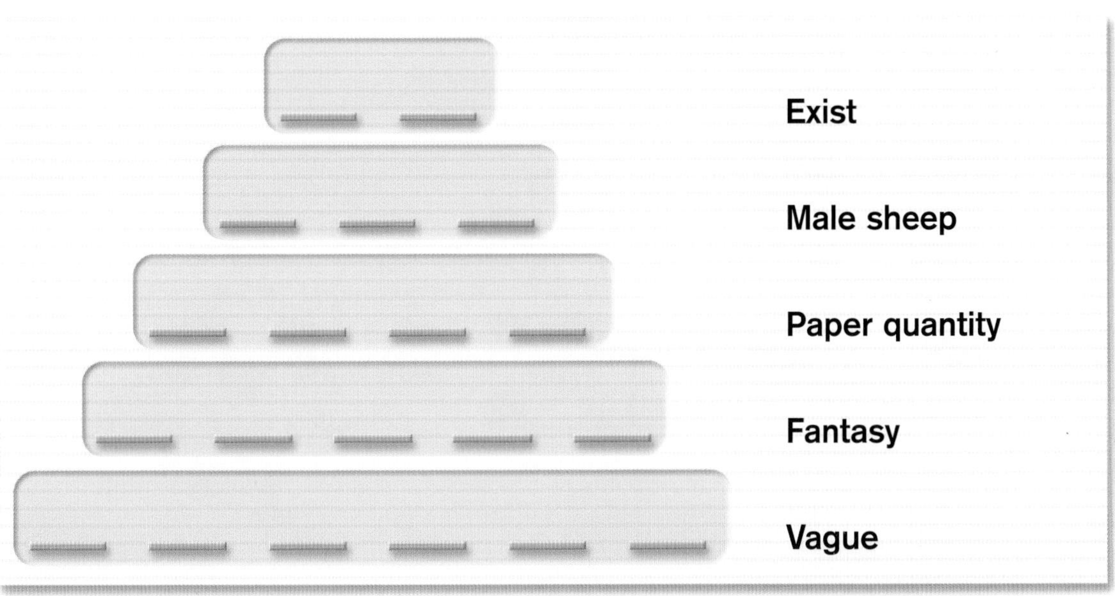

Exist

Male sheep

Paper quantity

Fantasy

Vague

WORD BLOCK-INS

Arrange the letter blocks into their correct position in the grid to form a symmetrical crossword. Several rows contain two words, and the Down words will appear once you have the blocks correctly placed. You may find it helpful to cross off each box as you go.

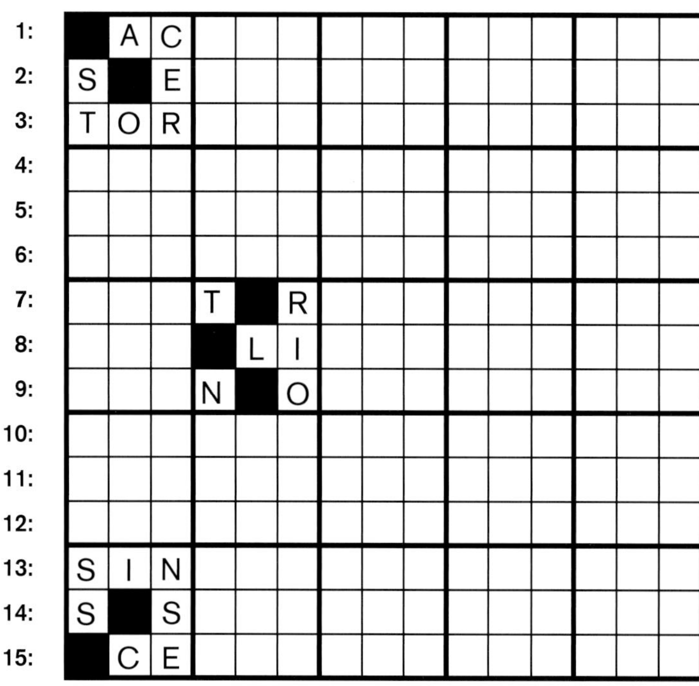

32

Block-in 1

Using the **Across** clues featured below can you place the given word blocks in their proper places? A few have been provided to get you started.

Row 1: Admit • Push forcefully
Row 2: Dried grass
Row 3: Windstorm • Tableland
Row 4: Manipulate
Row 5: Vine fruits • Water boiler
Row 6: Recuperate
Row 7: Female relative • Sports side
Row 8: Driving permit (British spelling)
Row 9: Divisible by two • Affirm
Row 10: Strange
Row 11: Reproductions • Royal residence
Row 12: Got together
Row 13: Earnest • Version of events
Row 14: Jog
Row 15: Middle • Martial art

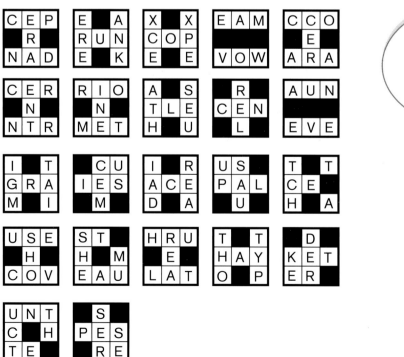

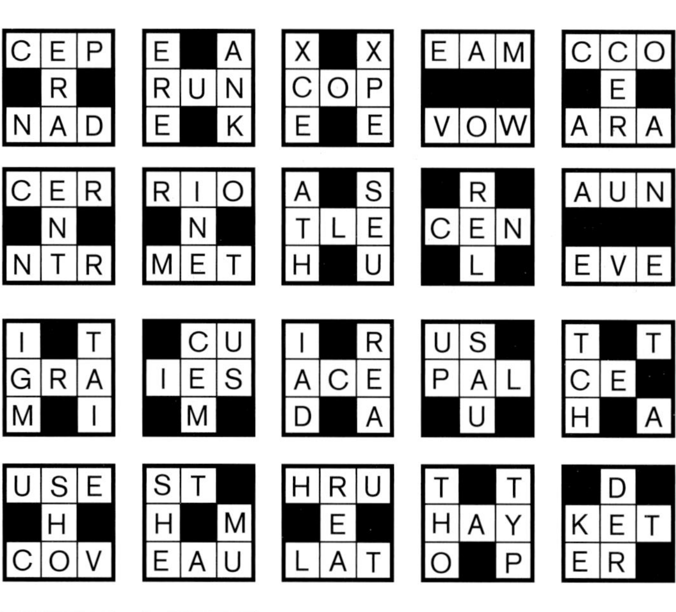

The clues here are for solutions that read across only, so you can disregard words that read down.

33 Block-in 2

Here are some **Across** clues:
Row 1: Vital (9). Row 3: Coal carrier (7)
Row 5: Sudden, violent thrust (6).
Row 9: Trial (10). Row 13: N. American bison (7)

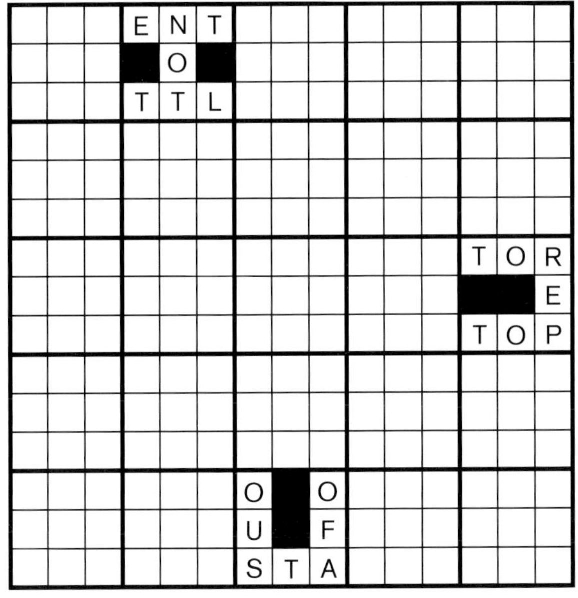

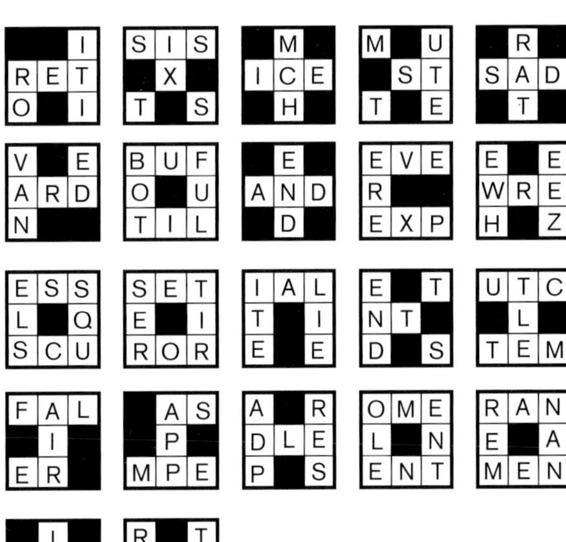

34 Block-in 3

Here are some **Across** clues:
Row 2: Conscious (5). Row 6: Personnel (5)
Row 10: The 'feeling' organ (5)
Row 14: A way of living (9)

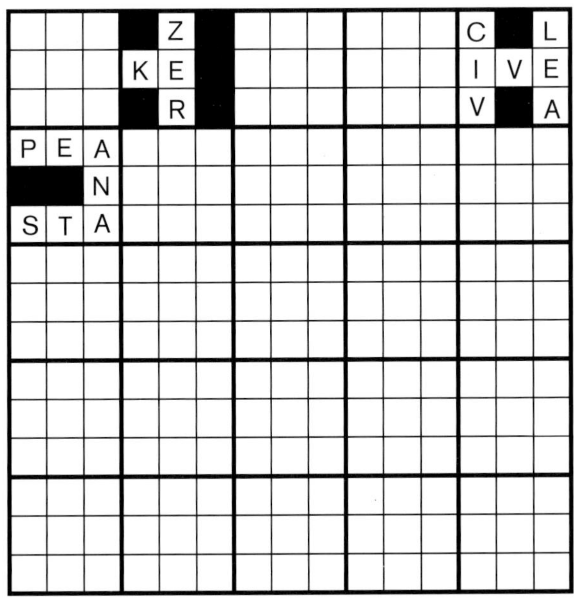

CONCISE CROSSWORDS

Concise or 'quick' crosswords test your vocabulary and general knowledge, making them great puzzles to get you warmed up for some of the more difficult word challenges that lie ahead.

Across

1. Normal score for golf hole (3)
4. Material for funeral fire (4)
8. Burden (4)
10. Mass of baked bread (4)
11. Affectations (5)
13. Dad's sister? (4)
14. Necessitating (9)
16. Twisted so as to expel moisture (5)
17. People who perform (5)
18. Female custodian of a child (9)
22. Period of fasting for Christians (4)
23. Type of fabric (5)
24. Every one separately considered (4)
25. Inert gas (4)
26. Mixture of black and white (4)
27. Practical skill (3)

Down

1. Bishop of Rome (4) **2.** Soon (4) **3.** Corrosion (4) **4.** American fellows living in flat territory (9) **5.** Youthful (5) **6.** Called phone (4) **7.** Newt (3) **9.** Fit for a voyage (9) **12.** Fathers (5) **15.** Entices (5) **17.** Unpleasant word for slow learner (5) **18.** Close by (4) **19.** Region (4) **20.** Stravinsky's first name (4) **21.** Small depression (4) **22.** Stage of race (3)

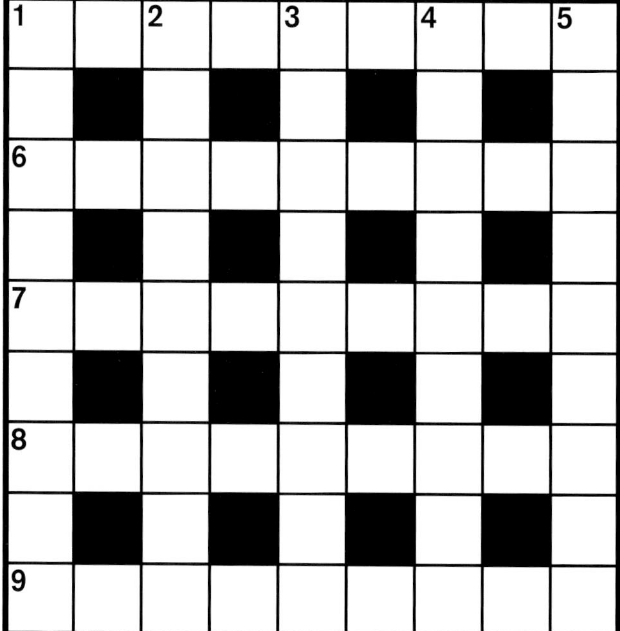

Across

1. They emit exhaust from US cars (9)
6. Carnage (9)
7. People who have them want to travel (5,4)
8. Hugging (9)
9. Territory of an Arab chief (9)

Down

1. Desirable quality in food (9)
2. Quick-tempered (9)
3. Ride often given to children (9)
4. Corrupted (9)
5. A plan to gain advantage (9)

37

Across

1. Male charmer, flirt (6,3)
6. Tool for picking up sugar cubes (5)
7. Untruth (3)
8. Judge's gown (4)
10. Mark as correct (4)
13. Choose (3)
14. Minor road (5)
16. Assess, review (4,5)

Down

1. At a following time (5)
2. Mouse-coloured (3)
3. The Orient (4)
4. Soldier's civilian clothing (5)
5. Point of an ink pen (3)
9. Indonesian method of cloth decoration (5)
11. Lightweight canoe (5)
12. Wading bird worshipped by the ancient Egyptians (4)
13. Dismissed as a batter (3)
15. Go a-courting (3)

38

Across

1. Prohibited by social custom (5)
4. Small ornamental sphere (3)
6. Unable to bite? (9)
7. Birds of the crow family (4)
8. Part of milk separated from the curd (4)
10. Driver's measuring device (4,5)
12. Annoying bark (5)
13. Upright and rigid (5)

Down

1. Make knotted lace (3)
2. Disguised explosive device (5,4)
3. Darts players' line (4)
4. Invitation to visit at any time (4,5)
5. Bearskin hat (5)
7. Wharf (5)
9. Gape rudely (4)
11. Consume (3)

Across

3. First digit (5)
6. Expensive edible shellfish (6)
7. Dutch relative? (5)
8. Item's name derived from a person (6)
9. Black tar residue (5)
12. Smooths with rough paper (5)
15. Crowd together (6)
16. Main artery carrying blood from the heart (5)
17. Fixed grin (6)
18. Abnormal occurrence (5)

Down

1. Shortness of sight (6)
2. Pelted with rocks (6)
3. Card of the master suit (5)
4. Not abridged (5)
5. Furniture timber (5)
10. Legally charge (6)
11. Hard area of skin (6)
12. Employees (5)
13. Carer for sick people (5)
14. Large predatory fish (5)

Across

1. One of the conspirators in Shakespeare's *Julius Caesar* (5)
4. Fundamental (5)
7. Non-amateur (3)
8. Singing with closed lips (7)
9. Elderly (4)
10. ___ of Dogs, London region (4)
13. Maths exercise (3)
15. Warms and dries (laundry) (4)
16. Sprites (4)
19. Looked (for talent) (7)
21. Self-importance (3)
22. Be anxious (5)
23. Dangerous, chancy (5)

Down

1. Point of land running into the sea (4) **2.** Freeloader (7)
3. Insects which attack plants (6) **4.** Minor collision (4) **5.** Take part in a winter sport (3)
6. Baby swan (6) **11.** Late meals (7) **12.** Poland's capital (6) **14.** Personal bodyguard (6)
17. Remain (4) **18.** John ____, edible fish (4) **20.** Rowing stick (3)

41

The answer to each **Across** clue is a place in the country or region specified.

Across

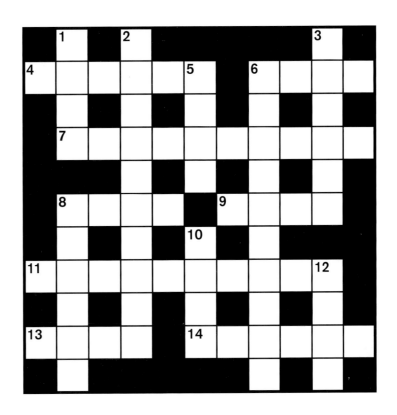

4. In Saudi Arabia (6)
6. In Peru (4)
7. In Kent (10)
8. In NE England (4)
9. In Moravia (4)
11. In California (10)
13. In NW England (4)
14. In Greece (6)

Down

1. Record (4)
2. *Little Lord* _______ (10)
3. Early stage of life (6)
5. Part of foot (4)
6. Mazes (10)
8. Interruption (6)
10. Jane Austen's heroine (4)
12. Noise of pig (4)

42

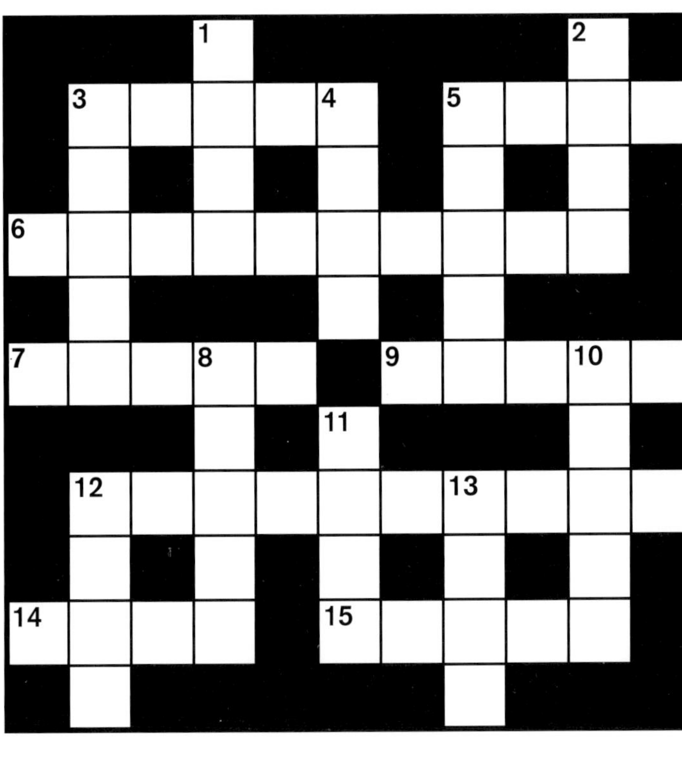

Each **Across** clue is a quotation from a poem, and the solution is the surname of the poet who wrote it.

Across

3. Wee, sleekit, cow'rin', tim'rous beastie (5)
5. Let not ambition mock their useful toil (4)
6. Earth has not anything to show more fair (10)
7. The moon is up, and yet it is not night (5)
9. Was it a vision, or a waking dream? (5)
12. But when she was bad she was horrid (10)
14. What a beautiful Pussy you are (4)
15. Things fall apart; the centre cannot hold (5)

Down

1. Parched (4)
2. Curse (4)
3. Plunder (5)
4. Stitched (4)
5. Ravine (5)
8. Possessor (5)
10. Implements (5)
11. Dubious (4)
12. Sediment (4)
13. Jump (4)

CRYPTIC CROSSWORDS

Each clue in a Cryptic Crossword is a puzzle by itself. The clue will contain some form of wordplay as well as a standard definition. Either of these two parts of a clue may come first. The two parts strung together may provide a deceptive meaning. The keys to solving Cryptic Crosswords are recognizing where the two parts separate, which is standard definition and which is wordplay.

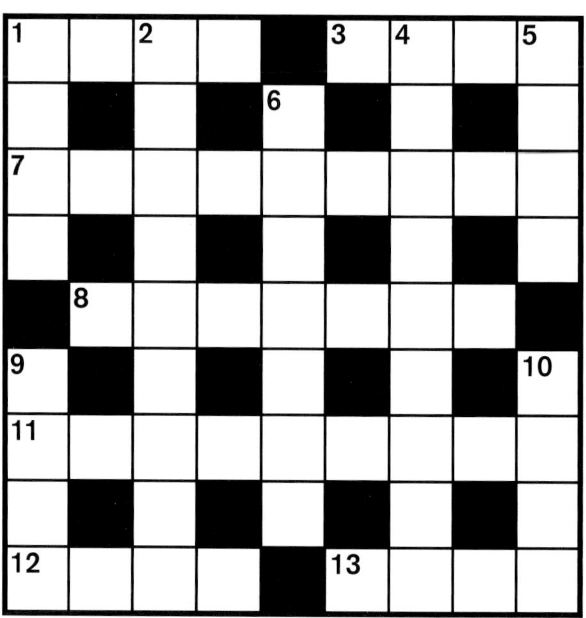

Across

1. Search for the crest (4)
3. Touch down on the earth (4)
7. Sid backs answers then vanishes (9)
8. Squeeze round it to find text (7)
11. Teach about cool confection (9)
12. Flower grew (4)
13. Take off for Cape Elizabeth bridge (4)

Down

1. Secret message with fish starter (4)
2. Fungi give character to quiet spaces (9)
4. Benefit of distributing vegan data (9)
5. Satellite receiver on vessel (4)
6. National Trust starts right in cool command (7)
9. Point to vehicle with mark (4)
10. Robust reservoir (4)

When rearranged the letters in the blue boxes will give the name of a state in the USA.

Across

1. Make film about twig (5)
4. Put on platform (5)
8. Printed true composition, then disturbed (11)
9. True shellfish changes brightness constantly (7)
10. Pigment found in Kent (3)
12. Number south of nine (3)
13. It sits in visor of traveller (7)
15. Set apart, I sigh in dust storm (11)
16. North African country where every grain you plant thrives at first (5)
17. Quick round, early start at banquet (5)

US State:

____

Down

2. Found summons in delivering script (11) 3. Crumble a scone in the seas (6) 5. Sort of printed letter (4)
6. New buildings for young plants (11) 7. Flat fish one finds dazzling (9) 11. Miniscule record (6)
14. Ban on putting balls in pockets (4)

Across

1. Just blonde (4)
4. Right award for gown (4)
7. Fix oil platform (3)
8. Holiday home featuring an ice-cream flavour (7)
10. Require the French pointer (6)
12. Light-sounding bucket (4)
13. Press metal (4)
15. Monster to continue tediously (6)
19. Frightful house I'd redeveloped (7)
20. Sports kit includes downhill racer's item (3)
21. Release at no cost (4)
22. Nobody fails to finish at midday (4)

Down

2. Corner fish (5)
3. Five in Scottish dance make merry (5)
4. Call for item of jewellery (4)
5. Modelling wood, a thick piece taken up (5)
6. Threateningly wave cereal bowl? (8)
9. *Lost City*, at last in translation (8)
11. Part of ordinary racket (3)
12. Dad swallows eastern vegetable (3)
14. Give instructions to group of monks (5)
16. Rinse out sap (5)
17. Great enthusiasm got us upset (5)
18. Manage company exercise class (4)

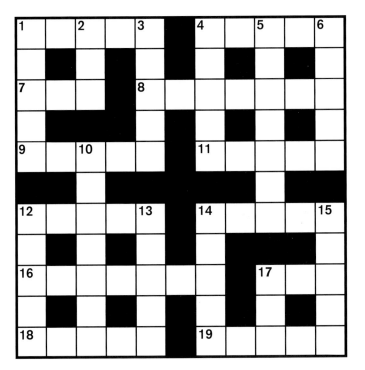

Across

1. District surrounding northern stadium (5)
4. Mum and boy stone worker (5)
7. Starts to observe weedy little bird (3)
8. Two vehicles outside a mobile home (7)
9. Piece of land is said to be shadowed (5)
11. Laurel's partner is frost resistant (5)
12. Precise former law (5)
14. Car race to get better (5)
16. Eat bird (7)
17. Health resort in Surfer's Paradise (3)
18. Admit the French can (3,2)
19. Ancient Italian manor renovated (5)

Down

1. Concerned with a boxing match (5)
2. Reveal every other fish (3)
3. A Caledonian racecourse (5)
4. Spoil quiet fenland (5)
5. More than a few cut off, almost all (7)
6. Childminder's goat (5)
10. Insistent worker follows first man (7)
12. Lease out artist's stand (5)
13. Part of a parrot, a long claw (5)
14. Oarsman, one who argues? (5)
15. Long, long time before start of night (5)
17. Consumer holding quantity of money (3)

47

Across

1. Holly, for example, is always naive (9)
6. Money for loaves (5)
7. Wine holder's duty (3)
8. Healthy water source (4)
10. Requests not to begin tasks (4)
13. Small drink for toddler (3)
14. Desert plants found during botanic activity (5)
16. Gets eager to exchange chocolate gift (6,3)

Down

1. Joint presented in enamel bowl (5)
2. Sheep trapped in sewer (3)
3. Divine creatures, playful dogs (4)
4. Mr Presley lives, surprisingly (5)
5. Fishing mesh in marine trawler (3)
9. Louts damage water lily (5)
11. Discard catapult (5)
12. Care about area of land (4)
13. Draw garment for the neck (3)
15. Signal for actor to get snooker stick (3)

48

Across

1. Every peach unstarted (4)
3. Went along with a selfish desire (6)
8. Gets in the way of picnic baskets (7)
9. Musical twosome in arduous surroundings (3)
10. Funny man's journey in cartoon story (5,5)
13. Poorly co-ordinate the painting and papering (10)
17. Historical age for section of the peerage (3)
18. Washrooms vandalized by spray can (7)
19. Scandinavian's vegetables (6)
20. Prevent the return of pots (4)

Down

1. Speech often includes repeated sound (4) **2.** Brief film role came to nothing (5) **4.** Fuel gossip (3) **5.** More mature tree (5) **6.** PS – door, being damaged, hangs down (6) **7.** Nero is moving higher in rank (6) **11.** Planet featured in NASA turnabout (6) **12.** Snakes and ladders has not started (6) **14.** Trace broken packing case (5) **15.** Start where film actors work (5) **16.** Cut film extract (4) **18.** Mimic primate (3)

49

Across

6. Doctor of the French navy is up-to-date (6)
7. Mother's sister likes flaked tuna (4)
8. Ryan's in rave about annual celebration (11)
9. Prepared notice before delivered speech (9)
11. Amused to register part-time soldiers to eat in mess (11)
13. Fillet second one (4)
14. Large number of the feminine type (6)

Down

1. Point out man in trouble at the summit (8,3)
2. Call up from harem in Dubai (6)
3. Between point and wound is curious (11)
4. Break-up in kitchen (4)
5. Send away igniter of components (11)
10. Thin surface of New York (6)
12. They see what those in agreement hear (4)

50

Across

7. I was grateful for a very soft rice and date pudding (11)
8. Sung at Christmas by girl (5)
9. Sore about you saying "money" (5)
10. Cat's foot on point of finding chess piece (4)
12. Reject southern vandal (4)
15. Ransack with firearm (5)
16. Astonish by a labyrinth (5)
18. An instant dessert for boxer's assistant (5,6)

Down

1. Take express using celebrity's trademark (11)
2. Drive on to railway siding (4)
3. Mid-section, brown, holding a couple of students (5)
4. There's merit in changing the automatic switch (5)
5. Holy man will bend and stiffen (6)
6. It's strange – grit finishes have little value (4,3,4)
11. Talk nonsense about batter pudding (6)
13. Spirited hothead found in Western Australia (5)
14. Artist leaves caramel for desert animal (5)
17. The smallest part of a male cat (4)

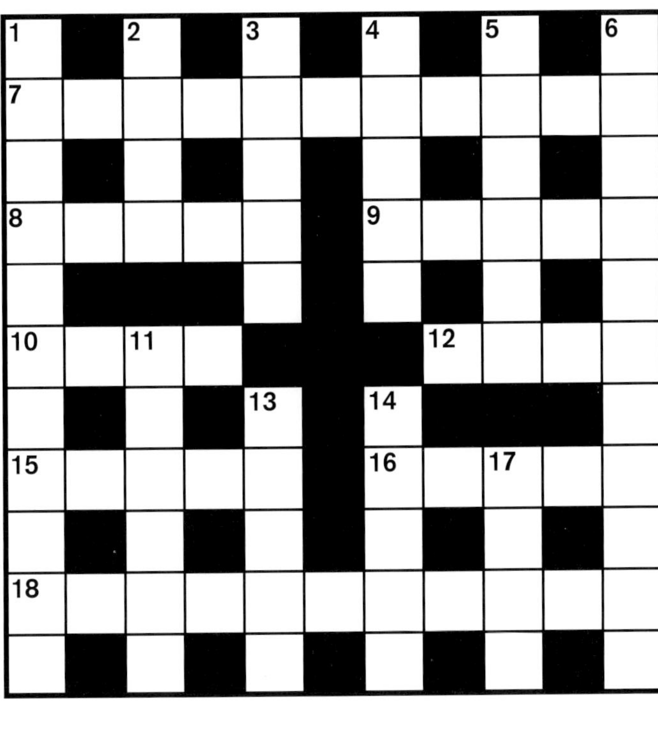

ACROSTICS

This novel take on an ancient puzzle asks you to solve the given clues and place the answers in the square grids provided. The result reveals initial letters which form a new word; a self-contained and neat solution.

51

In the next three puzzles, solve the clues by writing the answers into the grid across. Once complete, Column A will spell out a bonus word.

Row 1: Competent • Nought
Row 2: Dice shape • Savour
Row 3: Hire • Immense
Row 4: Promise • Worth
Row 5: Cow meat • Produce
Row 6: Absent • Child carer
Row 7: Steal • Fifty per cent

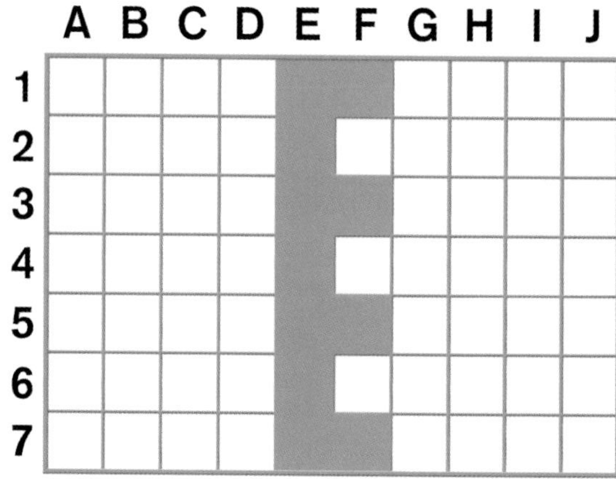

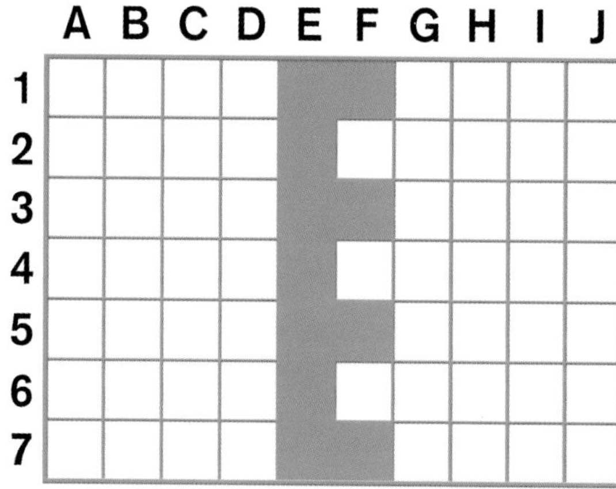

52

Row 1: Give up • Previous
Row 2: Second-hand • Thespian
Row 3: Female relative • Shove
Row 4: Young sheep • Deadly
Row 5: Heavy metal • Foray
Row 6: Squad • Arm part
Row 7: Sharp tug • Croon

53

Row 1: Shout • Unchallenging
Row 2: Follow orders • Start
Row 3: Equipment • Prison
Row 4: Injured • Rap
Row 5: Encourage • Final
Row 6: Fury • Rot
Row 7: Use a keyboard • Visage
(Bonus word in British spelling)

	A	B	C	D	E	F	G	H	I	J
1										
2										
3										
4										
5										
6										
7										

54

For the following three puzzles solve the clues in the main grid row by row, then transfer the relevant letters to form a quote below. Column A will spell out its author.

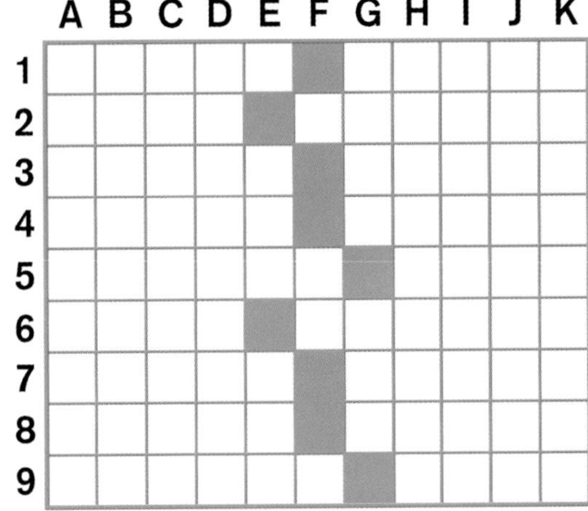

Row 1: Bravery award • Meadow
Row 2: Unsightly • Racket sport
Row 3: Clever • Pass out
Row 4: Slippery • Ability
Row 5: Beginning • Journey
Row 6: Bread • Ruddy
Row 7: Bury • Nominated
Row 8: Nude • Compose
Row 9: Ask over • Perspective

QUOTE:
3I; 6D/9I/7H; 1K; 9C; 8B; 7B; 4D; 2G/1G; 6H; 2C; 1J; 6I; 8G/7I; 9J/4I; 3G/5J/8H; 9F; 5H; 5B; 8K;1D; 2F/4H; 2J; 6G; 4B; 1A; 8D

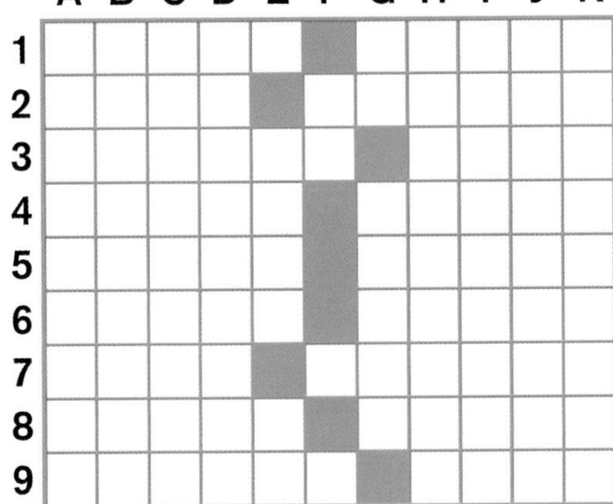

55

Row 1: Toss • Frightening
Row 2: Resound • Seem
Row 3: Delicate • Halt
Row 4: Unkind • Humped animal
Row 5: Cinema employee • Central area
Row 6: Magnificent • Topic
Row 7: Snake sound • Package
Row 8: Vacant • Entire
Row 9: Stress • Hold

QUOTE:
1E; 6H; 5I; 6G/2C; 7G; 9K; 2G; 5D; 9F; 4D/3C; 6D/3I; 5C; 6K/8H; 2I; 4H; 9I; 9B/1G; 9E; 4I; 8C; 8J; 1K/5G; 2F; 3K; 7F; 7J; 3D; 7D

56

	A	B	C	D	E	F	G	H	I	J	K
1											
2											
3											
4											
5											
6											
7											
8											
9											

Row 1: Emblem • Neckwear
Row 2: Notebook • Money reserve
Row 3: Pacific • Frequently
Row 4: Wash off soap • Male bee
Row 5: Pleasant • Kudos
Row 6: Heroic • Liquid
Row 7: Expel • Cup
Row 8: Lottery • Photo
Row 9: Dull colour • Hurt feelings

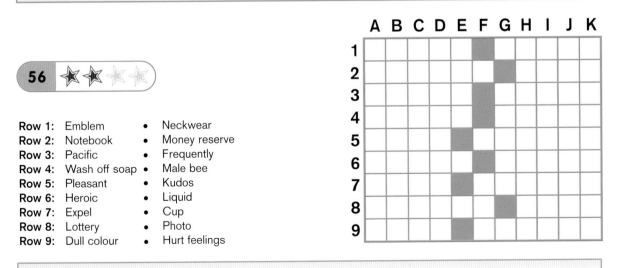

QUOTE:
7K; 2B; 2I/8I;1I; 6D; 8F/2D; 4I/6G; 5B; 3E; 1C/5I; 7F/9J; 3G; 7H; 4C; 2E/9I; 6H; 5J; 1E/1H; 8B; 2J/8D; 4B; 3K; 4G/6J; 8K/1K; 9F; 5G/9D; 8J; 7B

ANAGRAMS

Take a word, mix it up, and you have an anagram. Each of these words or phrases can be unscrambled to produce a single word – and they get harder as they go along. Beware – some of the harder puzzles may require a bit of lateral thinking!

Farmer's market

Here are ten anagrams for you to untangle. Each two-word phrase can be unscrambled to provide the name of a fruit or vegetable.

1. TOO APT
2. STARRY BREW
3. CASH PIN
4. NO GEAR
5. NEAT REIGN
6. CUTE LET
7. EGO CUTTER (British variation)
8. PIPE PANEL
9. ROOMS HUM
10. RIP COAT

Hollywood who's who

The first and last names of eight international film stars, past and present, are hidden in these anagrams. How quickly can you unscramble them?

1. COAL PAIN
2. NO JEAN FAD
3. NO NORMAL BARD
4. MONK'S HAT

5. THORN SEASON
6. SWOLLEN ROSE
7. SLOWER ULCERS
8. BESTIAL JUROR

Mixed bag

In the next eight anagrams you don't have a thematic link to give you a clue.

1. LISTEN
2. ADMIRER
3. CARTHORSE
4. DREADS

5. DIM NIECE
6. SAD PITCH
7. CRAM INTO
8. TEMPT ONCE

Confused countries

Can you find the eight places hidden in these anagrams? Each two-word phrase can be unscrambled to make the name of a country.

1. WE SEND
2. REAL DIN
3. OLD PAN
4. NEAR GYM

5. BIG MULE
6. TIME VAN
7. AGE LIAR
8. SAFARI TOUCH

Name game

Rearrange the letters of these phrases to find six girls' names. Then take the initials of each of the six and use them to make a boy's name.

1. EAT NAIL
2. ART BORE
3. FIND WIRE
4. ALE NAG
5. REAL ONE
6. HEN PAD

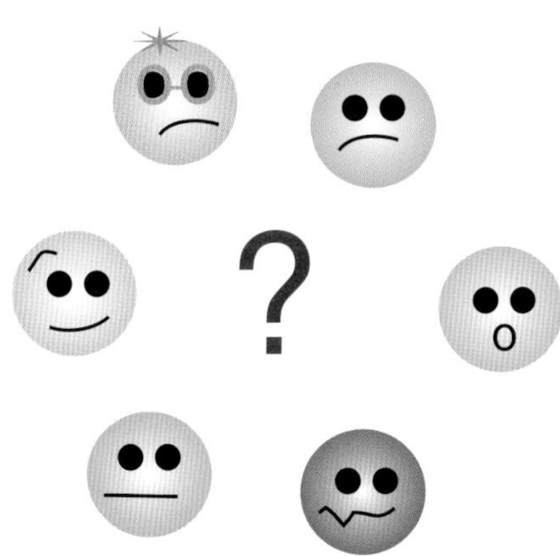

Tricky anagram

Rearrange the letters in this phrase to make a single word:

GROWN LADIES

DEFINITIONS

Test your word power and knowledge with these teasers. There is only one correct answer to the given definition and the remainder are designed to confuse you. This selection should be achievable, with those in **Word Challenges** proving more tricky.

Words, words, words

Test your vocabulary with these 15 words. We've provided four definitions for each, but only one is correct. Can you identify all 15?

1. **PUFFIN**
a seabird
b engine
c chocolate bar
d flower

2. **MOUSSAKA**
a Mexican bandit
b Polish song
c Greek dish
d Arab horse

3. **TANGIBLE**
a edible
b palpable
c uncomfortable
d depressing

4. **PICCOLO**
a Italian dance
b small puppy
c small flute
d large bucket

5. **CASCADE**
a type of nut
b cosmetic
c marketplace
d waterfall

6. **CANASTA**
a Easter hymn
b card game
c sweetmeat
d white flower

7. **SAVVY**
a shrewd
b sausage
c flavour
d rude

8. **TRIDENT**
a three-sided figure
b milk teeth
c sports car
d three-pronged spear

9. **REEK**
a root vegetable
b stagger
c smell
d seashell

10. **HISTRIONIC**
a Spanish
b melodramatic
c old-fashioned
d argumentative

11. **MURAL**
a dungarees
b gloomy
c earthy
d wall painting

12. **YOKEL**
a rotten egg
b country bumpkin
c farm tool
d Alpine singing

13. **CLOUT**
a bulb
b soil
c hit
d miss

14. **LARCH**
a type of fish
b type of tree
c type of butter
d type of roof

15. **GNARLED**
a shouted
b confusing
c wrestled
d weather-beaten

Don't be misled

Can you see the wood for the trees? We've provided four definitions for each of these 15 words – one of them correct, the other three misleading. Can you avoid being led astray?

1. **IMPECCABLE**
a exaggerated
b faultless
c difficult
d mistaken

2. **PRISE**
a turn round
b beat up
c close down
d force open

3. **HAUGHTY**
a arrogant
b harmful
c stiff
d concealed

4. **ENVISAGE**
a illustrate
b disguise
c imagine
d explain

5. **SEVER**
a strict
b cut off
c reach
d decide

6. **ENTREATY**
a peace agreement
b rear entrance
c appeal
d illness

7. **ERODE**
a cunning
b establish
c evaporate
d wear down

8. **SERENE**
a tranquil
b lunar
c serious
d shadowy

9. **TIDINGS**
a vegetable peelings
b information
c large crowds
d seawater

10. **NONCHALANT**
a inexperienced
b unmusical
c theoretical
d unconcerned

11. **BALDERDASH**
a wall decoration
b loud music
c nonsense
d cycle race

12. **CENSURE**
a reproach
b reassure
c refresh
d refuse

13. **TURBULENT**
a ramshackle
b stormy
c successful
d irritating

14. **BETROTHED**
a married
b engaged
c betrayed
d confused

15. **NURTURE**
a support
b countryside
c notice
d disapproval

Vibrant vocabulary

68

How word-wise are you? Test your vocabulary with these 15 words. There are four definitions for each – but only one of them is right. How quickly can you pick the correct meanings?

1. MYNAH
a Chinese emperor
b Asian bird
c deep-sea fish
d Indian headdress

2. INDEFATIGABLE
a watertight
b bottomless
c irresistible
d tireless

3. FRACAS
a cotton
b soup
c brawl
d donkey

4. ODIOUS
a smelly
b lazy
c angry
d hateful

5. ACUMEN
a sharpness
b crossword
c brigade
d feather

6. SUPPLE
a willow
b flexible
c snack
d clever

7. PEDICURE
a type of bicycle
b horse-race
c foot treatment
d religious ceremony

8. EPICURE
a chiropodist
b archbishop
c pickle
d gourmet

9. FLUNKY
a footman
b cowardly
c river
d lucky

10. PRELATE
a early
b anticipate
c bishop
d balding

11. TINE
a side of a mountain
b prong of a fork
c feather of a wing
d fraction of a second

12. CASSOULET
a cloud formation
b palm tree
c flightless bird
d type of stew

13. CURB
a dog
b restrain
c twist
d corner

14. THWART
a obstruct
b dark-coloured
c crunch
d leg bone

15. MALCONTENT
a computer virus
b overfull
c dissatisfied
d inappropriate

Speaking in tongues

69

You may think you have a large vocabulary – but do you only use English words? Our language has absorbed many words and phrases from all round the world. Study these examples and decide (or guess) which of the four definitions is the correct one.

1. SAUTÉ (French)
a saucepan
b white wine
c hot
d fry

2. SPRINGBOK (Afrikaans)
a right-angle
b jack-hammer
c antelope
d tropical flower

3. TERRA INCOGNITA (Latin)
a unknown land
b space exploration
c an allotment
d not guilty

4 SOTTO VOCE (Italian)
a orchestral music
b cooked with prawns
c in a quiet voice
d underwater

5. GUNG HO (Cantonese)
a canvas belt
b ginger sauce
c death penalty
d trigger-happy

6. MACAW (Caribbean)
a sandy beach
b colourful bird
c coconut palm
d flying fish

7 GLASNOST (Russian)
a greenhouse
b satellite
c angry argument
d open discussion

8 YETI (Tibetan)
a fermented yak's milk
b abominable snowman
c hemispherical tent
d snowshoes

9. CAFTAN (Turkish)
a ice cream
b loose-fitting robe
c wild dog
d woven carpet

10. ANGST (German)
a jealousy
b bigotry
c insanity
d anxiety

11. CRAVAT (Croatian)
a rivet
b neckwear
c small coin
d thick steak

12 FUTON (Japanese)
a type of fish
b type of balloon
c type of bed
d type of rifle

13. FAUX PAS (French)
a mistake
b ballet step
c artificial flower
d toasted bread

14. LEVIATHAN (Hebrew)
a money-changer
b sea monster
c clay oven
d holy book

15. JUJU (Hausa)
a red berry
b type of cattle
c magic charm
d dance music

16 PECCADILLO (Spanish)
a scaly anteater
b joyful song
c trifling misdemeanour
d ball game

WORD CIRCLES

These 'roundwords' have only five clues, and the answers read clockwise round the circle. The end of each word overlaps the beginning of the next by one or more letters. We've given you at least one letter to get you started. How quickly can you complete the circle?

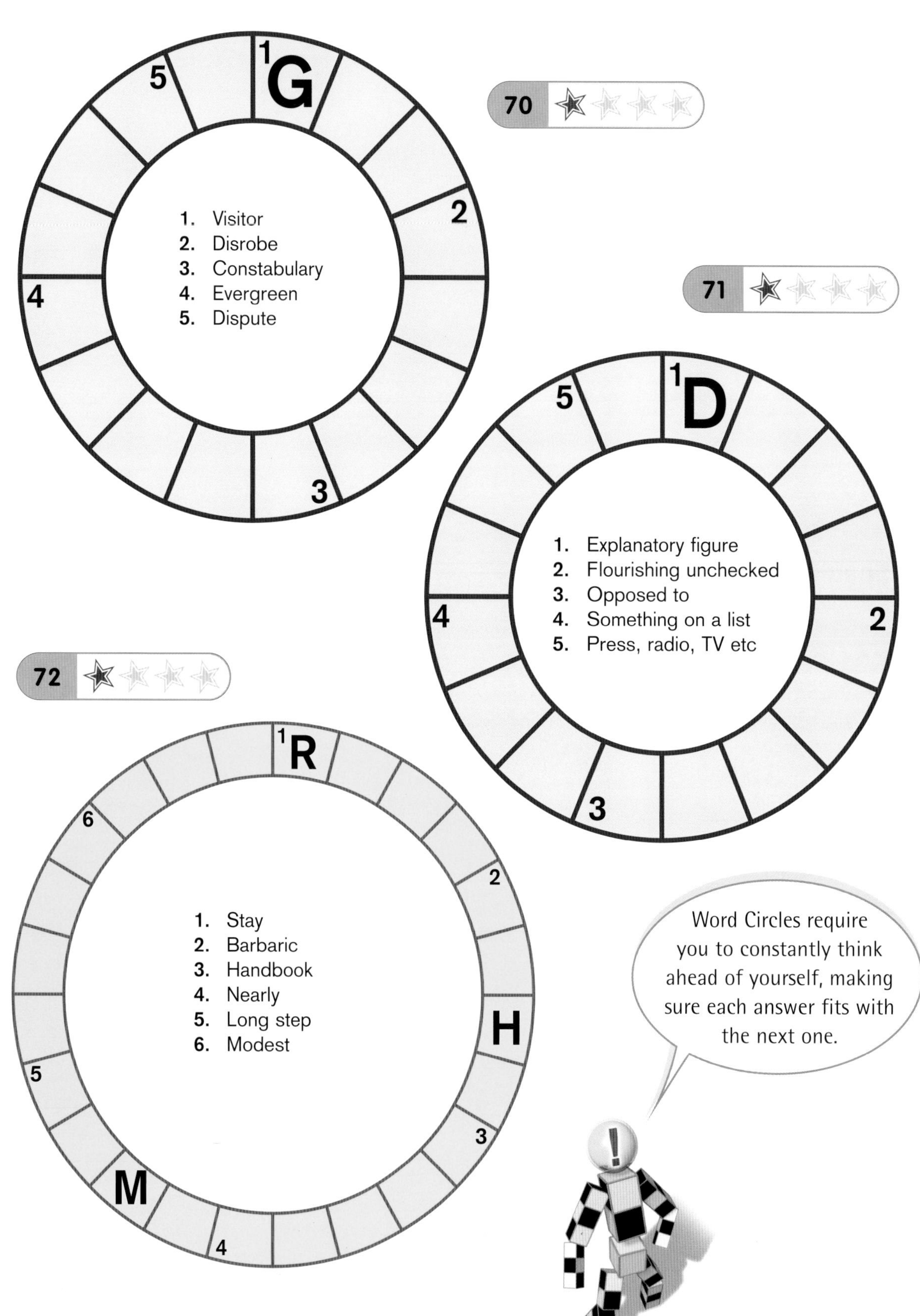

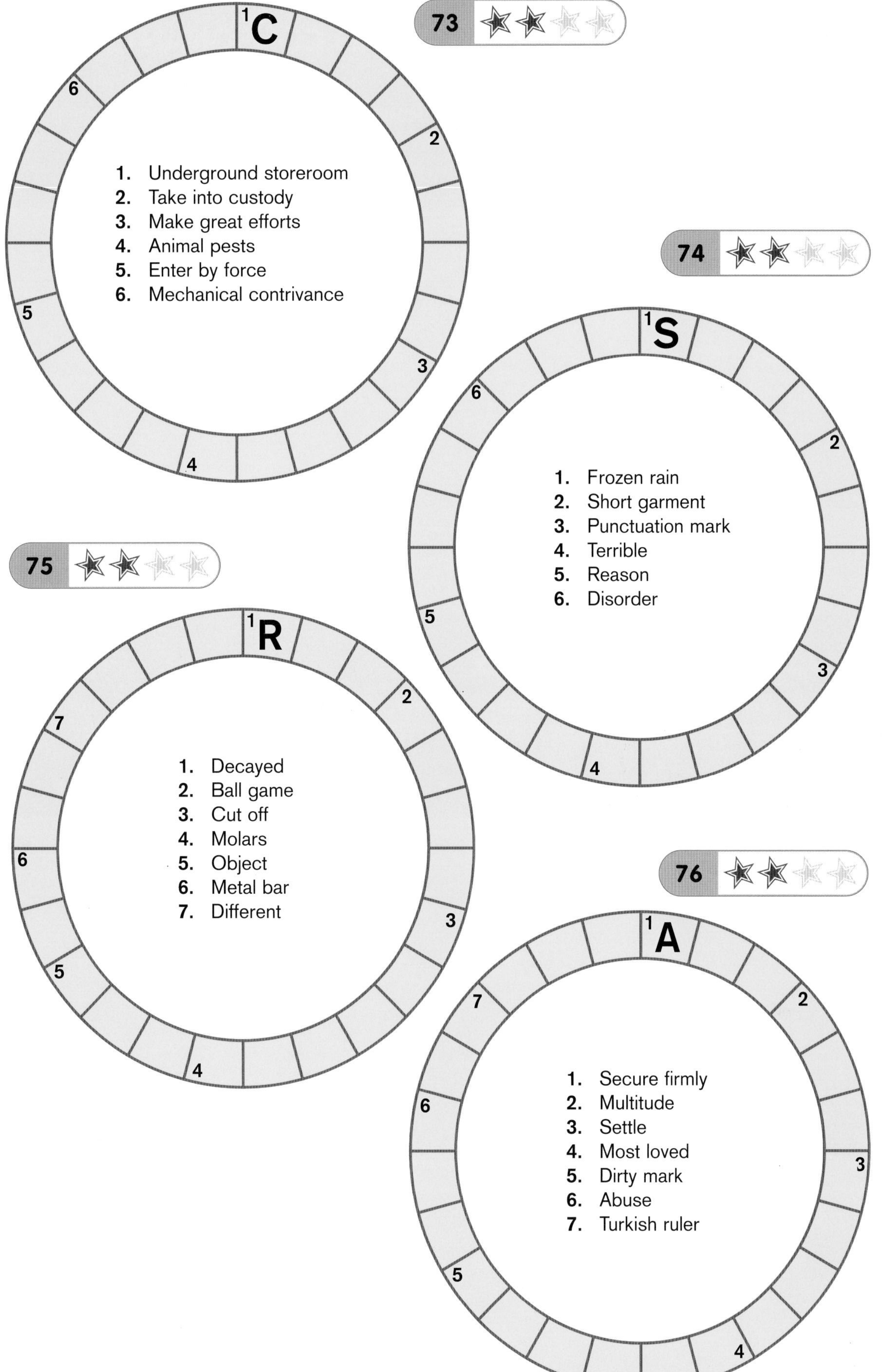
73
1 C
2
3
4
5
6
1. Underground storeroom
2. Take into custody
3. Make great efforts
4. Animal pests
5. Enter by force
6. Mechanical contrivance
74
1 S
2
3
4
5
6
1. Frozen rain
2. Short garment
3. Punctuation mark
4. Terrible
5. Reason
6. Disorder
75
1 R
2
3
4
5
6
7
1. Decayed
2. Ball game
3. Cut off
4. Molars
5. Object
6. Metal bar
7. Different
76
1 A
2
3
4
5
6
7
1. Secure firmly
2. Multitude
3. Settle
4. Most loved
5. Dirty mark
6. Abuse
7. Turkish ruler

WORD OPPOSITES WITH MISSING CONSONANTS

The challenge here is to find an opposite for each of the words in the left-hand column. For instance, the opposite of **'heroic'** could be **'cowardly'** or **'timid'**. To point you in the right direction we've given you some of the letters to each answer – but to make it harder, we've removed all the consonants.

77

Forget	- E - E - - E -
Ordinary	U - U - U - -
Bored	- - - E - E - - E -
Unobtainable	A - A - - A - - -
Gentle	- E - E - E

78

Enlarge	- I - I - I - -
Fascinating	- O - O - O - O - -
Cared for	- E - - E - - E -
Nearby	- A - A - A -
Unconventional	O - - - O - O -

LANGUAGE EQUATIONS

When a combination of numbers and initials are put together, they make a language equation. Have a go at working out what phrase or saying each of these language equations represent, thus giving your word association skills a really good work out.

79

What does this signify?

12 S O T Z

80

Can you make sense of this phrase?

26 L I T A

81

What does this represent?

7 W O T W

82

How quickly can you figure out these cryptic phrases, which all start with a number in the 50s?

52 W I A Y

54 C I A P (I J)

57 HV

These puzzles are all about time and place.

30 D H S

50 S I T U S A

60 M I A H

Can you work out the song lyrics hidden in these equations?

10 G B H O T W

24 H F T

50 W T L Y L

76 T L T B P

Can you fill in the words to complete three phrases which all begin with 9?

9 S B B

9 L O A C

9 P I T S S

MISSING LINKS

Test your powers of word association by finding a word that follows the first word in the clue that will make a new word or phrase. Your word must also make a new word or phrase when preceding the second word in the clue. For example, the answer to **top.........stand** would be hat – top **hat**, and **hat**stand.

86

1. cow .... friend
2. full .... proud
3. flower .... luck
4. part .... bomb
5. blind .... palm
6. bath .... dance

87

1. bowling .... cat
2. side .... dancing
3. door .... bar
4. rain .... string
5. Christmas .... stump
6. tall .... teller

ALPHA DICE

All of the dice blocks have a six-letter word written on them, but you can only see three sides. Try to solve the clues based on the letters you can see and enter the answers in the grid below. The correct letters in the first column will form a new word.

Clues
1. Salad vegetable
2. River
3. Usual
4. Colour
5. Fruit
6. Used for sewing

1						
2						
3						
4						
5						
6						

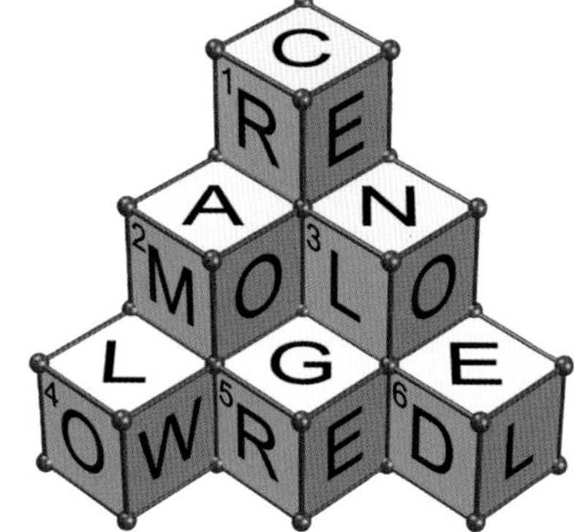

Clues
1. Something hidden
2. Open up
3. Thin
4. Tedious
5. On fire
6. Sport
7. Head protection
8. Take in
9. Chinese food
10. Laugh

1						
2						
3						
4						
5						
6						
7						
8						
9						
10						

Clues
1. Afternoon nap in hot countries
2. Knob
3. Gas
4. Vegetable
5. Rabbit's home
6. Money to live on
7. Feeling of sickness
8. Loiter
9. Place of work
10. Heated

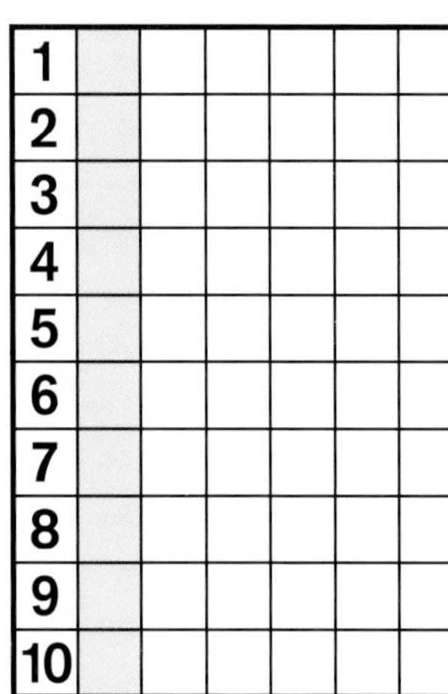

Clues

1. Beverage
2. Get away
3. Poster
4. Skill
5. Frail
6. Killing
7. Specialist
8. Pill
9. Come back
10. Use

1						
2						
3						
4						
5						
6						
7						
8						
9						
10						

Clues

1. Yarn
2. Obstacle to be overcome
3. Referee
4. Handbook
5. Where bread is made
6. Bring to shine
7. Thief
8. Stick of frozen water
9. Stinging plant
10. Need of a drink

1						
2						
3						
4						
5						
6						
7						
8						
9						
10						

Clues

1. Smoked herring
2. Girl's name
3. Beginner
4. Pungent vegetable
5. Lack of food
6. Style of writing
7. Sew
8. Genuine
9. Vitality
10. Where aircraft take off

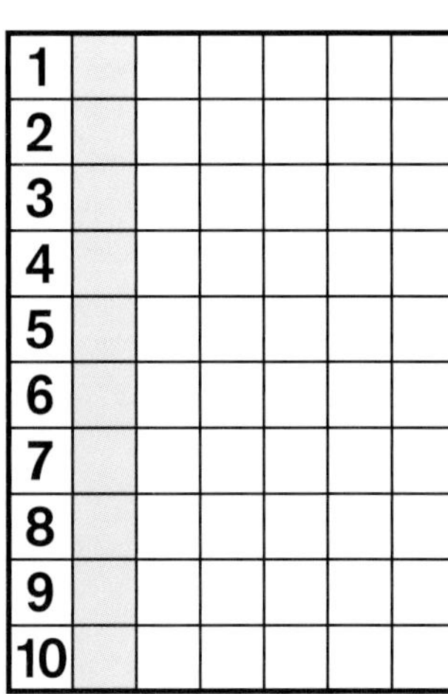

1						
2						
3						
4						
5						
6						
7						
8						
9						
10						

PROOFREADING

How good a proofreader are you? While the spell check on a computer will pick up most of your mistakes, it won't spot literal errors where the word is spelled correctly but used wrongly. The following fictional excerpts are packed with spelling errors, easily confused words and grammatical howlers. See if you can pick them all out.

94

Wish you were hear

Dear Chris and Mary,

We are having a marvelous time out here in Tenerife. The weather is terific and the sea feels like its heated! The local bars and restaraunts are lovely, though we're a bit to squeemish to try some of the more exotic dish's!

See you soon, Dave and Sue

20/10/81

The third largest Volcano, Teide Volcano, Tenerife

Chris and Mary Smith
Honeypot Cottage
Topsham Village
Bristol
BS20 4PP

95

Deer sir

Dear Mr. Reeman,

I write with regard to the parking ticket I recieved last thursday in the cul-de-sac leading off St. Stevens Street. My undertsanding is that parking I this area is unlimited for dis-abled drivers like myself. Therefore, I was extremly shocked to return to my vehicle to find a ticket on the windshield. I would be greatful if you could please advize me of the regulations which apply to this particuler road before I forward my payment by cheque.

Yours Sincerly

Mrs. A Hammond

96

Reed all about it!

STOP PRESS!

In an unpresidented move last night, the former head of the Ministery of Transport, Sir Rupert Walker stepped down in the middle of the latest pay despute with the nations train drivers. Having stalled in negociations with union representitives for the last two weeks, sir Rupert decided that enough was enough. Since taking up the post, he has been almost constently in the newspapers for his stiff oposition to the various unions. A union spokespersen commented that modern industry wasn't the place for Sir Ruperts Victorian values. The talks will procede under the guideance of Lord Belmont.

97 Book excert

The epitaphs on Roman tombstones were addresed to passers-by. One from the 2nd century BC describes the qualitys of a dutyful Roman wife: 'Stranger, I have only a few words to say. – This is the tomb of a lovley women. Her parents named her Claudia. She loved her husband with all her heart. She beared two sons; one she leaves here on earth, the other she has already placed under it. She was charming in speach, yet pleasent and proper in manner. She managed the house well. She span wool. – I have spoken. Go on your way.'

98 Book reveiw

An epic thrilling swashbuckling adventure, **Curse of the Seven Sea's** is a tale of sword fights, hidden treasure and ancient piracey on the waves and coastlines of yester-year. Following the exploits of young sea farer, captain Jack True, were taken on a journey through dangerous straights, trecherous weather and pirate ridden waters in a quest to return a mistical stolen treasure. Shrowded in mystery and spoken of only through whispers, True knows that the magical treasures healing property's could be his last hope of saving his loved ones, struck by a curse placed on them by the evil warlok Shargad. Armed with his sword, a map and a band of trusty ship mates, Captain Jack True sets of in search of hidden treasure and revenge – whatever the cost!

99 Recipe for sucess

Whole meal bread

Ingrediants

1lb wholmeal flour
1 tespoon salt
1 teaspoon bicarbonate of sooda
1 teaspoon crème of tartar
1oz melted butter or margerine
½ pint milk, idealy sour or buttermilk

Method

Heat the oven to 2000°C/gas mark 6. Place the flour, salt and razing agents together in a bowl and mix thoroughly. Make a well in the mixture and pore in milk and melted fat. Stir in carefuly. Shape the dough into a loafe and place on a greased and flowered baking sheet. Brush with milk and bake for 30-400 minutes, until browned and well-risen.

KNIGHT'S MOVE

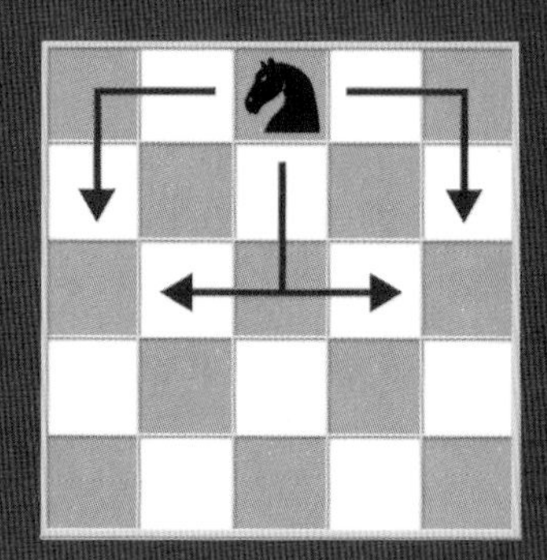

In chess the Knight moves hippogonally (from the Greek meaning *horse*). This means that it moves either two squares across and one square up or down, to form an 'L' shape, or it moves one square across and two up or down (as shown in the example on the right). Starting at the arrow use a combination of these moves to help you find a phrase in the squares below.

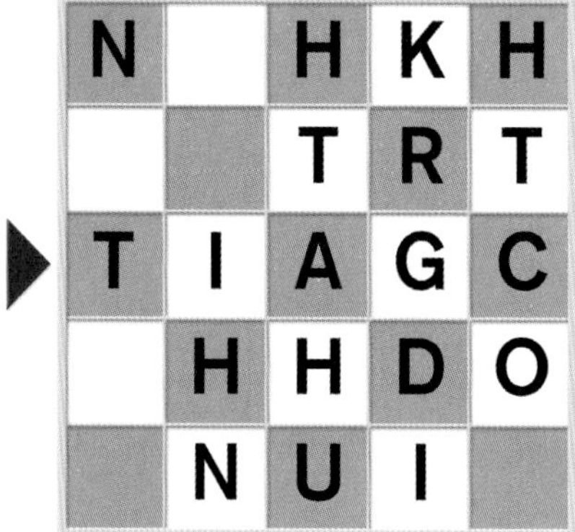

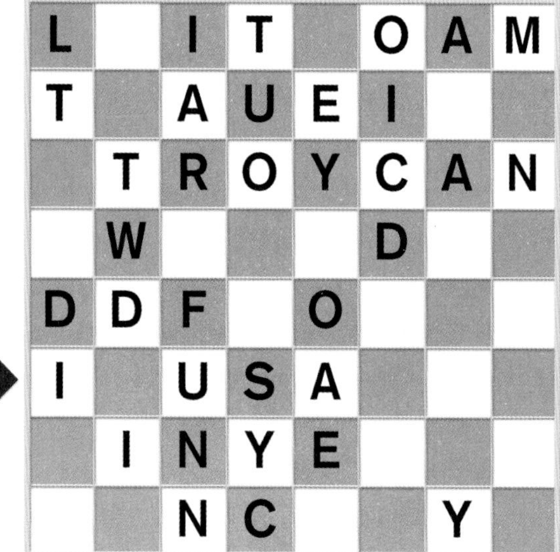

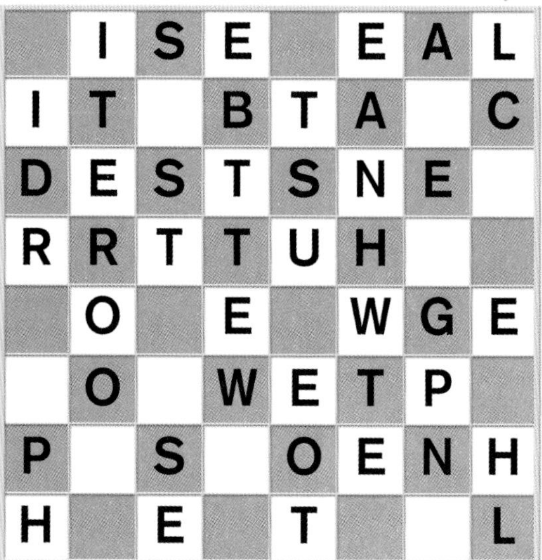

HETERONYMS

Heteronyms are words or phrases that use the same letters, in the same order, but are usually pronounced differently and mean different things. Use these clues to figure out the heteronymic pairs.

The name's the same

Use these pairs of clues to identify four heteronyms. Remember that each word is spelt the same, but has a different pronunciation.

1. plant seeds / female pig
2. turn down / garbage
3. tiny / period of time
4. abandon / dry place

Many heteronyms are the result of one word being a verb and another being a noun.

Sounds different

Heteronyms are another way of increasing your word power – and keeping a check of your spelling. Use the following clues to identify five heteronyms.

1. captivate / way in
2. fruit and veg / create
3. line / argument (British expression)
4. take exception / thing
5. turned / injury

MONOGRAMS

The puzzles here are visual representations of a word or words formed by a circular arrangement of the letters of the alphabet. In each case the answer can be found by moving around the circle from letter to letter, following the red lines.

If the letter is four letters away or less it is found by tracing around the circumference. In the event of double letters, the letter in question is visited just once. In each puzzle, a cryptic clue is provided – the figures in brackets denotes the number of letters and words in the solution.

Clue: Unlucky for some (6, 3, 10)

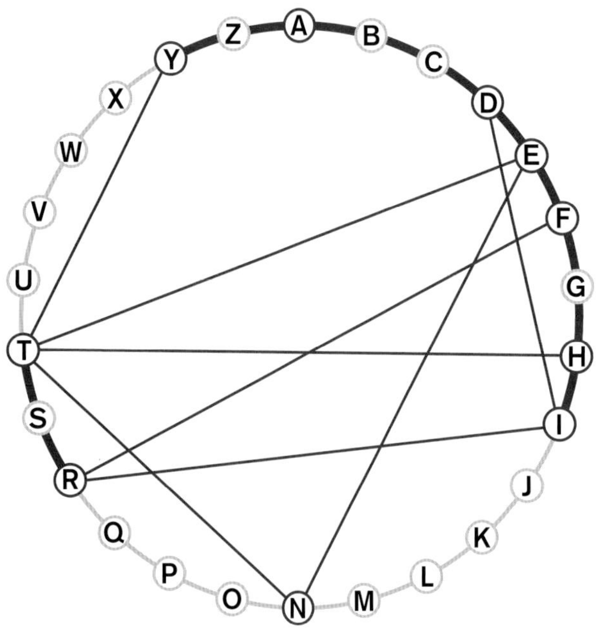

When following a line around the circumference of the circle, ignore letters in yellow circles.

107

Clue: Old timer (11, 5)

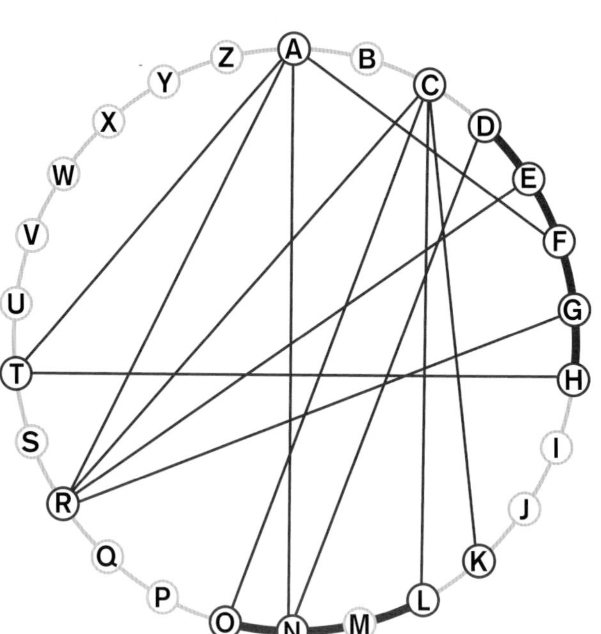

Clue: A storm in a teacup (4, 3, 5, 7)

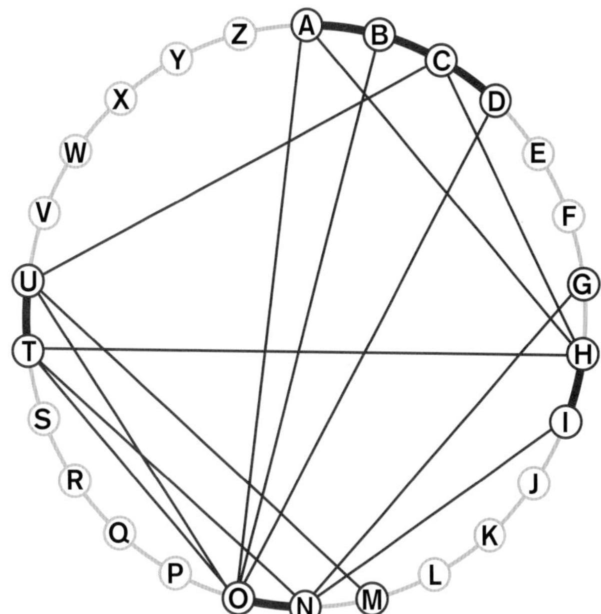

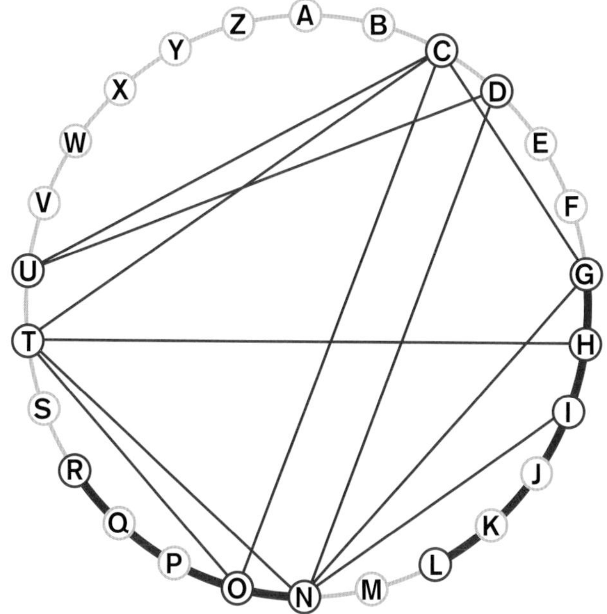

Clue: Might there be a strike if he gets the orchestra playing too fast? (9, 9)

Clue: Where an enigmatic primate may climb (6, 6, 4)

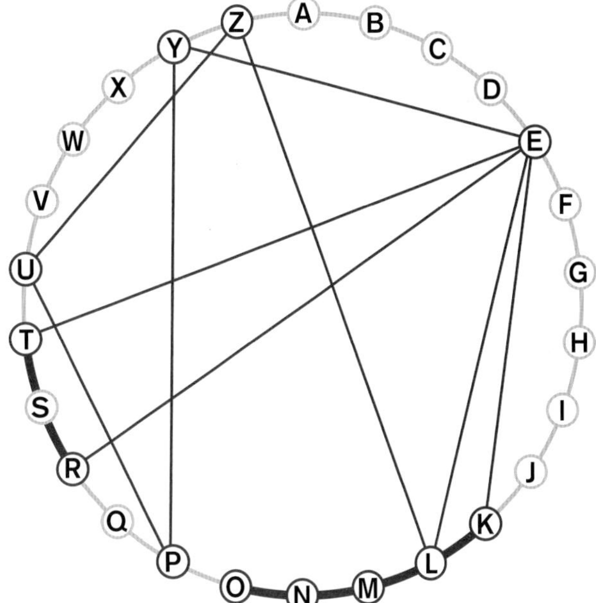

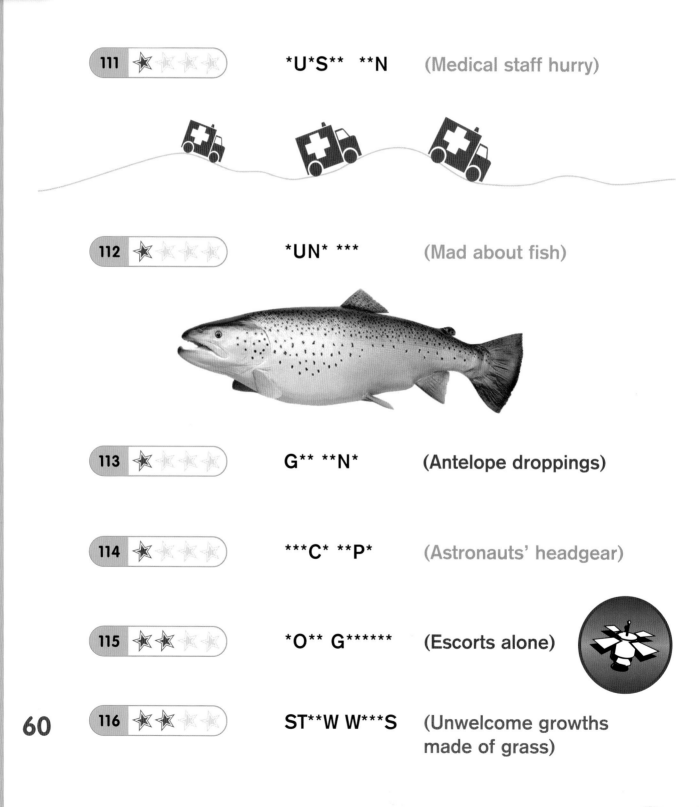

PALINDROMES

A palindrome is a word or phrase that reads the same forwards or backwards, though you may need to ignore the spaces between words – for example, DRAWN ONWARD. Using the clues supplied, and a little ingenuity, how quickly can you work out these two-word palindromes? We've supplied the odd letter to get you started.

111 *U*S** **N (Medical staff hurry)

112 *UN* *** (Mad about fish)

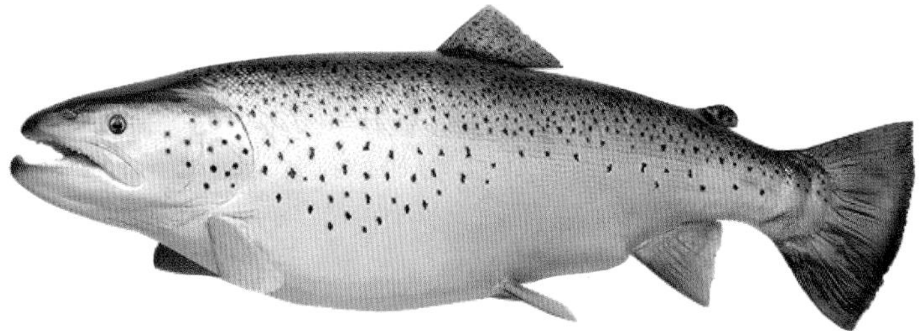

113 G** **N* (Antelope droppings)

114 ***C* **P* (Astronauts' headgear)

115 *O** G****** (Escorts alone)

116 ST**W W***S (Unwelcome growths made of grass)

** G**** *EE **D? (Fowls' divine insight?)

*O **M***, N* ****N (Absence of fruit)

W** *T * *** * S**? (Did I spot a rodent?)

(My mother's generous, too)
*A ** *S ***FL*** *S * *M

(Oh, Lucifer watches Miss Kinski)
*H, **T*N S**S N**AS*A

(Rare animal dozed)
*AN** *** ***

(Will you hoist as well?)
**L* ** I* * **L* **

(Strange sort of number)
V **D ** ***N

(Spirit is homicidal, old chap)
D *, S**, I* M*****

WORD CENTRES

These short words have something in common – they can all be found at the heart of longer words. Your challenge is to supply the missing letters, indicated by the asterisks, to produce new words of between five and eight letters.

Back and forth 1

126

Only the first and last letters are missing here. See if you can restore the original word.

Sometimes there is more than one answer to these puzzles – especially if you have a large vocabulary.

1. *ROB*
2. *HEM*
3. *COW*
4. *LENT*
5. *CHIN*
6. *ACRE*
7. *LOWE*
8. *IGUR*
9. *ATHE*
10. *ATUR*

Back and forth 2

127

Identify the ten eight-letter words represented here by their middle parts.

1. **LEND**
2. **WART**
3. **VEND**
4. **OGRE**
5. **AMEN**

6. **REST**
7. **EASA**
8. **IGIN**
9. **VENO**
10. **NICU**

Back and forth 3

Can you identify these seven-letter words from the three-letter words that lie at their centres?

1. **LID**
2. **TAN**
3. **SIP**
4. **BAR**
5. **URN**
6. **BIN**
7. **RVE**
8. **URI**
9. **ISO**
10. **CTU**

Back and forth 4

The words listed below are all found in the middle of words that are twice as long. Can you supply the missing letters to produce ten eight-letter words?

1. **STAB**
2. **PROP**
3. **WILD**
4. **SINE**
5. **MINE**
6. **LOSS**

7. **ADLI**
8. **THDR**
9. **NSIB**
10. **ARNI**

WORD SQUARES

Square puzzles like these have been around since Roman times. To solve them, write the answers to the clues in the grid so that they read the same across as down.

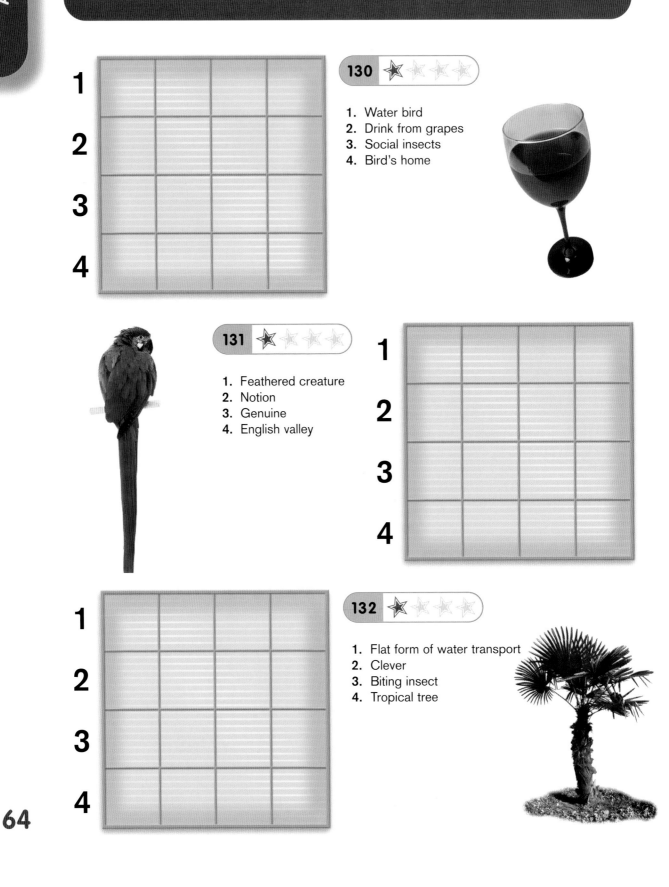

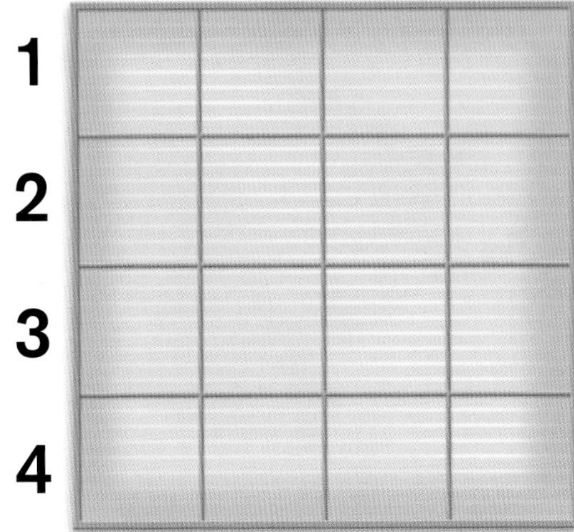

130

1. Water bird
2. Drink from grapes
3. Social insects
4. Bird's home

131

1. Feathered creature
2. Notion
3. Genuine
4. English valley

1
2
3
4

132

1. Flat form of water transport
2. Clever
3. Biting insect
4. Tropical tree

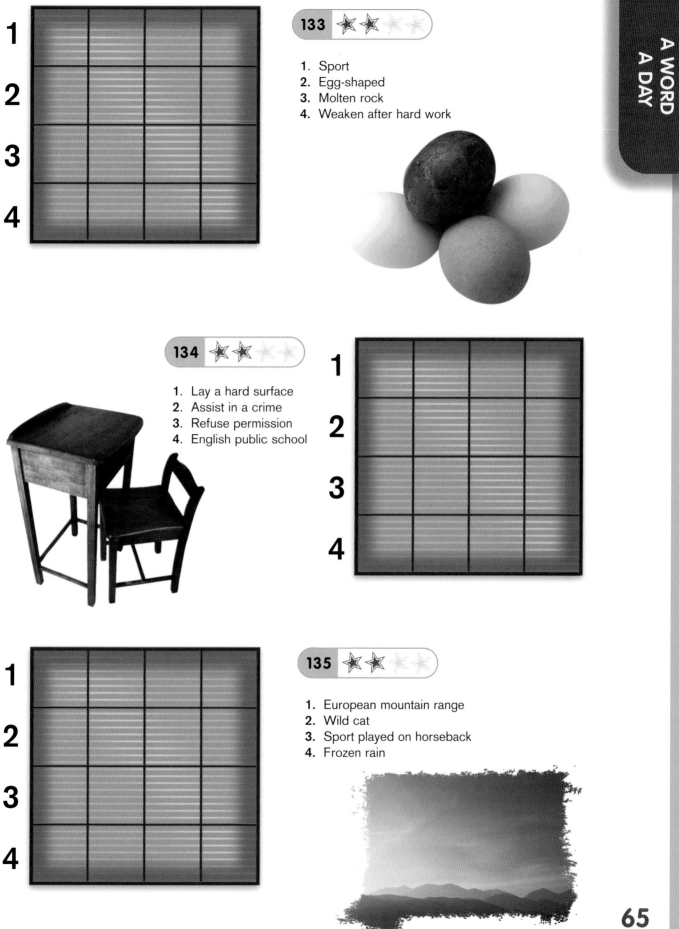

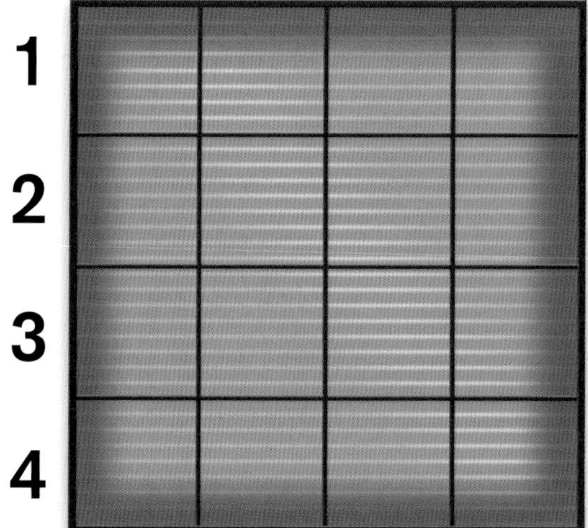

133 ★★

1. Sport
2. Egg-shaped
3. Molten rock
4. Weaken after hard work

134 ★★

1. Lay a hard surface
2. Assist in a crime
3. Refuse permission
4. English public school

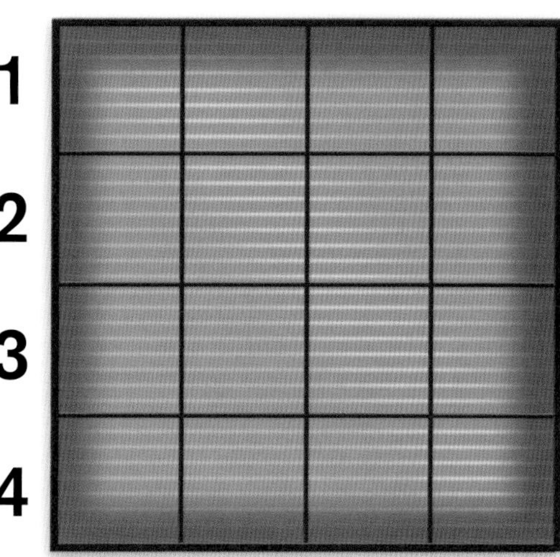

135 ★★

1. European mountain range
2. Wild cat
3. Sport played on horseback
4. Frozen rain

ARROW WORDS

The clues to these puzzles are in the blue squares on the grid – all you have to do is work out the answers and insert them as indicated by the arrows. Use the example on the right as a guide.

Perform on stage ▸	A	Managed wood / Animals' den	C	Long, narrow passage	Eager
Outer garment / Basic food stuff	C	L	O	A	K
S	T	A	P	L	E
On which films are projected	Piece of land in the sea / Fee	I	S	L	E
S	C	R	E	E	N

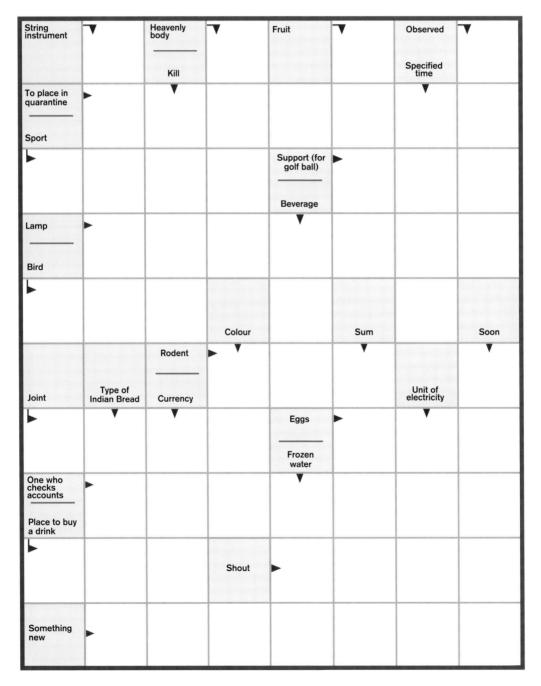

136 ★

String instrument		Heavenly body / Kill		Fruit		Observed / Specified time	
To place in quarantine / Sport							
				Support (for golf ball) / Beverage			
Lamp / Bird							
			Colour		Sum		Soon
Joint	Type of Indian Bread	Rodent / Currency				Unit of electricity	
				Eggs / Frozen water			
One who checks accounts / Place to buy a drink							
			Shout				
Something new							

You don't have to fill in answers in sequential order. Try inserting all of the answers you know straight away – it is amazing how difficult answers become much more obvious when you have some letters to work with.

Water fowl		No more than / Overdue		Stage		At liberty / Night bird	
One entitled to vote / Fruit							
				Female sheep / Rub out			
Church tower / Insect							
			Drink made from apples		Cleanse	Relating to birds	Lure
Perceptive	Tidy	Measure of the purity of gold					
Herb		Fabric / Leave					
				To weaken			
Distress							

NOVELTY CROSSWORDS

These puzzles are a fun and more challenging take on the regular crossword. Apply both word skills and logic to solve these unusual brain-teasers.

This is an anagram crossword. All you have to do is unscramble the letters of each clue to spell out a new word. Because some clues can make more than one anagram, you'll have to work out which fits.

Across

1. Binary (6) **4**. Nectar (6) **9**. Tor (3) **10**. Among (5) **11**. Pay (3) **12**. Peat (4) **14**. Pike (4) **16**. Lea (3) **18**. Binge (5) **19**. Later (5) **21**. Rat (3) **24**. Dire (4) **25**. Rely (4) **28**. Own (3) **30**. Trove (5) **31**. Doe (3) **32**. Hearty (6) **33**. Header (6)

Down

1. Beater (6) **2**. Tap (3) **3**. Mean (4) **5**. Moor (4) **6**. Any (3) **7**. Stripe (6) **8**. Glean (5) **13**. Pedal (5) **15**. Layer (5) **16**. Tan (3) **17**. Era (3) **20**. Finger (6) **22**. Bream (5) **23**. Decree (6) **26**. Shop (4) **27**. Dust (4) **29**. Raw (3) **31**. Roe (3)

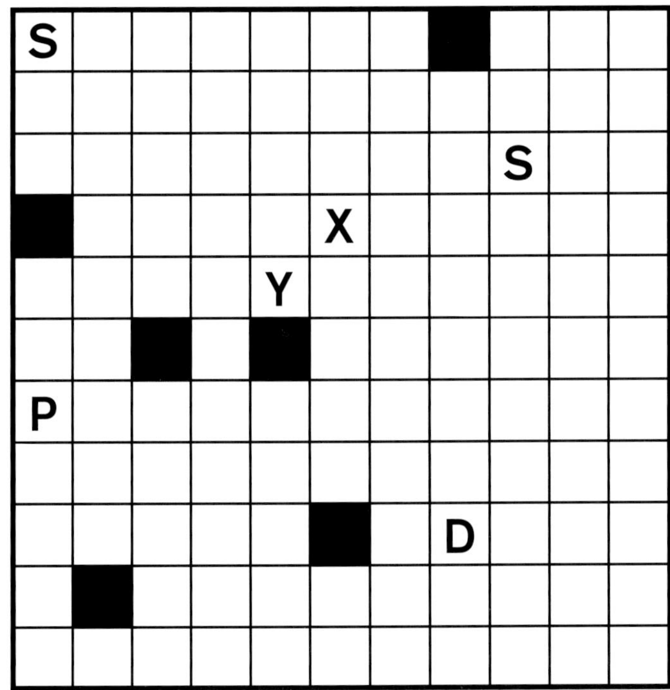

139

Here's a crossword with a difference. As well as solving the clues, you must also work out where the missing black squares go. To make things easier, we've given you a small head start.

Across

1. Not a failure (7)
5. Arrow firer (3)
7. Lawn (5)
8. Fertile part of a desert (5)
9. Wood chopper (3)
10. Foolish (5)
12. Perceive (5)
14. Spaghetti (5)
17. Red-breasted bird (5)
19. As well (3)
20. Celestial path (5)
21. Smell; Aroma (5)
23. Sailor (3)
24. Knives and forks (7)

Down

1. Droop (3) **2.** Move on hands and knees (5) **3.** Composition (5) **4.** Footwear (5) **5.** Bathroom sink (5) **6.** Cowboy film (7) **10.** Give backing (7) **11.** Illuminated (3) **13.** Self-importance (3) **15.** Not drunk (5) **16.** Loft (5) **17.** Sleeping place for birds (5) **18.** Penniless (5) **22.** Beam of light (3).

140

Use the same method as in the puzzle above, to tackle this tougher crossword.

Across

1. Musician (6)
4. Mastermind (6)
9. Suppose (7)
10. Step (5)
11. Bamboo stem (4)
12. Technique (3)
14. Plunge (4)
15. Wood pattern (5)
17. Topmost (5)
19. Damp (5)
21. Subdued (5)
24. Zone (4)
25. Affirmative (3)
26. Fury (4)
30. Performed softly (music) (5)
31. Weather (7)
32. Hypodermic instrument (6)
33. Sofa (6)

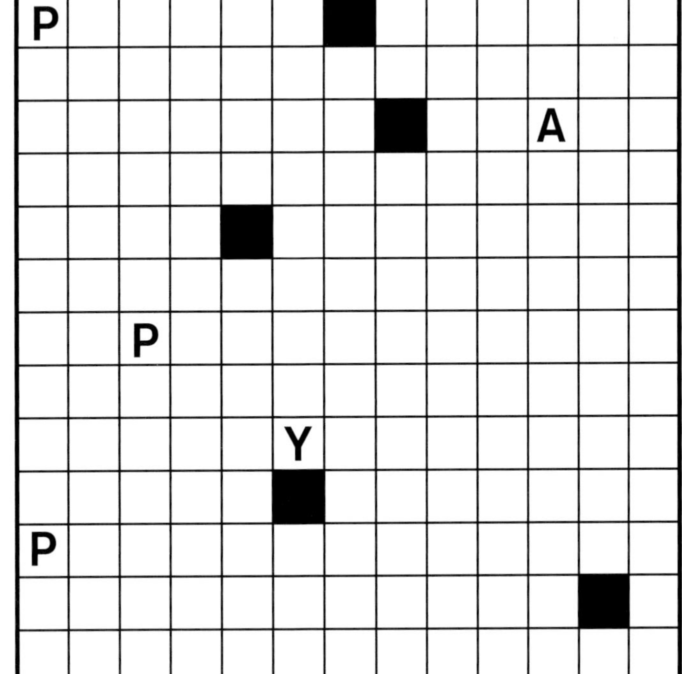

Down

1. Royal family member (6) **2.** Once more (5) **3.** Wicked (4) **5.** Effortless (4) **6.** Slanting typeface (7) **7.** Poll (6) **8.** Pedestrian crossing (5) **12.** Range (5) **13.** Uses a stopwatch (5) **15.** Receive (3) **16.** A sign of assent (3) **18.** Make ready (7) **20.** Occur (6) **22.** Clemency (5) **23.** Strict (6) **27.** Separated (5) **28.** Dish (4) **29.** Conceal (4)

WORD PLAY

Try your hand at the following crosswords. There is a regular puzzle, a cryptic teaser and a 'pieceword' to test your word skills to the maximum.

141 General knowledge crossword

Across
2. Large vehicle, red in London (3)
4. Yorkshire town, famous for its racecourse (5)
6. ___ King Cole, singer (3) **8**. MP3 player (4)
9. Rain falling as ice (4) **12**. German dictator (6)
13. Inflate (a balloon) (4,2) **15**. Expire (3)
16. Camp ___, Barcelona FC's ground (3)
18. Main underground part of a plant (7)
21. Capital of Norway (4)
23. Jerome ___, US songwriter (4)
27. Hare's murderous partner (5)
30. Sri ___, country whose capital is Colombo (5)
31. Construction of a house by its eventual occupier (4-5)
35. Wordless (4) **36**. Early stringed musical instrument (4) **37**. Jewish celebration, the Day of Atonement (3,6)
39. Hole ___, golfer's dream (2,3) **40**. Moshe ___, 1970s Israeli politician (5) **42**. Unit of typeface size (4)
45. Partner in conflict (4) **47**. Area of Hertfordshire with large film studios (7)
51.Total (3) **53**. Belonging to us (3)
54. Archers (6) **55**. ___ Hamer, Diane Keaton's role in The Lemon Sisters (6)
56. Insects that can lift loads fifty times their own weight (4)
57. Flank (4) **58**. Fish sometimes jellied (3)
60. Aberdeen ___, cattle breed (5)
61. Canine animal (3)

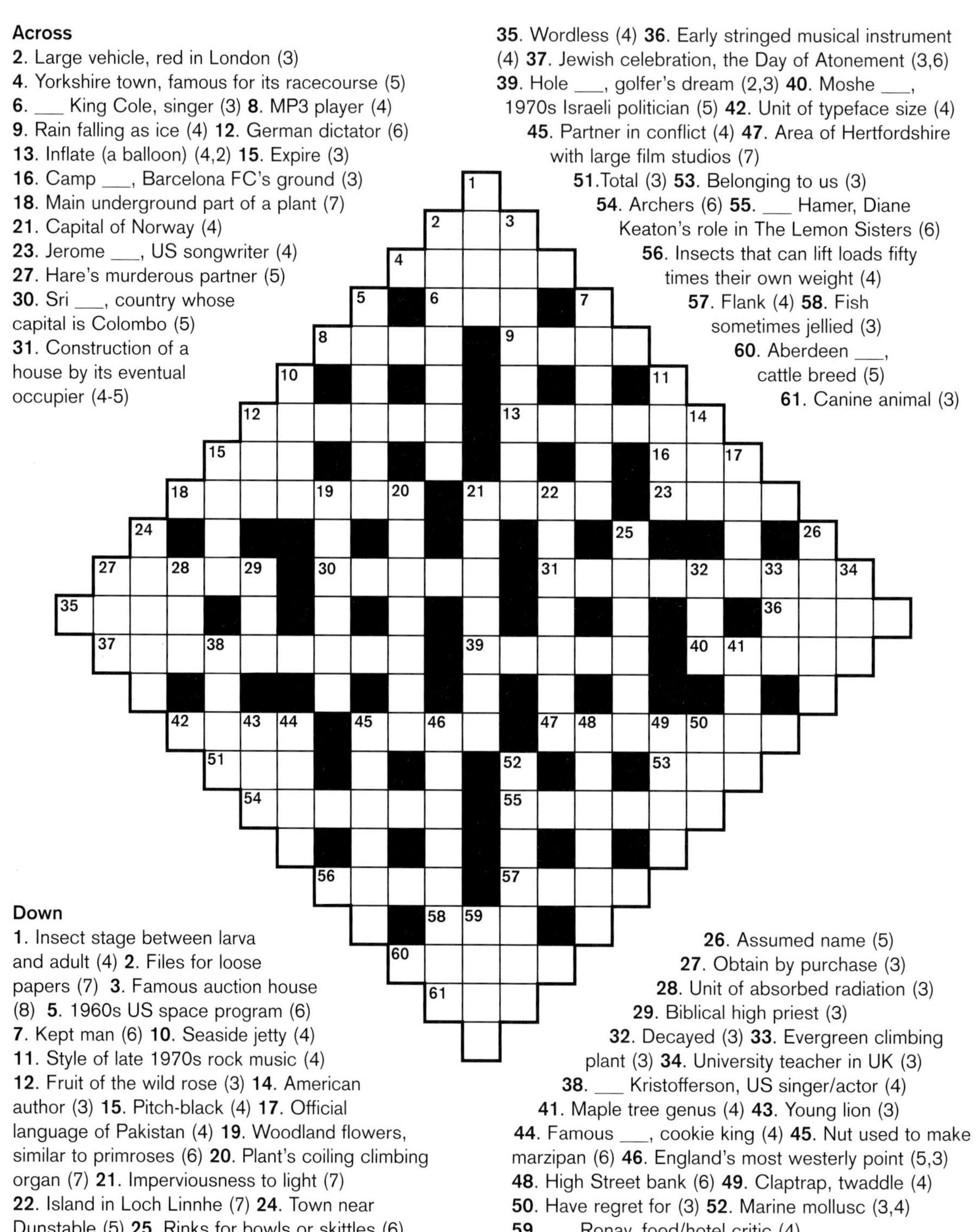

Down
1. Insect stage between larva and adult (4) **2**. Files for loose papers (7) **3**. Famous auction house (8) **5**. 1960s US space program (6)
7. Kept man (6) **10**. Seaside jetty (4)
11. Style of late 1970s rock music (4)
12. Fruit of the wild rose (3) **14**. American author (3) **15**. Pitch-black (4) **17**. Official language of Pakistan (4) **19**. Woodland flowers, similar to primroses (6) **20**. Plant's coiling climbing organ (7) **21**. Imperviousness to light (7)
22. Island in Loch Linnhe (7) **24**. Town near Dunstable (5) **25**. Rinks for bowls or skittles (6)
26. Assumed name (5)
27. Obtain by purchase (3)
28. Unit of absorbed radiation (3)
29. Biblical high priest (3)
32. Decayed (3) **33**. Evergreen climbing plant (3) **34**. University teacher in UK (3)
38. ___ Kristofferson, US singer/actor (4)
41. Maple tree genus (4) **43**. Young lion (3)
44. Famous ___, cookie king (4) **45**. Nut used to make marzipan (6) **46**. England's most westerly point (5,3)
48. High Street bank (6) **49**. Claptrap, twaddle (4)
50. Have regret for (3) **52**. Marine mollusc (3,4)
59. ___ Ronay, food/hotel critic (4)

142 Cryptic clues

Across

1. Searchingly examine front of pretty gown (5)
4. Studies marsh grasses, we hear (5)
9. Rock sounding more courageous (7)
11. Maintained, medical faulty (7)
12. Amphibian pulled along, say (4)
13. Bless me! A red stain inside (5)
14. Some cyst? Yes, it's a swelling (4)
17. Spotted by a mud-slinger (11)
18. Fixed description of speeding bullet (4,3,4)
24. Mosque leader, male, enters at 01:00hrs (4)
25. Very strict, some Easterners (5)
26. Goddess in the racing game (4)
29. Saw cheat torn between wife and daughter (7)
30. Pulpit's redesigned for divorce (5,2)
31. Join one with energy (5)
32. Goes first to Yorkshire city, reportedly (5)

Down

2. Background talk of stalks (7) **3**. Small county where people go to retire? (4) **5**. Return manufactured cheese (4) **6**. Edward, after short march, had been given a lower rank (7) **7**. Calm sailor dined (5) **8**. Goodbye to something that may be cast in gold (5) **10**. Dance with odd graduate (5) **11**. Handiwork on boat (5) **15**. American queen first sacks employers (5) **16**. Costa Rica tree to die (5) **18**. Listen to a couple of quintets and give cheer (7) **19**. Rebellious cadet played a part (5) **20**. Pub game sees violin knocked over (5) **21**. Gave medical help – for nothing? (7) **22**. Fights round western scenes (5) **23**. Lighting providing fifty amperes (5) **27**. Short note written during lunch, I think (4) **28**. Enemy left in sheet of ice (4)

143 Pieceword

This crossword has been taken apart and split into smaller squares. Using the across clues to help you, can you transfer the jigsaw pieces into the blank grid to form a crossword that is symmetrical from top to bottom and left to right?

Across

Row 1:	Stops, ceases • Natty dressers
Row 3:	Woodland spirit • Marine forces
Row 5:	Harder to come by • From the beginning
Row 6:	Mimic • Zodiac lion
Row 7:	Thick, soft, fine hair of certain animals • Horned viper
Row 8:	Dingy and stuffy • Bring upon yourself
Row 10:	Broad spade-like tool • Kitchen cutting tool
Row 12:	Burden of responsibility • Inventors' copyrights

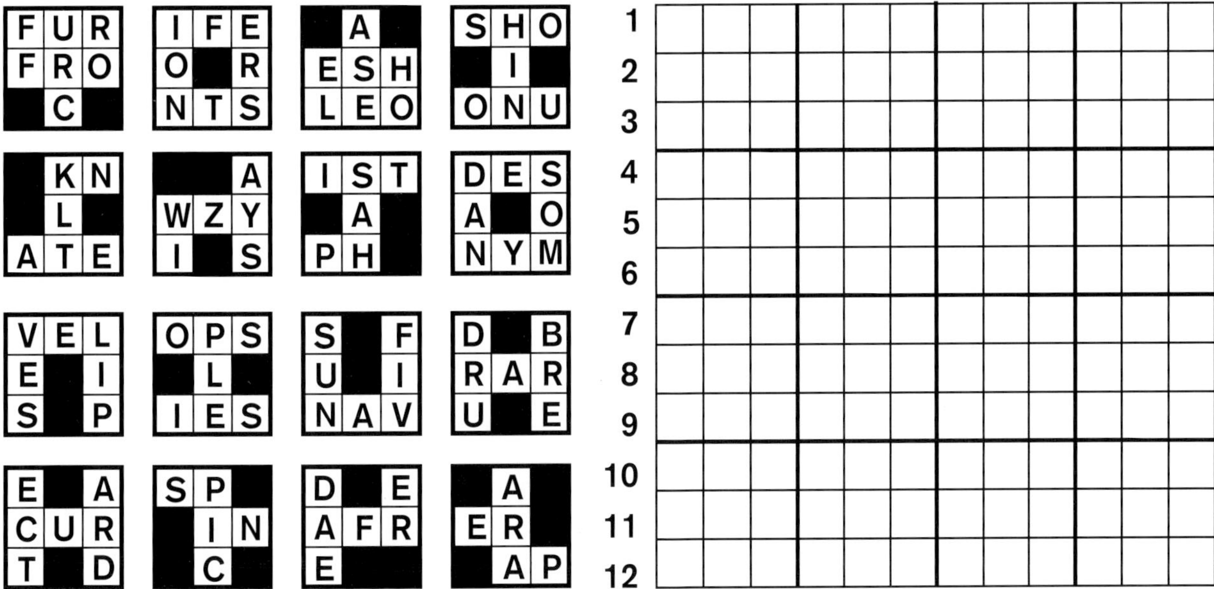

THREE-DIMENSIONAL CRYPTIC CROSSWORD

Not all crosswords are two dimensional – solve these humourous crossword clues and plot the answers into the cube. Hint: some of the answers may continue over the edge of the cube, so enter them accordingly.

144 ★★☆☆

Consider the cryptic clues to this crossword carefully – they are designed to challenge and confuse you. If you enjoy this kind of crossword, try the more complex version on page 288.

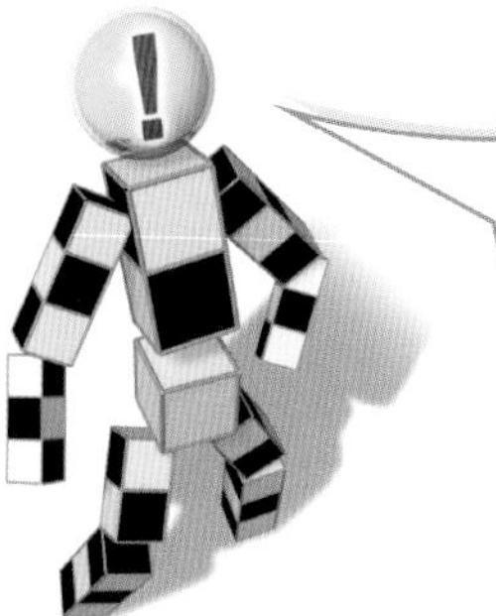

Use your powers of reasoning to recognize the devices used in each clue, and uncover what they are really saying. Each clue usually has two clues within it – one obvious and the other hidden. See 'How to do Cryptic Crosswords' on pages 19-20 for further guidance.

Across

6. Trust in coral to develop voice (9)
7. Fruit can cause a foot problem (5)
8. Peep round pail of pudding (5,3)
9. Back under coach (3)
11. Summer treat for one of the church elite (3,5)
13. Holly, for example, always young (9)
14. Place to keep silver in shop (7)
18. Special addition that is consumed (3)
20. My chum, he rants about flower (13)
21. Find fringe benefit through the king (4)

22. Direction in which to find tea store (4)
24. Song first heard when my back started niggling (4)
25. These natural surroundings get hot (7)
28. Put slug killer down to find a dish (4-2-3-4)
(Hint: British food)
30. Back favourites on stage (4)
31. Pip, the eccentric (3)
32. Insects grow fat on church candle (7)

Down

1. Jostled? Run away having lost blood (9)
2. Ruin international organization's party (4)
3. Translate Pinter's 'Spring' for the newspaper publishers (8,5)
4. Bail out onto island (4)
5. Sponsor in danger pot exploded (9)
10. Security at harbour (7)
12. Crisis for a hundred in New York under surface (9)
15. Stresses Bill has little money (7)
16. Reverberation disturbs Ruth in den (7)
17. Ecstasy! Politician and queen meet and love the king (7)
19. Monk takes soup with hesitation (7)
23. Meander after reptile (5)
26. The incident of the seven tickets (5)
27. Fail to notice the young lady (4)
29. This beverage provides support I'm told (3)
30. Holy man says yes to animal house (3)

DISC WHEELS

Similar to crosswords but arranged in the round, the answers to these puzzles need to be placed in the discs. Each answer ends with the same letter, given in the centre of the disc.

145 ★

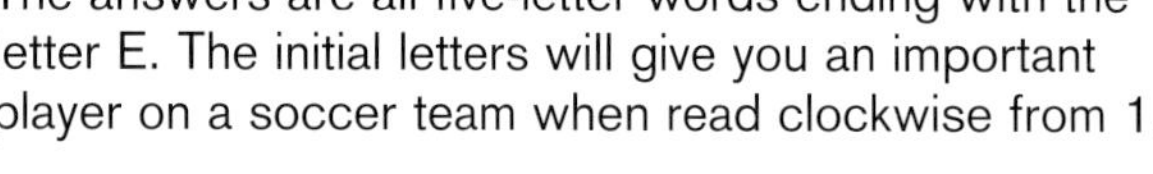

The answers are all five-letter words ending with the letter E. The initial letters will give you an important player on a soccer team when read clockwise from 1.

1. Came out of Aladdin's lamp
2. Small imperial measure of weight
3. Central passage in a church
4. Home of a beaver
5. Kitchen tool
6. Rub out
7. Force out of one's country
8. Fairy-like creature
9. Run away to marry
10. Type of firearm

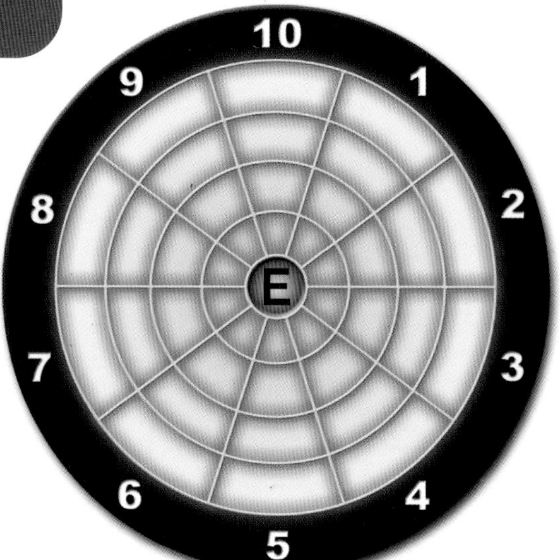

146 ★

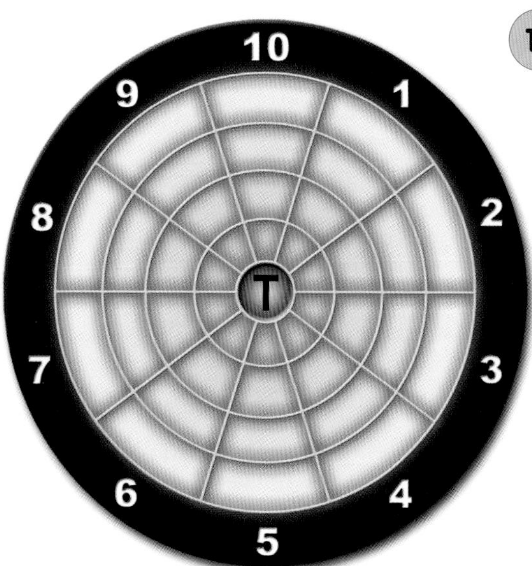

Each five-letter answer ends with the letter T. In this puzzle, the initial letters will reveal an important member of a wedding party when read clockwise from 1.

1. Explosion
2. Pay
3. Fool
4. Be skeptical
5. Overflow
6. Holy person
7. French painter of water lilies
8. Watchful
9. Contribution
10. Deter

147 ★★

The outer letters of the answers in this disc wheel will reveal the name of a state in the USA.

1. Manmade waterway
2. Heavenly creature
3. Even
4. Idealized pastoral scene
5. Untamed
6. Projecting window
7. French composer
8. Work of fiction
9. Force
10. Land around a lagoon

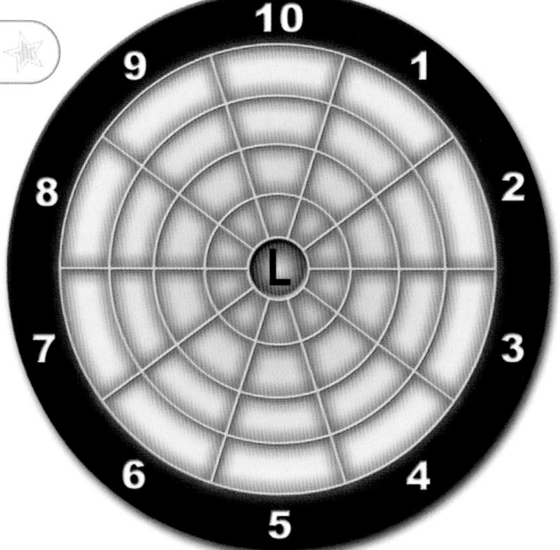

WORD RINGS

Rearrange the letters in each circle to find a word, using all the letters once only. Once you have found the anagram, test your word skills and powers of concentration further by seeing how many three letter words you can make from the letter selections in each ring.

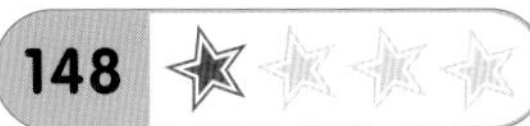

You may find it easier to work out the anagrams if you write the letters out in a straight line on a separate piece of paper. That way you can play with the order of the letters and see them in written form.

OXYMORONS

An oxymoron is a figure of speech in which two words of opposite meaning are linked together to produce a phrase – for example: **new antiques, advanced beginner**.

In the following two puzzles, 30 words are listed in columns in no particular order. To complete the puzzles, pair up all of the words to produce 15 oxymoronic phrases. Hint: Oxymorons are apparently contradictory terms, not necessarily direct opposites.

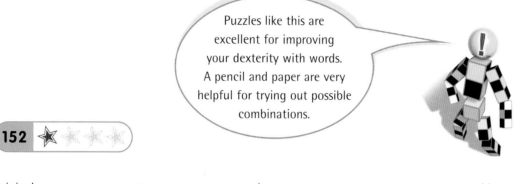

Puzzles like this are excellent for improving your dexterity with words. A pencil and paper are very helpful for trying out possible combinations.

152 ★

original	sweet	good	peace	whisper
nothing	vacation	copy	health	history
accurate	dead	force	cold	climb
again	grief	loud	shade	bitter
living	estimate	modern	ill	sweat
working	down	never	sun	much

153 ★★

together	sweet	chaos	definite	end
identity	same	confusion	alone	teacher
live	part	reality	difference	organized
random	secret	surprise	front	whole
open	order	student	orderly	virtual
expected	recording	unknown	tart	maybe

RHYMING PAIRS

Each clue leads to a phrase made up of a pair of rhyming words – for example, the clue **fast deception** leads to the answer **quick trick**, and the clue **perfectly correct** leads to the answer **quite right**.

154

pleasing gift

set adrift vessel

absurd goat

personnel chortle

express load

attractive tune

gnaw on footwear

aquatic meal

without support

small snack

humble Athenian

distant celestial body

moderately cold body of water

silent revolution

audible hurrah

not at any time

In these puzzles it is often easier to think of the second word first.

155

save fruit jam

more crafty member of religious order

bloodthirsty tale

sylvan flower seller

firm and level piece of furniture

big expense

hoard money

large black birds snooze

pilfer breakfast

little Jack's secret hideaways

more self-satisfied robber

nimbler purchaser

measure parts of limbs

approaching glade

frightening sprite

liquid food ladle

A TO Z OF SYNONYMS & ANTONYMS

Synonyms are words that are similar in meaning, such as **eager** and **keen**. In the following puzzles (156–159) you have to find a synonym for each of the words in the left-hand column. To get you started we've given you one specific letter that features in each synonym.

Antonyms are words that are opposite in meaning, such as **near** and **far**. In the second set of puzzles (160–163), try to find the correct word that is the antonym to the word in the left-hand column. The answers contain at least one letter of the alphabet that has been provided to give you a helping hand.
How many words can you identify?

Synonyms

156 ★☆☆☆

VISTA	*A***A*A
UNCONVENTIONAL	*CC*****C
SHARE	D***D**D
EBULLIENCE	E**E**E**E**E
ENTERPRISE	I*I*I**I**
MEMENTO	K*****K*
APT	*PP**P*****

157 ★★☆☆

IMMERSE	*B***B
EMPHASIZE	H**H***H*
COMPETENTLY	***L**LL*
IMPETUS	M*M****M
INFALLIBLE	*OO***OO*
IMPLICATE	**V**V*
HERITAGE	*Y****Y
GLARE	**ZZ**

158 ★★★☆

BEWILDER	**FF**
TOTAL	*GG**G***
REGULATE	**J***
OBSTACLE	**RR**R
FIGURINE	*T*T**TT*
LAVISH	*U*U***U*
PEAK	*****X

159 ★★★★

BANNER	**NN*N*
GROUP	***Q**
DEPRIVE	**S**SS*SS
GROVEL	**W**W

In these puzzles, the letter clues offer you suggestions to the solutions. It's a fun way of adding to your vocabulary and making sure you have a variety of words to use descriptively.

Antonyms

LONG-WINDED	**CC**C*
CLEAR	**DD**D
LIMP	***FF
PART	J***
TINY	M*MM***
VARIED	*O*O*O*O**
DELIGHT	**RR*R
ENLIGHTENING	**ZZ****

161

VULNERABILITY	I**I**I*I*I**
FAÇADE	***K
LEGITIMATE	*LL***L
HANDY	*N**N**N**N*
TRANSPARENT	***Q**
CONSTANT	**T****TT**T
ORDINARY	U*U*U**
TREACHERY	**Y***Y

162

SEPARATE	A*A**A*A**
SILENCE	**BB*B
OPEN	H**H – H**H
SENSE	P*PP*****
RATIONALITY	S**S***SS**SS
EXHAUST	**V*V*

163

DISRESPECT	*E*E*E**E
IRRESOLUTE	**GG**
OBEDIENT	W**W***
UNDO	****X

LOGOGRAMS

The test with logograms is to find a keyword by answering clues to smaller words within the keyword. Each clue tells you which sequence of letters in the keyword make up the answer, for example in the keyword ANOTHER, the word NOT is letters two to four. The clue to the keyword itself is always in the last line.

1. My one to four is a swirling cloud,
Five to Seven is always allowed,
Seven to Nine gets a foot in the door,
My whole at Christmas loving couples adore.

2. One to four is audacious cheek,
Two to four everything you seek,
Five to seven this insect works hard,
Seven to nine an attempt to regard,
Two to six finds Poe's second name,
Courage and chivalry may win the game.

1. Five to nine an access to gain,
One to four this fish may complain,
One to three on the road you will find,
Four to seven is shut and confined,
Four to six an enclosure or quill,
My all a profession of ancient skill.

2. One to five is my place of rest,
Two to five as high as my crest,
Five to eight a beast I admire,
A male like me, I am entire.

WORD PAIRS

In each puzzle are listed, in random order and column, 20 pairs of words that make up well-known phrases. Try to deduce which word goes with which.

166 ★

mix	brain	secretary
key	dog	thunder
believe	distance	moth
rubber	struck	up
piece	mind	round
stage	hot	tape
low	rolling	make
stamp	general	bending
clap	playing	ticker
luck	feather	museum
duty	role	rate
pin	middle	ball
table	second	
pot	free	

167 ★★

scale	cast	on
extra	bean	weight
dividend	dry	over
off	man	killer
herring	vaulter	cut
zero	line	cap
white	clean	made
anxious	perpetual	large
tip	terrestrial	ice
paper	carve	giant
motion	bone	die
pole	range	drip
up	bag	
collar	long	

168 ★

hot	stock	teller
opera	four	can
age	boiled	fork
do	general	wheel
back	laughing	cop
hard	dimensional	felt
drum	cross	run
fortune	air	lift
soap	think	double
hero	old	pop
in	up	snare
up	tank	tipped
purpose	out	
three	worship	

169

examine	change	swing
knuckle	home	never
cat	win	fair
cart	cost	walk
weather	apple	low
win	effective	kind
guess	stretch	jam
level	cross	hot
off	quick	state
wing	white	stock
never	spread	solid
lift	red	eagle
joint	second	
log	hearted	

LINE BY LINE

Each line of the verse in these puzzles will produce a single letter. The letters, read down in order, form a word, which is indicated by the final line of the verse.

172

My first is in witch but not in broom,
My second's in fragrance but not perfume,
My third is in apple but not in pear,
My fourth is in seldom but never rare,
My fifth's in a goblin but not in a sprite,
My sixth is in water but never tight,
My seventh's in candle but not in stick,
My eighth is in concrete but never a brick,
My ninth is in candy and jellybean,
My whole is a time when costumes are seen.

170

My first is in publish but not broadcast,
My second's in banquet and also repast,
My third is in spirit but not in ghost,
My fourth's in profusion but not in host,
My fifth is in mortise but not in lock,
My sixth's in a pendulum but never a clock,
My seventh's in jettison but not discard,
My eighth's in respect but not regard,
My ninth is in stretched but never taut,
My whole in Nirvana is often sought.

171

My first is in winter but not in spring,
My second's in circle and also ring,
My third is in region but not domain,
My fourth is in polished but not urbane,
My fifth's in beautician but never shampoo,
My sixth is in greenbacks and overdrew,
My seventh's in canopy but not in tent,
My eighth is in slope but not ascent,
My ninth's in encourage and also cheer,
On my whole an acrobat may appear.

173

My first's in alfresco but not open-air,
My second is in antique and also rare,
My third's in Utopia but not Thomas More,
My fourth's in Tyrannosaurus and carnivore,
My fifth is in Christmas and also Wise Men,
My sixth is in chlorine but not halogen,
My seventh's in frost but not in bite,
My eighth is in spendthrift but never tight,
My ninth is in calling but not career,
My whole is a sign when winter is here.

ENIGMAGRAMS

In each puzzle four eight-letter words, all on the same theme, have been jumbled. Solve the four anagrams and enter the answers next to them, reading from left to right or top to bottom. Next, transfer the coloured letters to the key anagram to find a fifth word (nine letters long) on the same theme.

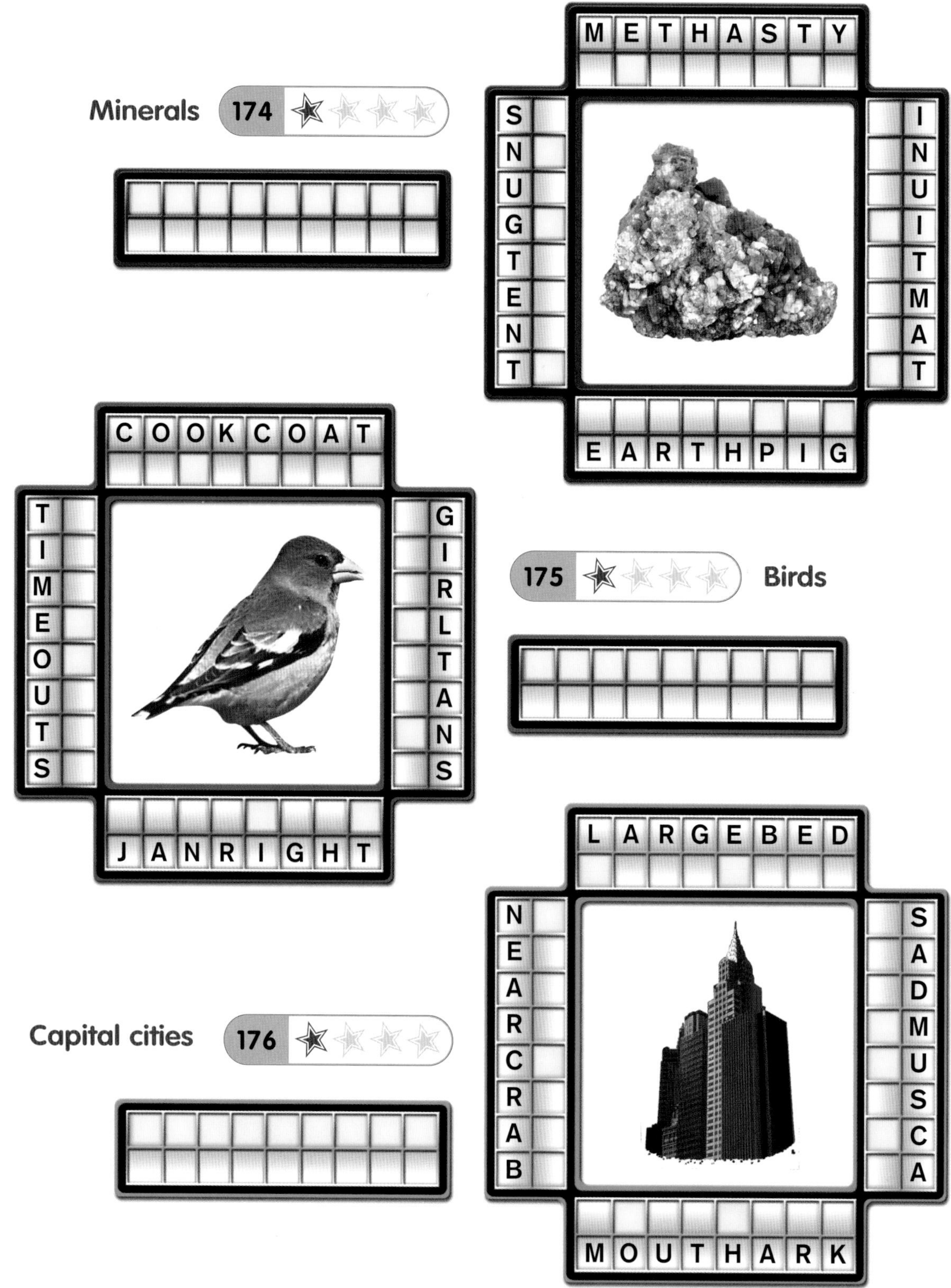

177

Sports

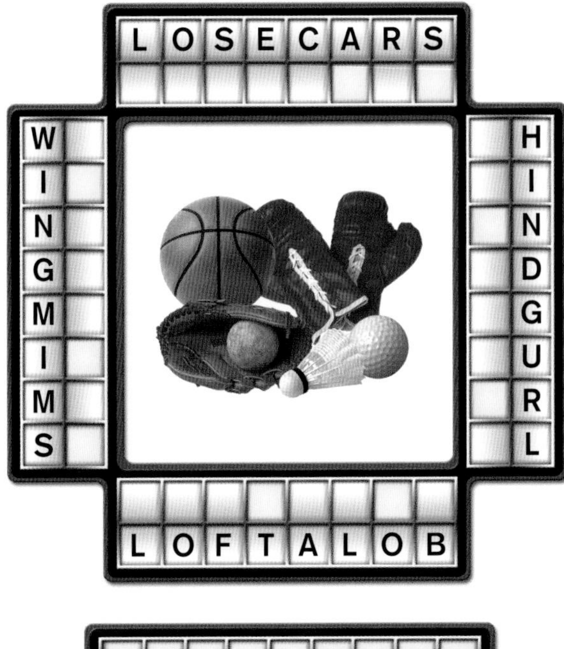

Sailing vessels

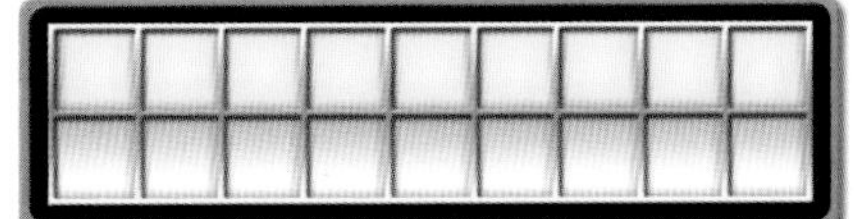

Musical instruments

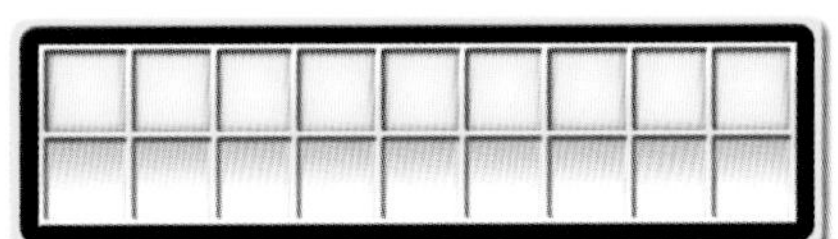

Let's dance

BRACKET WORD

In each of the following puzzles, place two letters in each set of brackets so that they complete the word on the left and start another word on the right. Once complete, put the letters in brackets together to form another eight- or ten-letter word.

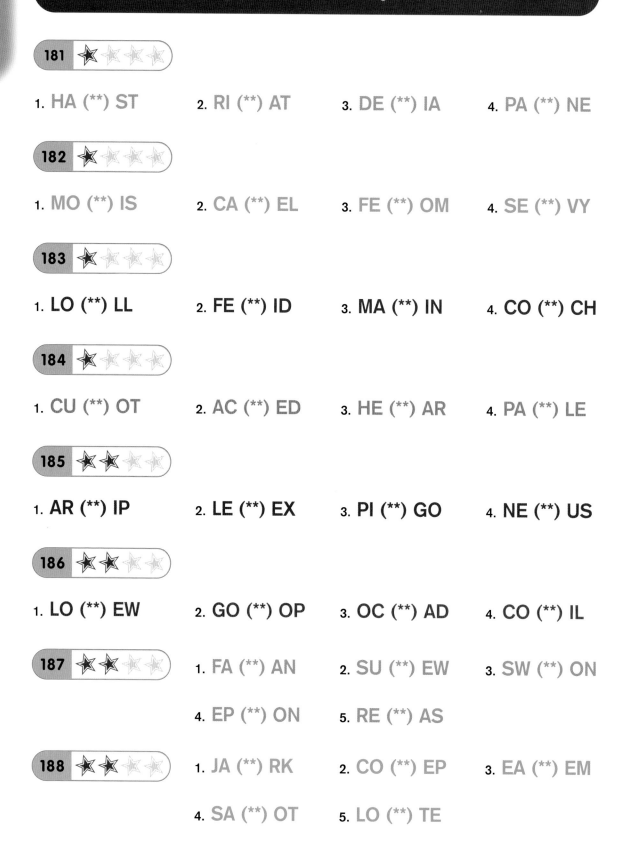

181 ★☆☆☆

1. HA (**) ST
2. RI (**) AT
3. DE (**) IA
4. PA (**) NE

182 ★☆☆☆

1. MO (**) IS
2. CA (**) EL
3. FE (**) OM
4. SE (**) VY

183 ★☆☆☆

1. LO (**) LL
2. FE (**) ID
3. MA (**) IN
4. CO (**) CH

184 ★☆☆☆

1. CU (**) OT
2. AC (**) ED
3. HE (**) AR
4. PA (**) LE

185 ★★☆☆

1. AR (**) IP
2. LE (**) EX
3. PI (**) GO
4. NE (**) US

186 ★★☆☆

1. LO (**) EW
2. GO (**) OP
3. OC (**) AD
4. CO (**) IL

187 ★★☆☆

1. FA (**) AN
2. SU (**) EW
3. SW (**) ON
4. EP (**) ON
5. RE (**) AS

188 ★★☆☆

1. JA (**) RK
2. CO (**) EP
3. EA (**) EM
4. SA (**) OT
5. LO (**) TE

ODD WORDS OUT

Although it helps to know the meaning of the words in these puzzles, what you really need to work out is what other feature singles them out as not belonging to the sequence given.
Hint: Look for pairs, sequences and hidden words.

189 Which word is the odd one out?

APLOMB, BEMUSE, COMMAND, ENGULF, GARNISH.

190 Which word shouldn't be here?

MUSICAL, LACIEST, RESTORE, FRAMED, DEMAND, CONTORT, TROTTER.

191 The following words all have something in common except one.

BEMUSE, ALTITUDE, HYPHENATE, NARROWLY, MAGNUM.

192 Can you pick out the word that doesn't belong in this group?

GARDENING, FREIGHTER, DENOUNCE, UNDERGROWTH, EXISTING, BRUNETTE.

193 Which of these five-letter words is the odd one out?

OCEAN, BASIC, UPSET, MOGUL, SOLAR.

194 Can you find the rogue word in this large group?

ABORIGINAL, TRAIN, AMISS, MAGISTRATE, PROSECUTOR, ALIGN, CONCERTINA, PERIPHERAL, ORGAN, TREAT, SNAPDRAGON, COURT, ENTHUSIASM.

HIDDEN WORDS

In these puzzles, you will find the answer by solving a clue that is hidden somewhere within the puzzle itself – remember, the letters in it may be jumbled and separate from one another.

Cuckoo in the nest

Each sentence in these puzzles contains, in the correct order, the letters of a word that is opposite to the meaning of the sentence, e.g. **c**l**o**se t**o** b**o**i**l**ing (4) = **cool**

195

Completely without reasoning process and incapable of analytical thought. (7)

196

Not easily yielding to pressure and firmly resistant. (4)

Think of several words that fit the clue first before looking for the specific letters – doing this may mean the answers immediately jump out at you.

197

Magnanimous, benevolent and charitable. (4)

198

Lacking in drive, energy and devoid of any emphatic determination. (7)

Cryptograms

Each puzzle consists of one cryptic clue, the answer being an anagram found within the clue. The number of letters in the word you are seeking is given in brackets.

Approval and support for one cute German in disarray. (13)

Hunted near mess down below. (10)

Redraw tennis cartoon with trepidation. (13)

Play for time until satanic report rewritten. (13)

Themed passage

Find six words, all on the same theme, which are hidden within other words in the following passage.

I considered myself fortunate to have obtained a complimentary ticket to the first night opening of the new *Planet of the Apes* movie. When the spotlight fell on the parade of celebrities, I remarked to the cloakroom attendant just how overwhelmed I felt by the display of high fashion on show on the red carpet outside the theatre.

VERBOSITIES

In the following puzzles a number of familiar proverbs have been disguised by the use of flowery language. Simplify the verbose words and phrases, and see how many proverbs you can identify.

EXAMPLE:

Retiring before it is late, and getting up soon, causes a person to become vigorous, affluent and sagacious.

SOLUTION:

Early to bed and early to rise, makes a man healthy, wealthy and wise.

I am producing grass mowed and cured for use as fodder during the time that the luminous orb, the light of which constitutes day, emits radiance. What am I doing?

In a somewhat risky manoeuvre I am travelling on a vessel in nearby proximity to the air in motion by which it is propelled. What am I doing?

In order to exercise caution I am scrutinizing what is ahead prior to making a light springing movement in a forward direction. What am I doing?

In an attempt to disguise my hilarity I am maintaining an uncurved and undeviating countenance. What am I doing?

These puzzles will help you to improve your fluency of expression and use of words because they require you to think of simple alternative words or phrases that are more succinct, but have the same overall meaning as the original.

LETTER CHANGE

In each of the following puzzles, change one letter only in each of the words to produce a familiar phrase.

EXAMPLE:

Plan in works becomes Pla**y** **o**n wor**d**s

208 ★☆☆☆

1. Line too pens if I nod
2. So I bank (British expression)

209

1. Bed on tie lace
2. Is fan an ore cat bell

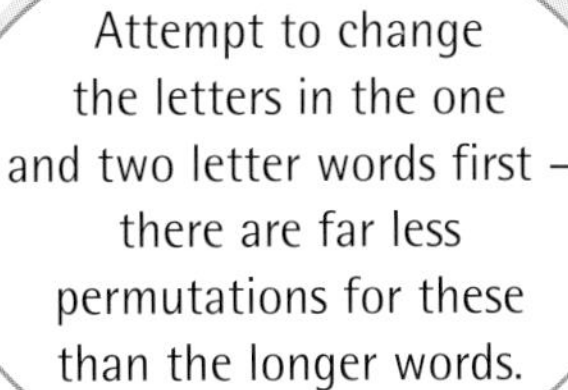

Attempt to change the letters in the one and two letter words first – there are far less permutations for these than the longer words.

210 ★☆☆☆

1. Bread on dam
2. May it say our

211

1. In chat to
2. Pack us she will

212 ★☆☆☆

1. As case
2. Let in wish if

NETWORK

In each of the six puzzles in this section, work from letter to letter to spell out a 14-letter word. Every letter must be used once, but once only, and each consecutive letter in the word must be connected by a line.

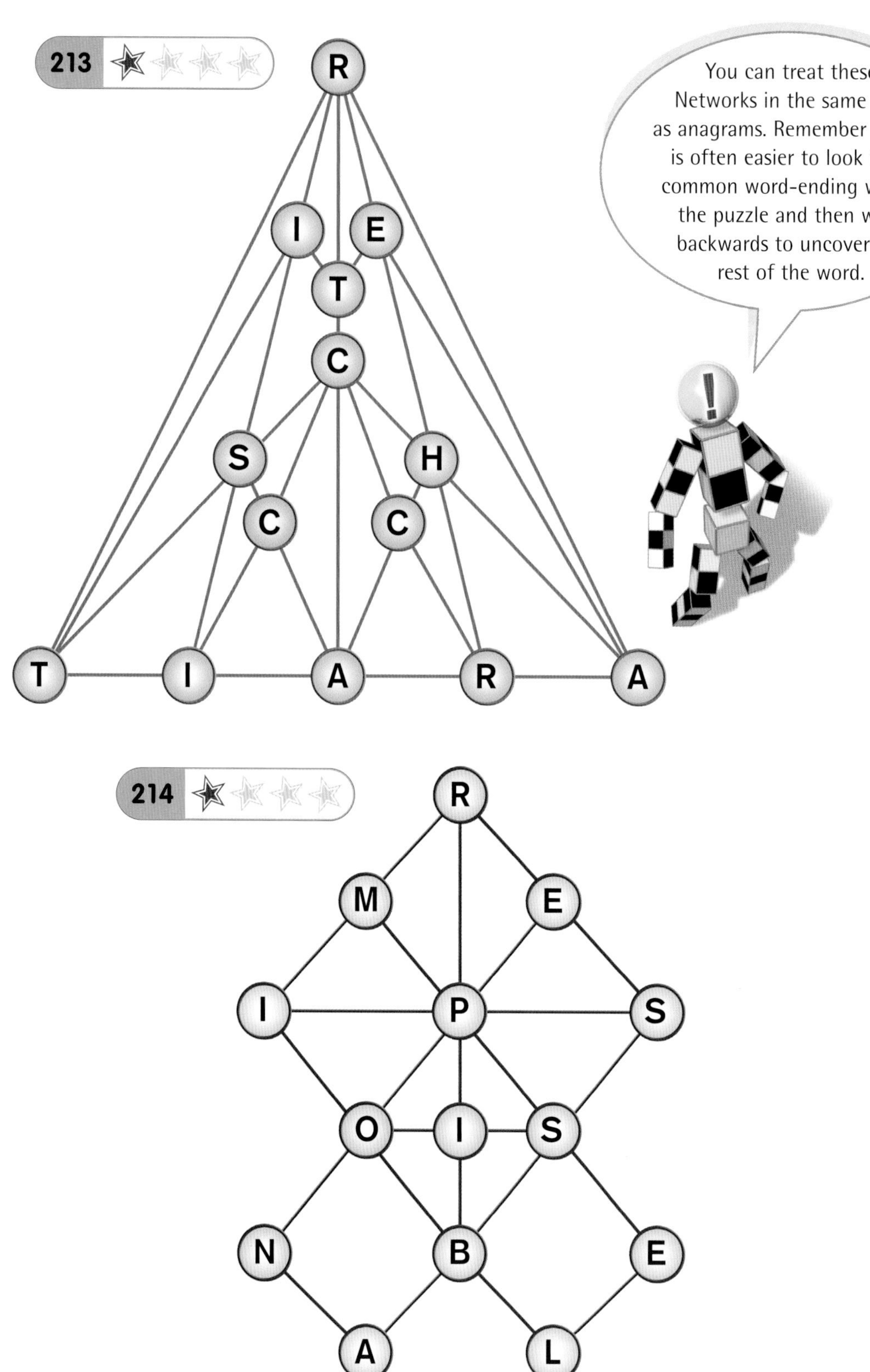

213
R
I
E
T
C
S
H
C
C
T
I
A
R
A
You can treat these Networks in the same way as anagrams. Remember that it is often easier to look for a common word-ending within the puzzle and then work backwards to uncover the rest of the word.
214
R
M
E
I
P
S
O
I
S
N
B
E
A
L

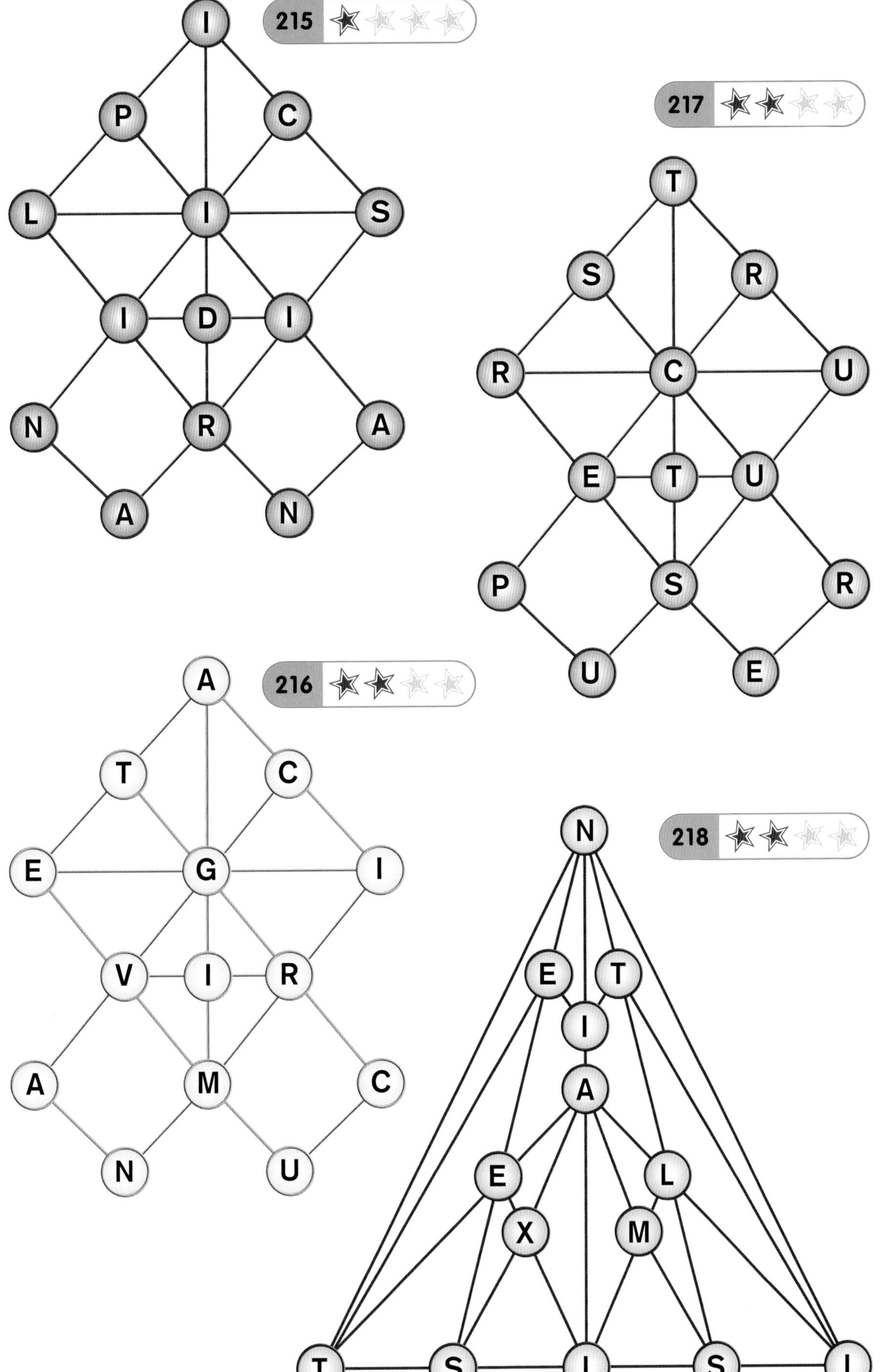
215
I
P
C
L
I
S
I
D
I
N
R
A
A
N
217
T
S
R
R
C
U
E
T
U
P
S
R
U
E
216
A
T
C
E
G
I
V
I
R
A
M
C
N
U
218
N
E
T
I
A
E
L
X
M
T
S
I
S
I

HOMOPHONES

A homophone (sometimes known as a homonym) is a word in the English language which has the same sound as another, but has a different meaning and a different spelling.

Examples of homophones are: **aloud/allowed, build/billed** and **chord/cord**.

Each of the clues in the puzzle below leads to a two-word phrase in which the two words are homophones: for example the clue, **dispatched U.S. currency**, would lead to the answer **sent cent**.

219 

1. Catch sight of the ocean.
2. Revolting hen.

220 

1. Avoided haze.
2. Junior underground worker.

221 

1. Reduce period of learning.
2. Jaded and weary group of directors.

Once you have completed these puzzles, try thinking of some more homophones and then write clues of your own. Remember there can be more than two words that sound alike.

222 

1. Stupendous fireplace.
2. Prague bank draft.

223 

1. Charming set of hotel rooms.
2. Coarse high tight collar.

224 

1. Regrets artifice.
2. Dreadful stainer.

THE LINCOLN CIPHER

During the American Civil War, the US president used his own very special code when sending messages. In the code he used the signature Ale Inn Cann, instead of his usual signature which was, of course, A. Lincoln. The sound was exactly the same, but the words were quite different.

Now decode the following, which all use the same system.

Reading the phrases aloud will make the solutions much more obvious.

A saying
Hugh Khan hot bees ear eye house.

A saying
Hiss Tory re Pete's hits elf.

A saying
Two more Ho! His Anne hoe third Hey!

A Shakespeare quotation
Weirs hutch thins Gaz D. Rheims arm aid off.

A film and book title
Juan flu hover thick hook who's hen hest.

An English proverb
Men he think Czar loss T. four one T. off ass king.

This could have been a message sent by a character from history to one of Lucretia Borgia's suitors
Dee rope inn four dine her, wood yew lie Kay whine, Watt hiss yore poise son?

An English proverb
Her Horace Hall way sin hay her Hay!

A Russian proverb
Two ass kiss snows in hand two beer he fuss eddy snow Kay Lamb hit he.

A Chinese proverb
I few R. Pat hen tin Juan mow mean toff hangar Hugh while scape hay undread daze off sore hoe.

THE GALLOPERS

These puzzles combine anagrams and synonym-type clues, and are similar to those used in crosswords. They are called 'The Gallopers' after the original name for the popular fairground ride, now better known as the Carousel.

The object is to complete the words in each 'spoke', all of which end in the letter 'G'. The scrambled letters in the segment to the right of each spoke are an anagram of a clue to the adjacent 'spoke' word.

You don't have to complete the puzzles in strict order. Complete the simpler anagrams first and then move on to the longer, more challenging ones.

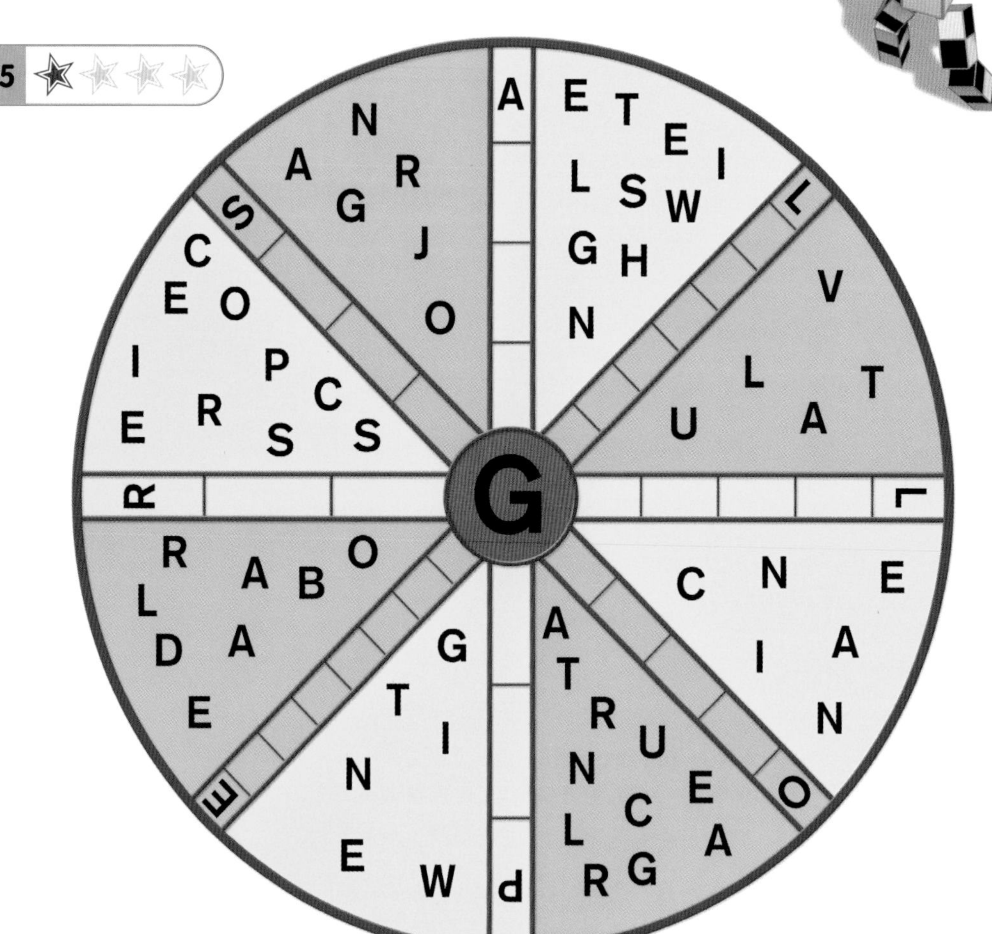

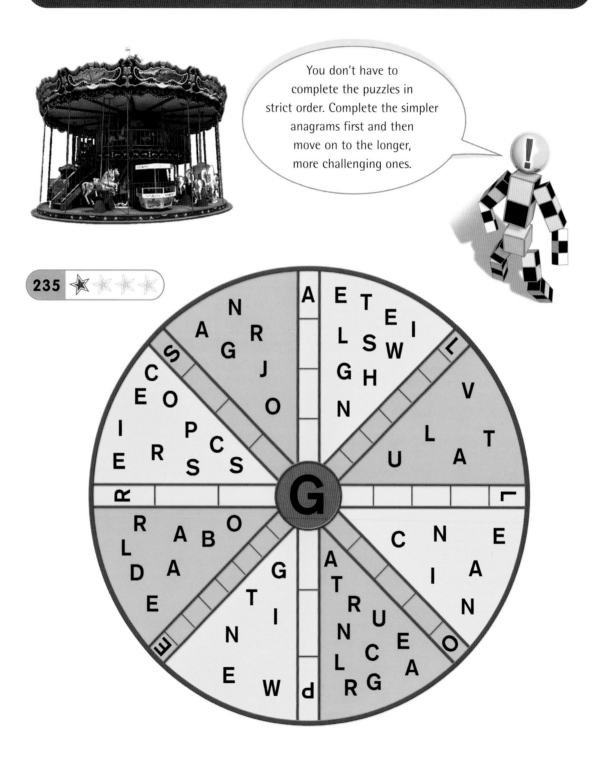

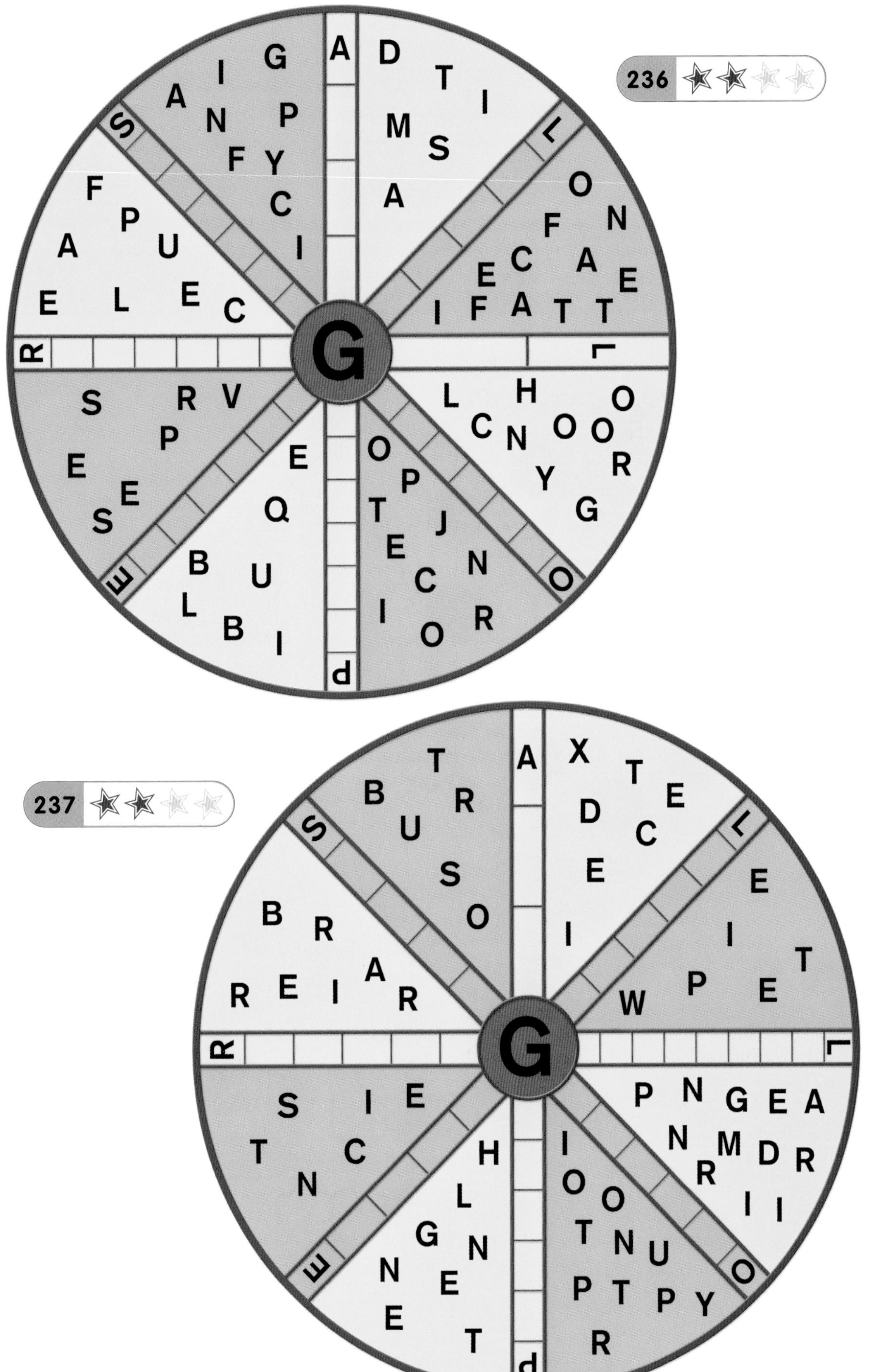
236
237

HEXAGONS

To complete the puzzles, fit each of the listed words into the six spaces around a number, so each word correctly interlinks with the words in the hexagons on either side. Each word has two consecutive letters in common with the adjoining words.

The words need to be inserted clockwise or counter-clockwise according to the instructions provided and the colour code of the number. Orange means a word must be entered clockwise and yellow means a word must be entered counter-clockwise.

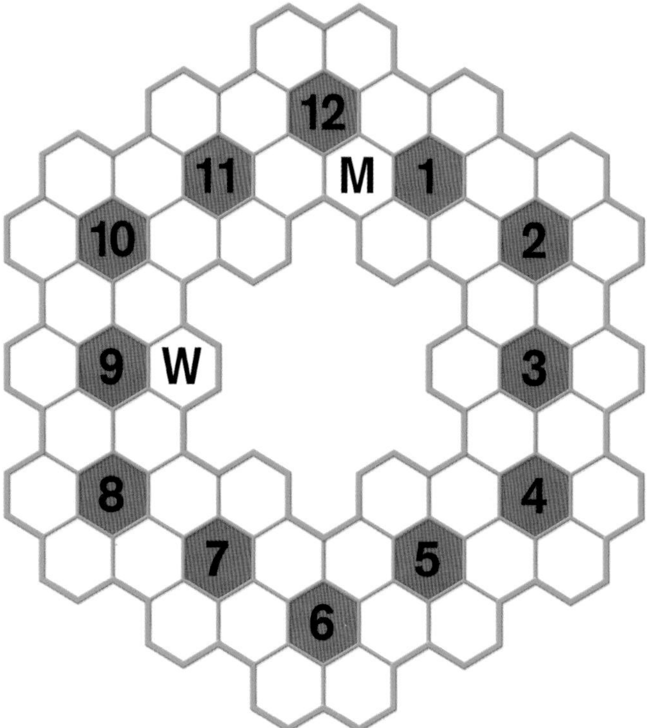

238

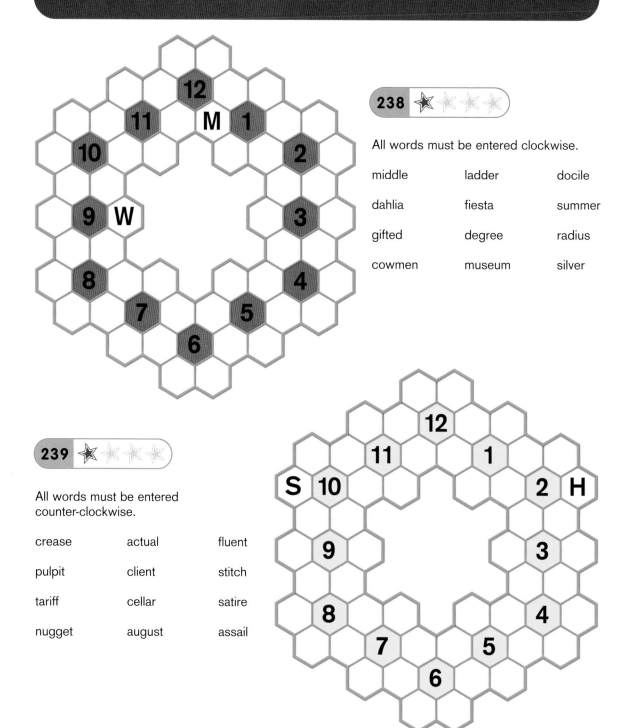

All words must be entered clockwise.

middle	ladder	docile
dahlia	fiesta	summer
gifted	degree	radius
cowmen	museum	silver

All words must be entered counter-clockwise.

crease	actual	fluent
pulpit	client	stitch
tariff	cellar	satire
nugget	august	assail

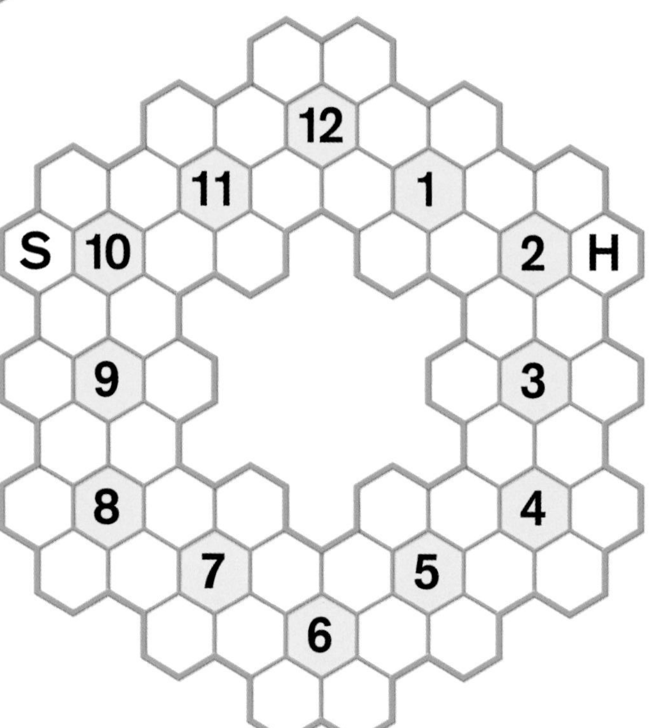

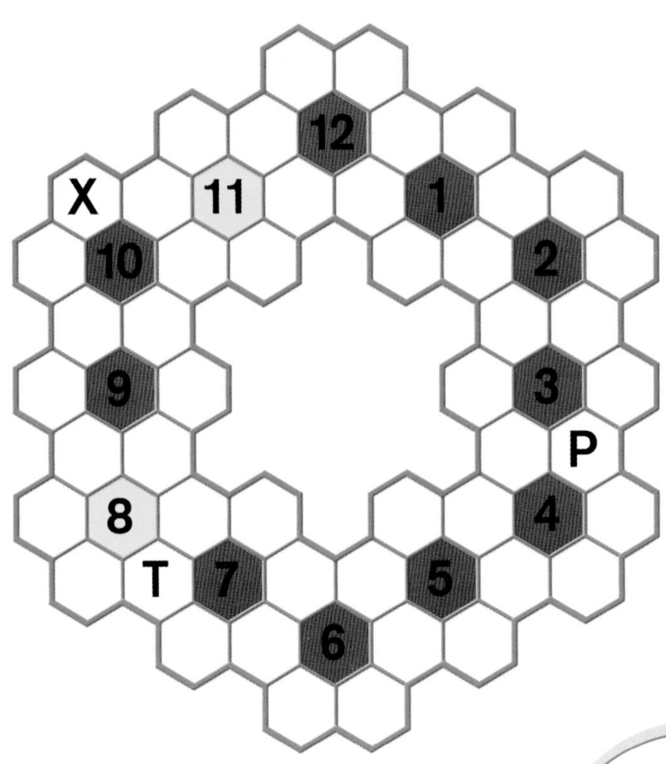

240

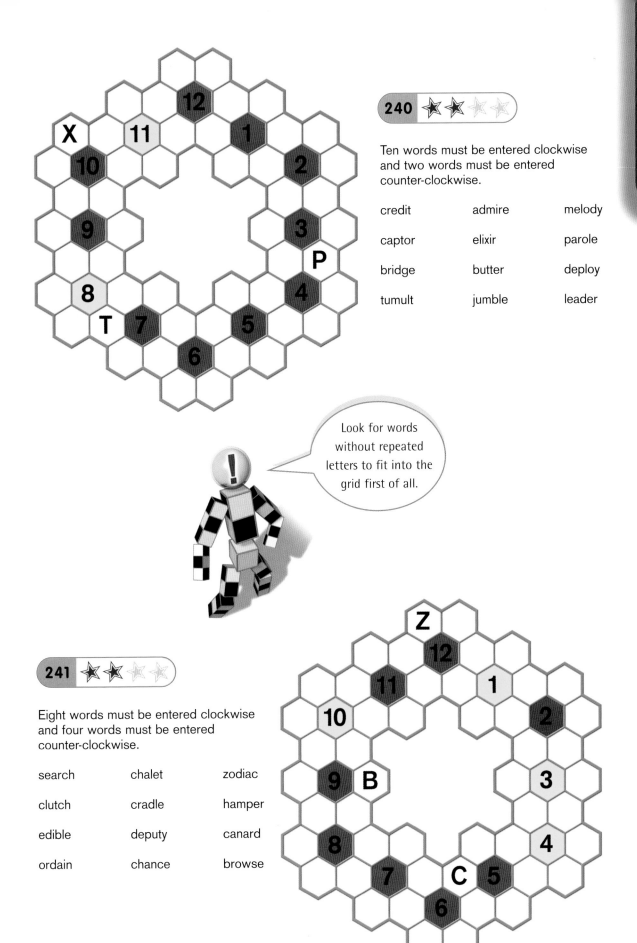

Ten words must be entered clockwise and two words must be entered counter-clockwise.

credit	admire	melody
captor	elixir	parole
bridge	butter	deploy
tumult	jumble	leader

Look for words without repeated letters to fit into the grid first of all.

Eight words must be entered clockwise and four words must be entered counter-clockwise.

search	chalet	zodiac
clutch	cradle	hamper
edible	deputy	canard
ordain	chance	browse

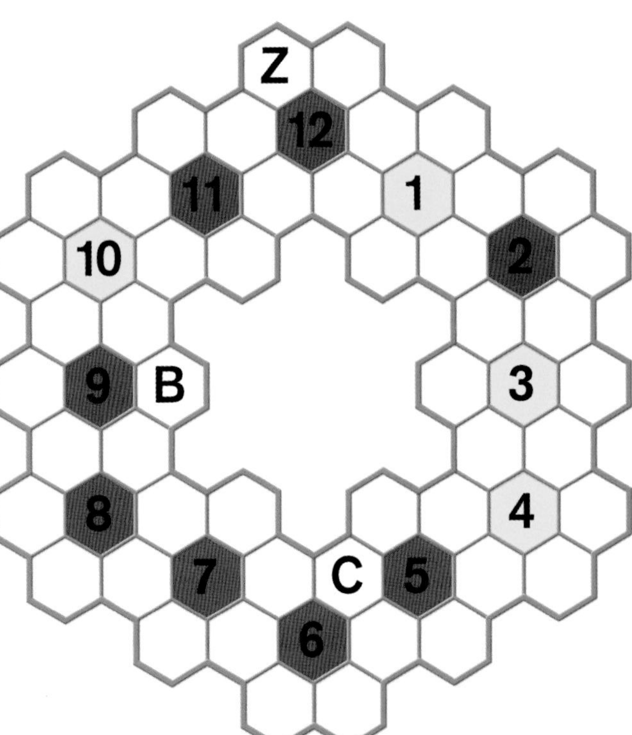

CONUNDRUMS

One definition of the word 'conundrum' is 'a difficult problem'. Many conundrums are clever plays on words in which the answer may be a punning joke.

Others appear in the form of a riddle or puzzle in which the answer must be determined by logical deduction from the various clues provided.

242

What does luminous paint contain that can only be seen on the continent of Europe?

243

What is it that is long and flowing, can guide or teach, can move people and objects, can be fast or slow, can sometimes let off steam, but always provides a drink before inclement weather?

244

What is the correct English language translation of VOLVII ?

245

I won three individual sports races at my local sports gala, but I did not once pass the finishing line. How was this possible?

246

Which Biblical king finds his father when he casts aside six?

247

Why is it that when you are searching for something you have misplaced you inevitably find it in the last place you look?

248

A tourist stuck these letters on his suitcase. Where was his holiday destination?

249

This riddle has a one-word answer.

Mix me up for a magic spell,
A piece of music that sounds swell,
An animal that's a little mad,
Or a long walk when feeling glad,
Maybe it's the time of year,
Look and you will find me here.

250

Arrange two numbers side by side so that the number on the right is twice as large, but the number on the left is twice as many. (Hint: There is more than one solution to this puzzle.)

251

What relative is a child to its father who is not its father's own son?

252

If half of nine is four, and half of twelve is seven, what is half of thirteen?

253

What fish is most cherished by a lady on her wedding day?

PYRAMID LABYRINTH

In each of the following puzzles you must spell out a 15-letter word by going into the pyramid, one room at a time. You may only visit each room once, but you may go into the passage as many times as you wish.

You may find it easier to write the 15 letters down on a piece of paper and treat them as basic anagrams. Then when solved, you can check your answer against the pyramid configuration.

254 ★★

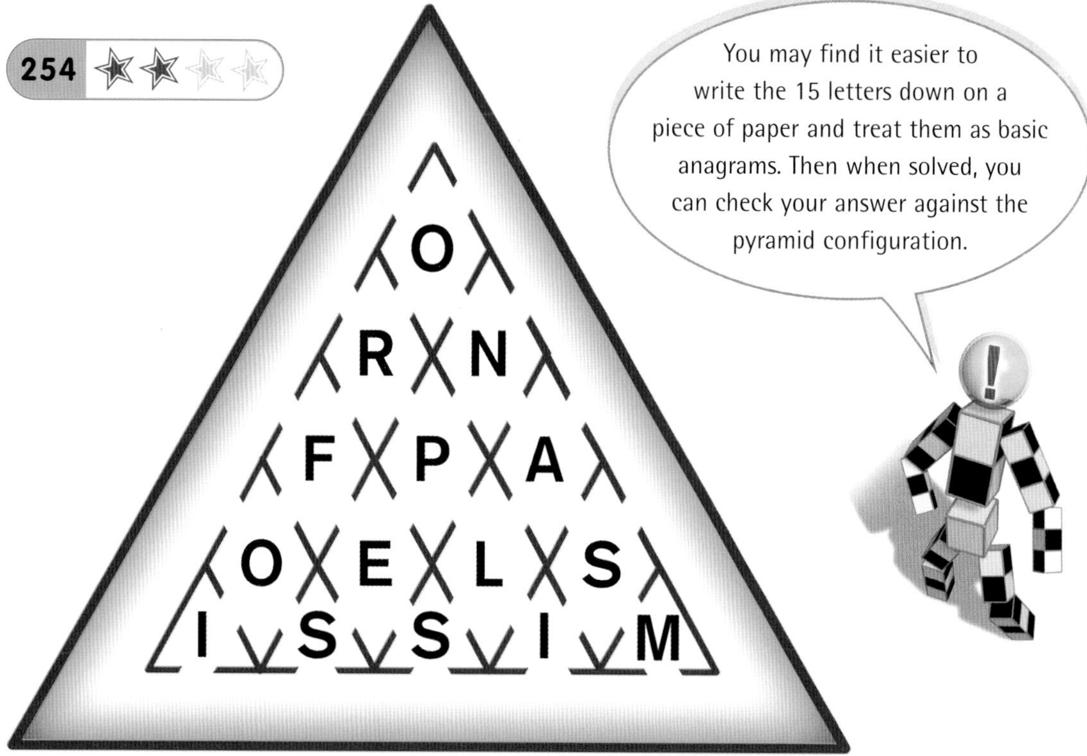

255 ★★

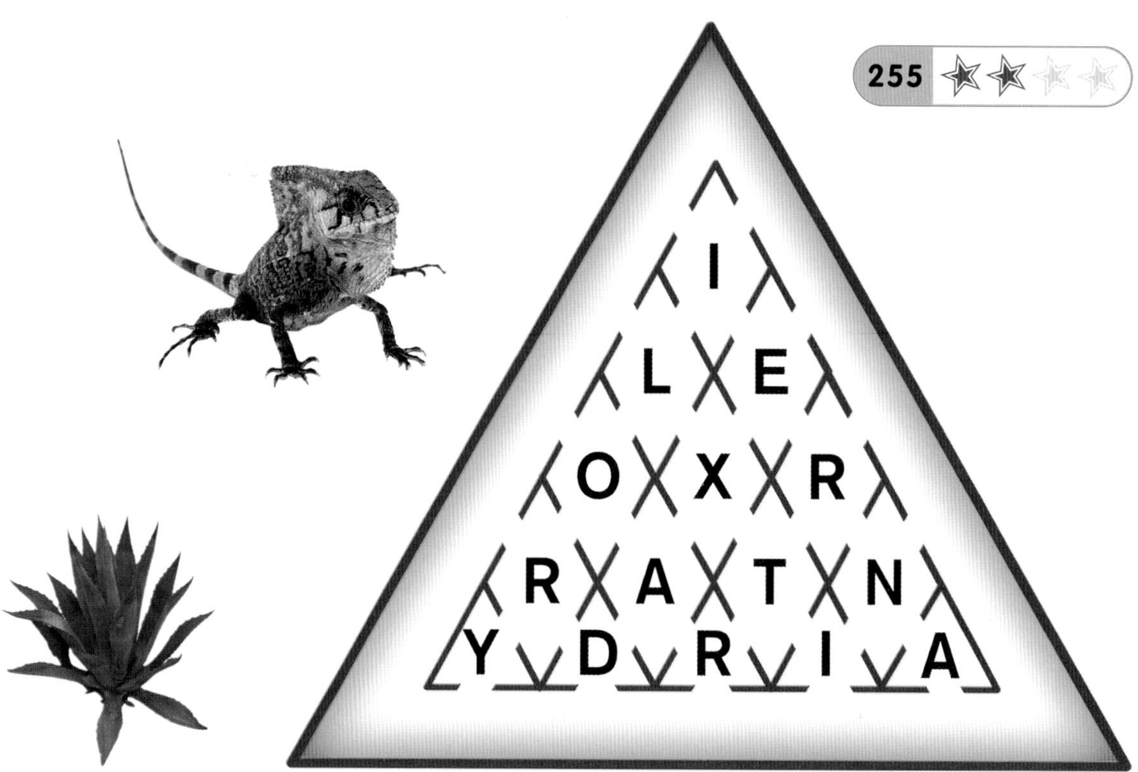

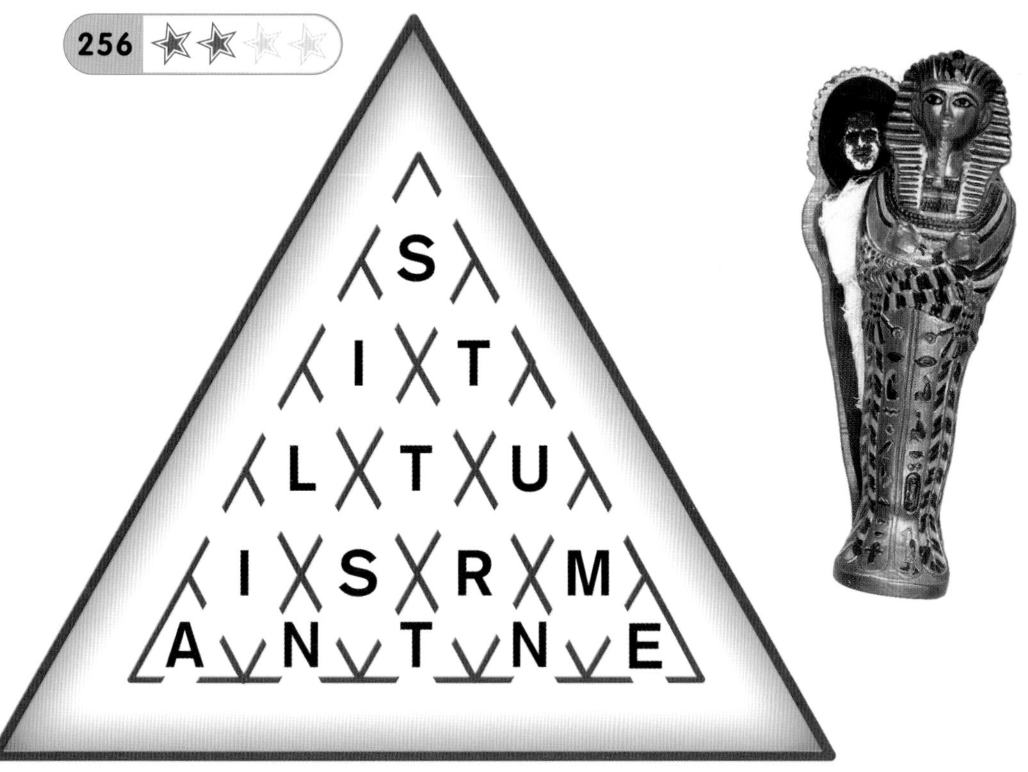
256
S
I T
L T U
I S R M
A N T N E

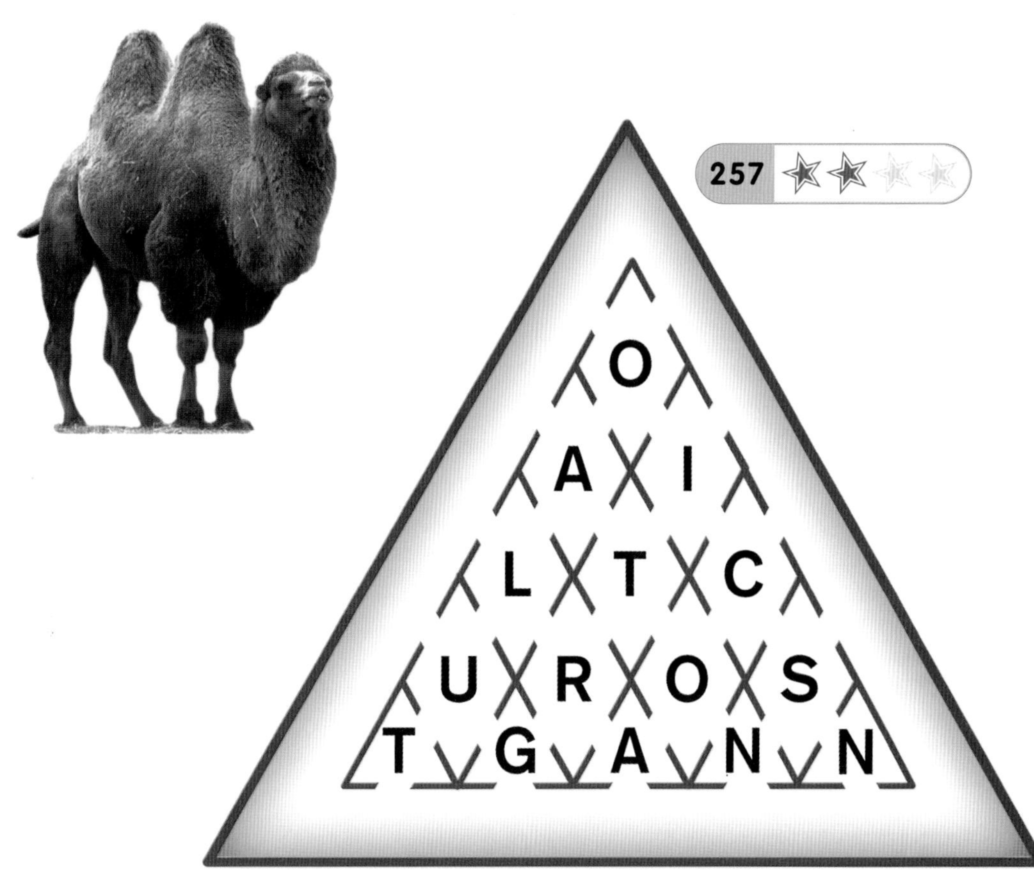
257
O
A I
L T C
U R O S
T G A N N

WORD POWER

Test the extent of your vocabulary and increase your word power with these quizzes.

Column A contains a list of ten definitions and column B contains a list of ten words. The problem is that they have all been mixed up. Can you match each of the ten words with their correct definition?

258

A

short-lived, transitory
intermittent or occasional
laughable or ridiculous
acclaim, glory
give or promise
ice-cream of Italian origin
disease, desperate condition
pang, turmoil
blunt, rude
sealed, airtight

B

throe
hermetic
brusque
cassata
sporadic
kudos
ephemeral
risible
malady
vouchsafe

A healthy etymology and understanding of word roots will assist here. When consulting a dictionary, remember also to look for word origins.

259

A

occurring during the day
coarse or bawdy behaviour
small round piece of meat
the description of a coat of arms
diamond-like mineral used as a gemstone
way out
to show or reveal clearly
heron or other variety of wading bird
a werewolf
record, recount

B

chronicle
noisette
diurnal
ribaldry
blazon
egret
egress
lycanthrope
zircon
evince

260

A

shaped like a snail shell
to improve or to make better
room just under a pitched roof
discoloured, as from a bruise
decoration around an opening
stand for supporting a book or notes
carnation, pink or related flower
foam or froth on the sea
still in existence
gum or resin used as varnish

B

dianthus
mastic
cochleate
garret
spume
extant
ameliorate
architrave
livid
lectern

261

A

bric-a-brac
to question on a point of government
hole in a fortification
insert in conversation or change a manuscript
resembling an eagle
preferring to use force
remedy for all diseases or ills
type of aquatic mammal
back or side gate
milk protein

B

casein
embrasure
postern
interpellate
hawkish
interpolate
curio
aquiline
panacea
cetacean

THE MIND'S EYE

THE MIND'S EYE

THE MIND'S EYE

Although we perceive our world primarily through sight, it is still a fallible sense. By training our brains to distinguish what's real from what's not, we allow ourselves a greater understanding of our experiences.

'I SAW IT WITH MY OWN EYES' is a phrase often used to confirm that an event has really happened. But, although the eyes and the brain are closely connected, this saying is not necessarily accurate. Whatever the nature of the 'real' signals the brain receives from the eyes, it can still be easily deceived – something that magicians and illusionists use to advantage. It is this mismatch between what is physically registered on the retina of the eye and its interpretation by the brain that forms the basis of most visual puzzles. Most rely strongly on the fact, well known to proofreaders, that we see what we expect to see, not necessarily what is actually there.

VISUAL PUZZLES ARE FASCINATING AND CHALLENGING ways of testing how well you can train your brain to focus on the true nature of an image in all its detail, including nuances of colour and perspective, irrespective of what the brain 'thinks' it sees. Such puzzles also make use of the fact that a flat, two-dimensional image reproduced on a piece of paper can be interpreted in three dimensions by the brain.

VISUAL REASONING involves being able to use your powers of analysis as well as your visual skills and imagination to resolve a visual problem. One way of exercising this ability is to look up in the sky and 'see' in the clouds recognizable objects to which you can give names or more complex images or configurations. This kind of visual reasoning is known as pareidolia.

The brain has an amazing capacity to interpret and rethink visual stimuli in order to create images that it can make sense of.

My name is Percy Ving, and I will give you advice throughout this section on picture puzzle-solving techniques and ways to improve your powers of perception.

MANY VISUAL ILLUSIONS INVOLVE GEOMETRY, as geometric objects can easily be turned into puzzles, most famously in the Tangram from ancient China. The combination of five triangles of varying sizes, a square, and a parallelogram (which total 32 half and 16 whole squares of equal size) can be combined to make thousands of different images, as well as puzzles of varying difficulty. If you enjoy Tangrams you may like to buy a wooden set, or make a set from card.

REARRANGING AND FITTING GEOMETRICAL SHAPES TOGETHER (in matchstick puzzles for example), spotting the 'odd one out' or finding the next in a sequence are other types of geometrical puzzles you will find in this section. Your visual imagination and reasoning will also be tested with puzzles solved by connecting a series of points with lines. Observation is especially important for the ever-popular 'spot the difference' puzzles, whose difficulty usually depends on the level of detail in the images themselves and the subtlety of the visual differences.

THE WORLD'S OLDEST MAZES are over 4000 years old – the most famous being the ancient labyrinth of Crete to contain the mythical Minotaur. Now strictly for entertainment, with false trails and dead ends, mazes exist not only on paper but also in living form, as in the hedge maze at Hampton Court. To challenge yourself as much as possible, try solving the mazes in this section without using the acetate and pen. Instead, trace your path, literally, in your mind's eye.

PUZZLES INCORPORATING CUBES, in which you either have to count the number of cubes shown, or replace one or more missing cubes in a configuration, demand that you use your mind's eye to visualize elements of the puzzle that you cannot see in the illustration. With the counting versions, a systematic approach, as well a paper and pencil to keep a tally of each row, are useful assets.

WITH YOUR VISUAL SENSES HONED, and your brain alerted to the unusual, your visual acuity and powers of observation will undoubtedly improve. Heightened visual awareness is enormously useful if you enjoy any kind of craft or hobby that relies on colour, shape and dimension, such as painting, card and model making, or even DIY. It can even be helpful in sports such as soccer, tennis and hockey in which you need heightened spacial awareness and the ability to visualize in advance your own or your opponent's actions.

VISUAL CLASSIFICATION

To solve these puzzles, you need to study each of the first boxes and then work out which other box meets the same conditions. This may be for a variety of reasons and so you may have to approach these questions with an open mind and explore different possibilities.

EXAMPLE:

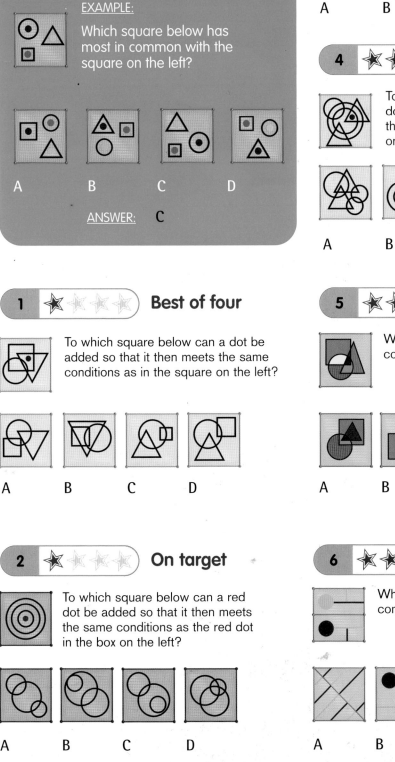

Which square below has most in common with the square on the left?

   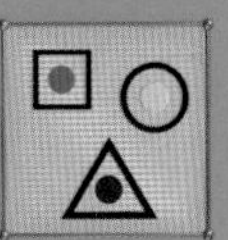

A B C D

ANSWER: C

1 Best of four

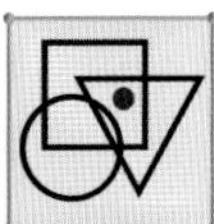

To which square below can a dot be added so that it then meets the same conditions as in the square on the left?

A B C D

2 On target

To which square below can a red dot be added so that it then meets the same conditions as the red dot in the box on the left?

 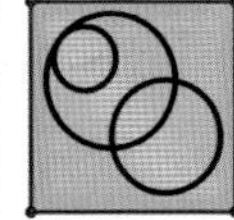 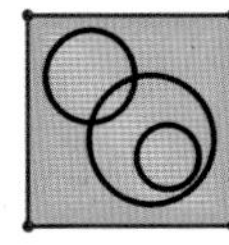 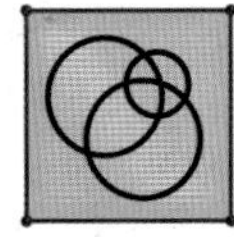 

A B C D

3 Chain reaction

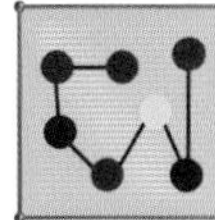

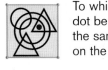

Which of the five squares below has most in common with the square on the left?

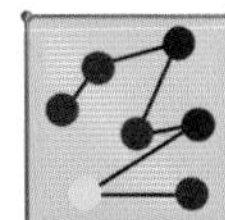 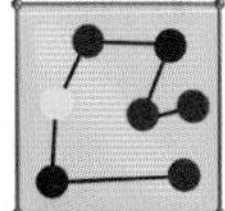 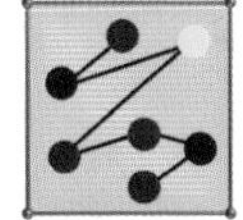 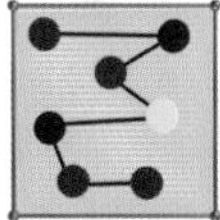

A B C D

4 Group theory

To which square below can a blue dot be added so that it then meets the same conditions as in the square on the left?

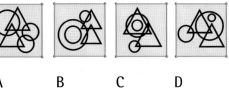

A B C D

5 Similar rules

Which square below has most in common with the box on the left?

 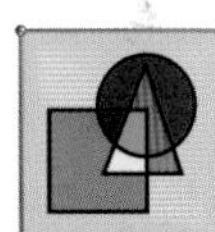  

A B C D

6 Be reflective

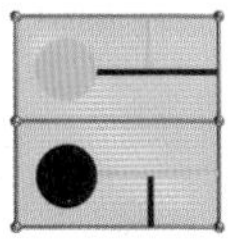

Which square below has most in common with the square on the left?

 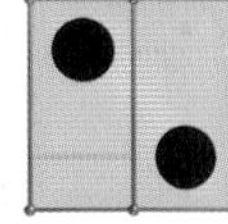 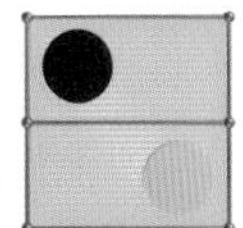 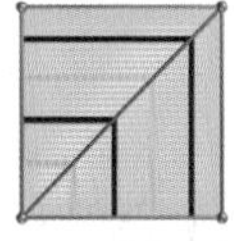

A B C D

SPOT WHAT'S WRONG

How observant are you? Take a look at the images that follow. Now look a bit closer – things are not quite as they seem. Can you spot the oddities?

7

Dim sum

Take a close look at the picture here and see if you can determine what shouldn't be there.

Study this

Can you spot the six unusual things in this mixed-up room?

Culinary chaos

Take a close look at this seemingly harmonious scene and spot the six inconsistencies.

Child's play

There are no fewer than ten oddities in this bedroom. Can you find them all?

VISUAL SHAPE PUZZLES

These puzzles will help you to start training your powers of analysis and logical reasoning. Some are more, and some less obvious than they may seem at first glance.

THE MIND'S EYE

11 Best of four

Which design will replace the question mark?

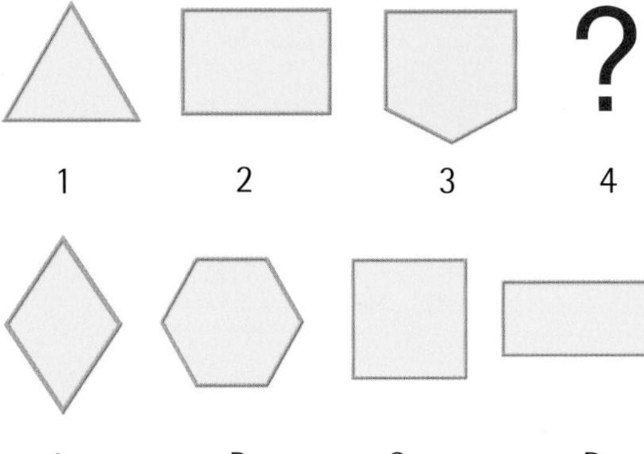

12 Tiles of fun

Which tile completes the wall?

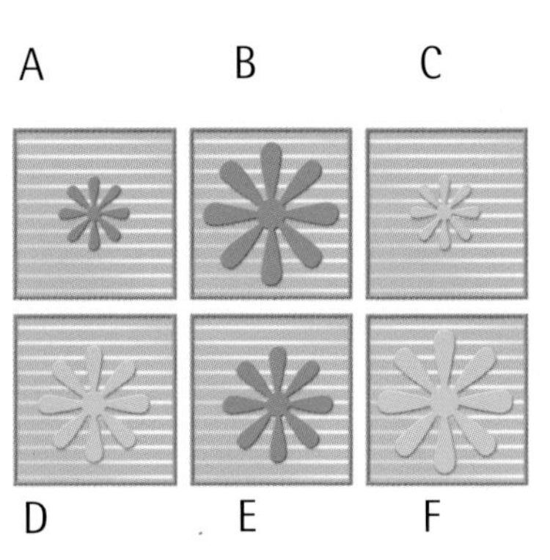

13 Tri and match

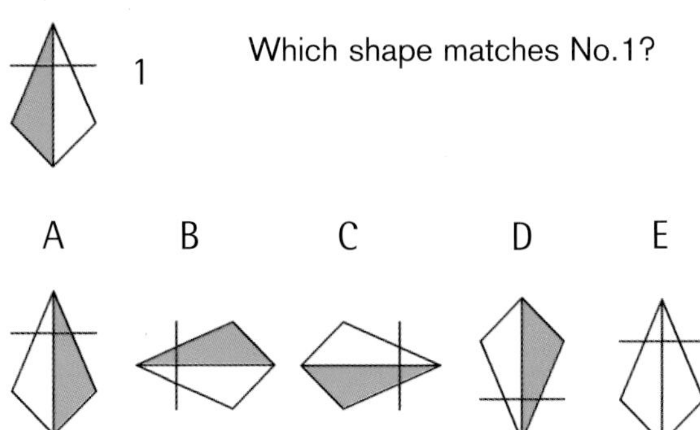

Which shape matches No.1?

14 What the hex?

The ten hexagons may look identical at first glance, but they're not. They can be divided up into five pairs of identical designs. Can you match them up?

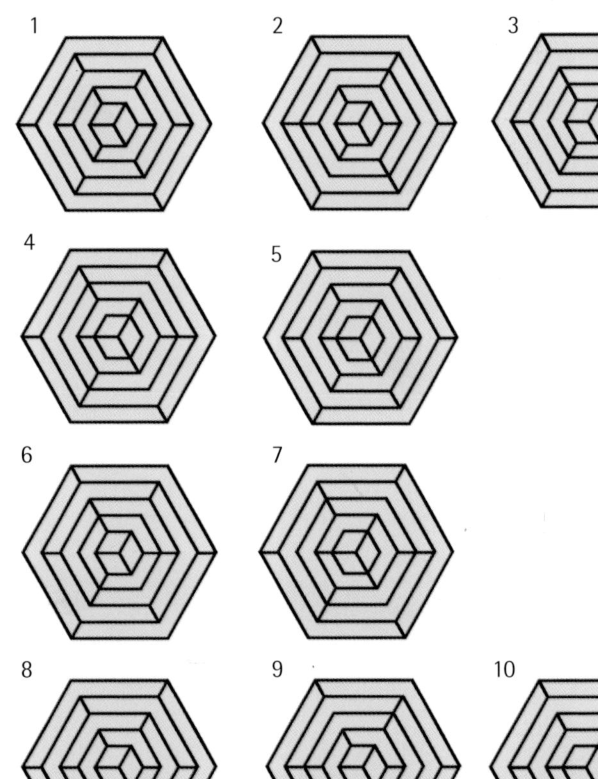

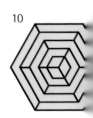

15 Identity parade

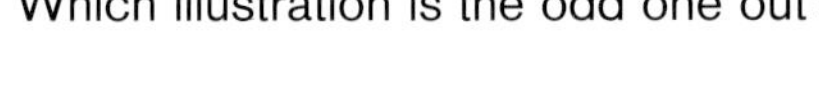

Which illustration is the odd one out?

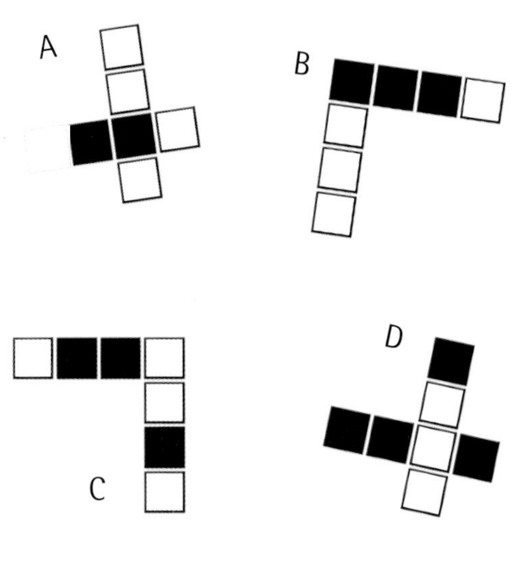

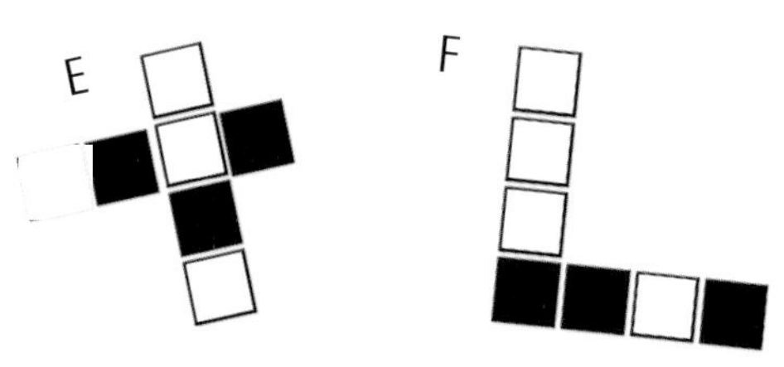

16 Six of the best

Divide this drawing into six identical parts so that each will contain five different objects.

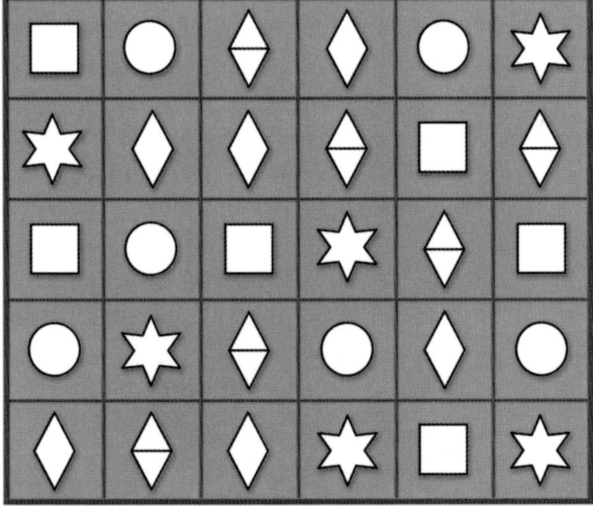

17 Figure it out

Each different symbol represents a figure from 1 to 9. According to the given totals, can you tell which figures were used?

●	□	◇	◇	■	20
■	□	△	△	●	22
●	◇	✶	■	●	15
▲	△	△	▲	■	20
□	○	○	■	■	35
21	30	20	21	20	

18 Box links

Fit the ten pieces into the grid so each line across and down contain six different symbols. To give you a clue we've already added some shapes in the grid.

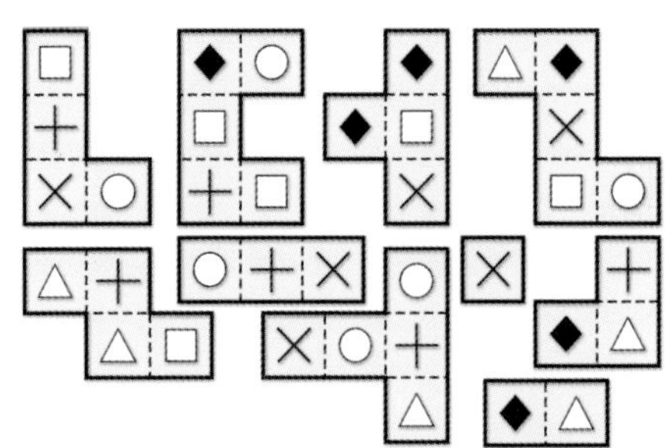

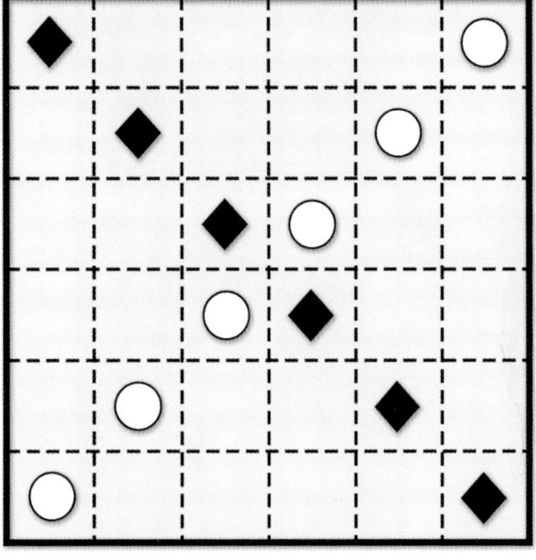

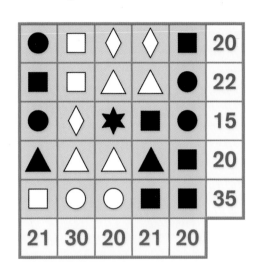

CLOSE-UPS

The human brain notices objects and makes sense of them by piecing together fragments of visual information to put them in context. Here we reverse that process. Can you work out what each object is by scrutinizing these close-up views?

Close encounters 1

19 ★

1

2

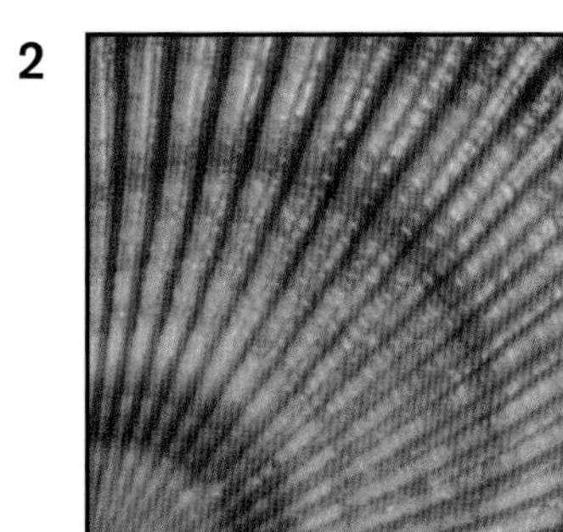

3

4

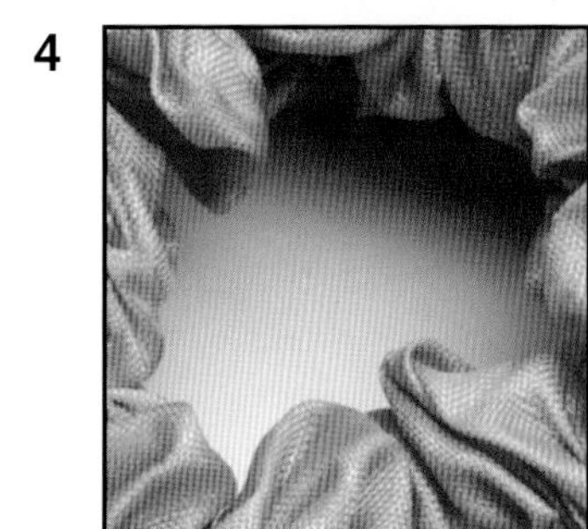

Close encounters 2

20 ★★

1

2

3

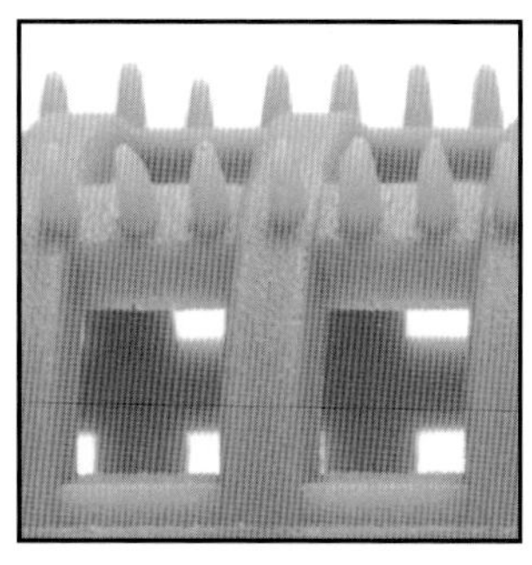

4

Close encounters 3

1

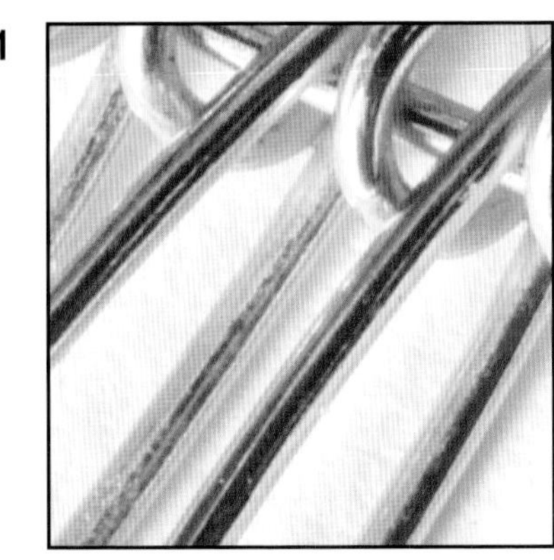

2

3

4

Close encounters 4

22

1

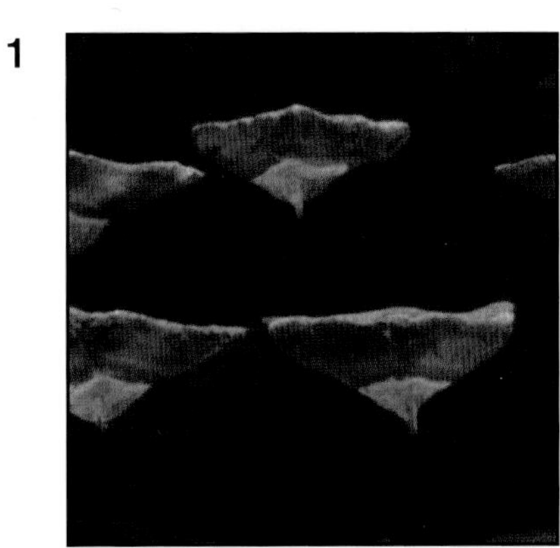

2

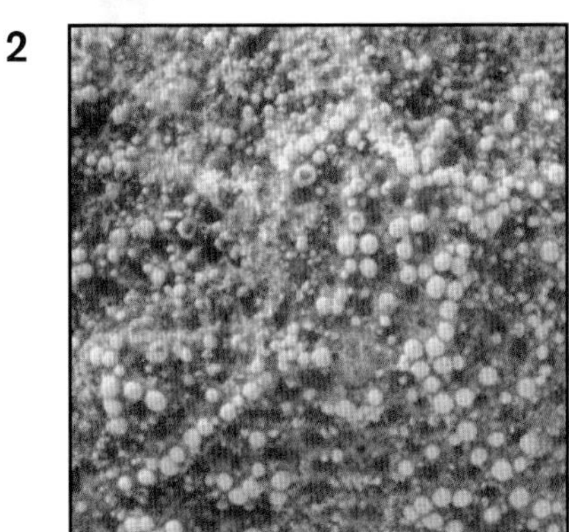

3

4

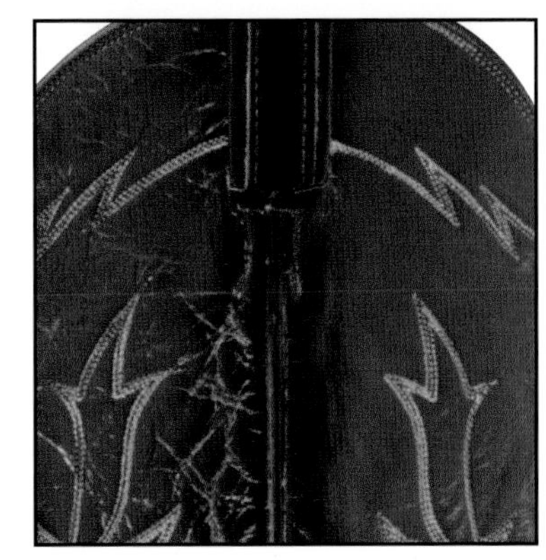

TANGRAMS

These ancient Chinese geometrical puzzles – invented by a man called Tan – consist of a square cut into seven pieces (literally *ch'i* or *ch'iao t'u*: 'ingenious puzzle figure of seven pieces'), which can be arranged to make various other shapes. These visual tricks test both your aptitude for logic and spatial reasoning.

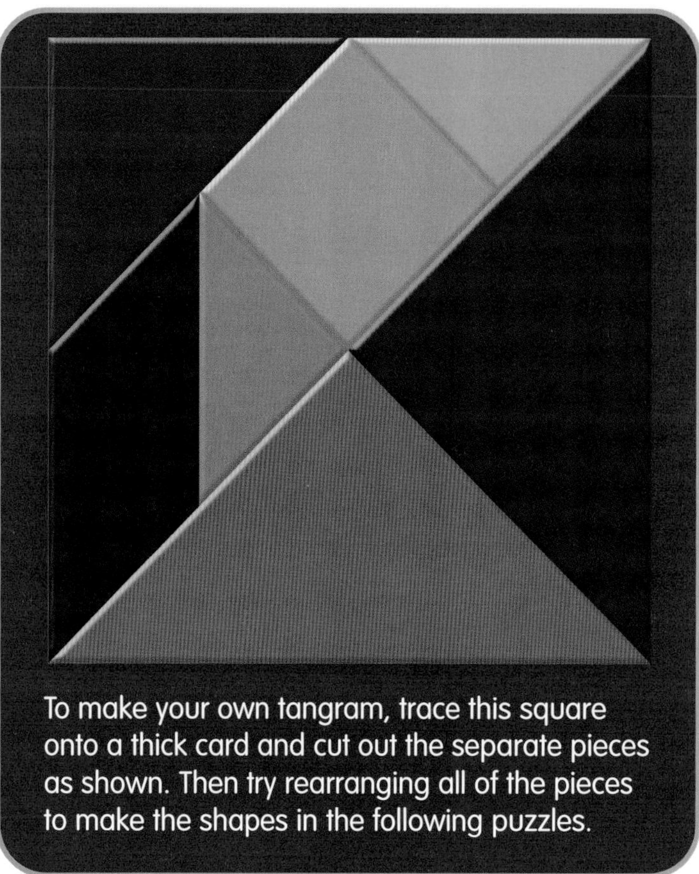

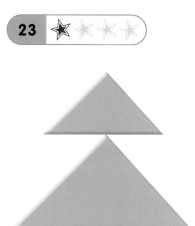

To make your own tangram, trace this square onto a thick card and cut out the separate pieces as shown. Then try rearranging all of the pieces to make the shapes in the following puzzles.

Christmas tree

23

Bird in Egypt

24

David Beckham?

25 ★★☆☆

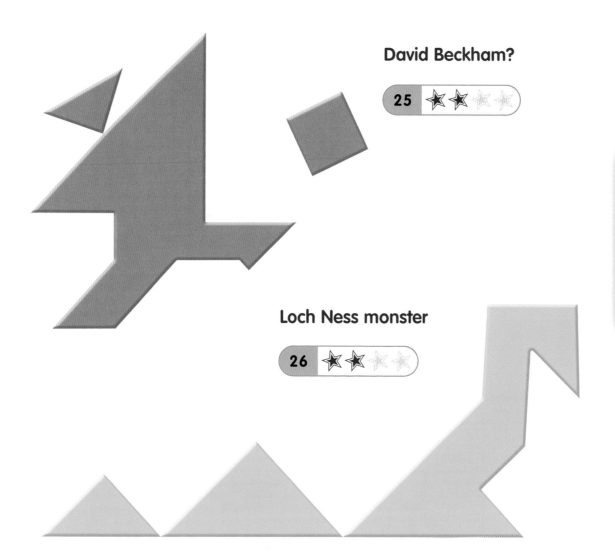

Loch Ness monster

26 ★★☆☆

Ghost or elephant?

27 ★★☆☆

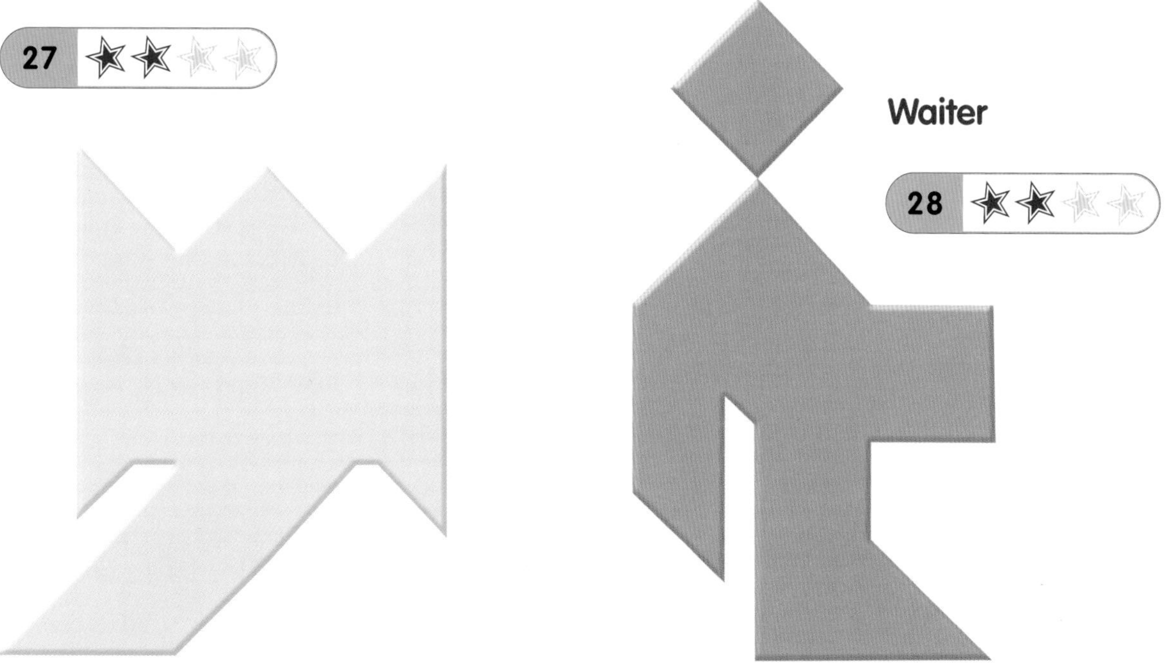

Waiter

28 ★★☆☆

PICTURE MAZES

These puzzles combine the skill of working your way through a maze with an added twist – find the correct path from the entrance to the exit, avoiding dead ends, to reveal a surprise picture in the completed puzzle. If you take a wrong turn at any point, the picture will become distorted, so each maze has only one unique solution.

To get the best image, shade in the whole width of the correct path through the maze, as shown in the example started for you in 'Fairytale fun'.

Fairytale fun

Starting from the entry arrow, work your way around the maze, colouring in your path as you go. If you successfully complete this puzzle, you will be rewarded with a glimpse of one of the most endearing fairytale couples.

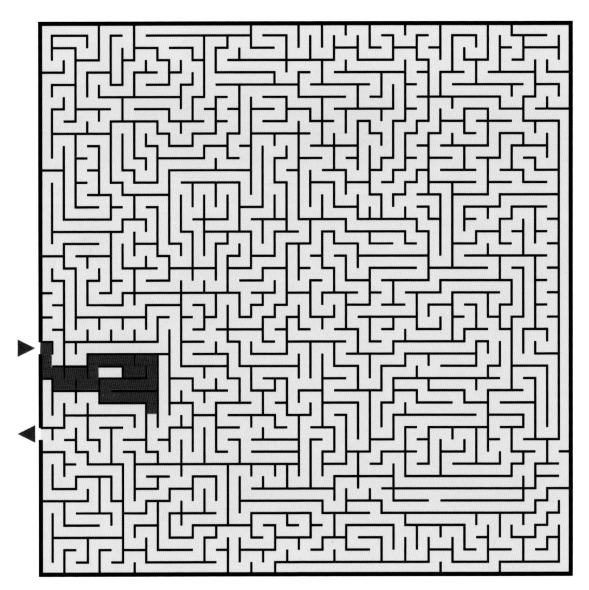

Farmhand

Choose your path to the exit carefully – if you colour it in, avoiding all the wrong turns and dead ends, you will end up with an image of a trusty farmhand.

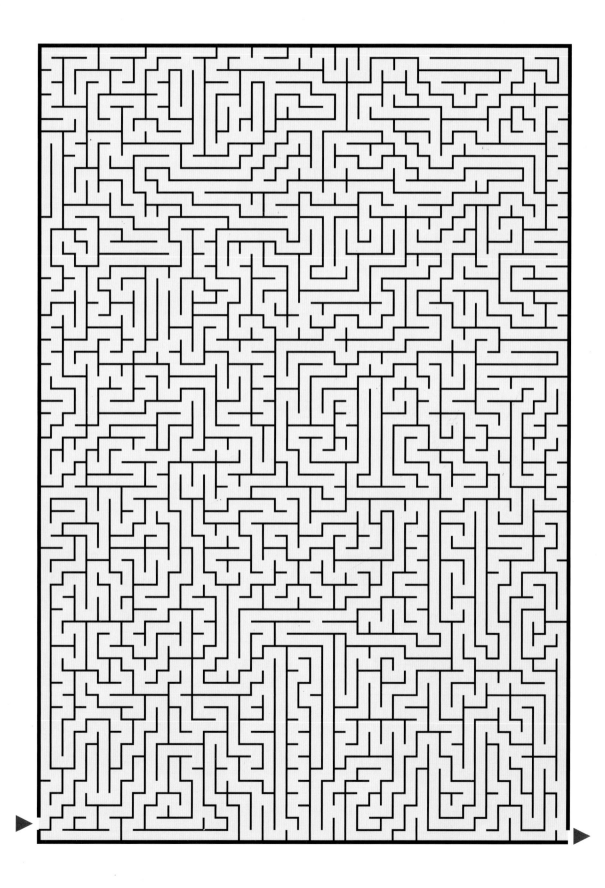

REARRANGE SHAPES

Geometric shapes can be arranged to form a variety of other shapes. Rearrange the smaller pieces in these puzzles, in the quantities specified, to make the main shape. Each shape should be used once only and they must not overlap one another at any point. For similar visual puzzles, try the Tangrams on pages 112-113.

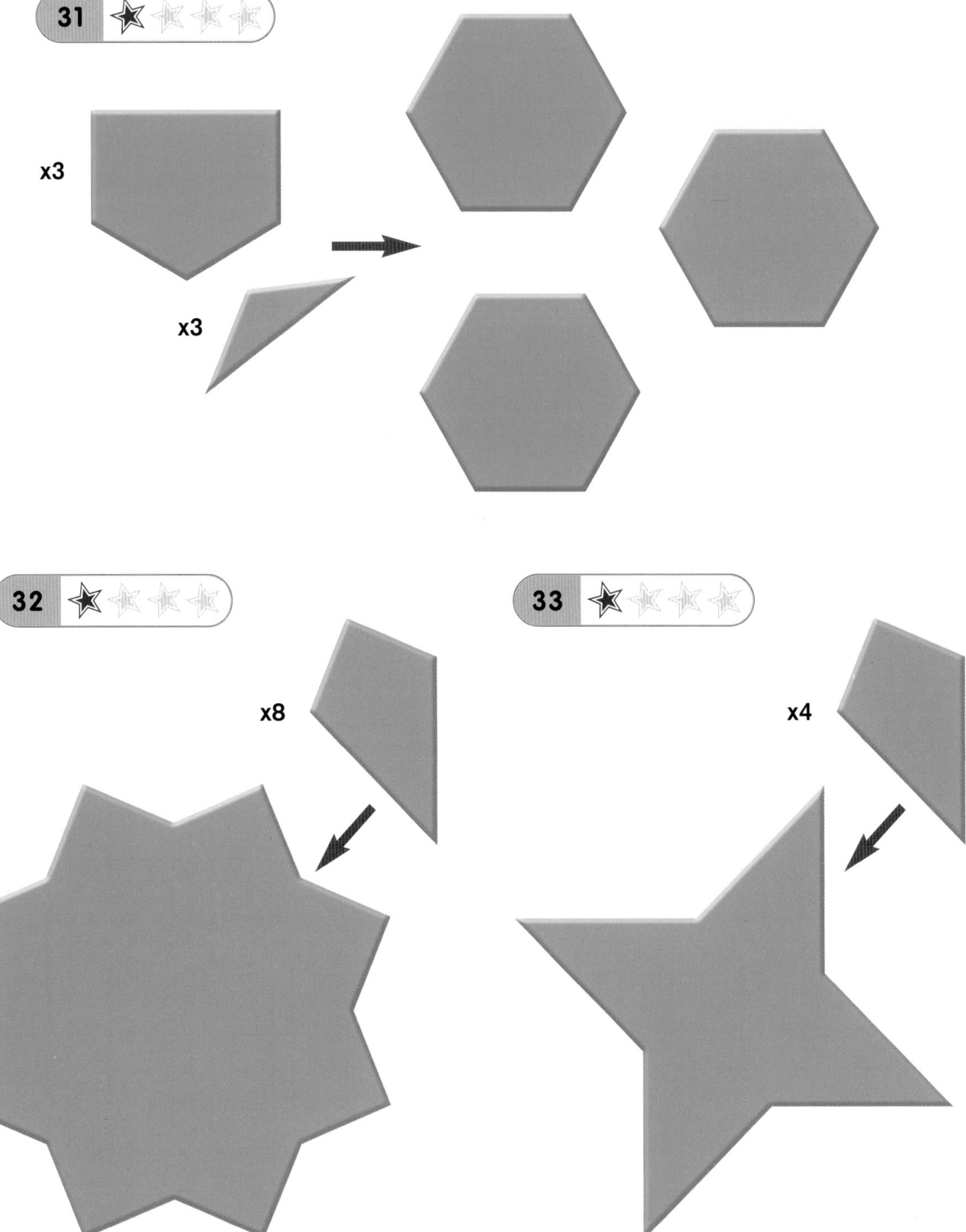

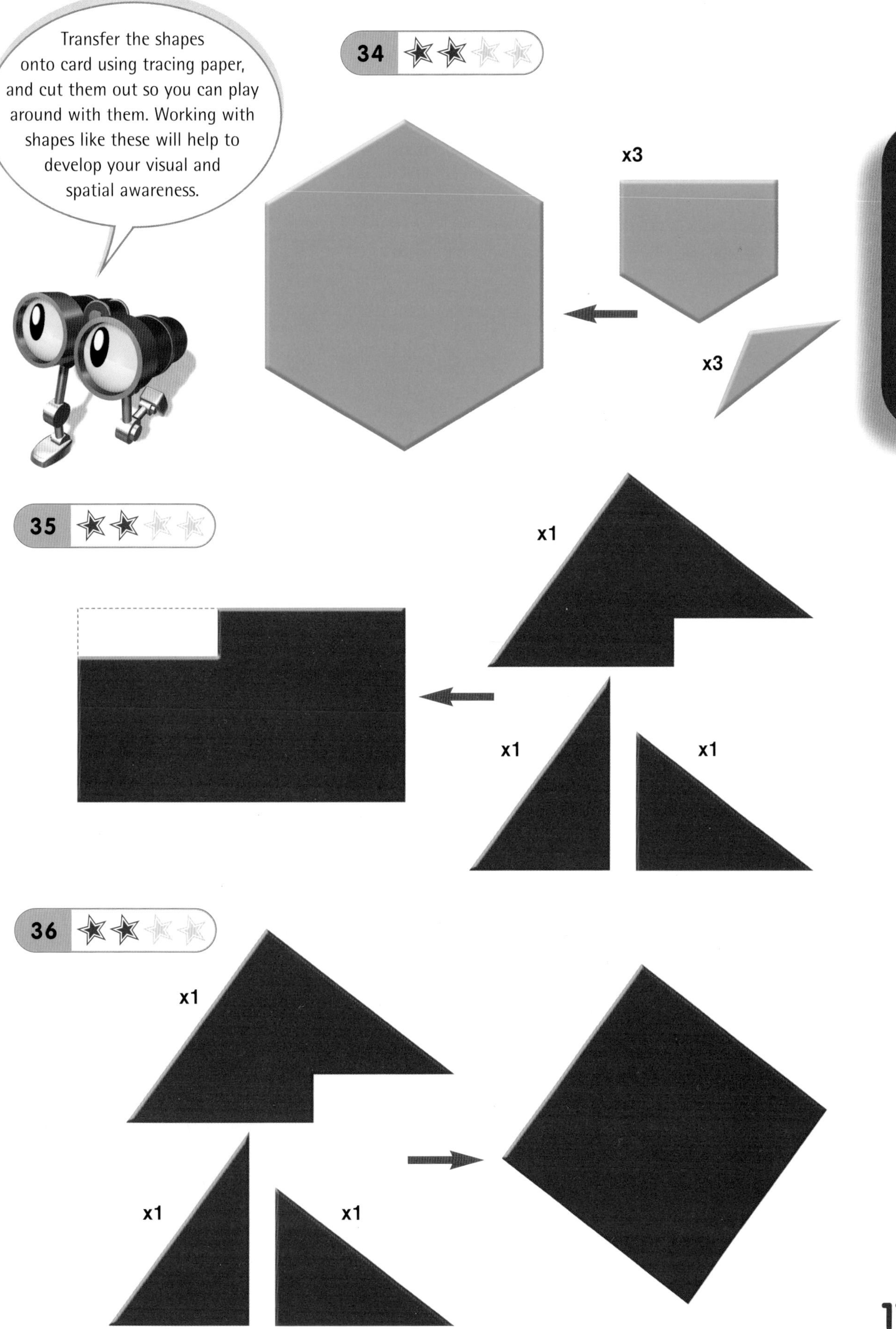
Transfer the shapes onto card using tracing paper, and cut them out so you can play around with them. Working with shapes like these will help to develop your visual and spatial awareness.
34
x3
x3
35
x1
x1
x1
36
x1
x1
x1

SYMBOL SUDOKU

Instead of numbers and letters, 16 different symbols are used in this sudoku puzzle. Fill the grid so that every row, column and 4 x 4 box contains one of each of the 16 symbols.

37 

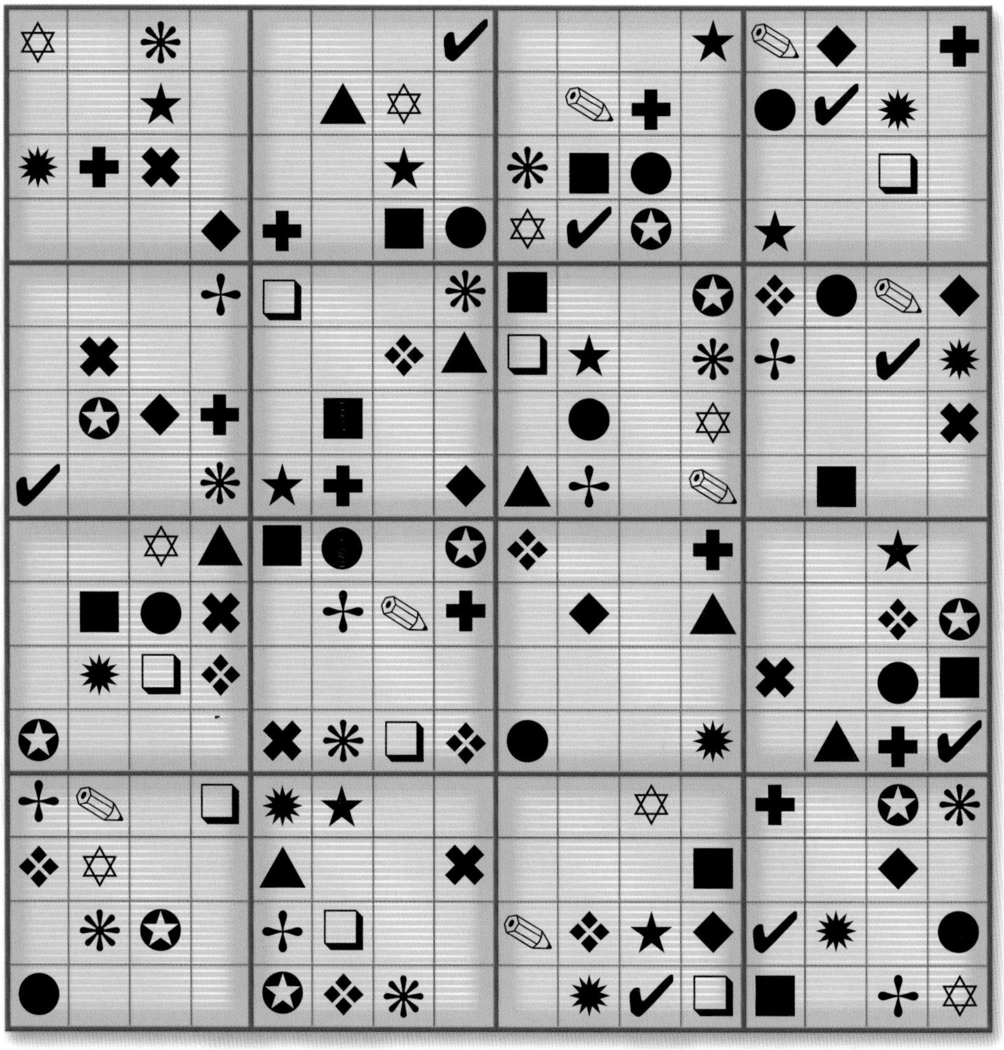

✡		❋					✔				★	✎	◆		✚
		★			▲	✡			✎	✚		●	✔	✹	
✹	✚	✖				★		❋	■	●				❏	
			◆	✚		■	●	✡	✔	✪		★			
			✢	❏			❋	■			✪	❖	●	✎	◆
	✖					❖	▲	❏	★		❋	✢		✔	✹
	✪	◆	✚		■				●		✡				✖
✔			❋	★	✚		◆	▲	✢		✎		■		
		✡	▲	■	●		✪	❖			✚			★	
	■	●	✖		✢	✎	✚		◆		▲			❖	✪
	✹	❏	❖									✖		●	■
✪				✖	❋	❏	❖	●			✹		▲	✚	✔
✢	✎		❏	✹	★					✡		✚		✪	❋
❖	✡			▲			✖				■			◆	
	❋	✪		✢	❏			✎	❖	★	◆	✔	✹		●
●				✪	❖	❋			✹	✔	❏	■		✢	✡

MORE TANGRAMS

Here are more Tangram puzzles for you to attempt. Rearrange the pieces (provided on page 112) to form the new shapes in the following puzzles.

Medieval lady

Vacuum cleaner

Aladdin's lamp

Candle

Remember to trace and cut out the shapes given on page 112 for use in these puzzles.

MISSING CUBES

These puzzles test your ability to judge three-dimensional depth in two-dimensional images. In puzzles 42-47 try to work out how many cubes are missing from each block.

44

47

CUBE SUMS

Using the same principles of judging spatial relationships, try the cube sums (48-53). These puzzles require you to work out how many cubes make up each stack – remember that perspective can be misleading and some rows of cubes may continue, unseen, behind others.

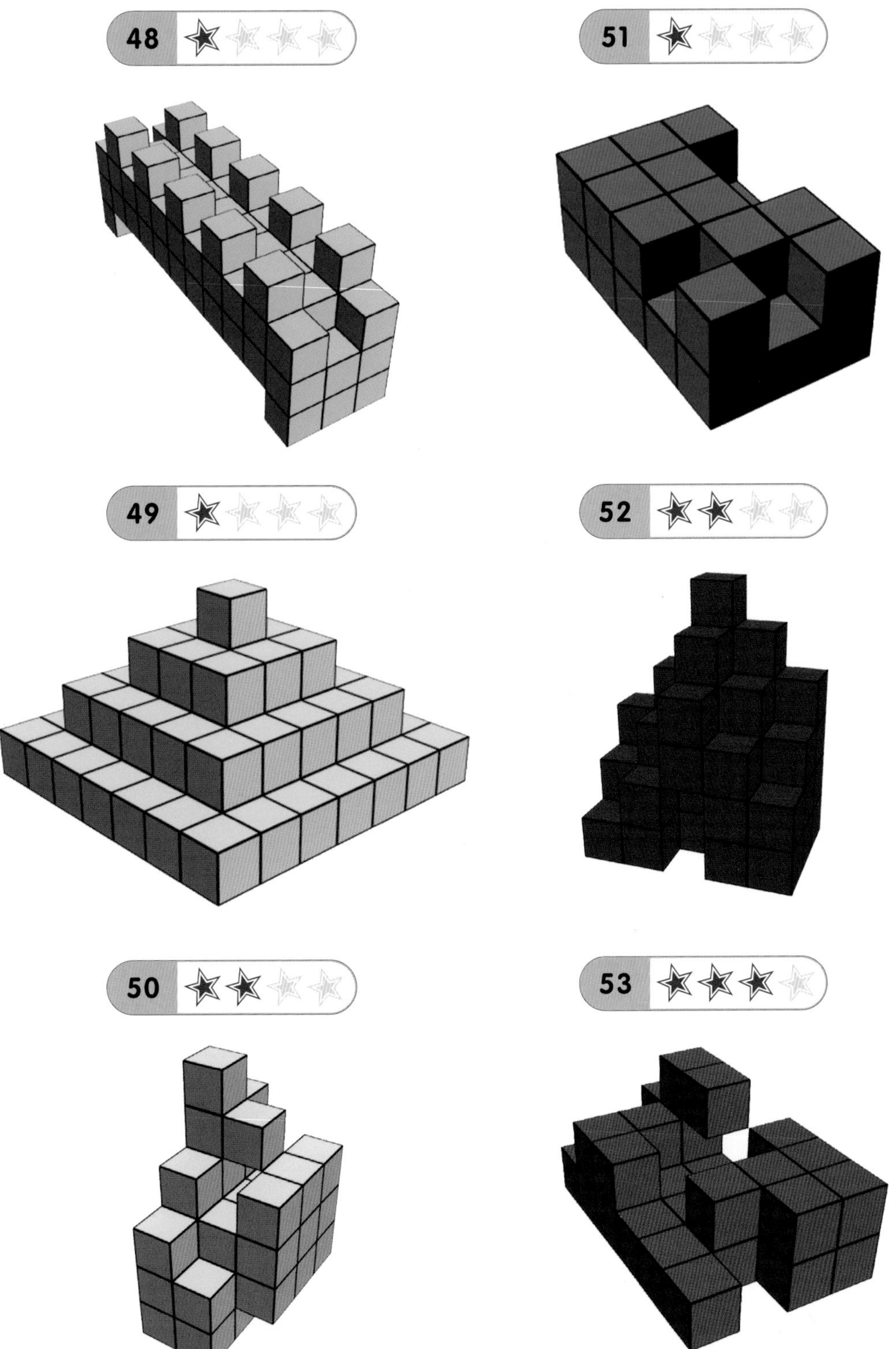

CUBES IN SPACE AND MIXED-UP BLUEPRINTS

The two puzzles on these pages test your powers of perception and creative thinking. Both **Cubes in space** and **Mixed-up blueprints** challenge you to look at cube-based shapes in different ways, and from different angles. The key here is to train your brain to overcome inbuilt perceptions and to recognize optical tricks.

Cubes in space

Amazingly, among these ten cube formations, there are three that are identical, and a further six that make three separate pairs. This leaves one formation that is unique and matches no other in the puzzle. Can you spot the pairs, the set of three and the odd one out?

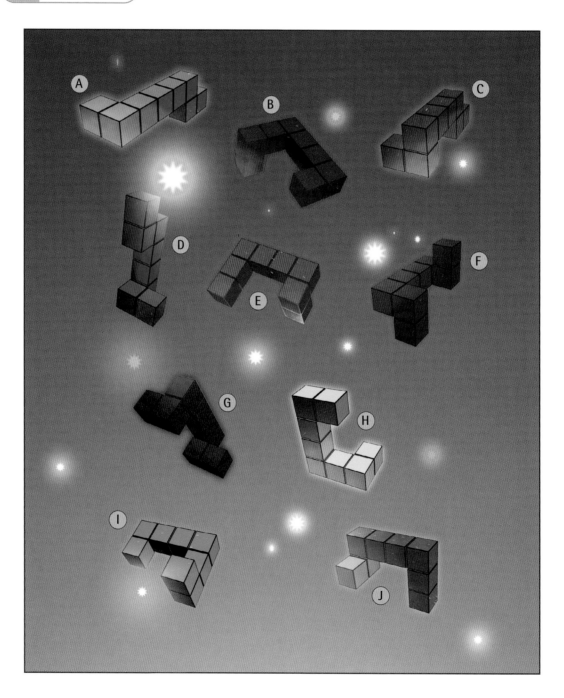

Mixed-up blueprints

Can you match the correct blueprint to each of the buildings 1–8? Bear in mind that the blueprints show either the front view or the top view of the buildings and only eight are correct, so you will need to consider each shape carefully and from all angles.

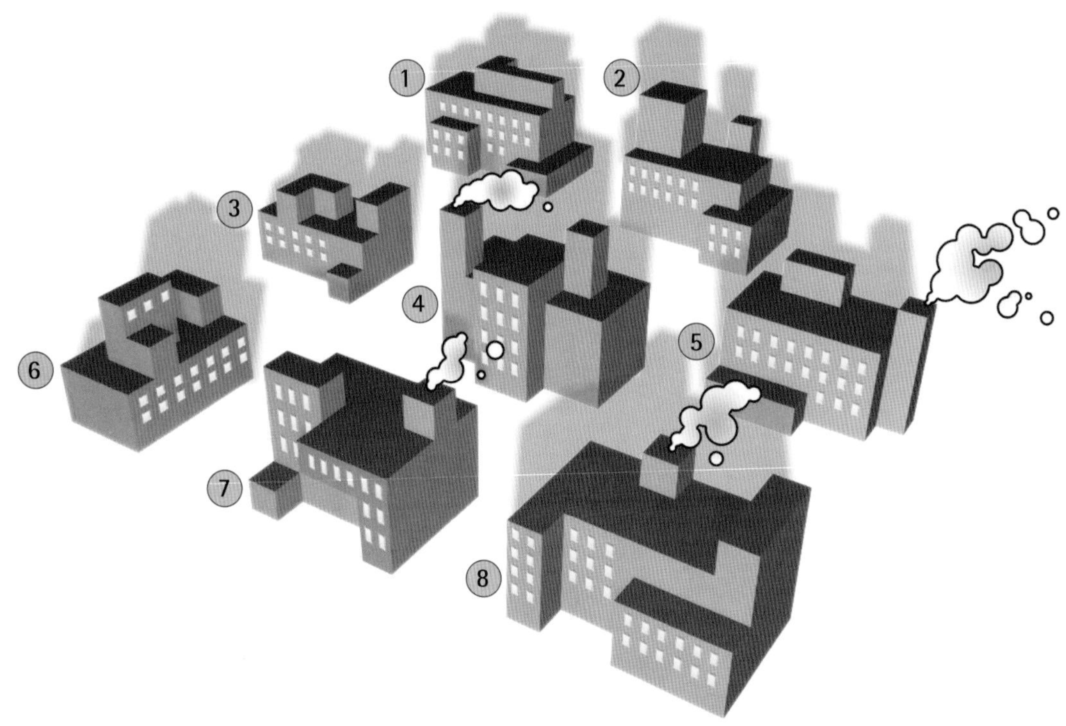

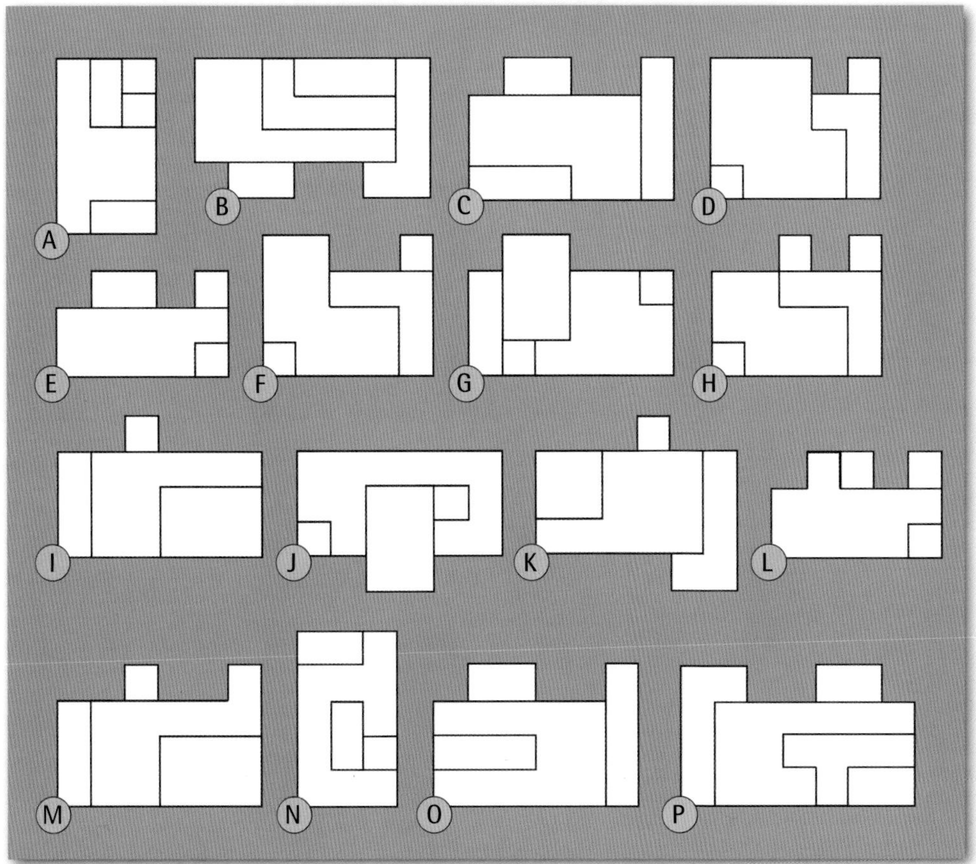

Try drawing your own blueprints and see how closely they match up.

ODD ONE OUT

In each of these puzzles, all of the images are similar to one another – all, that is, except for one. Your task is to work out what the common theme between each image is and, consequently, to decide which one is the odd one out.

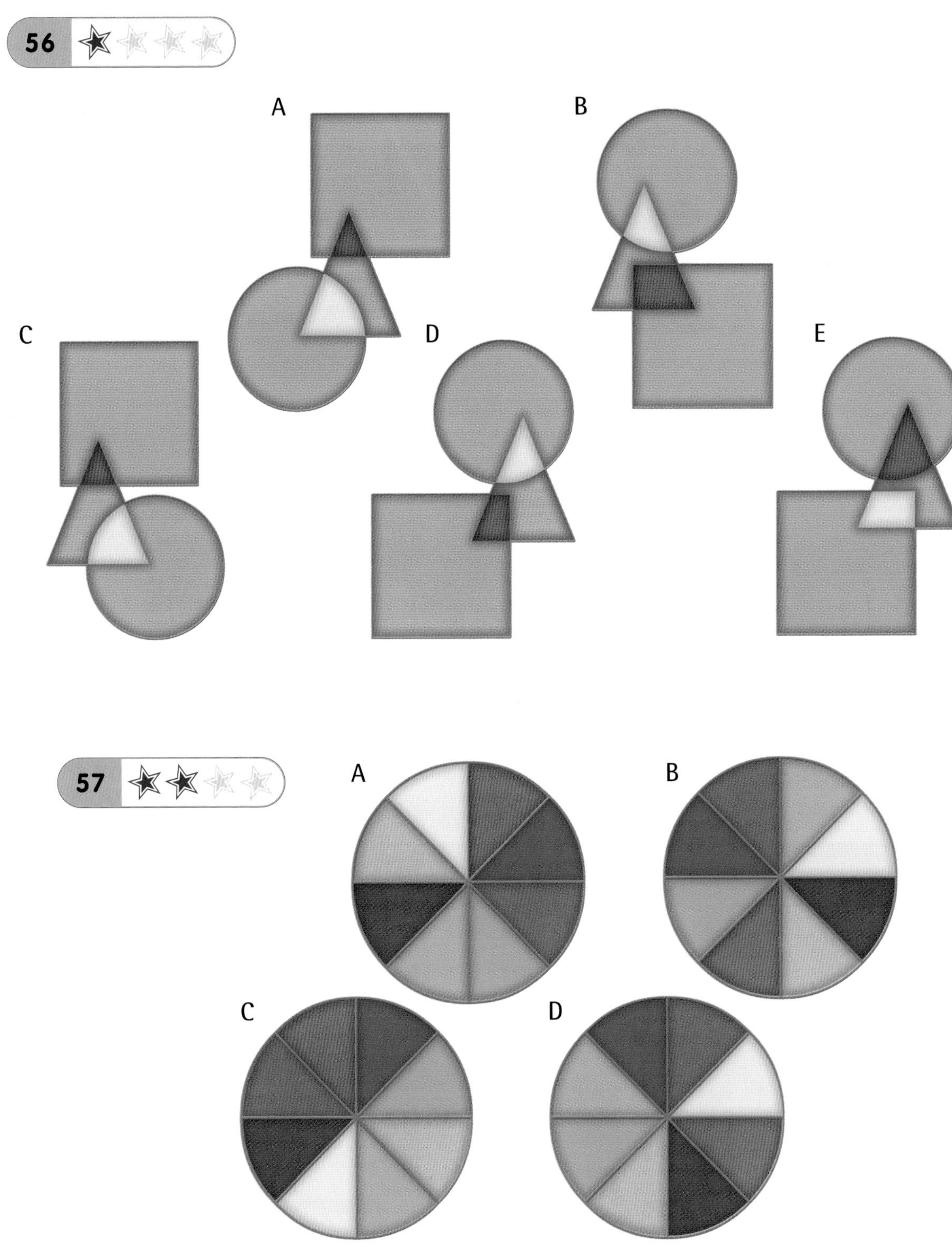

58 ★★★☆

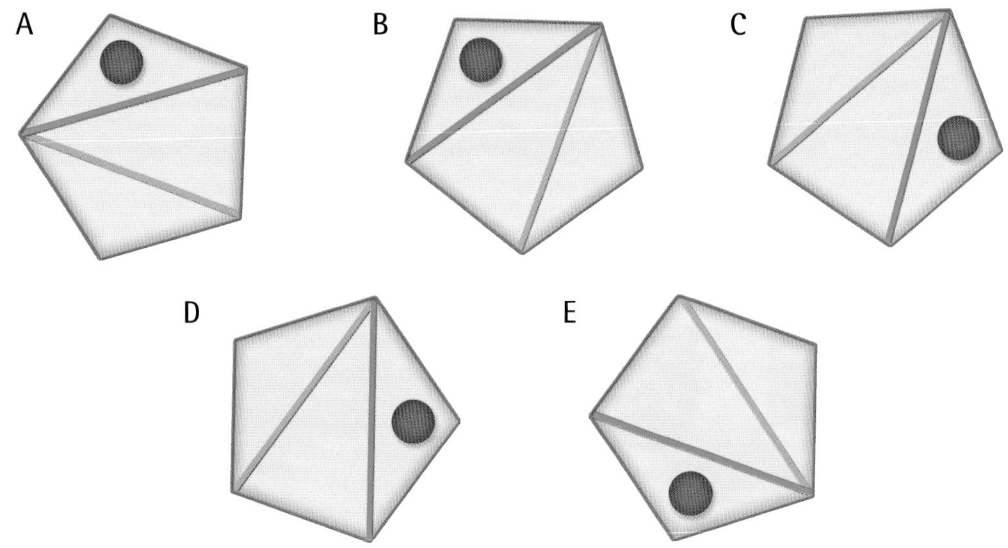

59 ★★★☆

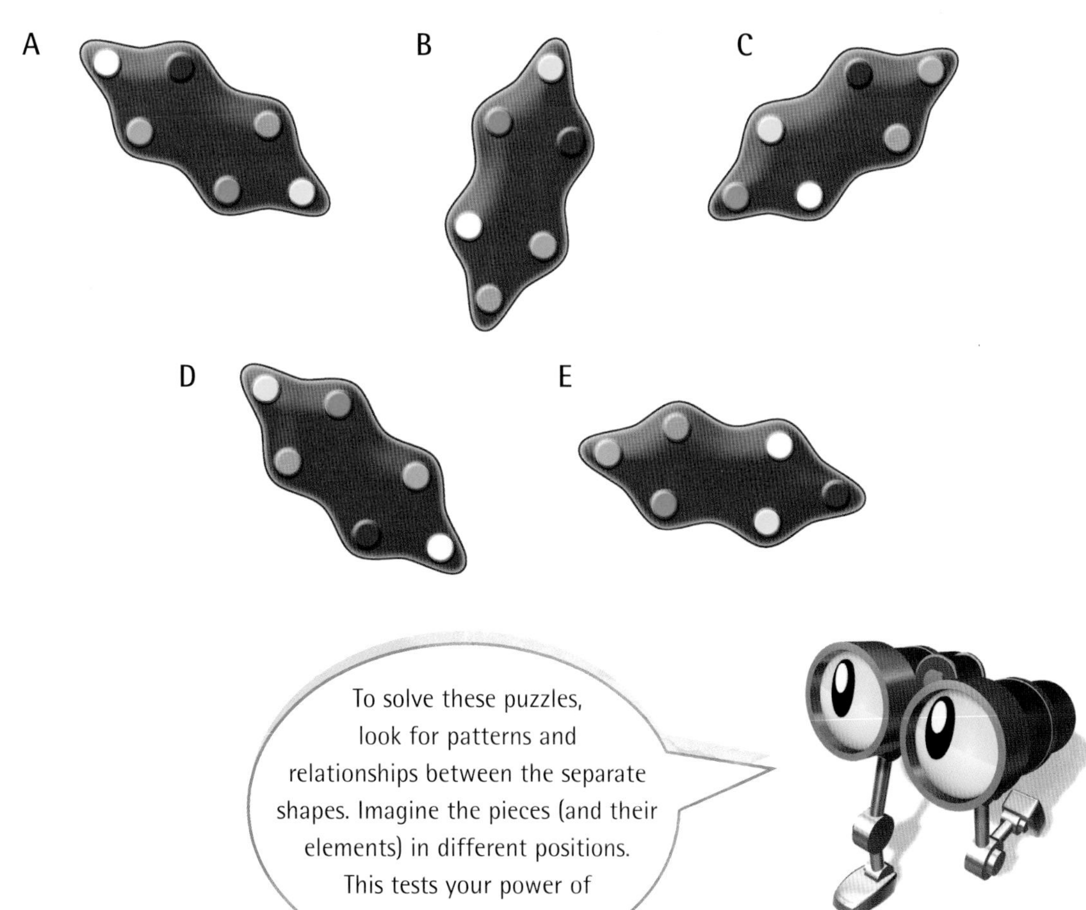

To solve these puzzles, look for patterns and relationships between the separate shapes. Imagine the pieces (and their elements) in different positions. This tests your power of spatial reasoning.

BOX CLEVER

Most of the time we observe the world around us in two or three dimensions. How hard is it to visualize something three-dimensional from a two-dimensional plan? In all the puzzles on these pages, you need to choose which of the three-dimensional alternatives was constructed from the flatplan provided.

60 ★

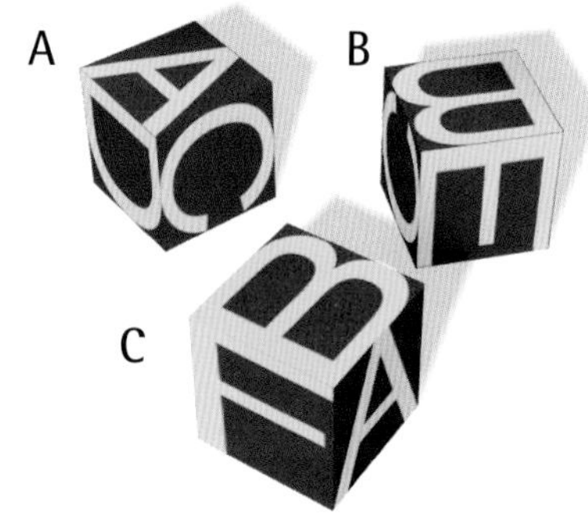

61 ★★

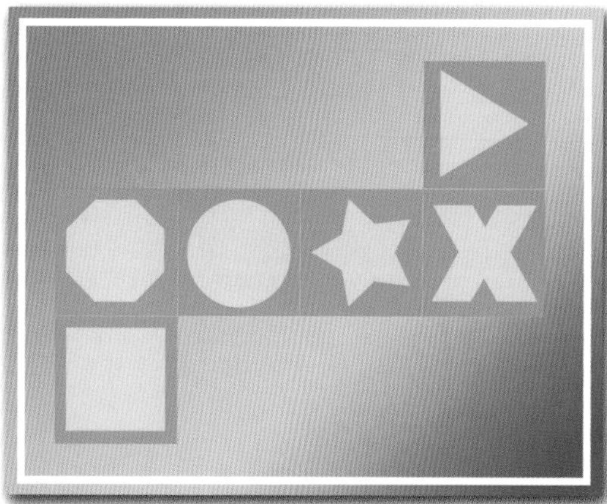

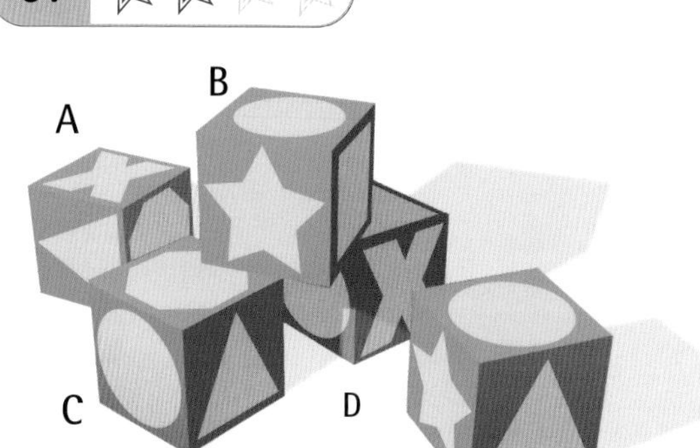

62 ★★

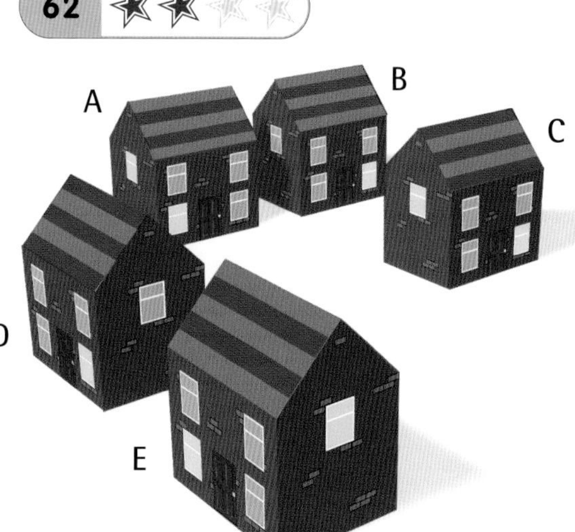

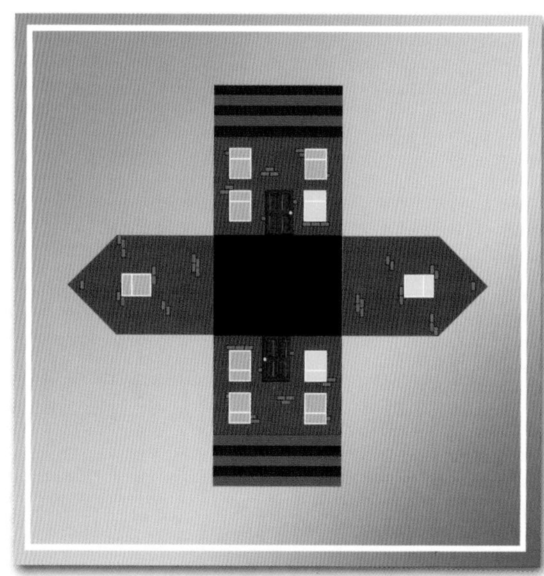

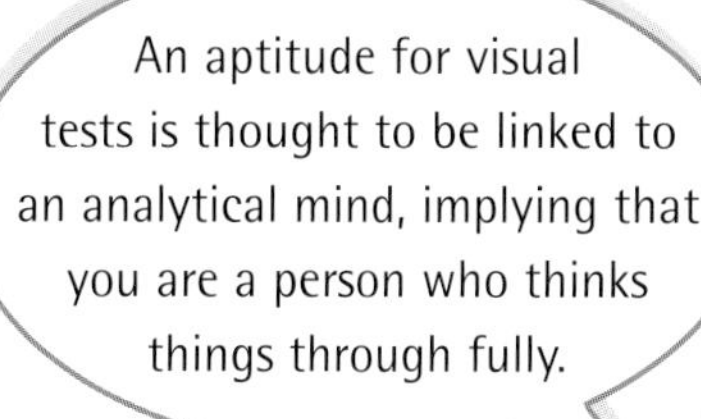
An aptitude for visual tests is thought to be linked to an analytical mind, implying that you are a person who thinks things through fully.

63

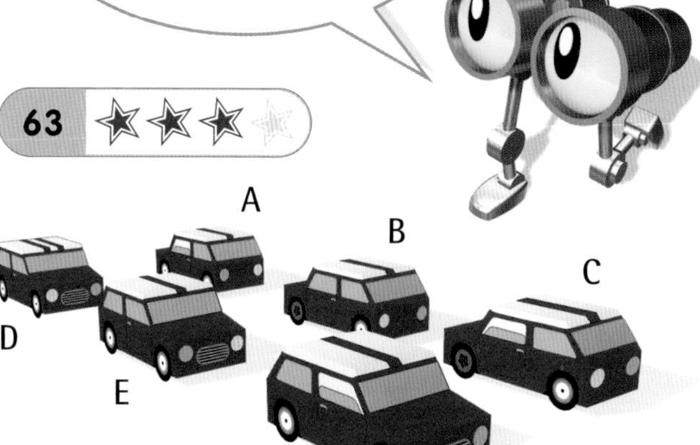
A
B
C
D
E
F

64

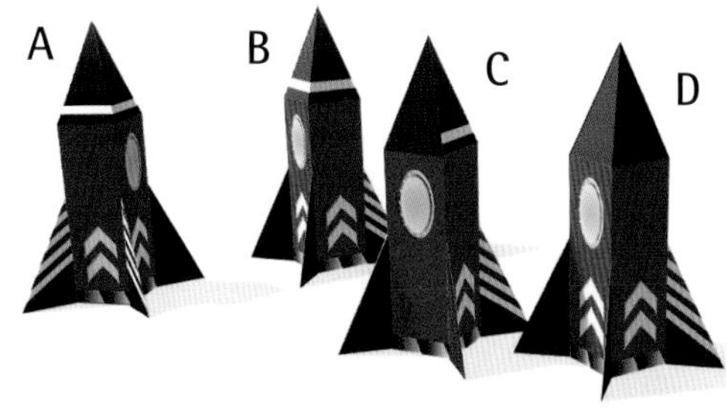
A
B
C
D

65

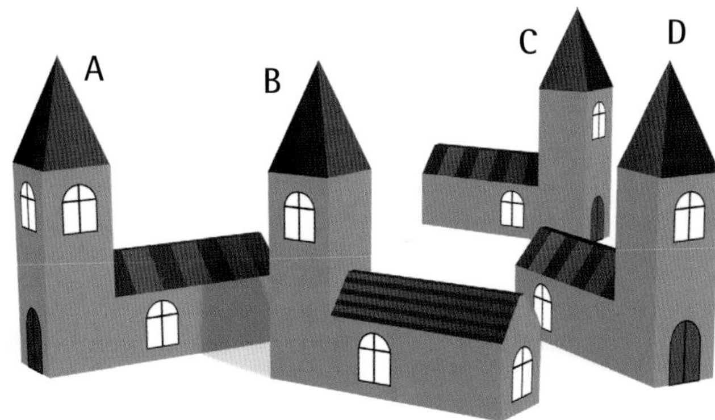
A
B
C
D

MAZES

Navigate your way through these geometric mazes to hone your visual perception skills and your powers of concentration. Start at the entry arrows and try and find your way to the middle or the exit, avoiding all of the misleading dead ends. To make them more challenging, try doing them in your head, without tracing your path with a pencil.

Can you find your way to the middle of this circular maze without getting caught out by the dead ends? To challenge yourself further, give yourself a time limit of five minutes to complete the puzzle.

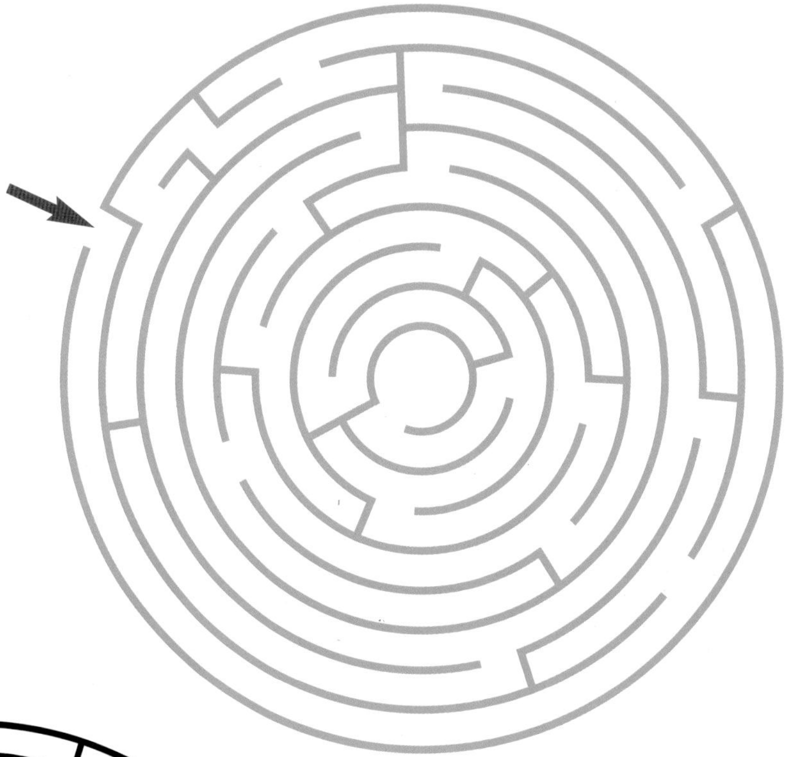

67

Start at the arrow and work your way around this intricate maze, to end up in the centre of the circle.

MAZES

Navigate your way through these geometric mazes to hone your visual perception skills and your powers of concentration. Start at the entry arrows and try and find your way to the middle or the exit, avoiding all of the misleading dead ends. To make them more challenging, try doing them in your head, without tracing your path with a pencil.

Can you find your way to the middle of this circular maze without getting caught out by the dead ends? To challenge yourself further, give yourself a time limit of five minutes to complete the puzzle.

67

Start at the arrow and work your way around this intricate maze, to end up in the centre of the circle.

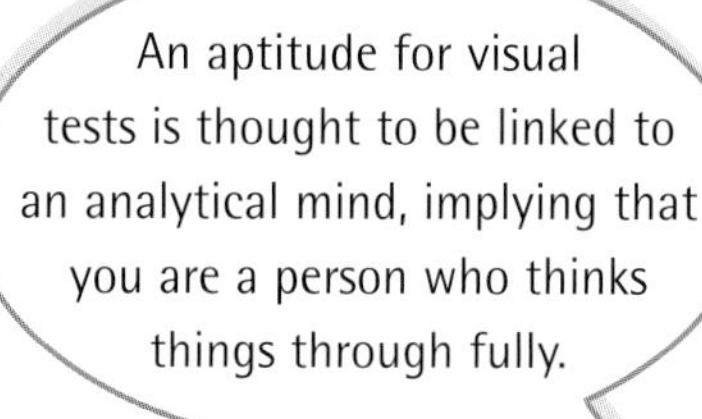
An aptitude for visual tests is thought to be linked to an analytical mind, implying that you are a person who thinks things through fully.

63

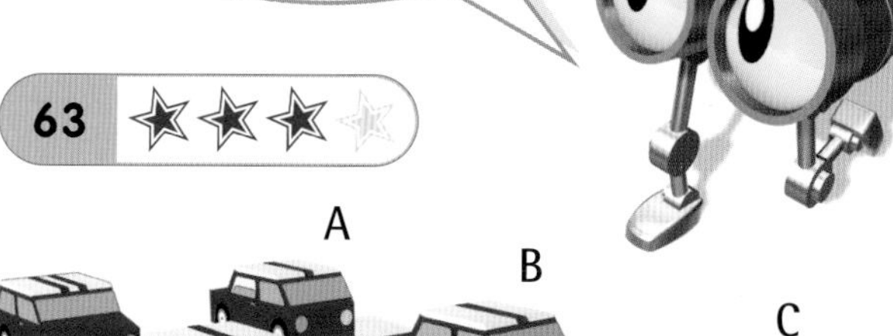
A
B
C
D
E
F

64

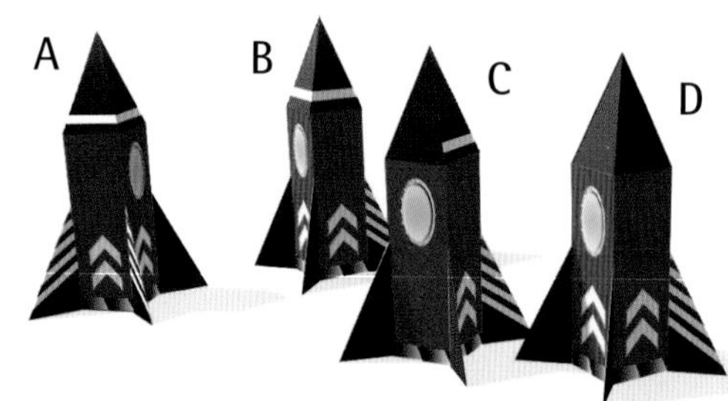
A
B
C
D

65

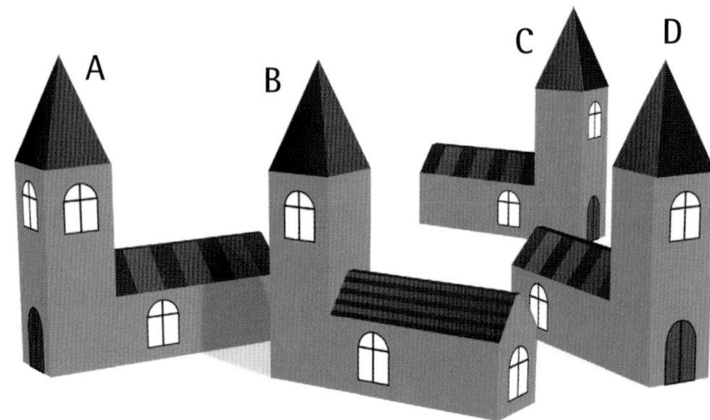
A
B
C
D

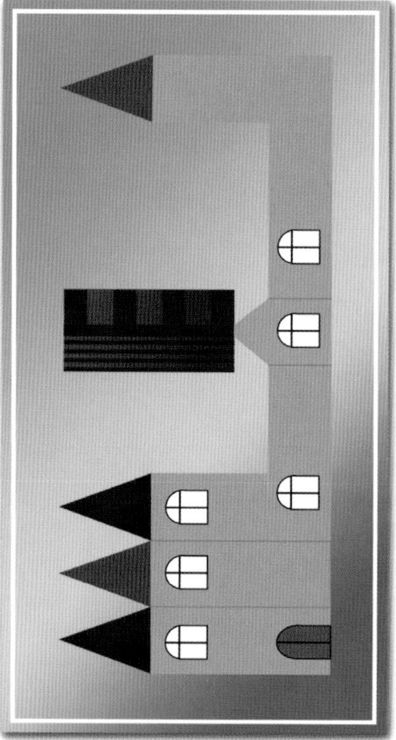

68 ★★☆☆ Work your way through the labyrinth from the arrow to the exit.

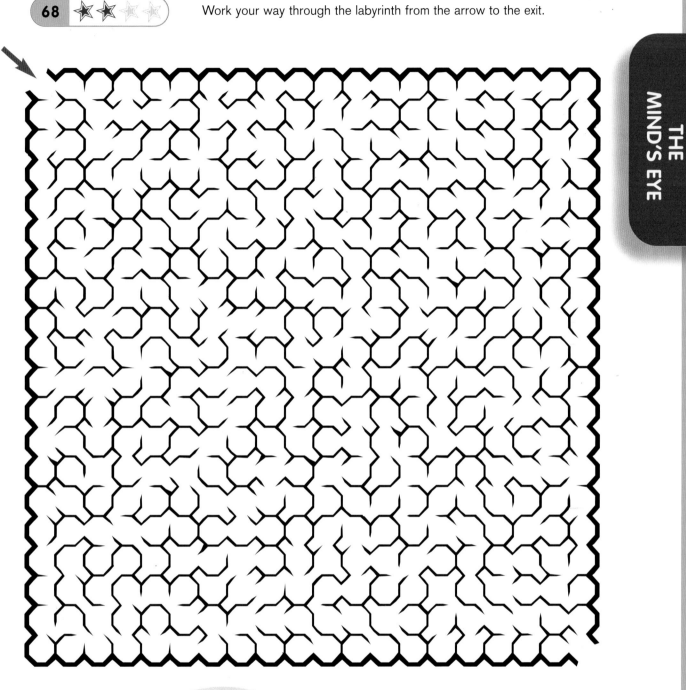

Practise doing mazes and visual tests and you'll get better at map reading. Both use the 'navigational' part of the brain.

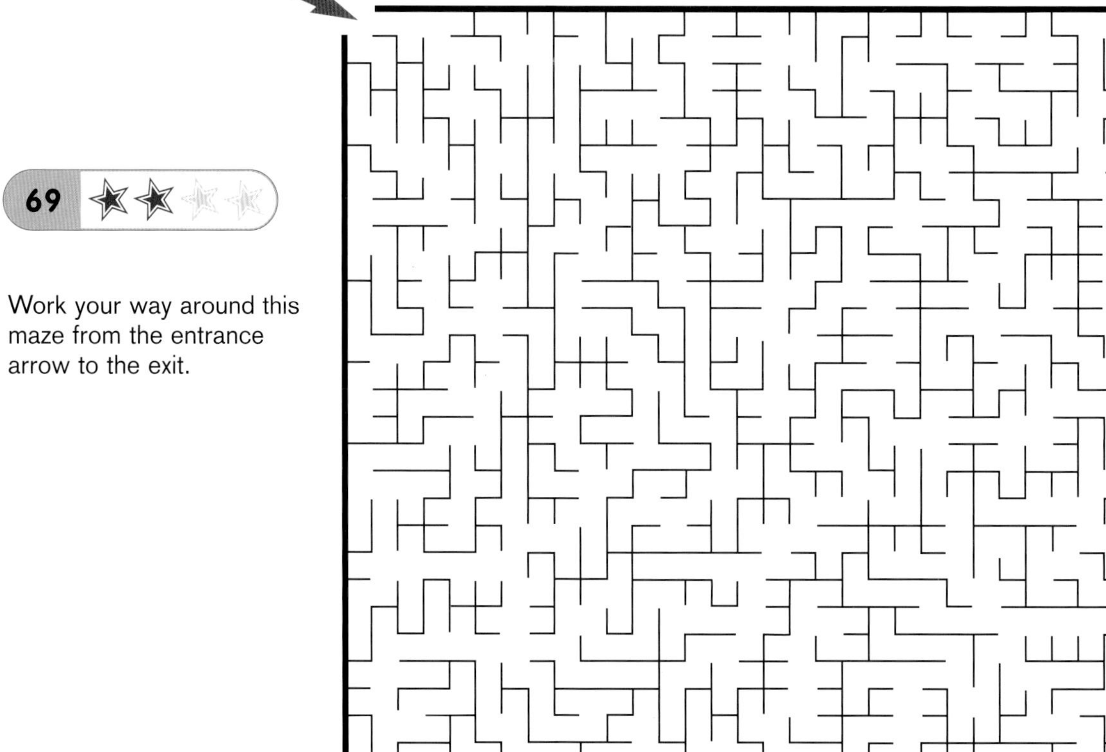

69 ★★☆☆

Work your way around this maze from the entrance arrow to the exit.

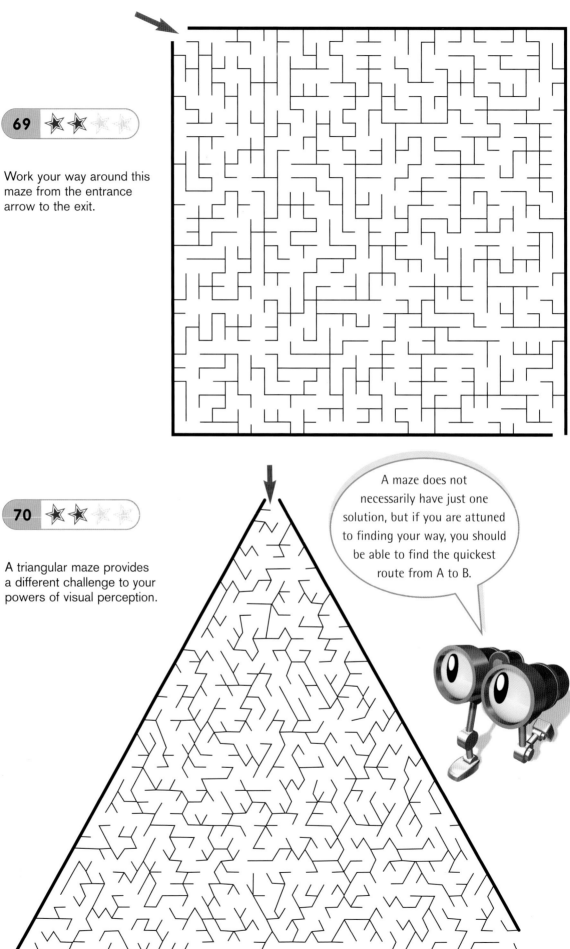

70 ★★☆☆

A triangular maze provides a different challenge to your powers of visual perception.

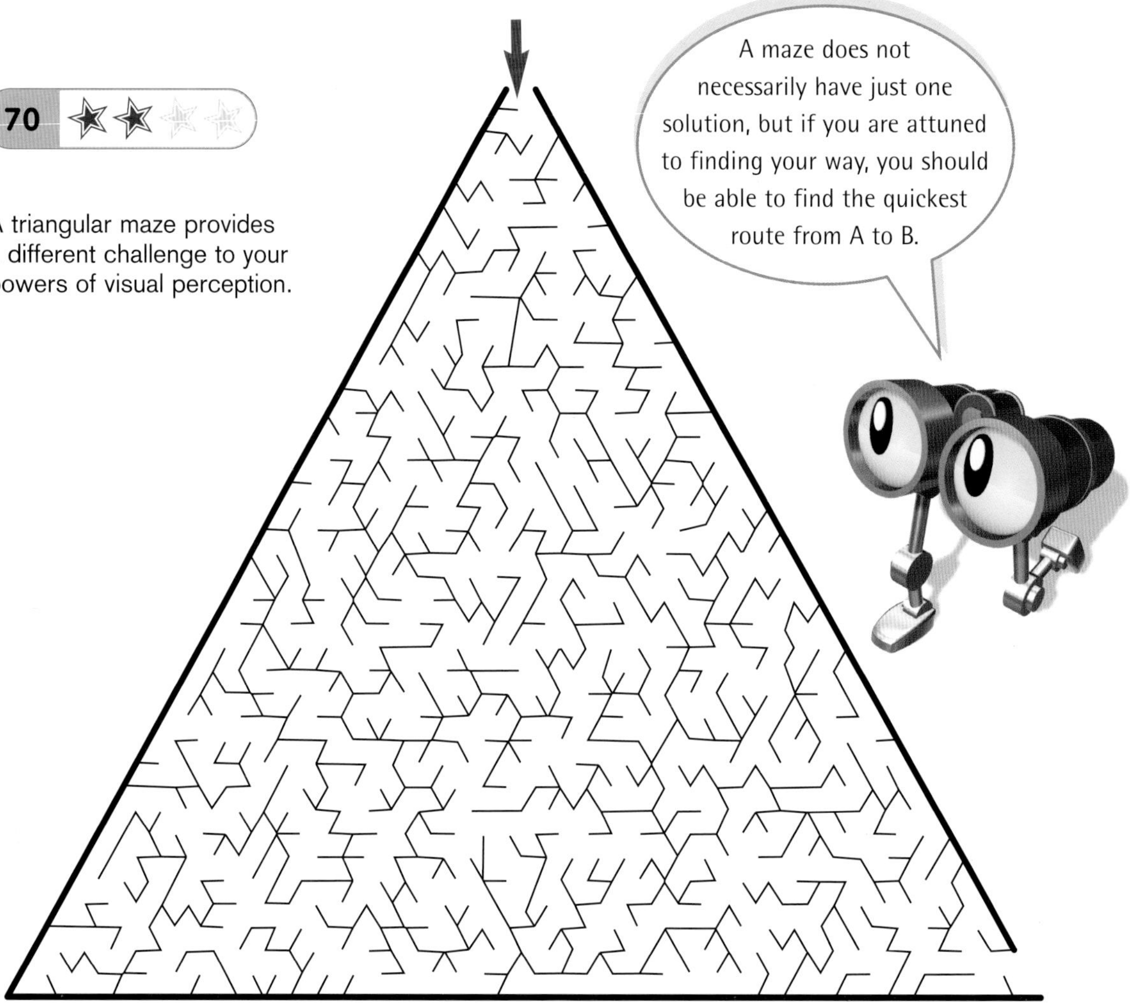

A maze does not necessarily have just one solution, but if you are attuned to finding your way, you should be able to find the quickest route from A to B.

Give yourself a time target for this puzzle, and then try to do it in your head.

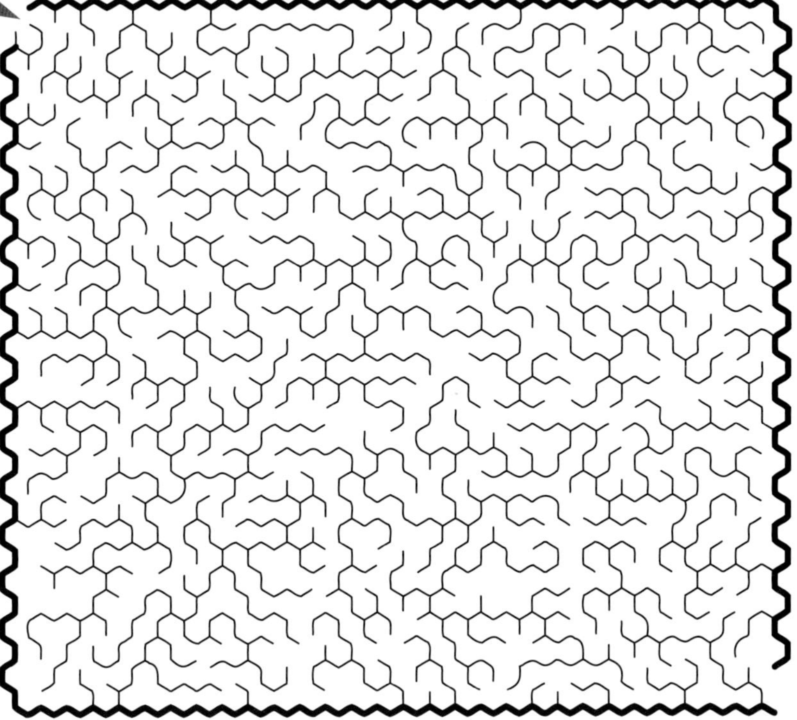

Try giving yourself less time to complete this maze – see how far you can get in three minutes.

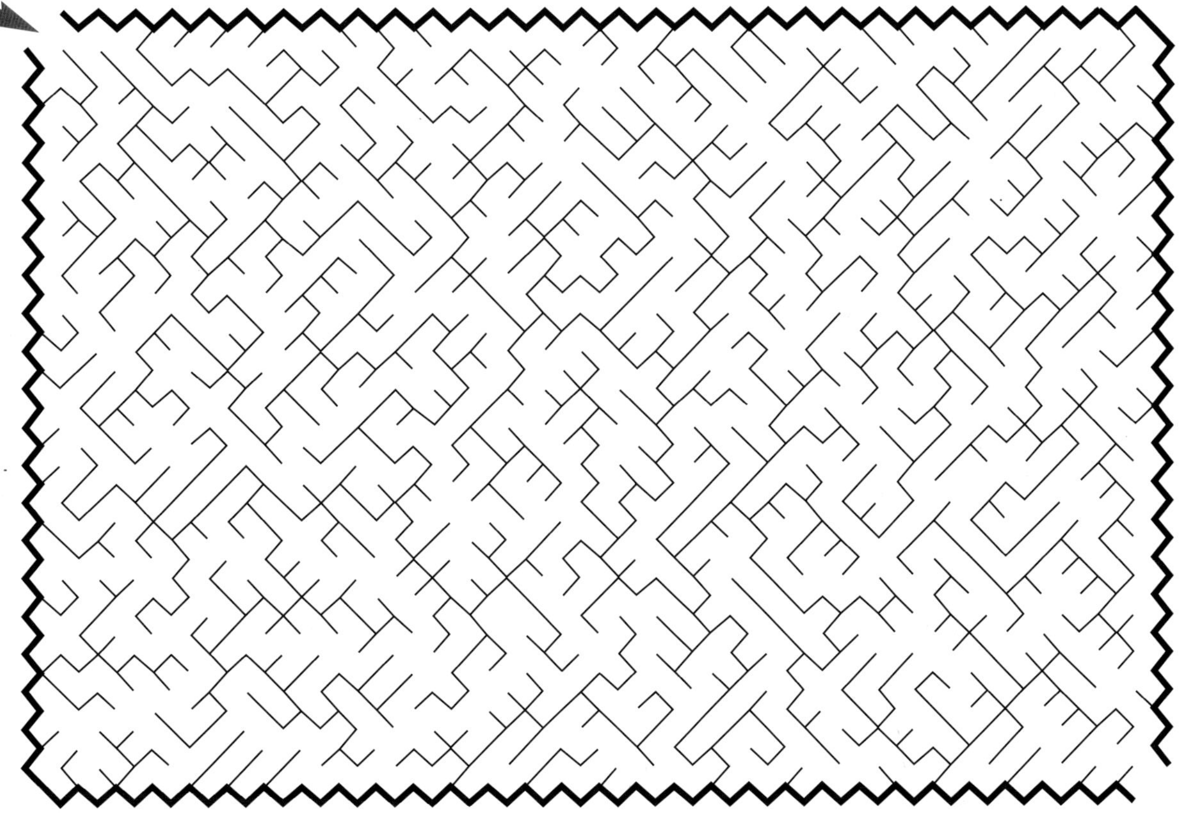

TWO OF A KIND

These puzzles test your ability to assess visual stimuli and to pick out small details. Scrutinise each picture carefully to find the answers.

73 

Techno twins

Which two of these robots are exactly identical?

A

B

E

C

D

F

Spot the difference

Study the two pictures of a chaotic train station. Can you spot ten differences between the first and second scenes?

THE MIND'S EYE

GET THE PICTURE

The following picture puzzles are rebuses, which work in a similar way to Egyptian hieroglyphics. Each image represents a word or part of a word, which when combined with its adjacent images, makes up a well-known phrase.

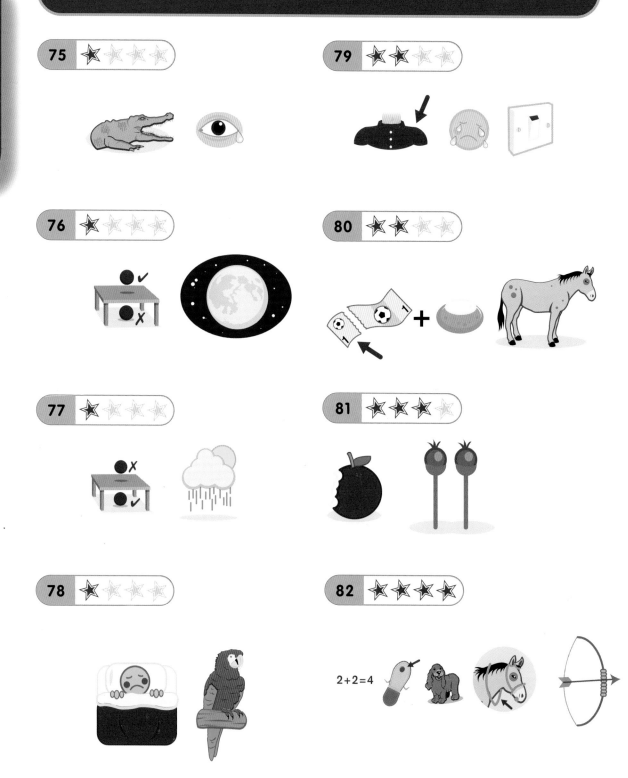

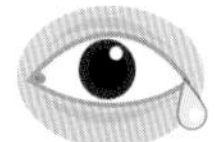

78

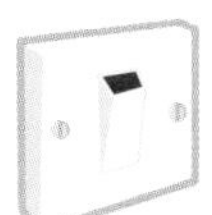

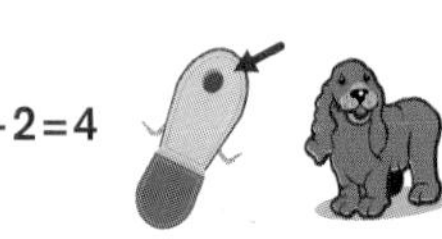

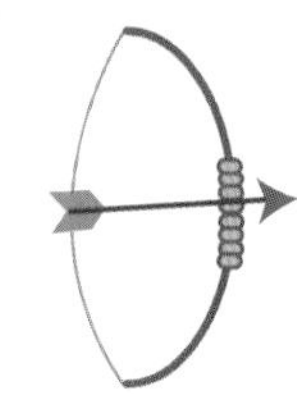

A MAZING VIEWS

This is a two-in-one visual test: complete the maze by finding a route from the entrance to the benches in the centre, then try to find where the three snapshots A, B and C were taken within the maze.

A

B

C

VISUAL PUZZLES

Every day our mind is besieged with thousands of images that have to be processed. The puzzles on the following eight pages are designed to improve your brain's visual perception.

THE MIND'S EYE

Sitting ducks

84 

There are three different kinds of duck in the diagram below. Position six more ducks on the two-dimensional pond, so that each of the five horizontal and vertical rows contain all three different kinds of sitting duck.

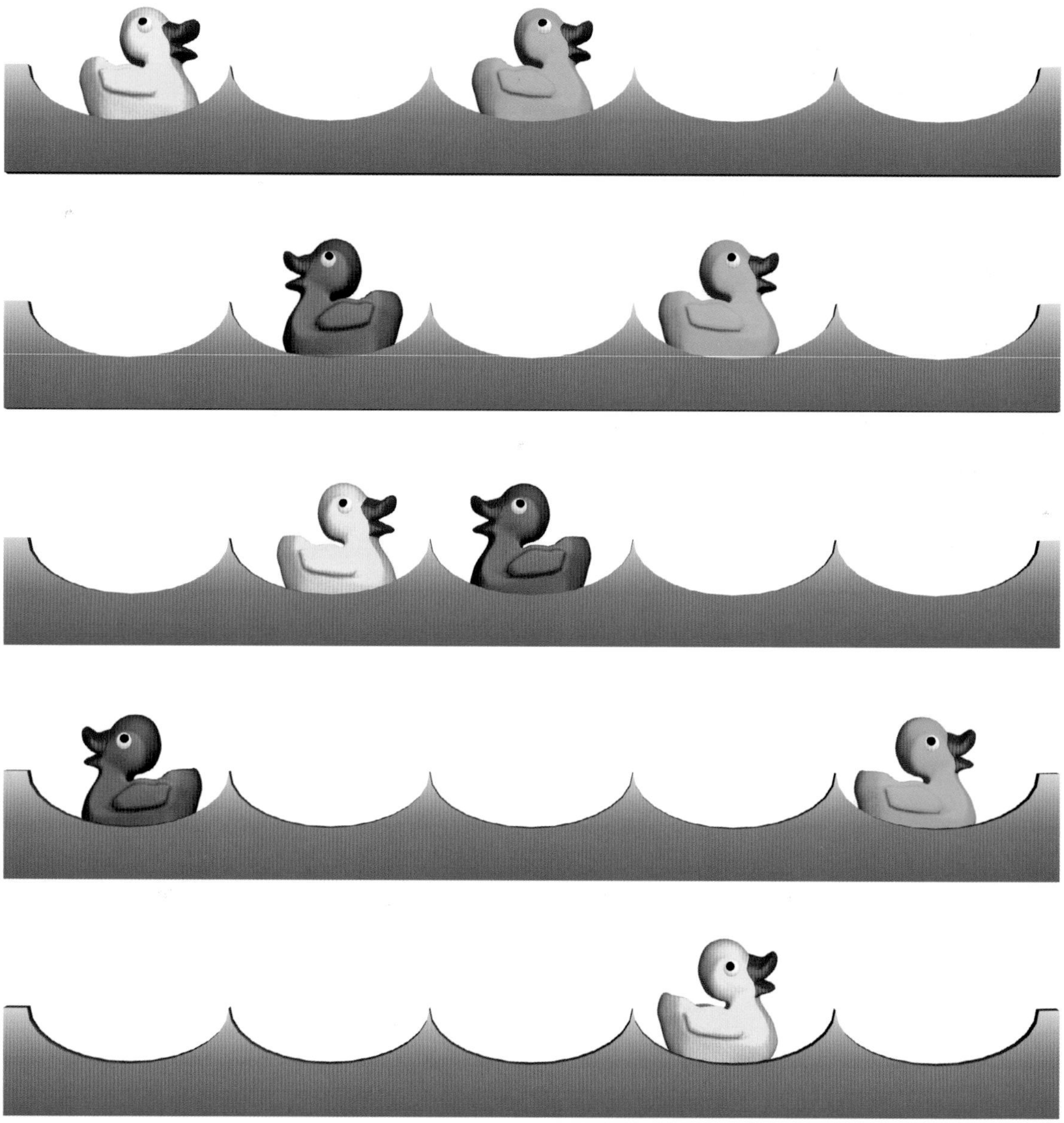

Match fish

85 ★

Take eight matches and make a fish, as shown in the following diagram. Now try the following:

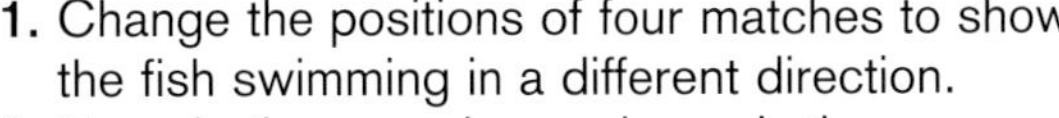

1. Change the positions of four matches to show the fish swimming in a different direction.
2. Now do the same by moving only three matches.
3. Now try it by moving only two matches.

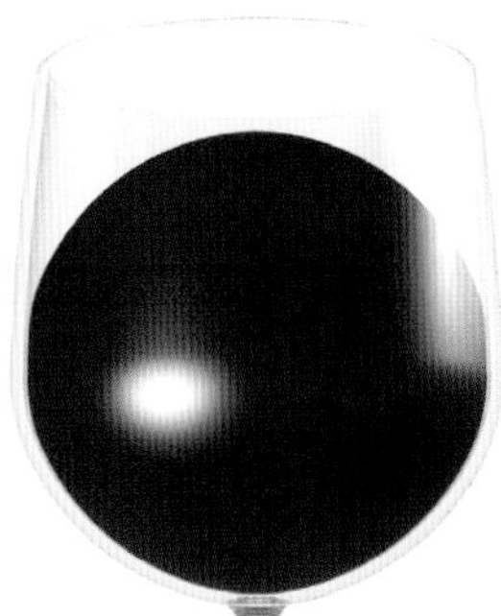

Wine glass

86 ★★

This totally clear wine glass has no decoration on it and nothing inside it but ordinary wine. Why is the surface of the wine curved in shape, and not flat?

Christmas lights

87 ★★

The lights on this Christmas tree are in a terrible tangle. Complete the circuit so that each light is passed through only once, and no steps are retraced.

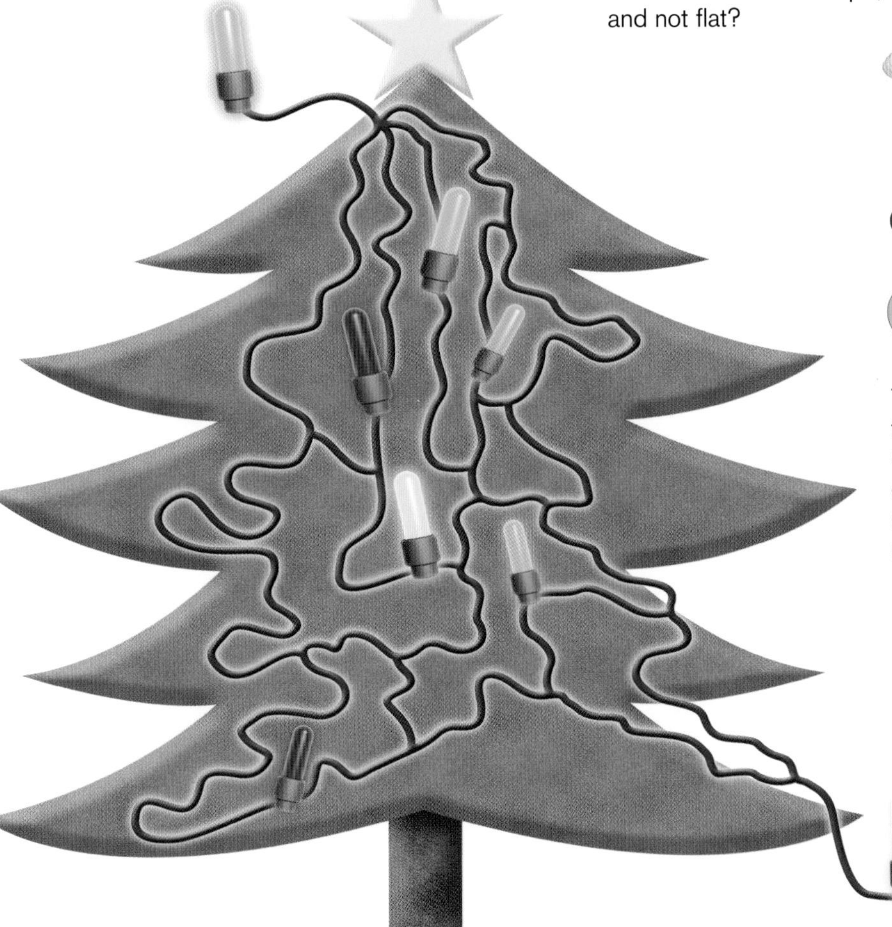

The birthday cake

88

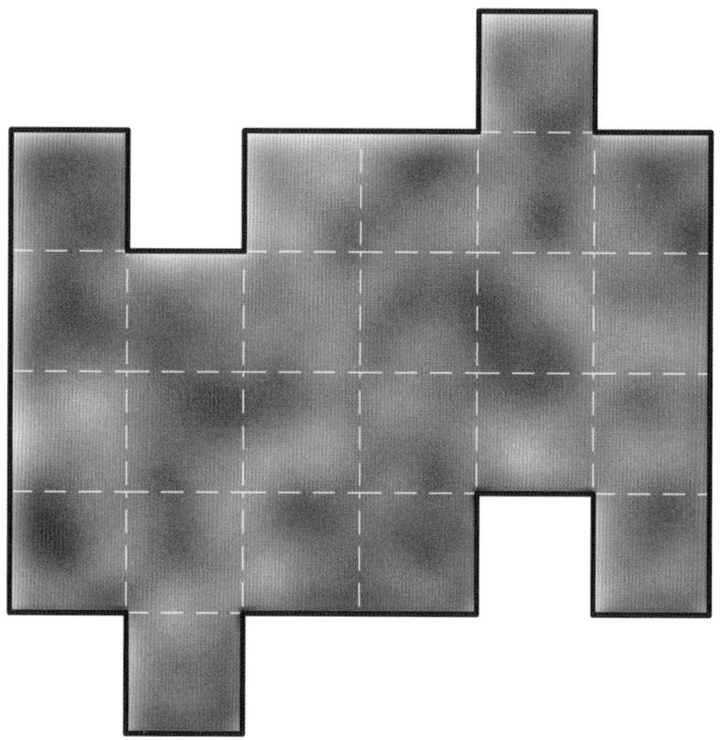

Mavis is having a birthday party and, as she is expecting 24 people to attend, she bought a cake with cuts for 24 pieces pre-drawn onto it. But she hadn't counted on diets and food intolerances, and it turns out that not many guests are actually going to have any cake. Mavis still wants to make sure that those who do have a piece of cake all get the same size and shape. Can you divide the cake into:

1. Twelve pieces?
2. Eight?
3. Six?
4. Four?

The pyramid puzzle

89

Two historians are staring at this pyramid, trying to find a pattern to this seemingly random collection of hieroglyphs. They have been studying the arrangement for hours without being able to decipher the code. Can you work out the reasoning behind the placement of the birds in relation to one another?

Jumping Jim

The diagram below shows a trampoline with varying tension in each square. Jumping Jim starts in the top left-hand corner, in the square marked with a **3**. He must always 'jump' the number of squares shown in the square on which he stands, and he is only allowed to jump either horizontally or vertically, and he can visit a square more than once. His object is to land exactly on the square marked **Goal**, from which a ladder will allow him to descend from the trampoline.

START

3	6	4	3	2	4	3
2	1	2	3	2	5	2
2	3	4	3	4	2	3
2	4	4	3	4	2	2
4	5	1	3	2	5	4
4	3	2	2	4	5	6
2	5	2	5	6	1	Goal

Three squares

Here is one way of making five enclosures by using three overlapping squares. What is the maximum number of enclosures you can make with three identical overlapping squares?

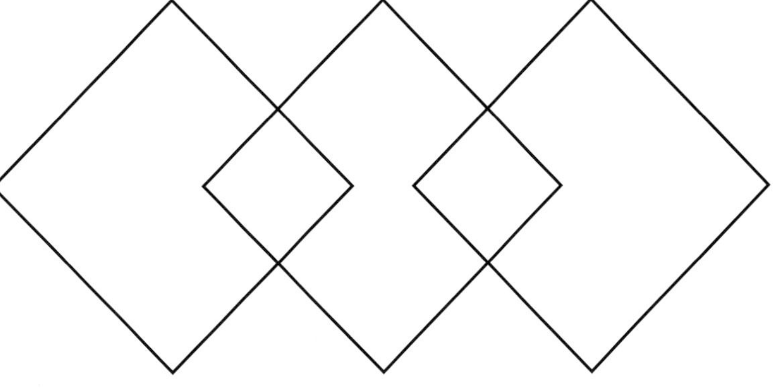

Poker patience

Using the scoring combinations to the right, which show how points are to be allocated, try to score as many points as possible in the following two puzzles.

Place a different card from each 30-card selection below in one of the 25 squares of its adjacent 5x5 grid.

The total score for each grid is an accumulation of the scores from each row, column, and the two diagonals.

EXAMPLE:

♥2 ♦2 PAIR (two cards of the same rank) = 1 point

♥2 ♦2 ♣Q ♠Q TWO PAIRS = 3 points

♣2 ♣5 ♣8 ♣Q ♣K FLUSH = 4 points (5 cards of the same suit)

♥2 ♦2 ♣2 THREE OF A KIND = 5 points

♥2 ♦2 ♣2 ♥7 ♦7 FULL HOUSE = 8 points (3 of a kind plus a pair)

♥2 ♦3 ♣4 ♥5 ♦6 STRAIGHT = 10 points (an ascending sequence using any suit)

♥2 ♦2 ♣2 ♠2 FOUR OF A KIND = 12 points

♣2 ♣3 ♣4 ♣5 ♣6 STRAIGHT FLUSH = 16 points (an ascending sequence in the same suit)

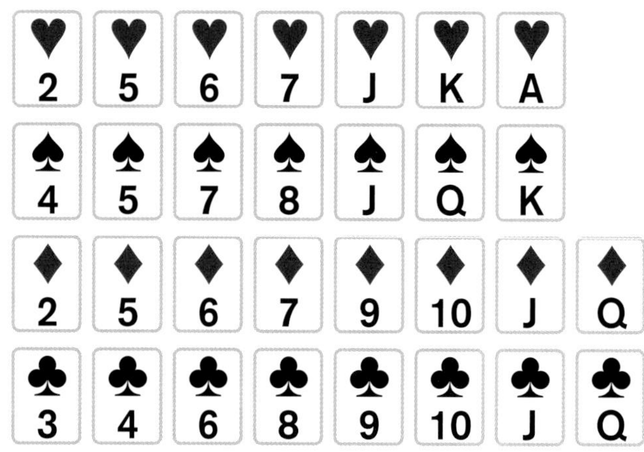

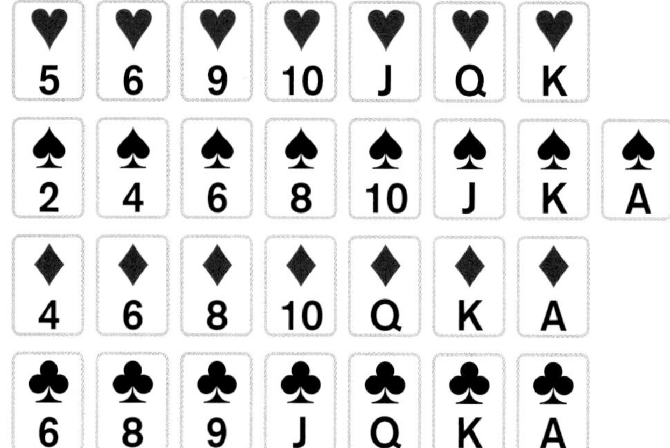

The black matchic

Draw the match heads on the remaining 32 matchsticks in such a way that each horizontal and vertical row of squares has the same number of match heads in them.

First work out how many match heads are required in each row and column before deciding where they go.

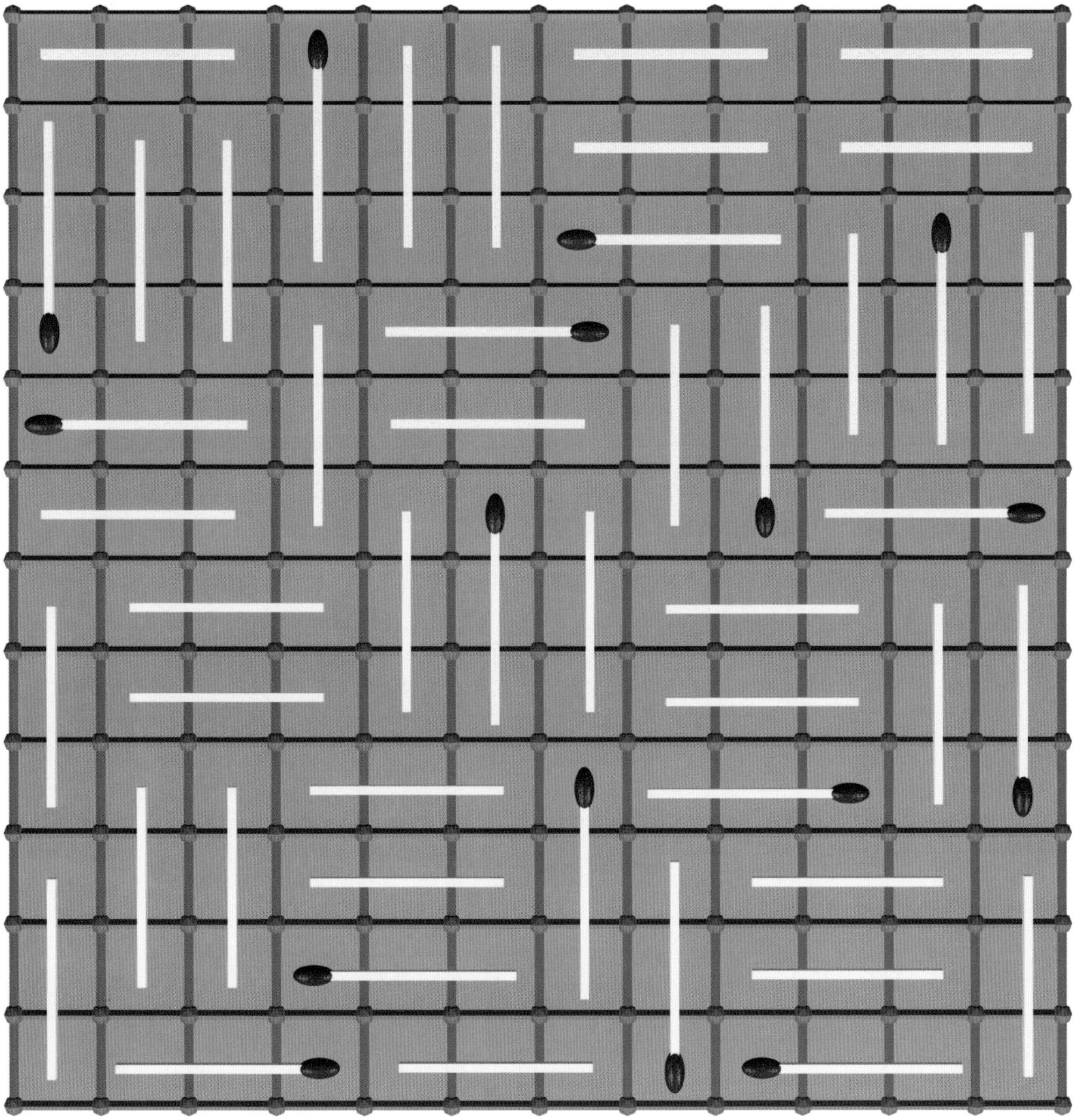

95 Park pathway

In this puzzle a hiker enters the park via one of the 14 entrances shown. The compass direction shown at the entrance he chooses will determine the side of the park by which he must eventually leave (N, S, E or W). To complete the puzzle, place three 'Ls' and three 'Rs' (to mark left and right turns). Correctly placed, these directions will always lead the hiker to the proper exit, whichever entrance he chose in the first place. The direction must always be from the hiker's viewpoint.

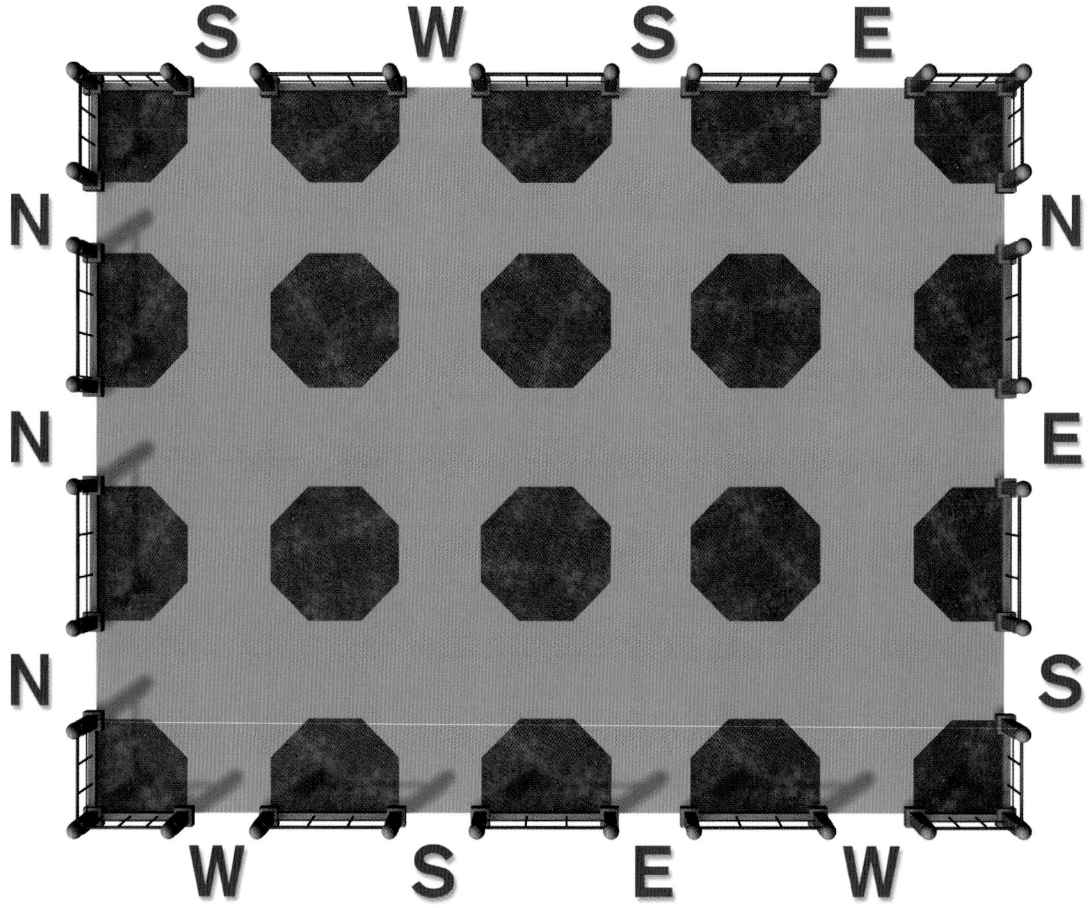

Domino dilemma

96

What are the values of the dominoes identified with question marks, and which way up should they be placed so that this puzzle makes sense?

Dennis' dust sheets

97

This puzzle was stumbled upon by Dennis the Decorator when he was painting his house. He had laid eight square dust sheets on the floor before he started painting. When he'd finished he was idly looking at the sheets while the paint dried, and it occurred to him that he could identify the order in which the sheets had been placed on the floor. Bearing in mind that all the sheets are the same size and shape, and none have been folded, can you do as well as Dennis and work out the order?

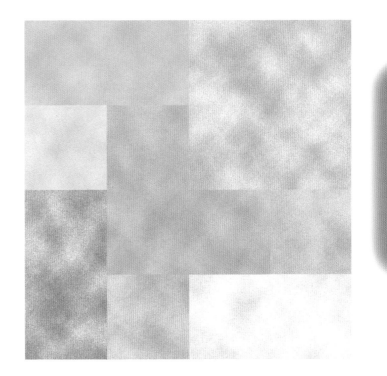

Dice maze

98

Think of a dice as a large carton that is too heavy to slide, but can be tipped end over end.

The letters stand for Low, High, Odd and Even. If a 1, 2 or 3 is on top of the dice, you can tip it onto a square with an L. If a 4, 5 or 6 is on top, you can tip the dice onto a square with an H. The rules are similar for Odd (1,3,5) and Even (2,4,6).

Place the dice on the starting square. Position the dice so that the 2 is on top and the 6 is facing the bottom edge of the page. As the dice is showing a 2, you can tip it onto the next square.

Can you return the dice to the starting square? There should be no tipping out of bounds or onto the blue areas.

START ↓							
				E	O	E	
			E	O		E	E
			E		O	E	O
			E	O	E		O
H				H			H
L	O			H	E	L	E
	H			O	O	L	
	O	L	E	H	L	L	

STORYBOARD

How adept are you at placing visual images in sequence? Look at the fragmented storyboard below and use your perception to put them in the correct order.

Double identity

Roger Regular, the criminal lawyer, led a double-life as a crimefighter. Key colleagues could call his private number to enlist his help against villainous activity in the city. Can you arrange the following scenes A to I in the correct order, to show how Roger prevented a bank robbery?

A

B

C

D

E

F

G

H

I

REARRANGE FACES

This puzzle tests your ability to remember both visual and written information, and your skill at linking the two. Are you able to look at these identity cards and remember all the faces as well as their names and birth dates?

Who was it?

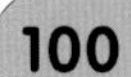

Study the faces, names and birthdays on the identity cards on the right, and memorize as many details of the people as you can in two minutes. Then cover over the identity card pyramid, leaving just those below the blue line visible. From memory decide whether each card is exactly the same as before or if it has been altered in some way.

We often meet new people in our everyday lives and this puzzle exercises your ability to recall names, faces and other relevant information.

John Bean
12th February

Kit Webb
20 May

Poppy Hamilton
6th August

Jen Wallace
27th November

Walter O'Malley
15th August

Marco North
6th June

Hugh Taverner
5th November

Tom Dupont
14th February

Sally Gordon
17th November

Gerry Ling
2nd December

Marco North
2nd December

Poppy Hamilton
6th August

Tom Dupont
12th February

Sally Gordon
17th November

Hugh Taverner
5th November

TANGLE PUZZLES

Trace each path through the tangles to match up each letter with a number. For an added challenge, try to follow the path without using your finger.

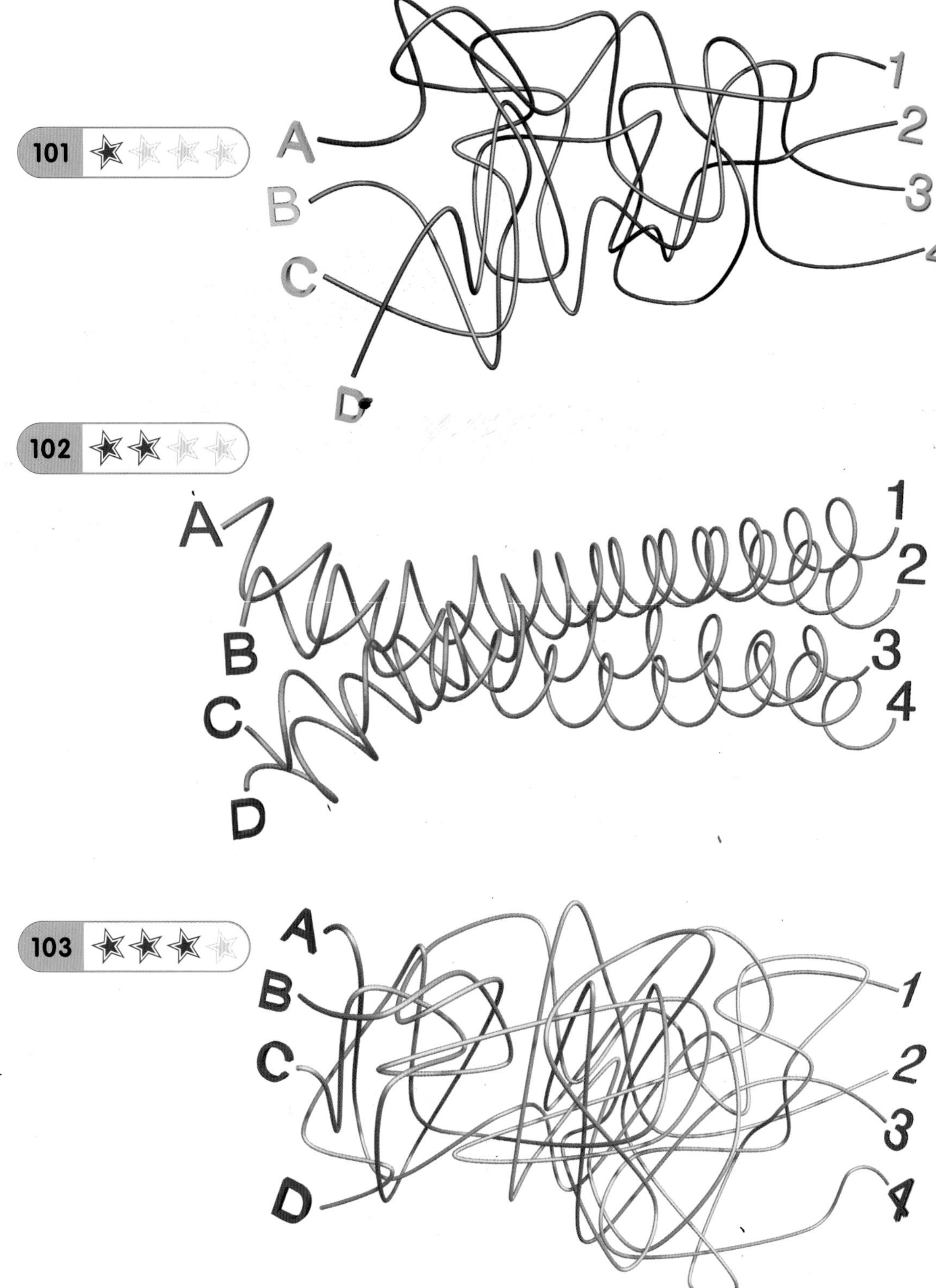

THINK OF A NUMBER

THINK OF A NUMBER

Although we have calculators to carry out complex mathematical calculations, mental arithmetic and numerical agility are still important everyday skills.

NUMBERS AND NUMBER PUZZLES HAVE AN ELEGANCE all their own, making them fun to tackle and fulfilling to complete. Even if you found math difficult at school, set aside your prejudices and trying some of the puzzles in this section. You will discover that many of them have as much to do with logic as they do with the mathematical manipulation of digits. Identifying all the elements and tackling each in turn is a key element of success.

WHETHER YOU ARE CALCULATING DISTANCE, working out how to manage your monthly budget or measuring the ingredients for a recipe, mathematical skills are essential to everyday life. And it is so much quicker to work out sums in your head rather than having to get out the calculator every time. As with all puzzling, practice with numbers will improve your performance, as well as exercising your brain.

MOST NUMBER PUZZLES are related to familiar concepts that were first learned in school (addition, division, subtraction, and so on). The harder puzzles in this section need an understanding of minus numbers and the basics of algebra, as well as angles, weights and measures, and speeds.

SIMPLER THAN 'REGULAR' MATH puzzles are those that use sets, or groups of numbers, such as Sudoku, in which the numbers 1 to 9 are grouped together so that they are not repeated in any rows, columns or 3x3 boxes in the grid. You need patience, a systematic, logical approach and the ability to assess the appropriateness of various solutions to solve these puzzles.

Being able to recognize and analyze numeric patterns is a skill that can be developed and used from day to day.

I am Count Zero, and wherever possible I will be giving you hints and tips to help you solve some of the more difficult puzzles in this section.

MOST OF US ARE BORN WITH AN INNATE ABILITY TO COUNT – even babies can tell the difference when presented with first one doll then two. Equally, both numeracy and logic are skills that largely involve the left side of the brain. Once you grasp the fact that numbers are a logical code and they relate to each other by means of certain rules, number puzzles become easier to solve.

IN MAGIC SQUARE PUZZLES, all the columns, rows and diagonals in a grid must add up to the same answer, but the number in each individual square has to be different. The minimum size of a Magic Square is 3 columns by 3 rows, and the answer has to be at least 15, but the possible combinations are infinite.

TO TACKLE THE MORE CHALLENGING NUMBER PUZZLES successfully, you also need to think laterally, not least because number puzzles can deceive in the same ways as cryptic clues in a crossword puzzle. A typical trick in number sequence puzzles, in which you have to find the next or a missing figure in a string of figures, is the use of commas to group numbers together to mislead you, when you actually need to study the numbers separately to find the solution.

IN SUCH PUZZLES, THE KEY TO SUCCESS is often the ability to recognize patterns (even if these are concealed by punctuation or some other device). A puzzle that appears to be a random succession of numbers will contain a pattern of some kind. Obvious patterns are a sequence of even or odd numbers, but you might get more complex patterns, such as 8, 36, 44, 80 – numbers that are all divisible by 4. or prime numbers such as 1, 3, 5, 7 and 9.

MANY NUMBER PUZZLES COMBINE BOTH MATHEMATICAL SKILLS and lateral thinking. For these, you need to get your sums right, and to think about how these sums might relate to, and impact upon, one another. Which is where you need to put the right side of your brain into play. These kinds of puzzles normally connect the numbers in some spatial fashion. To solve the puzzle, you may need to work out what pairs of numbers have in common, and the spatial as well as the mathematical relationship between adjacent numbers.

WITH ALL THESE NUMBER PUZZLES under your belt you should not only notice a marked improvement in your arithmetic speed and agility, but an increased problem-solving ability and a development in your powers of reasoning.

NUMBER SEQUENCES

The following puzzles are designed to test your numerical dexterity and quickness of thought. In each one there is a hidden pattern waiting to be uncovered, but sometimes you need to think flexibly and laterally to arrive at the correct solution – straightforward adding and subtracting are a good start, but you need to think beyond these.

Missing numbers

What number should replace the question mark?

100,99,96,91,84,75,?

Which is the missing section?

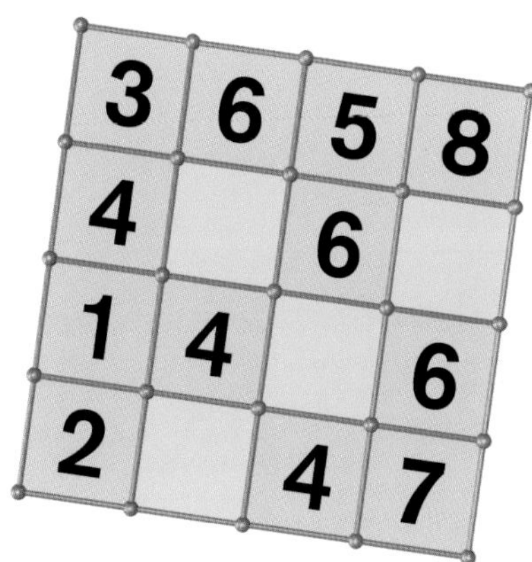

a.

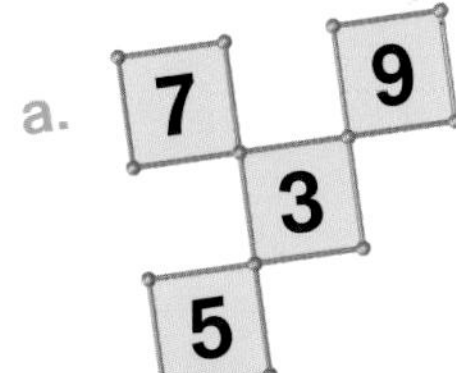

c.

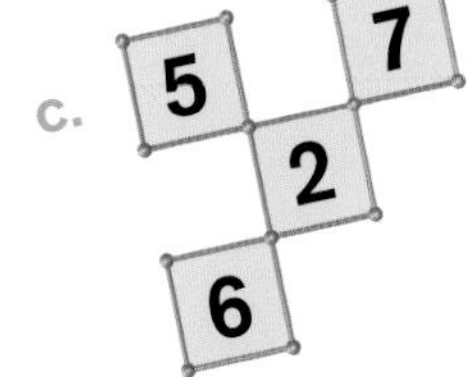

b.

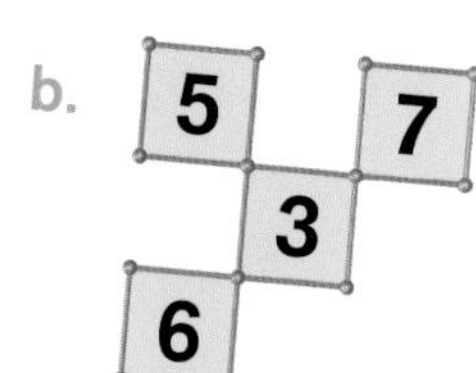

d.

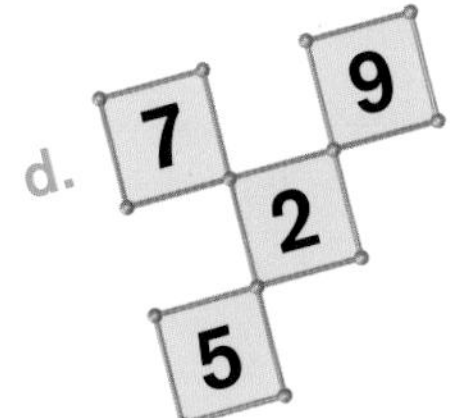

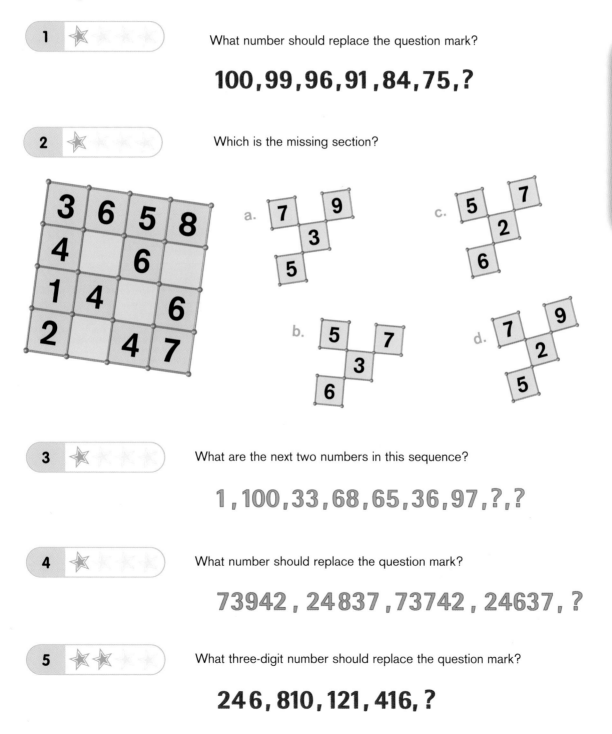

What are the next two numbers in this sequence?

1,100,33,68,65,36,97,?,?

What number should replace the question mark?

73942, 24837, 73742, 24637, ?

What three-digit number should replace the question mark?

246, 810, 121, 416, ?

749,683,274,968,327,?

What number should replace the question mark?

What number should replace the question mark?

8

What number should replace the question mark?

2397,378,168,?,32,6

What number should replace the question mark?

6	8
2	9

5	4
5	6

4	?
8	3

What numbers should replace the question marks?

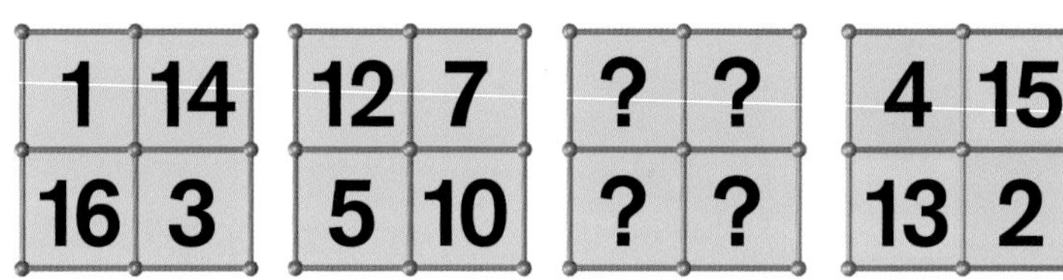

145,230,315,400,445,?

What number should replace the question mark?

Which is the missing section?

5	6	2	5	3	2	8
2	8	3	6	8	5	6
3	3	8	8	6	6	5
8	2	6			8	2
6			2	2	3	3
5	6	2	5	3	2	8
2	8	3	6	8	5	6

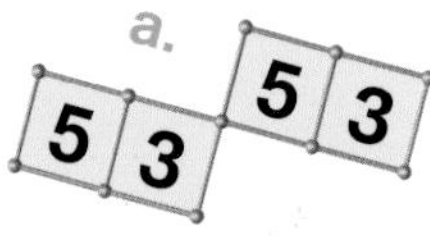

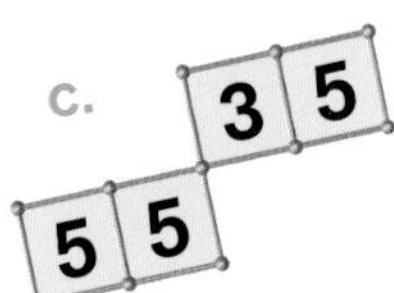

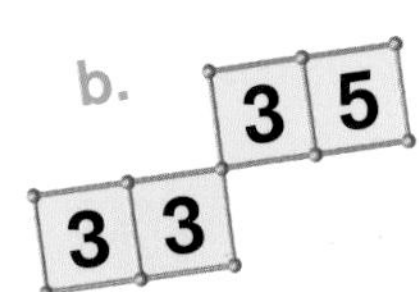

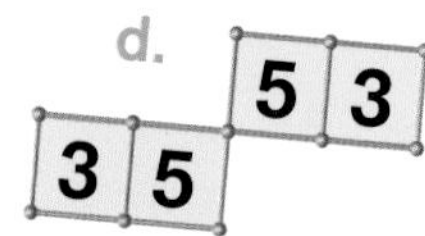

ALPHAMETICS

In alphametics puzzles a letter represents a specific number between 0 and 9. If solved correctly, the result should be a valid arithmetic sum. Throughout the sum, each letter will always represent the same number, and no line can begin with the number 0. Unlike conventional addition, with these puzzles it is easier to work from left to right.

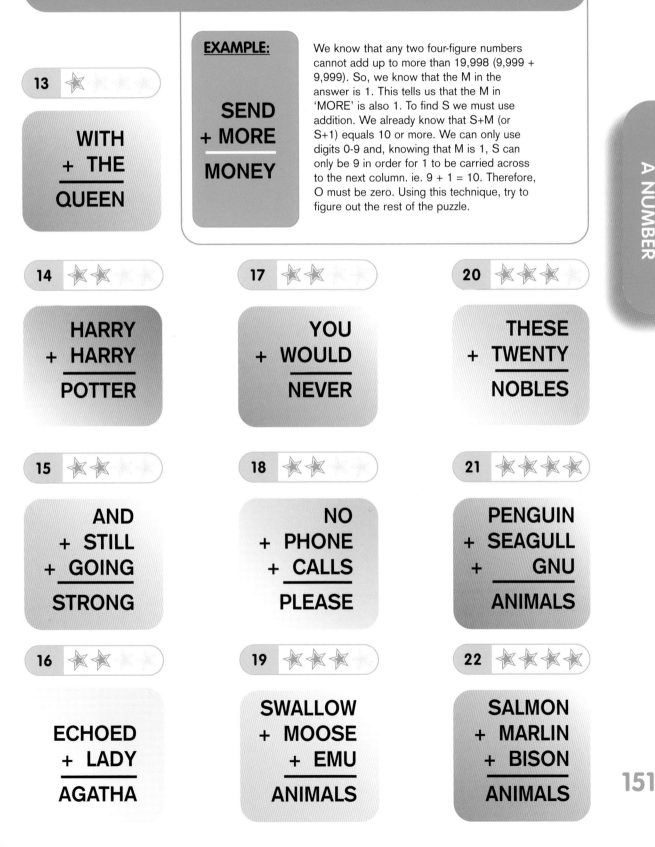

EXAMPLE:

```
  SEND
+ MORE
------
 MONEY
```

We know that any two four-figure numbers cannot add up to more than 19,998 (9,999 + 9,999). So, we know that the M in the answer is 1. This tells us that the M in 'MORE' is also 1. To find S we must use addition. We already know that S+M (or S+1) equals 10 or more. We can only use digits 0-9 and, knowing that M is 1, S can only be 9 in order for 1 to be carried across to the next column. ie. 9 + 1 = 10. Therefore, O must be zero. Using this technique, try to figure out the rest of the puzzle.

13 

```
   WITH
+   THE
-------
  QUEEN
```

14 

```
   HARRY
+  HARRY
--------
  POTTER
```

15 

```
     AND
+  STILL
+  GOING
--------
  STRONG
```

16 

```
  ECHOED
+   LADY
--------
 AGATHA
```

17 

```
     YOU
+  WOULD
--------
   NEVER
```

18 

```
      NO
+  PHONE
+  CALLS
--------
  PLEASE
```

19  

```
  SWALLOW
+   MOOSE
+     EMU
---------
  ANIMALS
```

20 

```
   THESE
+ TWENTY
--------
  NOBLES
```

21 

```
  PENGUIN
+ SEAGULL
+     GNU
---------
  ANIMALS
```

22  

```
   SALMON
+  MARLIN
+   BISON
---------
  ANIMALS
```

SUDOKU

Every column, every row and every 3 x 3 box of these Japanese number cross-words contains the numbers 1-9. All you have to do is work out which number goes in each blank space to ensure that each row, column and region contains only one instance of each numeral.

These puzzles simply require patience and logic. For hints and tips, visit **www.sudoku.com/howtosolve.htm**

23 ★

	1		5		8			
4		7		9		6		
	6		4	7		2	3	8
7	3			8	4	1		
	5	8	7	2				3
2			3		5			9
	7	1	9					6
		5					1	2
		4		5	6	3	8	

24 ★

8	7			9		3		5
1	9	3			7			6
	6				8	1	7	
			7	8				
3			9		1		8	4
	8	1		6			5	3
5		2				4	6	
		8		1	5	9		2
6	3			7	4		1	

25 ★

8		9				2	6	
		3			8	9	7	5
7	2		9		1		4	
		6				1	8	4
				4	6	5	9	
	8	7		5	9			6
3	7		5	9		6		
5	1	2	6	8				
	9		3		4			

26 ★

	4			8	7		2	9
2	5	9				8	1	
	1		2	5	9			3
		6	8	3		7		
9		5	7		2	6		
3		1		6			5	
	3		4	9				
5	6				1			2
1		7					4	6

27 ★

1	3	9		8		2		
4			1		3			9
6				4		3	5	
	6					8	2	5
7		4				1		3
	1				9	4		
3		6	8	9	1			2
		1	5					8
	8		3	2		9	1	4

28

9		4	1				3	7
		6	5	4	7		9	8
8	7			9	3			
6	1						2	5
	8	2			4			
	9	7		5		8	1	
					1	6	8	2
3	2		4		6	7		
1	6		7			9		

29

1		8	3	2			7	
		4			8	3		1
2	3		5			4	8	9
8		7		6		1	4	
6			1		2			
	2			7	5		6	3
	8	5	2					
3		9	8		1			
	1	2			9			8

30

	4		8		6		2	
5				4		1	7	
				9	5	4		3
7			5	6		8	3	
	2	8	7				6	
3		6			8	2		
	9	5	6		7			
8	7		3	2				
		2						8

31

	9			8	2		7	4
5		4	1		7			2
	8		5		9	3		
	5	6	3			4		
1				5	4	6		
8	4	3		1				
		8	7	9		1		
7								9
4	3						6	

32

		3		9		6	7	8
		2		8	3			
5	9				4	3	2	
				1				5
9	5		6				3	
	7	1			2			
3		9					6	7
1		7		4		2		3
6			8			9	1	

33

9			6			2		
		6			8	7		
	2	7					6	8
5					6	3	2	4
				8	4		7	
	6		7	5			8	9
8	1		2					6
		5	8	6	9			
		2	5		1	8		

34

	7			5		2	9	
2			1	8		7		
		4		2	7	8		6
	5				1	3	6	
4	3	7						
		1	5		3		4	
1	4	8	7					
7			4		5			3
		5					7	9

35

		7		2		6		
		1	3		4		2	
4	5				6	7	8	
	3							2
7				3			5	6
	1	8					3	7
6		5					7	
	8	9		6	5	3	4	
			2	4	9			

36

		5		9	1			8
	4				5		9	3
1				3		6		
			3	7	8	5		
5		9	1			3	6	7
7	1		9					
		6	7	4		2		
	7			6				4
2	3			1			5	

37

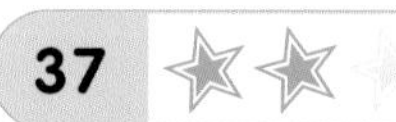

		7	9		3			1
	3	2		7				5
1	6	4	8					7
7		5			6	1	2	
	4			3	9		7	
6			7	1	5			
			5			4		
			3	9				2
2	7	8					5	

38

	8			1	4			6
6			8					1
		4	6		5			8
	6	1					9	
9				6		3		4
3		5			1	6		
				3	2		4	
			7			8	2	3
2	5	3		4			6	

39

5								9
	7			4	9			8
				5		6		2
				8			1	7
	5	8	7				6	
	2				1	8	9	
		2			6	5		
			9	7	8			
3	8	4	5					

40

	3	5				1		2
4					1	5		
1		9			2		3	
					4		8	1
					8	6		
	8	1	5	3				9
3	1			8				
		7	4					
9			2		7			

41

				5		4	8	2
		6			3			1
	9			1		6		5
						3	6	
9		3					4	
	2				6			9
2		1	4			9		
4			9	8				
6	7	9			2			

42

1					3	2		9
		2				7		
	9			6		4		5
				3				2
		5	7	1				
9						6	4	1
2	8	9			5			
					6			
4		6	9		2			7

43

6			7				3	2
	7		9			4		
			1	6		7		
2	5	9						
		3		4		5		1
							7	9
	2	4		5				3
3					6			
5				1	3	9		4

44

				4			3	2
				3	2		6	
		8			1		7	
						1	9	3
1	2							
	5	7						
			6			5		9
7	4	2	8					
9			4			2		

45

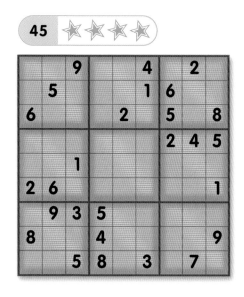

		9			4		2	
	5				1	6		
6				2		5		8
						2	4	5
		1						
2	6							1
	9	3	5					
8			4					9
		5	8		3		7	

MONEY PUZZLES

Hone your numerical agility skills by juggling with deduction, division, multiplication subtraction and all the tools of puzzle logic. By starting with the easier puzzles, you can use the skills you have amassed to progress with confidence to the more testing ones.

After a meal, you leave a 10% tip for the waiter, and later tip the taxi driver who takes you home $2.

If the taxi cost exactly half as much as the meal, and all you've got left is $2 from a $20 note, how much was the meal?

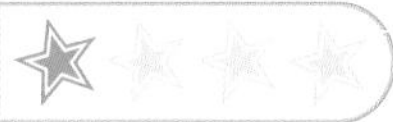

'Drat,' said Jim, 'I can't see how much the complete place settings are – they've piled the crockery in front of the price list.'

DINNER SERVICE BARGAINS!

$	
3.18	Set of six dinner plates
5.76	Set of six dinner plates & soup bowls
3.04	Set of four dinner plates & side plates
2.00	Set of four side plates and cups with saucers
??	Set of four **complete place settings**: dinner plates, soup bowls, side plates, cups with saucers

Given that there are no discounts, what price is missing?

Sally, Linda and Eric have $28 between them. Sally has twice as much as Eric, who has twice as much as Linda.

How much does Eric have?

$28

Tony sold his guitar at an Internet auction. He had to pay the website $3 to list his guitar and 10% commission from the price achieved at auction.
The buyer paid $25, which included $6 postage and packing. As Tony originally paid $20 for the guitar, how much had he lost?

Farmer Fred went to market.
He sold 3 cows, 5 sheep, 7 goats and 11 chickens for $980.
Each goat fetched 3 times the price of a chicken, half as much as a sheep, and only a quarter as much as a cow.

How much did he get for each goat?

Back home after a trip to England, Rob and Mary find themselves with some British coins. Rob has as many 20p coins as Mary has 5p coins. If Rob were to give Mary 90p, their financial positions would be reversed.

How much money do they have between them?

52

Dozy, Sleepy, Happy, Sneezy and Snow White are sharing out $100. Dozy gets as much more than Sleepy as Sneezy gets more than Snow White, and Sneezy gets as much less than Happy as Happy gets less than Sleepy.

How much does Happy get?

53

John noticed that the amount he was paying for his lunch was a rearrangement of the digits of the amount of money in his pocket – and that the money he had left was a further rearrangement of the same three digits!

How much did he start with?

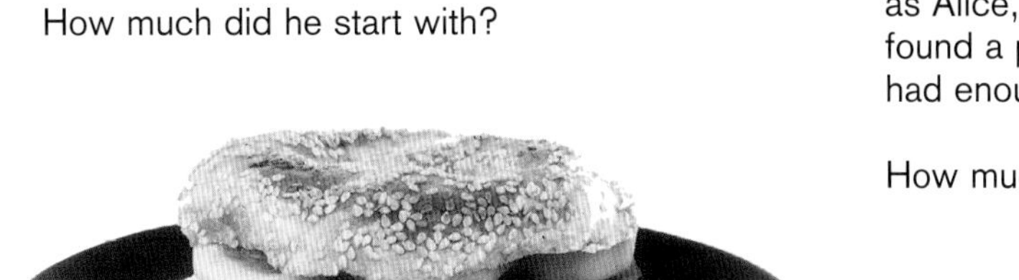

54

An old lady left half her money to her daughter, and half that amount to her son. She left a sixth to her brother, and the remainder, $1,000, to the dog shelter.

How much did she leave altogether?

55

A rich aunt left her nieces and nephews her fortune of $100,000. Each was to get $100 more than the cousin next younger than her or him. The youngest got $5,500. How many nieces and nephews were there?

56

Tom had twice as much money as Sally, so he paid for the 10-cent ice cream cones for himself, Sally and Alice. That left him with twice as much as Alice, and half as much as Sally. Luckily, they found a penny on the pavement, so they just had enough to catch the bus home.

How much was the bus fare?

57

Mom and Dad decided to buy all the children coming to the party a present. It was important to spend the same amount on each child – but they didn't know how many children were coming. There certainly weren't to be more than 10.

What is the minimum amount of money they needed, to be able to divide it equally between all the children, irrespective of how many came to the party, and without leaving any change?

NUMBER GRIDS

A playful twist on conventional crosswords, these puzzles replace word answers with numerical solutions. Working out the sums will put your arithmetic and mathematical skills to the test. Write your answers into the grids as figures.

58

1		2		3		4		5
		6						
7	8					9	10	
			11		12			
13					14			
			15	16				
17		18				19		20
		21						
22						23		

Across

1. 12 x 9
4. 1,223 – 469
6. 28,888 + 1,780
7. 64.5 x 8
9. 5,834 – 4,911
11. 1,335 ÷ 3
13. 424 x 4
14. 5,483 + 1,547
15. 0.6 x 200
17. 1,092 ÷ 4
19. 1,388 – 532
21. 28,532 + 17,890
22. 1,875 ÷ 5
23. 2,000 x 20%

Down

1. 312 – 187
2. 269 + 567
3. 210.5 x 8
4. 3,945 ÷ 5
5. 1,892 x 25%
8. 39,240 – 21,563
10. 17,887 + 7,458
11. 1,310 – 849
12. 30 x 19
16. 8,526 ÷ 3
17. 89 + 164
18. 23 x 15
19. 1,752 – 928
20. 3,840 ÷ 6

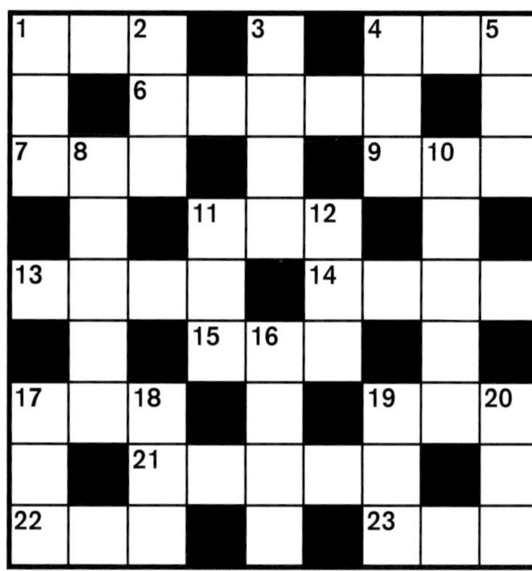

59

Across

1. 12 x 12
4. 25 x 15
6. 37,290 + 48,319
7. 45 x 8
9. 1,700 – 1,012
11. 2,586 ÷ 3
13. 61 x 25
14. 693 + 573
15. 196 x 5
17. 3,664 – 2,955
19. 4,842 ÷ 6
21. 23,338 + 37,657
22. 2,000 x 45%
23. 21 x 8

Down

1. 89.5 + 93.5
2. 600 x 80%
3. 404 x 400%
4. 12 x 33
5. 2,200 – 1,692
8. 3,025 x 20
10. 69,323 + 19,337
11. 3,436 ÷ 4
12. 700 x 0.3
16. 1,171 x 7
17. 3,645 ÷ 5
18. 800 x 1.2
19. 1,204 – 353
20. 599 + 189

60

Across

1. 11 x 11
4. 488 + 129
6. 100,000 x 61.5%
7. 3,166 – 2,907
9. 2,925 ÷ 5
11. 1,304 – 897
13. 2,108 x 4
14. 12 x 208
15. 1,866 ÷ 6
17. 583 + 382
19. 2,400 – 1,598
21. 10,000,000 x 0.1%
22. 4,428 ÷ 9
23. 97 x 8

Down

1. 426 ÷ 3
2. 13 x 13
3. 2,865 + 1,685
4. 3,025 ÷ 5
5. 29 x 25
8. 18,482 x 3
10. 84,996 + 2,994
11. 1,692 ÷ 4
12. 103 x 7
16. 910.3 + 898.7
17. 5,261 – 4,327
18. 4,096 ÷ 8
19. 229 + 578
20. 16 x 16

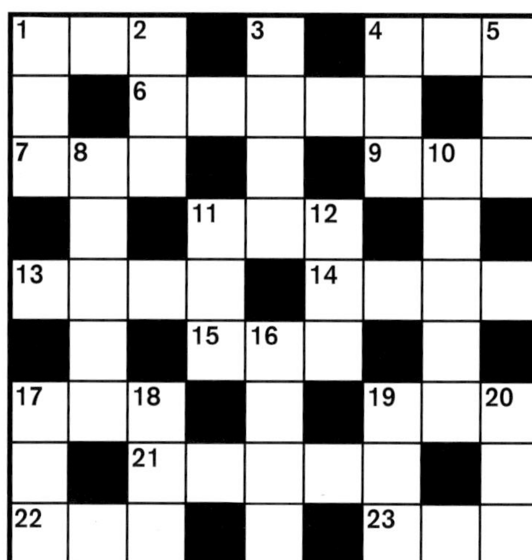

Across
1. 9,750 - 7,616 - 99
4. 5,344 ÷ 4
6. 0.0601 x 10,000
7. 6,080 x 0.3
10. 7,777 – 3,345 – 1,577
12. 130 x 2.5
14. 25,864 + 64,377 + 9,511
16. 12,732 ÷ 6
18. 9 x 33
20. 14,330 x 20%
23. 94,440 x 25%
26. 1,701 ÷ 7
27. 25,712 ÷ 8
28. 336 + 886 + 1,384
31. 476 – 282 + 187
32. 293 x 30
33. 1,818 + 4,989 – 2,582

Down
1. 2,439 ÷ 9
2. 905 x 40%
3. 341 + 686 + 648
4. 28,030 x 0.4
5. 139 x 5
8. 357 + 284 + 228
9. 2,866 + 3,489 – 5,920
11. 83 + 399 + 70
13. 1,998 ÷ 9
15. 4,656 ÷ 6
17. 9,876 - 5,432 – 4,318
19. 9,412 ÷ 13
21. 20.3 x 40
22. 3,271.5 x 20
24. 8,300 ÷ 25
25. 4,950 ÷ 33
26. 16,880 x 12.5%
27. 2,642 – 888 – 1,416
29. 13,640 x 5%
30. 1,212 – 667 + 70

62

Across
1. 1,627 x 5
4. 103 x 19
6. 23,700 x 2%
7. 821 + 496 + 874
10. 75,990 ÷ 15
12. 1,825 x 0.4
14. 74,252 x 25%
16. 6,366 + 9,633 – 7,099
18. 2,128 ÷ 19
20. 56,676 ÷ 12
23. 21,150 x 80%
26. 62.6 + 188.8 + 61.6
27. 2,444 + 8,666 – 5,076
28. 111,111 – 99,999 – 7,669
31. 6,123 – 2,896 – 2,956
32. 2,905 + 2,905
33. 50,500 x 3%

Down
1. 215.5 x 4
2. 9,870 ÷ 30
3. 6,388 + 2,977 – 4,945
4. 3,649.5 x 4
5. 49 + 285 + 442
8. 210 x 80%
9. 6,421 – 4,876 – 1,369
11. 5,580 ÷ 9
13. 2,648 ÷ 8
15. 4,336 x 12.5%
17. 39,960 x 2.5%
19. 4,220 ÷ 20
21. 18,750 ÷ 25
22. 6,884 x 5
24. 2.11 x 300
25. 710 x 40%
26. 4,024 x 75%
27. 38 + 779 – 162
29. 1,261 + 403 –1,259
30. 4,615 ÷ 13

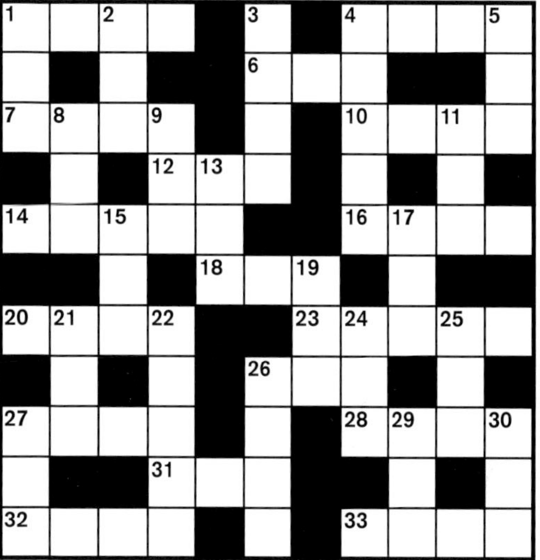

Put your general knowledge and math skills to the test by writing the answers into the grid as numbers not letters. Then add together each number from the 6 blue squares to reveal the mystery number.

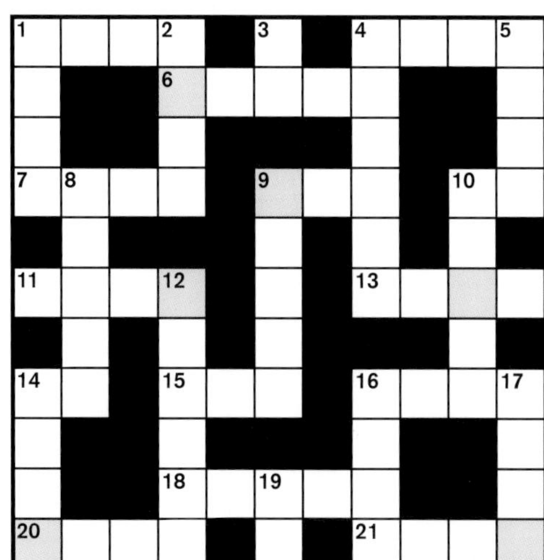

63

Mystery Number: _ _

Across
1. Pearl Harbor attack
4. Gagarin became the first man in space
6. Jules Verne's ..... Leagues Under The Sea
7. 388 minutes before 7 pm
9. Inches in 79 feet
10. Around The World in .. Days
11. Beijing hosts the Olympics
13. Henry VIII died
14. Number represented by the Roman numeral X
15. A sixth of 4,194
16. Walt Disney was born
18. 20 across multiplied by 19 down
20. A Space Odyssey sequel
21. England hosted soccer's World Cup

Down
1. Jim Morrison of The Doors died
2. Months in 101 years
3. Total number of states in the US
4. 11,209 x 9
5. .... Pennsylvania Ave, White House address
8. Height of Everest to the nearest 1,000 feet
9. Largest whole five-digit number
10. Seconds in a day
12. Pounds in 59,010 stone
14. Sinking of the Titanic in what year?
16. Alexander I became Czar of Russia
17. Great Fire of London
19. Letters in the classical Greek alphabet

Write the answers in the grid as numbers not letters. After solving the puzzle, add together each number from the 6 blue squares to reveal the mystery number.

Across

1. Signs of the zodiac
5. Apollo that spawned the infamous words, "Houston, we have a problem"
6. 470 minutes after midnight on a 24-hour clock
7. Bits in 853 bytes
8. Inches in 63 feet
10. Fahrenheit ... , Michael Moore film
12. A quick countdown
14. US dollars in 21,402,200 nickels
17. Ounces in 57 pounds
18. 45 degrees celsius in fahrenheit
19. 20p pieces in £634,640
21. 115.75 x 8
23. Convenience store chain
25. Pounds in 14 stone
27. When London hosts the Olympics
28. When World War I ended
29. Bo Derek and Dudley Moore film
30. Contiguous states in the US

Down

2. A Space Odyssey
3. James Bond
4. Number of the beast
5. Year in which Joan of Arc was born
9. Indy ... , world-famous motor race
11. Square 106
12. Next in series 29810, 29909, 30008, ...
13. One less than a gross
15. Double decker Boeing jetliner
16. Dalmatians in the sequel
17. UK emergency phone number
20. ... BC, year of Socrates' death
22. Synonymous with normal vision
24. George Orwell novel
25. Squares in this grid
26. Months in 51 years

Mystery number: _ _

Across

1. 35 squared
3. 1,051,316 ÷ 4
7. 8,003,642 – 5,456,787 – 1,538,286
8. 43,199.4 + 23,199.5 + 31,240.1
9. 13 across – 16 across
13. 1,263,611 x 5
15. 8 across – 2 down
16. 7,189,650 x 50%
17. 199,991 + 399,391 + 56,183
18. 20 cubed

Down

1. 847,847 ÷ 7
2. 166,166 – 82,289 – 25,004
4. 10,665 x 6
5. 1,985,750 + 3,750,985 + 3,099,475
6. 39,996 ÷ 4
10. 5,658,658 – 2,879,879 – 621,024
11. 7 cubed
12. 30,318 x 5
13. 14 down x 75%
14. 530,688 ÷ 6
15. 29,088 ÷ 8

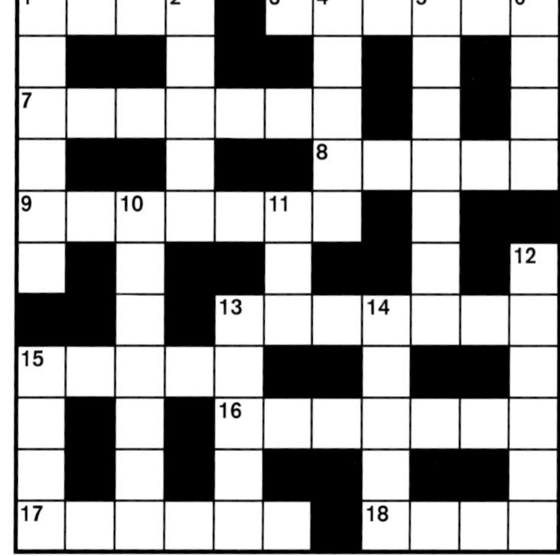

Across

1. 15 cubed
3. 505,344 ÷ 3
7. 12,600,500 – 4,825,750 – 1,979,000
8. 5,290 x 5
9. 5,000,000 – 2,804,625
13. 1,486,034 + 1,486,033
15. 227,696 ÷ 4
16. 9,086,454 x 50%
17. 135,788 + 79,866 + 44,653
18. 13 cubed

Down

1. 4 down x 5
2. 2,223 x 25
4. 58,577 + 24,889 – 22,441
5. 13,199,760 – 8,995,560
6. 11,000 x 81%
10. 7 across + 5 down
11. 9 x 9 x 9
12. 3,888,885 ÷ 5
13. 4,080 x 6
14. 5,580.5 x 4
15. 1 across + 18 across

MAGIC SQUARE PUZZLES

Magic square puzzles were developed by the ancient Chinese. They consist of an array of consecutive numbers in which all rows, columns and corner-to-corner lines (**line conventions**) add up to the same total.

67 ★

Insert the numbers 2, 4, 6, 8, 10, 12, 14, 16, 18, 20, 22, 24 once into the remaining blank spaces so that each row, column and corner-to-corner line totals 65.

15				
	19		23	3
21	25	1	7	11
5	9		13	
				17

68 ★★

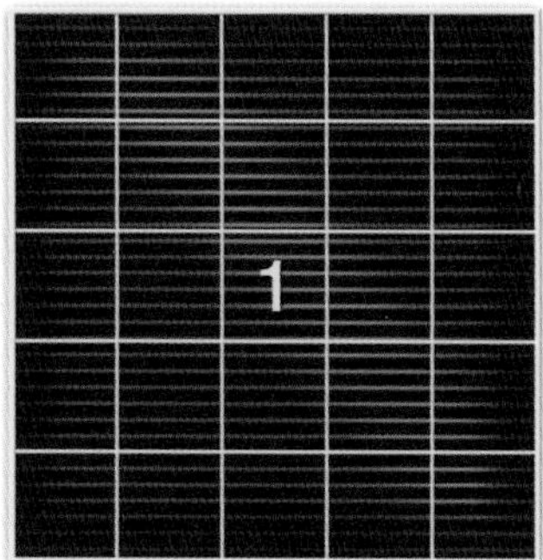

Place the tiles in the grid correctly in order to produce a Magic 65, where each row, column and corner-to-corner line totals 65.

25	5	4	13	3	11	24	14	17	15
21	18	8	10	23	7	6	19	9	22
					1	12	20	16	2

69 ★★

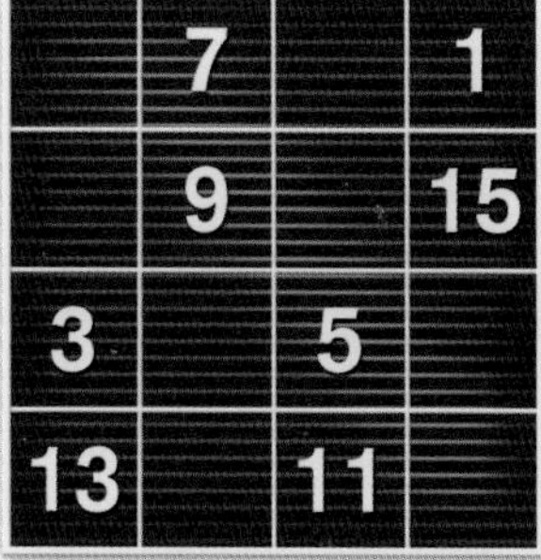

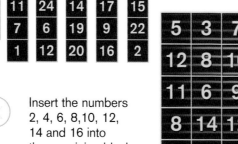

Insert the numbers 2, 4, 6, 8,10, 12, 14 and 16 into the remaining blank spaces so that each row, column and corner-to-corner line totals 34. The four corner squares, each block of four corner squares and the block of four central numbers should also total 34.

70 ★

This is an anti-magic square where none of the rows, columns or corner-to-corner lines total 34. Change the position of just four of the numbers in the grid (one per line) in order to produce a Magic 34, in which each line convention totals 34, as well as the four corner squares, the block of four central numbers and each block of four corner squares.

12	16	9	6
13	2	8	3
15	11	5	10
1	14	4	7

71 ★

Within the grid, identify a 3 x 3 block of 9 consecutive numbers, in which each row, column and corner-to-corner line adds up to the same total.

5	3	7	21	29	23	3	4	5
12	8	10	27	25	28	2	8	6
11	6	9	26	22	24	7	4	9
8	14	12	21	29	23	3	10	5
10	7	13	2	5	14	7	12	6
7	5	3	4	7	9	11	13	9
2	9	6	8	6	10	15	8	4
10	4	8	3	2	13	9	12	5
7	3	5	1	5	16	14	11	7

72

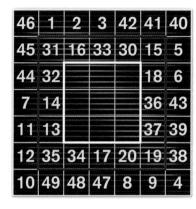

46	1	2	3	42	41	40
45	31	16	33	30	15	5
44	32				18	6
7	14				36	43
11	13				37	39
12	35	34	17	20	19	38
10	49	48	47	8	9	4

Insert the numbers 21, 22, 23, 24, 25, 26, 27, 28, 29 in the middle section so that a triple magic square is produced, whereby the grid contains the numbers 1–49 once only and the 7 x 7 grid forms a magic square where each row, column and corner-to-corner line totals 175 (a magic 175), the inner 5 x 5 forms a magic 125 and the inner 3 x 3 core a magic 75.

73

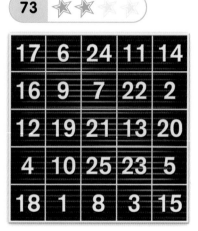

17	6	24	11	14
16	9	7	22	2
12	19	21	13	20
4	10	25	23	5
18	1	8	3	15

This is an anti-magic square where none of the rows, columns or corner-to-corner lines total 65. It is possible to move the position of just five of the numbers in the grid (one per line row) in order to produce a Magic 65, in which each line convention totals 65.

74

16	15	14	13
12	11	10	9
8	7	6	5
4	3	2	1

From the numbers within the grid aim to swap the position of four pairs of numbers to produce a Magic 34, where each of the line conventions total 34, as well as the four corner squares, each block of four squares as well as the block of four central numbers.

75

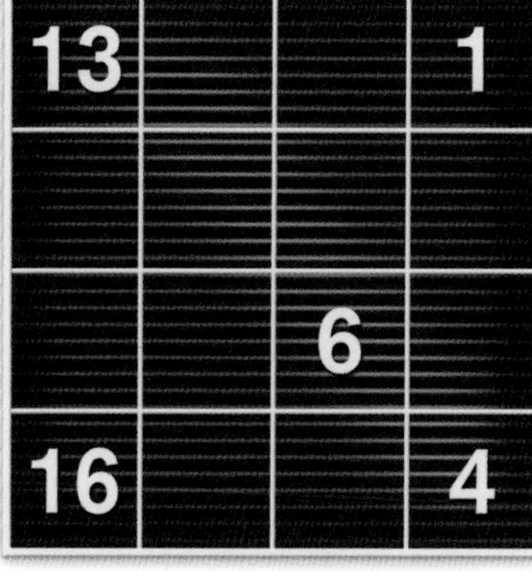

13			1
		6	
16			4

Insert the numbers from 2–15, once only, to produce a Magic 34. The aim is to make each line convention total 34, as well as the four corner squares, (these numbers have been inserted into the grid) each block of four corner squares and the block of four central numbers. Trial and error will get you there while patience will assist you.

76

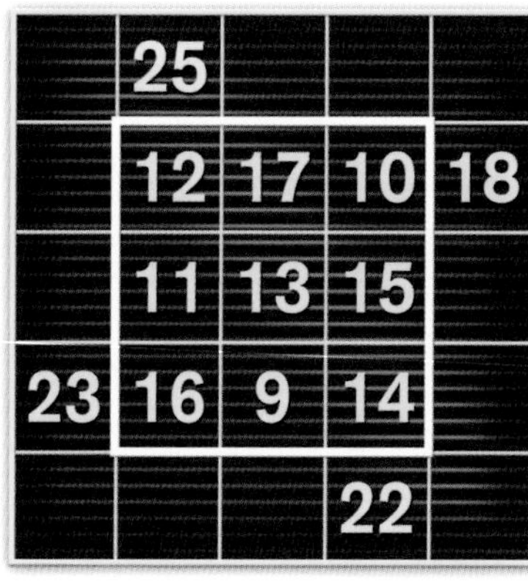

	25			
	12	17	10	18
	11	13	15	
23	16	9	14	
			22	

Insert the remaining numbers from 1–24, to complete a double magic square. The key placement of the numbers will mean that the 5 x 5 square is a Magic 65, and the inner 3 x 3 core square – in which all numbers have already been placed – is a Magic 39.

77

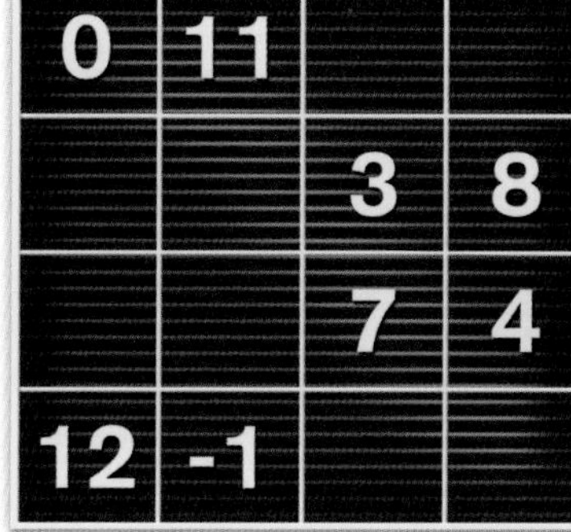

0	11		
		3	8
		7	4
12	-1		

Insert the following numbers in order to complete a Magic 18, where each row, column and corner-to-corner line totals 18: –3, –2, 1, 2, 5, 6, 9, 10.

78

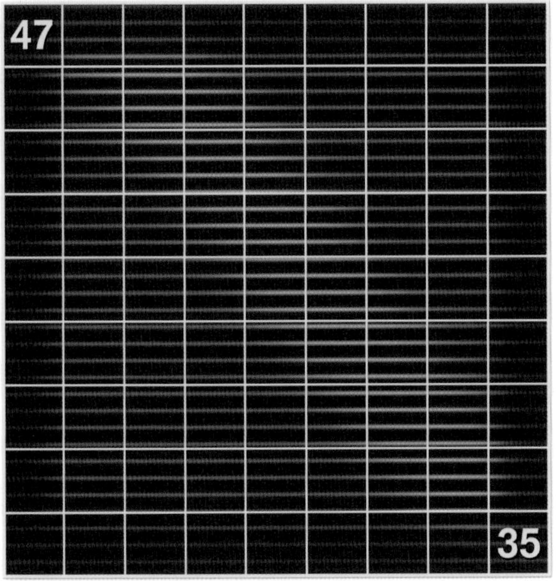

Insert the blocks into the grid to form a Magic 369, whereby each row column and corner-to-corner diagonal total 369.

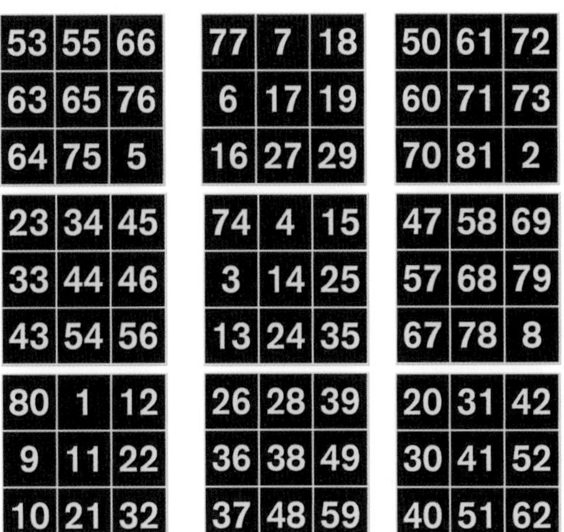

53 55 66
63 65 76
64 75 5
77 7 18
6 17 19
16 27 29
50 61 72
60 71 73
70 81 2
23 34 45
33 44 46
43 54 56
74 4 15
3 14 25
13 24 35
47 58 69
57 68 79
67 78 8
80 1 12
9 11 22
10 21 32
26 28 39
36 38 49
37 48 59
20 31 42
30 41 52
40 51 62

The magic square below left is a classic version where all lines add up to 15. The version on the right replaces the 9 with an 8, solve this making all lines add up to 15.

4	9	2
3	5	7
8	1	6

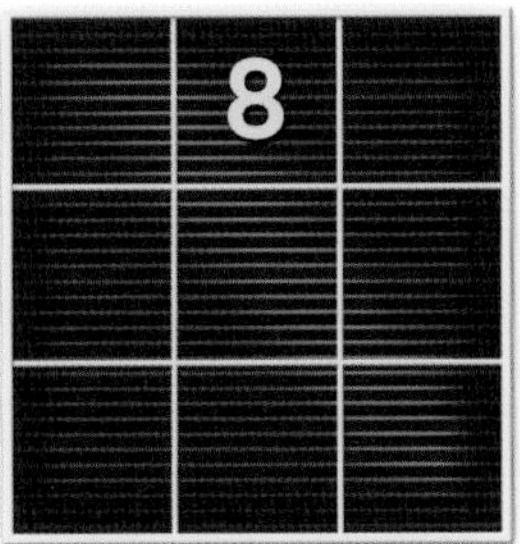

Insert the following numbers in order to complete a Magic Zero, whereby each row, column and corner-to-corner lines totals Zero: –1, –3, –5, –7, 2, 4, 6, 8.

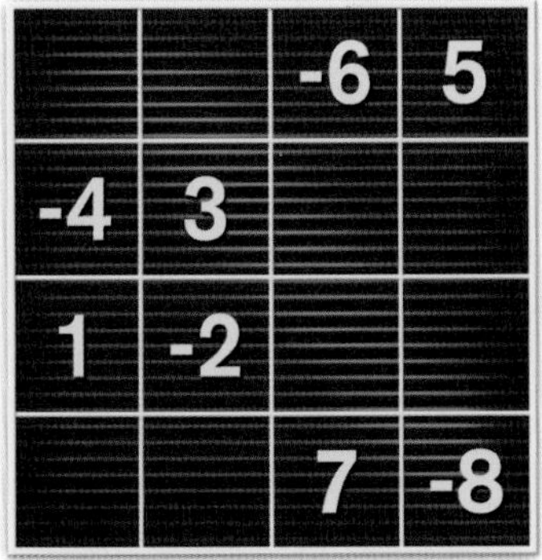

Fit all the pieces into the grid to form a Magic 111 whereby each row, column and corner-to-corner line total 111.

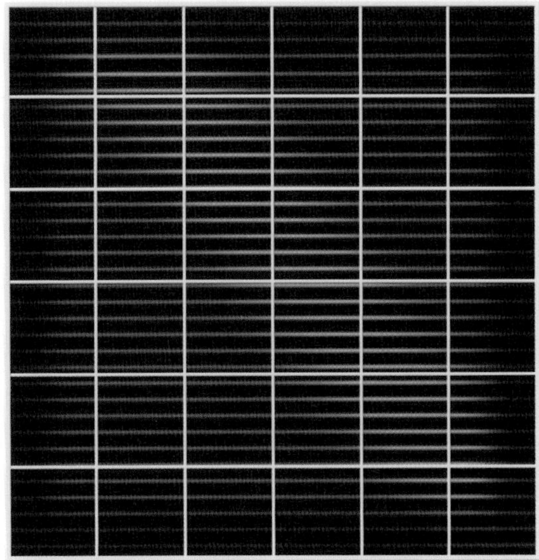

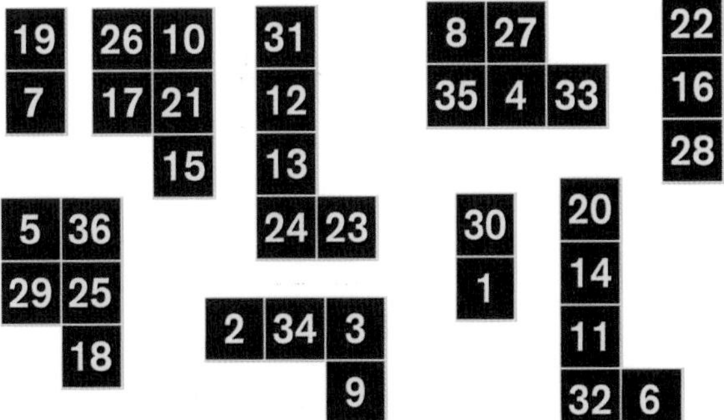

THINK OF A NUMBER

SYMBOLIC SUMS

These puzzles use a grid format often used in word puzzles. Instead of creating words, you have to find the numbers represented by the various symbols.

Suits you 1

The symbols ♦, ♥ and ♣ each represent a number from 1 to 9. If you add up the rows of three, horizontally, vertically or diagonally, you get the totals shown outside the square. What are the values of the symbols?

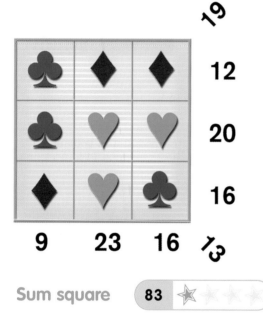

Sum square

Each of the three symbols in the square stands for a single-digit number. Beside and beneath them are the totals you get if you add the three in a row or column. Can you use this to work out the answer to this sum:

● + ▲ = ?

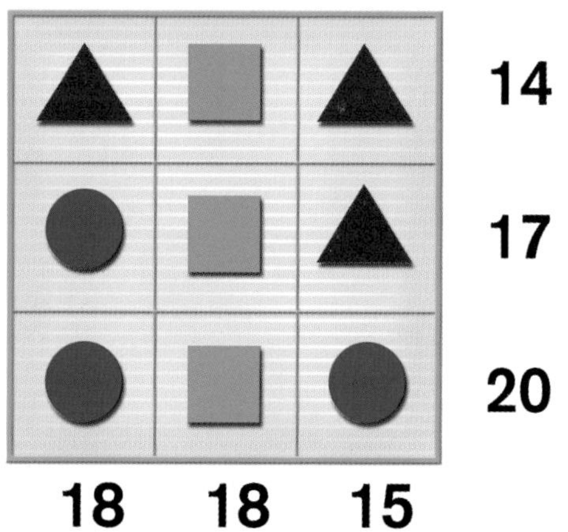

Add 'em up

Find the three single-digit numbers replaced by the symbols ✔, ✖ and ✪. When you add up rows of three, horizontally, vertically or diagonally, you get the totals shown outside the grid. Use this to find what the symbols represent, then do this sum:

✖ + ✖ + ✔ = ?

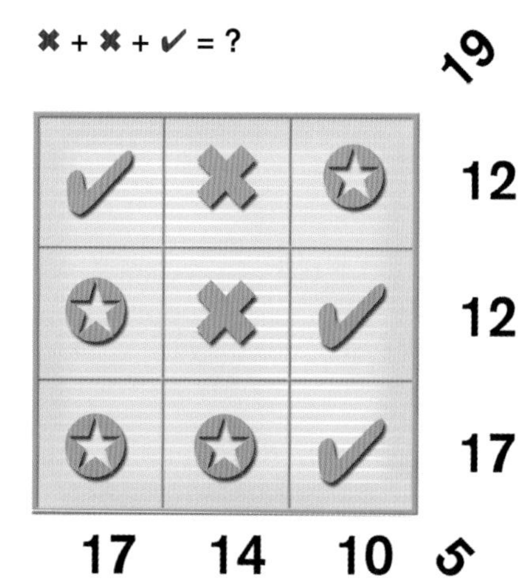

Shapely sums

The four shapes take the place of four different numbers between 1 and 9. Add up the numbers in each row and column to get the totals shown. Use the numerical values of all the shapes to complete this sum:

✚ + □ + ○ = ?

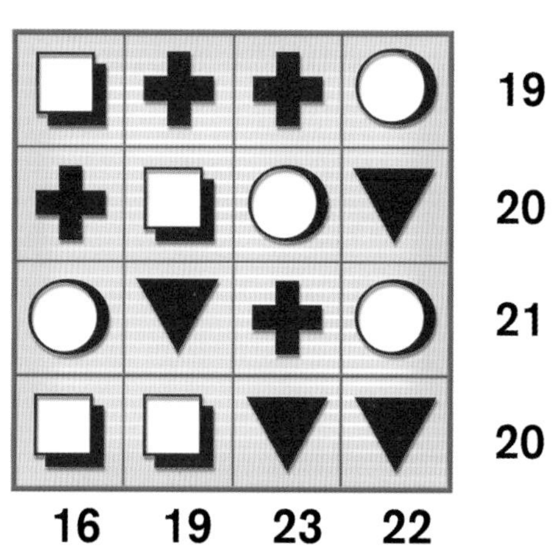

Suits you 2

86

The four playing card symbols each replace a different single-figure number. If you add up the numbers in each row and each column, you get the totals shown. Use the information given to work out the answer to this sum:

♥ + ♣ + ♦ = ?

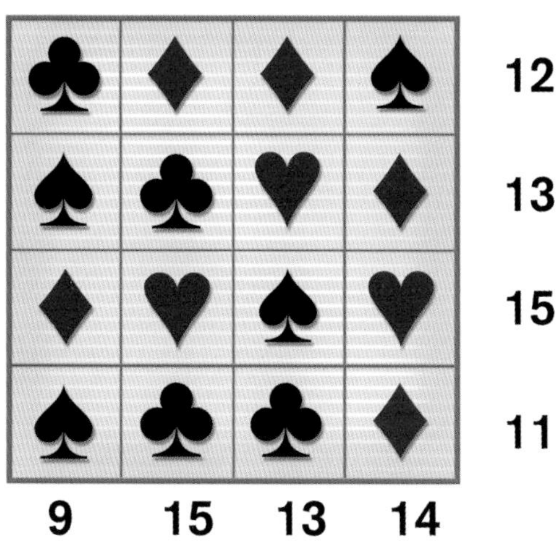

All Greek

Each of the three Greek letters in the square symbolize a number between 1 and 9. Around the grid are the totals you get by adding the four numbers in each row and column. Use this information to work out the values of each letter, then do this addition sum:

$\Sigma + \Delta + \Phi = ?$

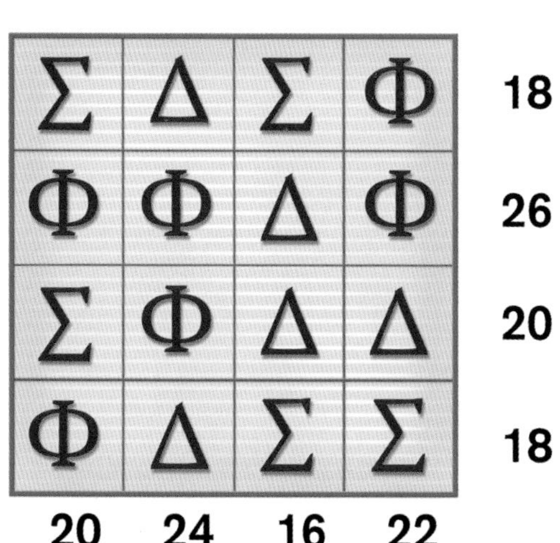

Letter adding

88

The five vowels are each a substitute for a different single-digit number. Add up the numbers in each row, column and diagonal and you get the totals printed alongside the grid. Work out what the vowels are worth numerically, then find the answer to this sum:

A + E + O + U = ?

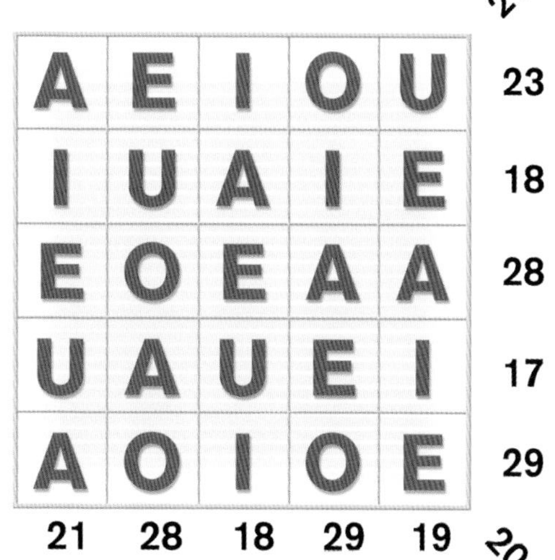

Tantalizing totals

Each of these symbols represents a single-digit number. If you add up the rows, the columns and the diagonals, you'll get the totals printed around the grid. Use these to deduce what each symbol is worth, then solve this addition sum:

♦ + ▲ + ● = ?

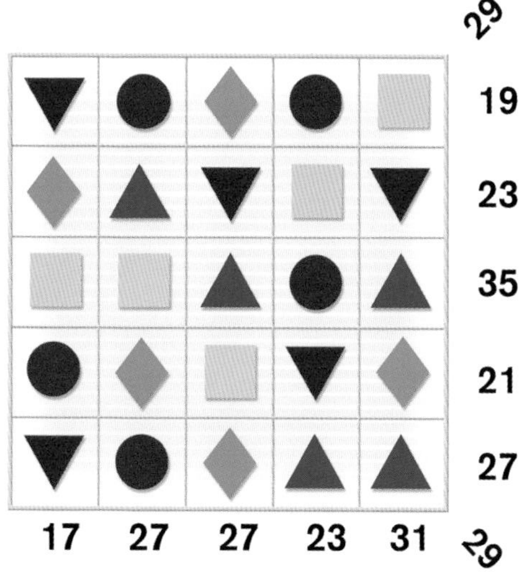

LATERAL THINKING NUMBER PUZZLES

Lateral thinking is a method of solving a problem by looking at it from many angles instead of trying to find an immediate solution. You will need to think 'outside the box' and develop creative approaches to problem-solving. Lateral thinking seeks to change our natural and traditional perceptions, concepts and ideas and increases our ability to tackle problems that would otherwise elude us.

Is it possible to arrange the digits below to form a three-figure number that will not divide by nine without remainder?

Complete the bottom set of numbers.

12	1112	3112
223	2213	221113
23		

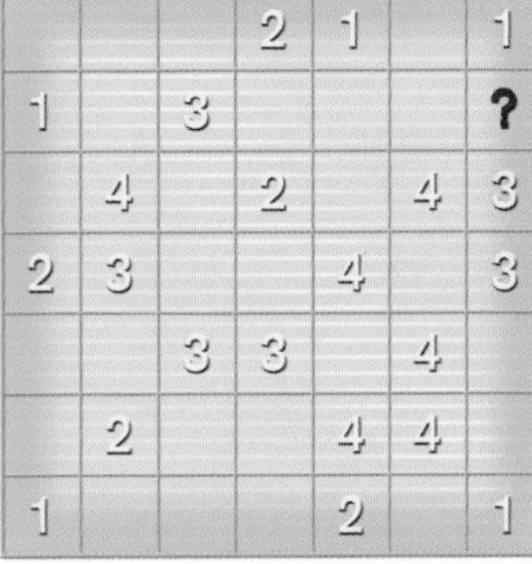

			2	1		1
1		3				?
	4		2		4	3
2	3			4		3
		3	3		4	
	2			4	4	
1				2		1

What number should replace the question mark here?

93

In my fish tank I have 18 measle fish. The male fish have 81 spots each and the female fish have 27 spots each.

If I transfer two thirds of the male measle fish to another tank, how many spots do the fish that now remain in the original tank have between them?

94

What numbers should replace the question marks?

4	23	8
7	41	2
9	27	8
3	51	5
8	?	6
3	72	?

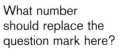

95

1	2	3	4
5	8	13	20
6	19	40	73
7	32	91	?

What number should replace the question mark here?

MISCELLANEOUS NUMBER PUZZLES

Test your mathematical and logical skills with this collection of intriguing and challenging number puzzles. Work through the levels to steadily improve your skills.

Test match

If a test score goes up 15% from x to 69, what was the previous score?

Railway trip

Between 50 and 100 people found a private carriage for a railway trip. They paid $2847. Each person paid the same amount, which was an exact amount in dollars.

How many people went on the trip?

Scales

Why do the scales not balance?

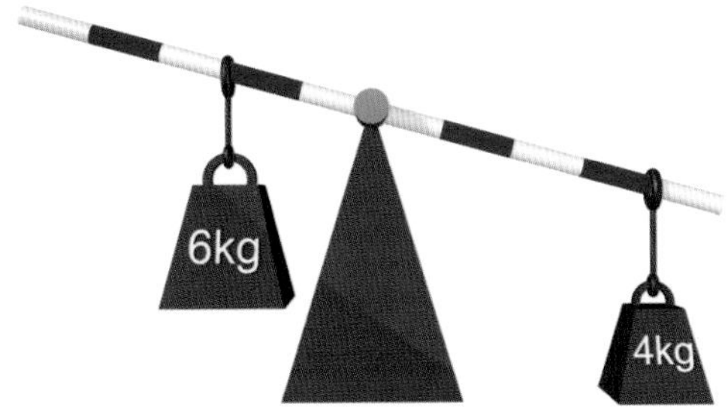

Numbers

Which number when added to 116 and 164 makes both of them square numbers?

Ages

The combined ages of Joan, Barbara and Matilda are as follows:
Joan and Barbara = 76
Joan and Matilda = 96
Barbara and Matilda = 140

How old are Joan, Barbara and Matilda?

Apples

A fruit grower has picked 667 apples from the trees in his orchard. He is packing these into sacks and wants to put an equal number into each sack using as few sacks as possible. How many sacks would he use?

Field

Man A can mow a field in 2 hours
Man B can mow the same field in 3 hours
Man C can mow the same field in 4 hours
Man D can mow the same field in 5 hours

If they worked together at their respective rates how long would it take to mow the entire field?

NUMERICAL MATRIX PUZZLES

Here, a matrix of numbers is displayed with one section missing. You have four different choices. Look across each line, down each column and at the matrix as a whole to find the number pattern in each puzzle and then match the correct missing section.

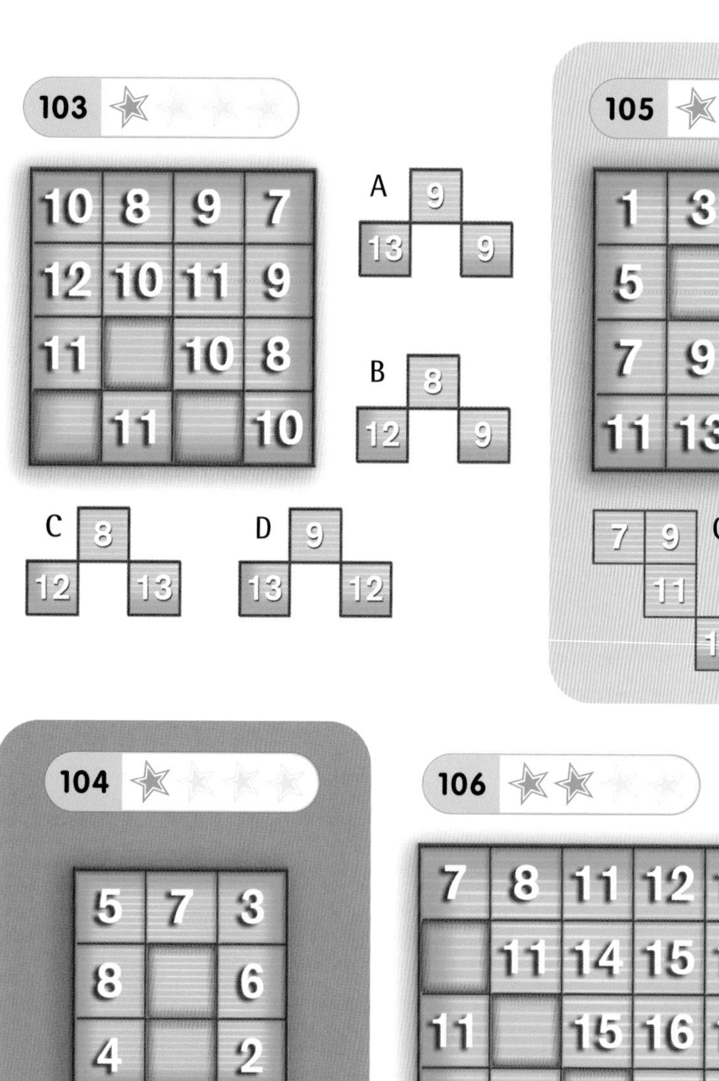

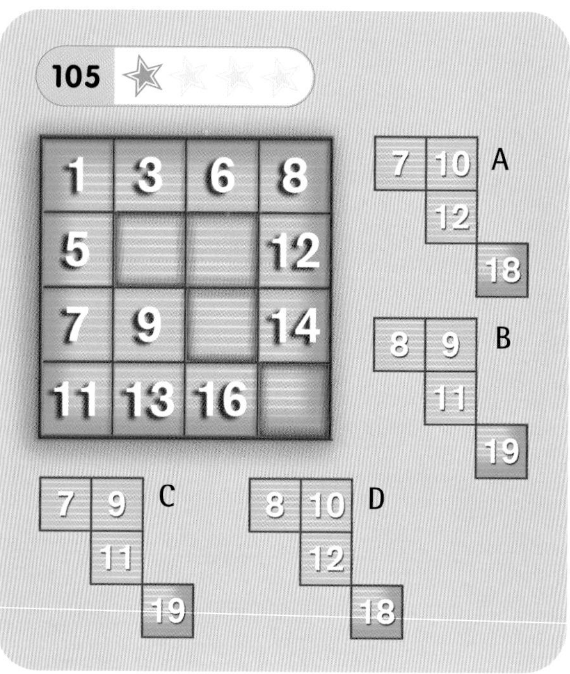

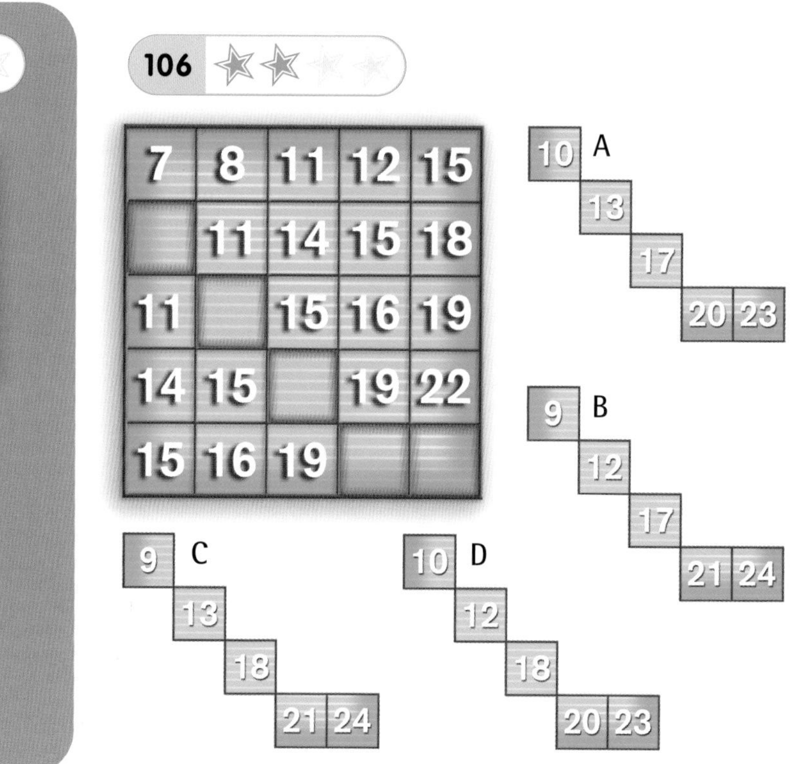

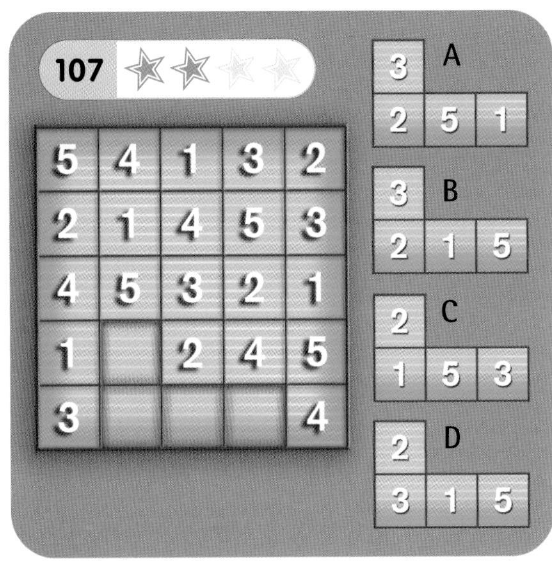
107

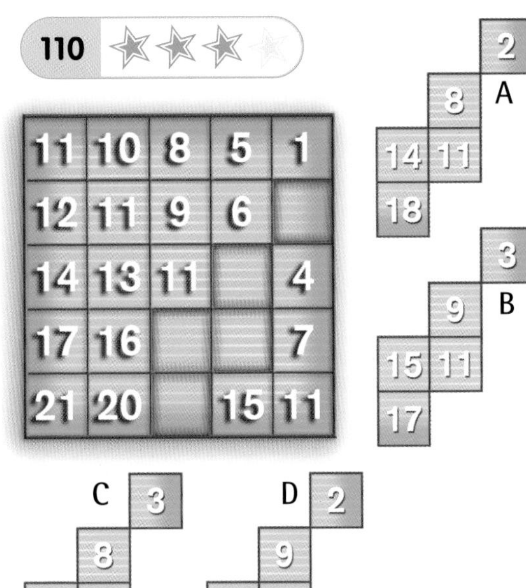
110

108

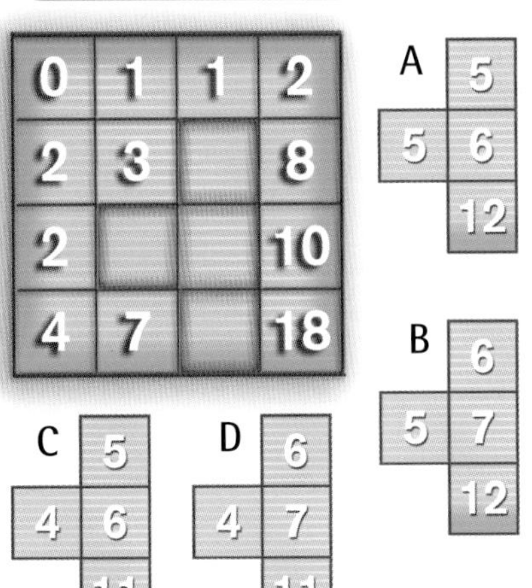

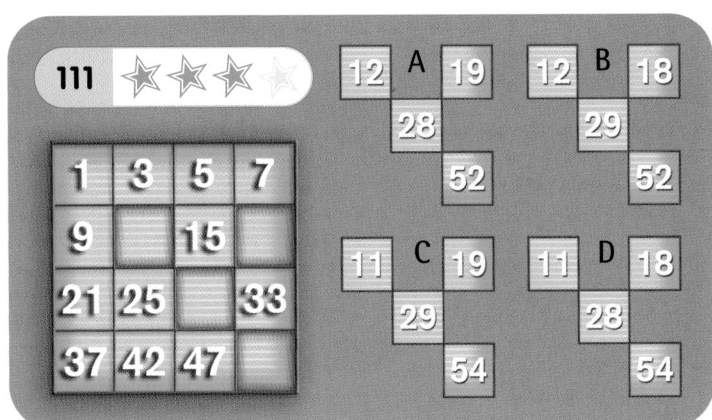
111

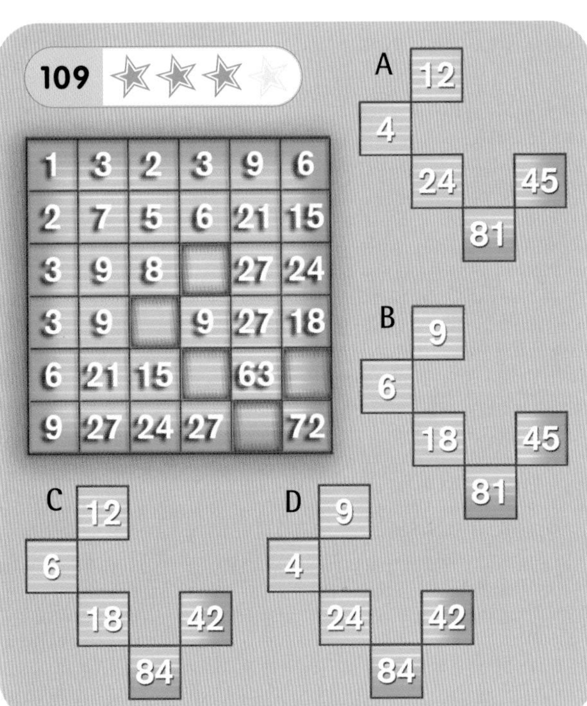
109

112

MISCELLANEOUS MATH PUZZLES

Challenge the mathematical part of your brain with these number-based problems that will test your powers of reasoning and probability. All you will need to solve these puzzles is a pen and paper, patience and a logical brain.

Store

At my local store they are offering a 5%discount for cash payment, 10% for long-standing customers and 20% during sale time.

To save the most money, in which order should I take the discounts?

Visitors

Three visitors to London walked into a pub for a drink and a meal but found the pub only had bags of chips to eat. The first visitor ate 1/3 of the total number of bags, the second visitor ate 1/3 of those left and the third visitor ate 1/3 of the remainder. This meant there were eight bags of chips remaining. How many bags of chips did the pub have at the start?

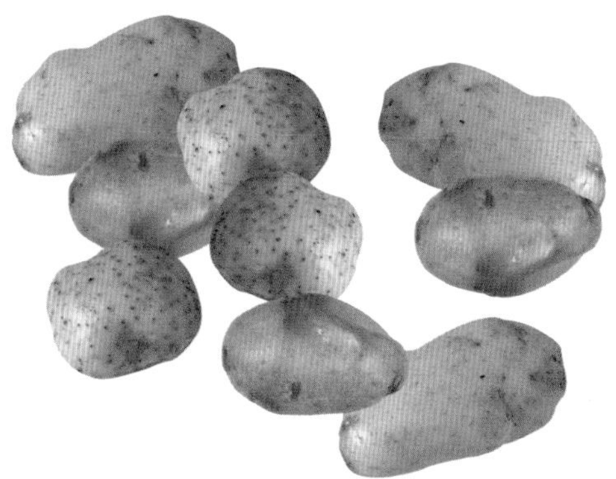

Grandad

A man who is aged between 50 and 70, and has a very large number of grandsons, said, 'Each of my sons has as many sons as brothers, and the combined number of my sons and grandsons is exactly the same as my age'. How old is the man, and how many grandsons does he have?

Lucky Andy

Andy won $300.00 playing the slot machines at Las Vegas, which meant he ended up with five times more money than if he had lost $300.00.

How much money did Andy have before he won the $300.00?

Hockey

Cristobal and David each want to be the top goalie on their hockey team. After one game played, Cristobal has a Save Percentage of .882, having allowed 4 goals on 37 shots against him. David is off to a better start. After two games, he's allowed only 3 goals on 66 shots.

What is David's Save Percentage?

Snooker

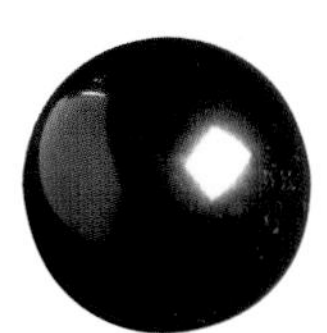

There are ten snooker balls in a bag – five black and five red.

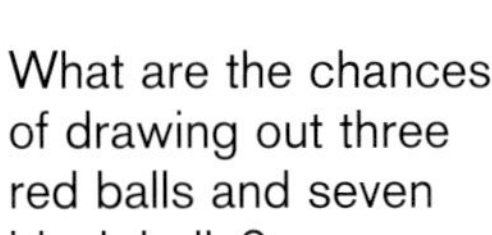

What are the chances of drawing out three red balls and seven black balls?

Stamps

I asked my son how many stamps he had. He replied 'The number, if divided by two, will give you a remainder of one. Divided by three will give you a remainder of two. Divided by four will give you a remainder of three. Divided by five a remainder of four, divided by six a remainder of five, by seven a remainder of six, by eight a remainder of seven, by nine a remainder of eight and by ten a remainder of nine.'

How many stamps did the boy have?

Lottery

The lottery uses the numbers 1-20. To win you must choose the same six numbers as picked at random by the lottery machine. How many different combinations of six winning numbers are possible?

lottery

Fence posts

Using his stock of fence posts, a farmer found that he could make a simple square enclosure, or two adjoining squares of equal size, or three adjoining squares of equal size. The distance between the posts had to be the same in every case.

What was the lowest number of posts he could use?

Aliens

We have been visited by aliens.

Some have four eyes
Some have six eyes
Some have eight eyes
Some have twelve eyes

There is an equal number of each type of alien.

The total number of eyes in the room is 5,120.

How many aliens are there?

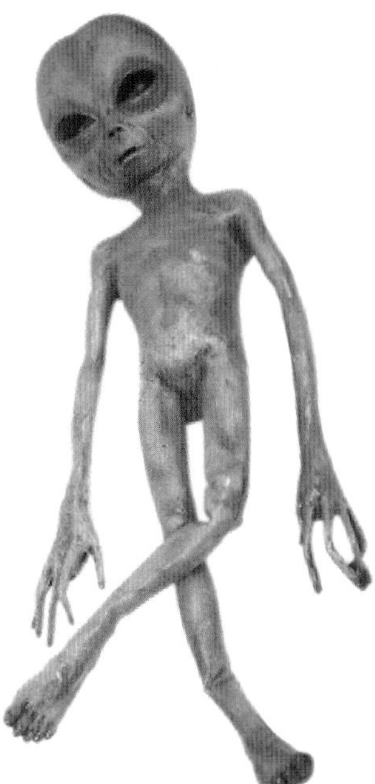

GRIDS AND SQUARES

These number puzzles test your skill with numbers. To complete each grid you will need to use the usual rules of arithmetic. In some cases you will have to add in + (plus), so – goes with (minus) and x (multiplication) signs; in more challenging calculations, you will have to deduce which numbers go where to complete the sums.

123

Each calculation contains a +, – and x. The number in each blue square is the sum of the four numbers at its corners. Can you complete the grid by adding in the appropriate math symbols to satisfy the sums?

2		5		3		6	=	15
	12		15		18			
4							=	7
	21		24		27			
12							=	40
–	30	+	33	+	36	–		
2							=	140
=		=		=		=		
18		28		9		31		

124

Each calculation uses the +, – and x signs. The number in each blue square is the sum of the four numbers at its corners. Finish the grid by adding in the relevant math symbols to complete the sums.

2		4		6		5	=	31
	10		18		30			
1							=	12
	20		36		50			
9							=	52
	30		48		70			
6							=	141
=		=		=		=		
60		11		219		27		

125

Again every row and column has a +, – and x. Totals for each line, across and down, are different numbers from 21 to 31 inclusive. Fill in all the missing numbers and signs.

5			x	2		6	=	22
–						x		
4	x			20	–		=	
+		x						
		3	–		+	9	=	
						+		
3		9		16		10	=	
=		=		=		=		
24				29				

126

Every row and column has to have +, – and x signs. The total for each line across and down is a different number from 11 to 20 inclusive. Work out which numbers and signs are missing.

5				21		2	=	
		–		+				
	x	17			–	21	=	16
+						–		
	x	3		20			=	
x		+				x		
3	+		x	5	–	3	=	
=		=		=		=		
						15		

127 ★★★

Can you find the value of each letter A, B, C, D, E to make the sums correct?

12	x	A	–	32	+	A	=	33
–		+		–		+		
B	+	C	x	D	–	A	=	58
+		–		x		–		
C	–	2	+	C	x	E	=	28
x		x		+		x		
B	x	11	–	D	+	E	=	42
=		=		=		=		
44		66		78		21		

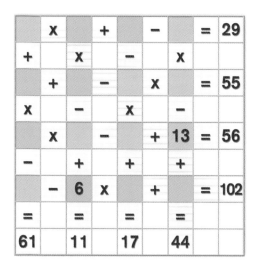

Playing with the sums on a piece of paper helps to get to the solution and brushes up your arithmetic as you go.

128 ★★★

Work out the values of A, B, C, D, E that will complete these sums.

23	–	A	+	B	x	C	=	75
+		–		+		x		
D	+	12	–	C	x	4	=	60
–		x		x		–		
17	x	B	+	D	–	A	=	96
x		+		–		+		
C	x	E	+	A	–	21	=	48
=		=		=		=		
70		23		74		27		

129 ★★★★

The numbers 1 to 16 are to be placed, one each, in the coloured squares. Blue squares contain odd numbers and green squares even numbers. Can you make the sums add up correctly?

	+		–	8	x		=	48
–		x		+		x		
	–		x		+		=	32
+		+		–		+		
11	x		–		+		=	14
x		–		x		–		
	x		–		+		=	18
=		=		=		=		
19		26		10		31		

130 ★★★★

Apply the same rules to this puzzle as those used in the grid above. Again, blue squares contain odd numbers and green squares even numbers.

	x		+		–		=	29
+		x		–		x		
	+		–		x		=	55
x		–		x		–		
	x		–		+	13	=	56
–		+		+		+		
	–	6	x		+		=	102
=		=		=		=		
61		11		17		44		

THINK OF A NUMBER

NUMBER MAZES

Solving these mazes requires a combination of logical thought and skill with numbers. Each puzzle tests different ways of dealing with numbers, but all of them require you to navigate from the entrance to the exit of the grid to complete the puzzle. All these mazes will help improve your facility with numbers.

131

Starting at the top, navigate through the maze, always moving the number of squares shown in the box in a straight line, across or down. Can you reach the bottom right hand corner?

↓					
3	1	4	1	5	1
1	1	1	3	3	5
4	1	3	4	1	2
3	2	5	4	1	2
3	3	2	3	3	5
3	2	5	5	4	0
					↓

Remember, you may need to move backwards to find the solution.

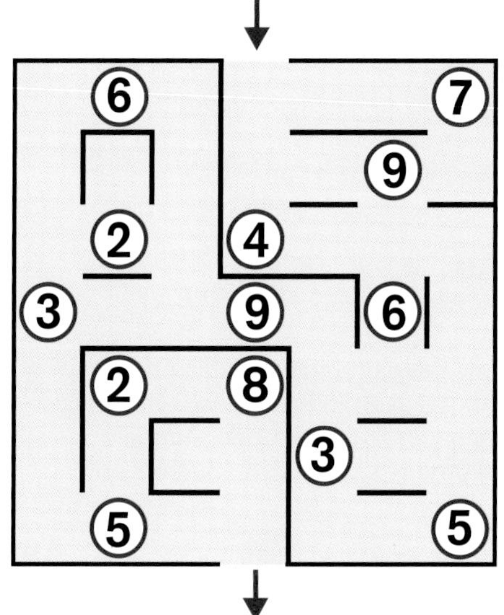

132

Starting at the top arrow, find a route through the maze, picking up points in the circles as you go. Can you get to the exit at the bottom without going back on yourself and, in the process, pick up exactly 58 points?

133

Starting from the 1 at the top of the puzzle, move through the maze, always moving the number of squares shown in the box, across or down only. Can you reach the red star?

				1				
2	4	2	9	7	2	4	4	2
8	5	1	2	3	2	5	6	1
2	9	2	4	3	3	1	4	6
8	6	9	2	6	2	2	1	2
3	1	1	2	5	3	2	7	3
4	4	1	2	2	2	2	1	2
1	5	7	4	4	9	5	4	4
8	7	1	2	3	3	9	4	3
7	4	5	2	6	7	1	4	2
				✸				

PERCENTAGE PUZZLES

These puzzles are based on the rules of arithmetic that involve percentage calculations. Use your mathematical brain to solve the problems given, trying your best to do so using just a paper and pencil, rather than with the aid of a calculator. You will find it much more satisfying when you get the right answers doing your sums the old-fashioned way.

134

The owner of a store raises his prices by 10 per cent on Monday and lowers them by 10 per cent on Tuesday. Before the price shuffle, notebooks cost one dollar. How much do they cost afterwards?

135

A Rolls-Royce Canardly depreciates by 10 per cent per year. This year it is for the first time worth less than half of what it cost. When was it bought?

136

The owner of a corner store bought some stock and priced it so that if it sold it would make him 20 per cent profit. However it wasn't selling, so after a month he put up a sign saying, '10% off.' What was his new profit margin?

137

Kevin has managed to average 85 per cent over the first four papers of his examination in Unclear Physics. Given that there is only one paper to go, what is the highest overall percentage he can get in this vague subject?

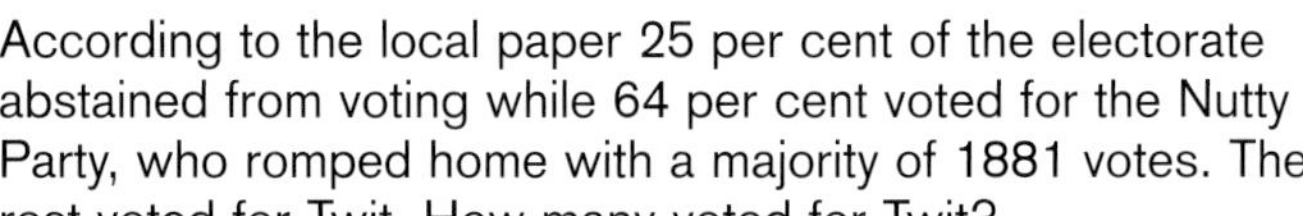

138

According to the local paper 25 per cent of the electorate abstained from voting while 64 per cent voted for the Nutty Party, who romped home with a majority of 1881 votes. The rest voted for Twit. How many voted for Twit?

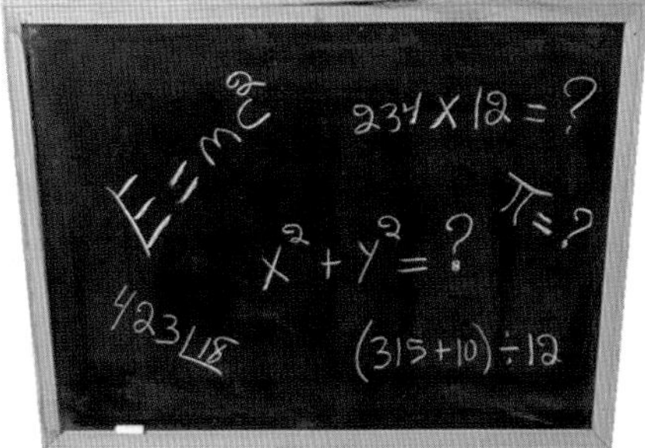

PROBABILITY PUZZLES

Probability is the branch of math that calculates the odds of chance, and it is used to determine the likelihood of an event whose occurrence is governed by a random phenomenon. Test your ability to cope with the rules of probability with these puzzles, which are also a real test of your numerical agility.

EXAMPLE:

A chandelier contains five bulbs. Two bulbs blow at random. What are the chances that they are next to each other?

ANSWER

Consider one of the blown bulbs. There are two bulbs adjacent to it, and two bulbs not adjacent to it. So the chances are 50:50.

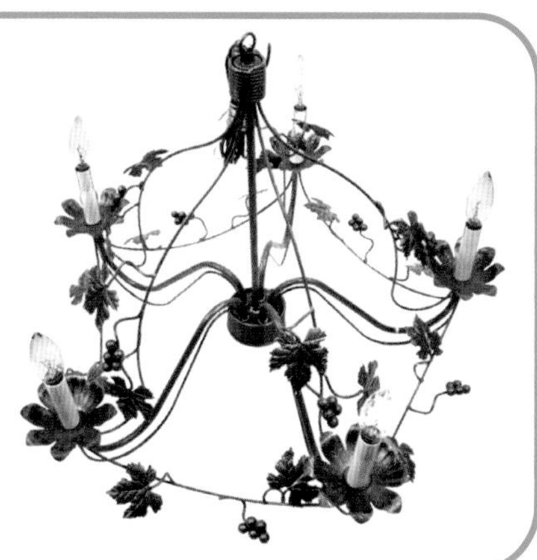

139

You are dealt the top 26 cards of a well-shuffled deck of 52 cards. Are you more likely to have all the hearts or none of them?

A dice has four white faces while the remaining two are black. Which of the following two outcomes of six successive throws is the more likely?

B W W W W W

or:

B W W W W B

141

Buses from Chilton to Milton go at 10 minutes past the hour and 25 minutes past the hour. You arrive at the bus stop at random and catch the first bus that comes along. How many times more likely are you to catch the 10-past than the 25-past?

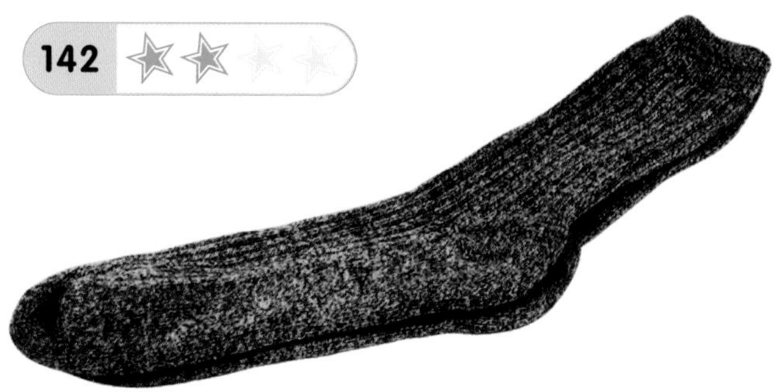

There are 12 socks in a drawer. Each sock is either white or black. The chances of withdrawing six socks at random and finding them to be all black is exactly 50:50. What are the colours of the remaining socks?

You and a friend take it in turns to toss a fair coin as many times as it takes to get two successive tails (you win) or a head followed by a tail (your friend wins). Who has the better chance of winning?

You have been given life imprisonment by a wicked ruler. All, however, is not doom and gloom. Once a year you are allowed to take part in the ritual of the three caskets. In this ritual three boxes made of lead, gold and wood are placed in front of you.

Your jailer has placed the key to freedom in one of these three boxes at random, and only he knows which one it is in. He challenges you to nominate a box. You do so. He then opens one of the remaining boxes and shows you that it contains no key. You are then offered the opportunity to swap the box you have nominated for the remaining box. Should you stick to the box you have chosen? Or swap?

Assume that if you had the box with the key in it, the jailer would show you the contents of either remaining box chosen at random. If you did not have it, the jailer would deliberately choose the empty one to show you.

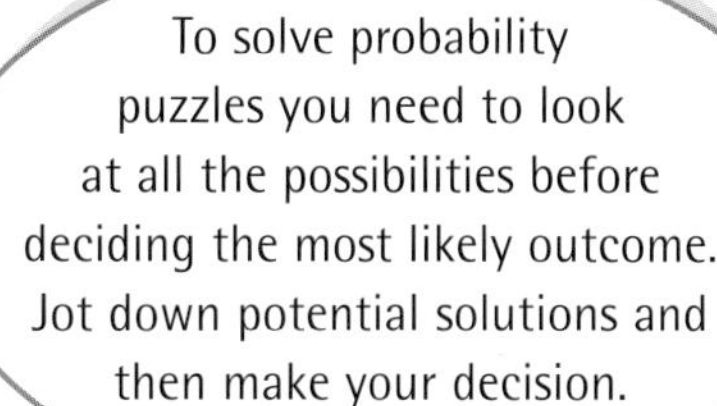

To solve probability puzzles you need to look at all the possibilities before deciding the most likely outcome. Jot down potential solutions and then make your decision.

145

A number with a hundred digits is divisible without remainder by 99. What are the chances that the number formed by reversing its digits will also be divisible without remainder by 99?

Tweedledum is 33.33 per cent likely to go to town if Tweedledee goes. Tweedledee is 50 per cent likely to go to town if Tweedledum goes. At least one of them must go. How likely is it that they both go?

The chances of seeing at least one shooting star in a given hour one night are 36 per cent. The trouble is, you have only half an hour to spare. What are the chances of seeing at least one shooting star in that time?

SUDOKU

These are sudoku puzzles but with a double challenge. They are solved in the same way as the normal grids, but in this instance you need to ensure that every row, every column and every 4 x 4 box contains the numbers 0 to 9 and the letters A to F. Hint: puzzles like this are actually more of a test of logic than numerical skill.

148 ★★★

					7		0			5		F	C	3	
	2	8				1	F				4		A		
	1	0	9				3	8		D	A				
		D	4		E	A					6	1	9	5	
				0		C			B	9	7		6		3
1			A		D		8	E	4					B	7
	5		C	4						2			1	9	
B	D	4			A			C	6						5
		C			4		B	0	2	E				8	F
				7	2		C	4			B	0	5		9
6		9		E		3		7			F	4	2		
	4	3	B	6					9	8			D	C	E
9			1						D	F		E		7	
E	6		F	2		B			5	4	C			D	1
7			D		0	F		A			E	5	4		
				C	6		E	1	7		2		8		

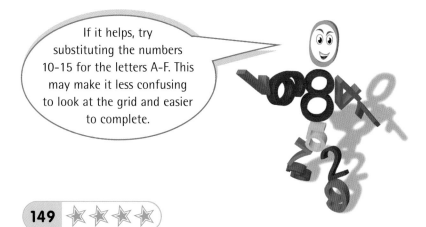

If it helps, try substituting the numbers 10-15 for the letters A-F. This may make it less confusing to look at the grid and easier to complete.

149

3	A	7		5					0				D	F	
E					D				C		A	1		8	
9				3	4	1	2				7		0		6
					F			8	3	B		9		4	7
2		3					E		D		F	B			8
	8	6	1				F	2			0		A		
		A						E		3	6	2	4	C	
		B		0	9		3							7	
			7		2	C		B	6		3				
8	D		0	7				1			2			5	A
			A			F					E	4	C		2
	2	C		D	1	3		0	A	5					
	5		6	1		7				D		8		2	4
4		F			6	8				A					B
A	9		D			4	B		2			C			
		2	3	C					4	0		7	9		

CONNECTIONS

These puzzles are designed to test your powers of concentration, logical analysis and mathematical prowess. To complete the connections, insert the numbers listed in the left-hand column into the circles so that – for any particular circle – the sum of the numbers in the other circles connected to it adds up to the value given in the right-hand column. See the example below for guidance.

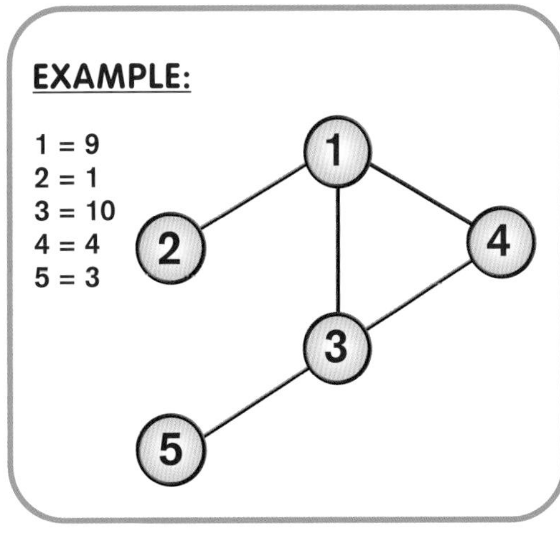

EXAMPLE:

1 = 9
2 = 1
3 = 10
4 = 4
5 = 3

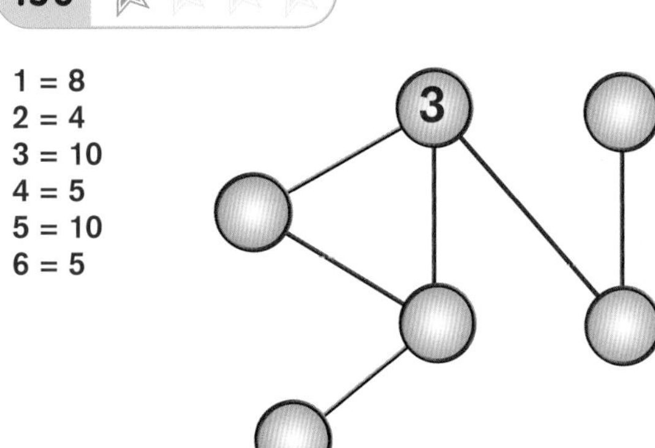

150

1 = 8
2 = 4
3 = 10
4 = 5
5 = 10
6 = 5

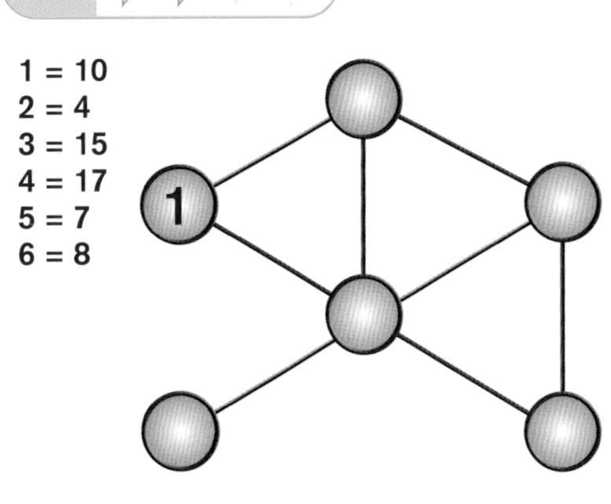

151

1 = 10
2 = 4
3 = 15
4 = 17
5 = 7
6 = 8

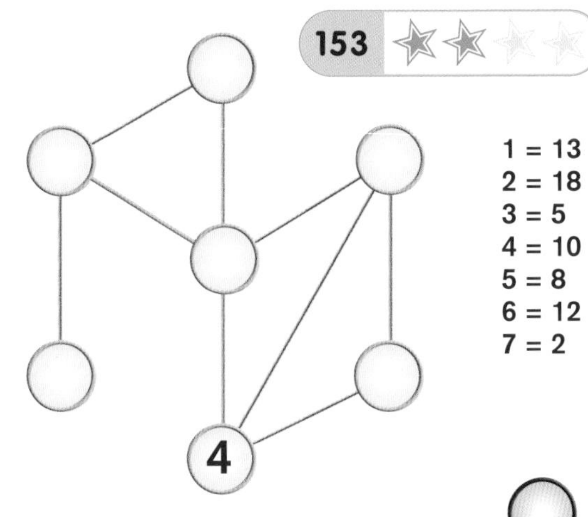

153

1 = 13
2 = 18
3 = 5
4 = 10
5 = 8
6 = 12
7 = 2

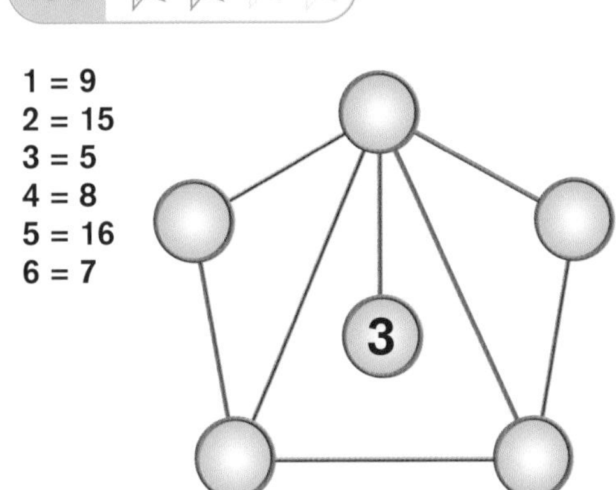

152

1 = 9
2 = 15
3 = 5
4 = 8
5 = 16
6 = 7

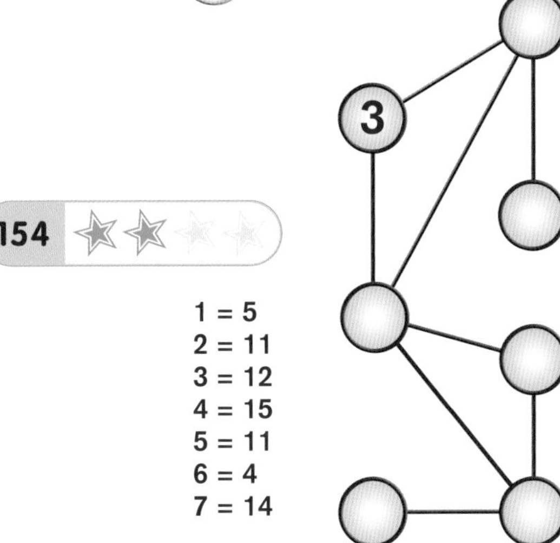

154

1 = 5
2 = 11
3 = 12
4 = 15
5 = 11
6 = 4
7 = 14

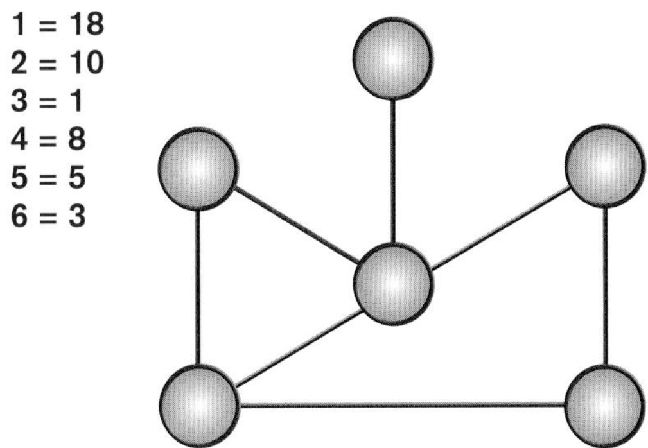

1 = 18
2 = 10
3 = 1
4 = 8
5 = 5
6 = 3

156

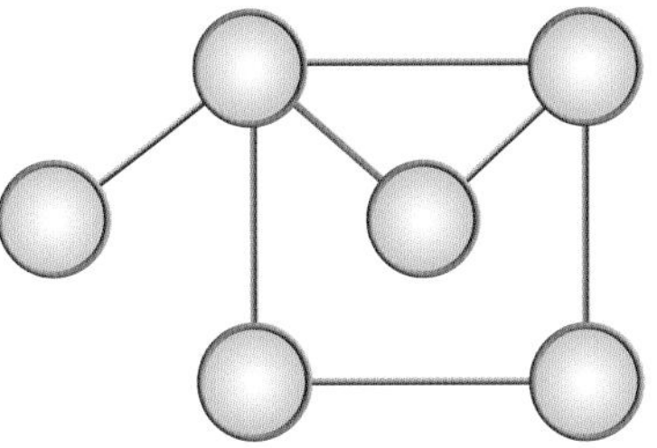

1 = 9
2 = 5
3 = 10
4 = 8
5 = 15
6 = 6

157

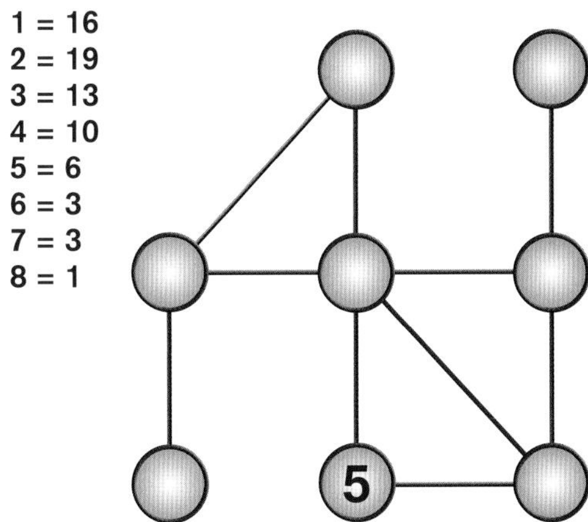

1 = 16
2 = 19
3 = 13
4 = 10
5 = 6
6 = 3
7 = 3
8 = 1

158

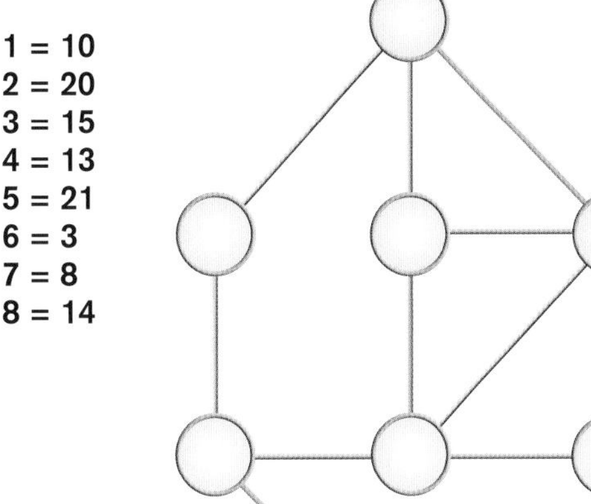

1 = 10
2 = 20
3 = 15
4 = 13
5 = 21
6 = 3
7 = 8
8 = 14

159

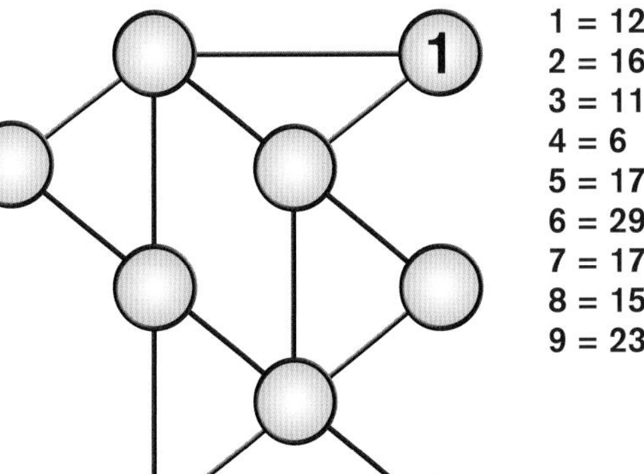

1 = 12
2 = 16
3 = 11
4 = 6
5 = 17
6 = 29
7 = 17
8 = 15
9 = 23

160

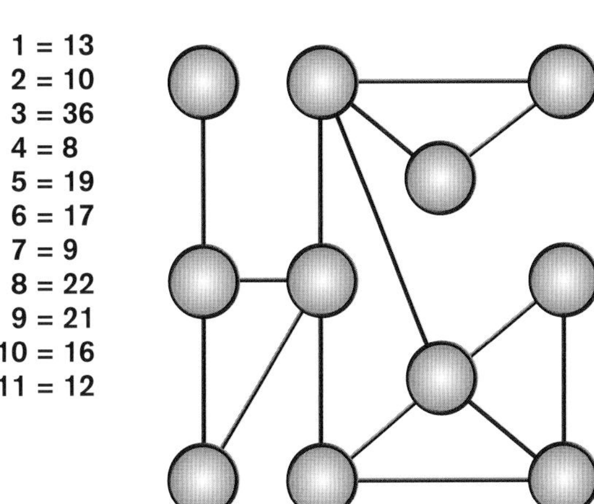

1 = 13
2 = 10
3 = 36
4 = 8
5 = 19
6 = 17
7 = 9
8 = 22
9 = 21
10 = 16
11 = 12

Start with the information you know for sure. Then use it to deduce the remaining solutions.

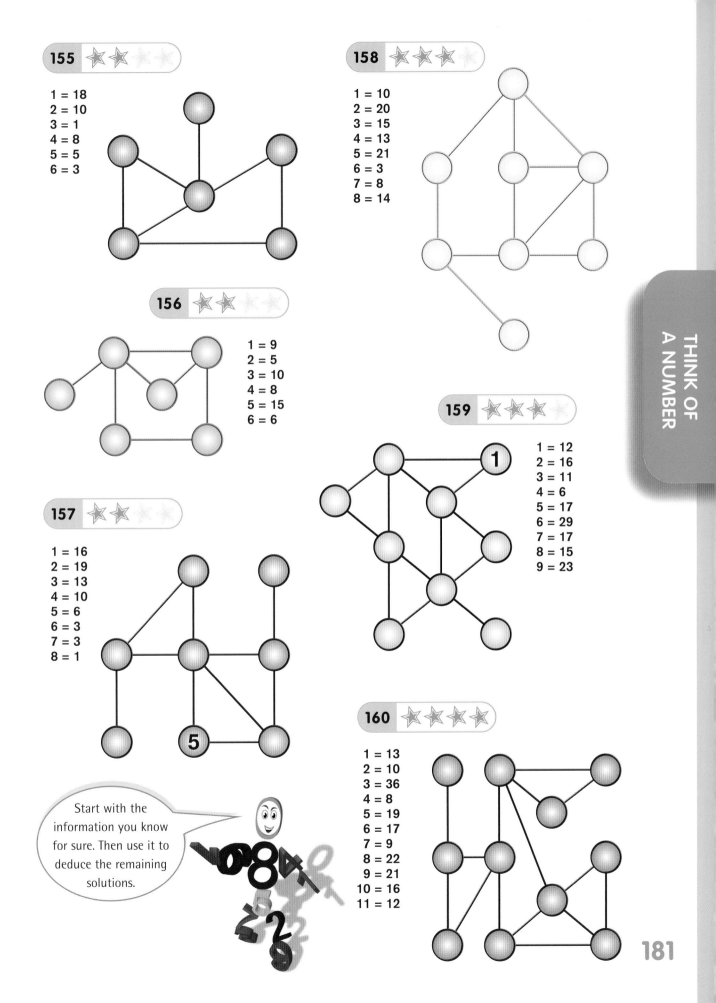

SAMURAI X SUDOKUS

Also known as 'Gettai-5' (five merged), these puzzles are a variation of the original Sudokus, but are much harder to tackle. The Samurai X Sudoku consists of four grids linked through another central one. Each grid must work individually and as part of the larger puzzle. As with simpler Sudokus, it should be possible to solve these number puzzles using logic alone.

Because filling in a number in one grid could give you clues to another, when working on an outer grid try to consider the numbers in the central grid at the same time.

161 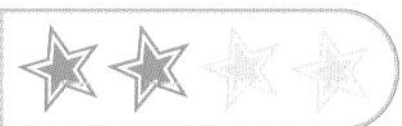

Fill in the grids with the numbers 1–9 so that every row, column and 3x3 box contains each number once only. Each grid should work independently of the other four, as well as part of the complete five-grid puzzle.

	1					7	2	5				1		5						
3					4										3	7				1
		2	1	9		3												5		
9				4									4				2		9	
5		4	7					9												5
								8						2	8	3		7		
8						5		2			6			9		5		2		4
							6		8		7									9
		3		6			7	1							7	4				
						1				3										
										4										
										6				7						
				9	8							9	4			7		2		
2									2		9		3							
1		7		2		6			1			8		2						9
		3		8	5	9						1								
6												5					3	9		7
	4		1				2									2				8
		9												6		3	5	8		
8				5	3										2					6
						3		1				2	5	4					3	

162

	1		8		4							3					4	1		
4				7		2	9									1	9			
	8	7		9	3										3	6		7	4	9
					5								1	4						
						3	4	9				9	2						3	
			4		2		5							5	9					
								7		3		8		1				4		
		3			7	9			1	2	7			3						2
			2								4	2						3		
								4		5			2	6						
						7	1	8	4	6	2	9	3	5						
						6	5			1		4								
		3						9	2								7			
5						2			8	4	5			9	8			7		
		7				5		1		9		7								
					2	9							7		4		2			
	3						2	5				2	9	6						
						7	8								5					
4	5	8		2	9										1	9		5	4	
			7	1									6	1		5				3
		2	5					8							7		8		1	

	8		4	3	7	9								4						
	1		9			3		8												6
			1	2								6	7	3	4					
			7					3								5		2		
	9							2							3			7	8	9
3				6		1														
				7					4	5							6			5
		8							3		1		2				5	8	1	
	6		3		2				6	2		3		7	1			6	9	
						3					8		7	4						
						1	6		7					5						
	2	3			7	6		1		9	2				5		8		9	
	5	7	2				4		1		6							6		
9			4							3	4					4				
														5		2				9
5	8	4			1							4							6	
		1		5								3					9			
					2	3	5	6								8	3			
7												6		4			1		2	
						4								8	2	5	4		7	

KAKURO

Kakuro puzzles are the numerical equivalents of crosswords, requiring you to complete a grid using numbers rather than words. The 'clues' appear in the black cells, either above or below a diagonal line; numbers in a top right corner are 'across' clues and those in a bottom left corner are 'down' clues. The aim is to insert digits from 1-9 in the blue cells to total the amount in the clue (see the example, right). No number can be repeated in any one entry, either across or down.

EXAMPLE:

164

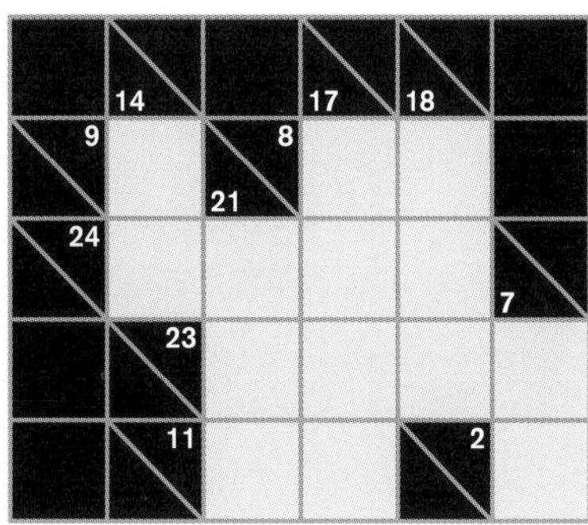

Start by solving the clues that have the fewest possible permutations; those with one, two or three squares for their answers.

165

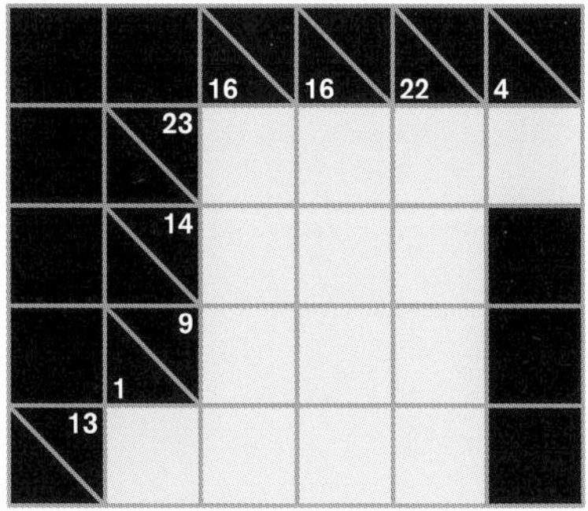

167

166

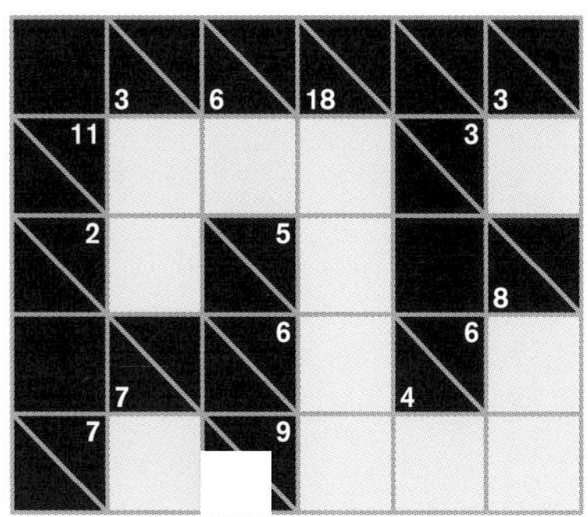

168

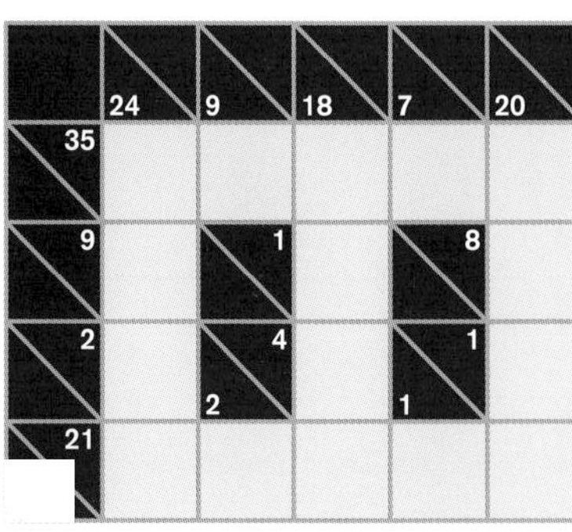

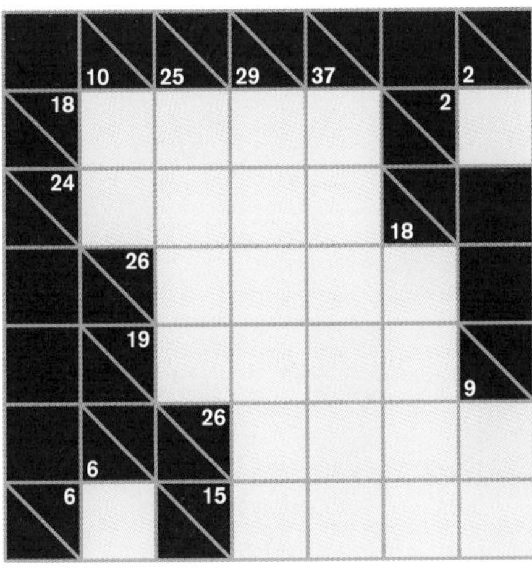

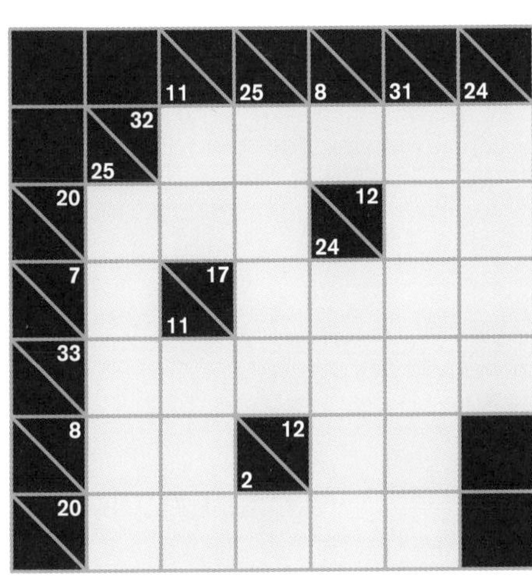

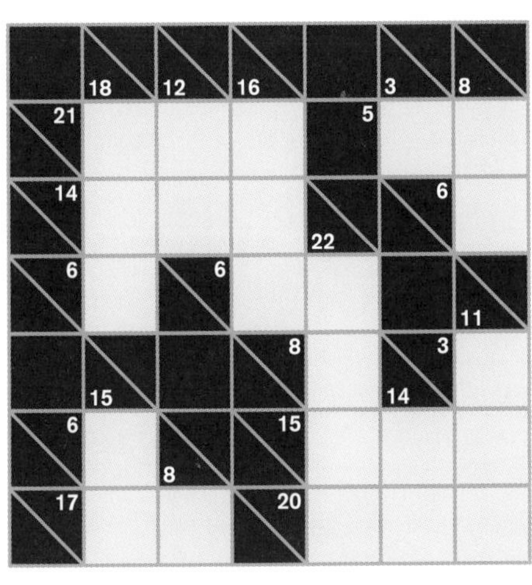

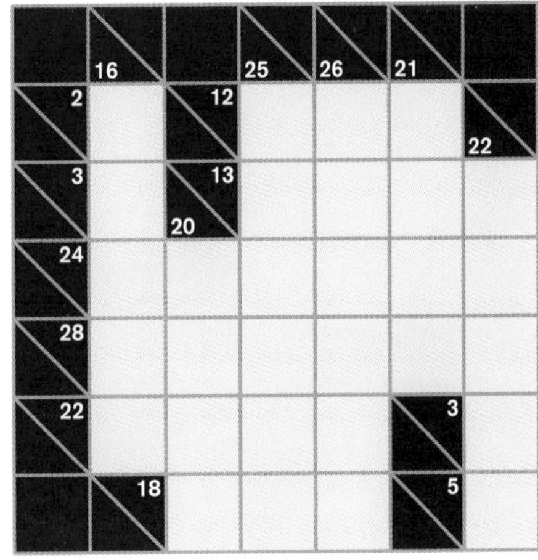

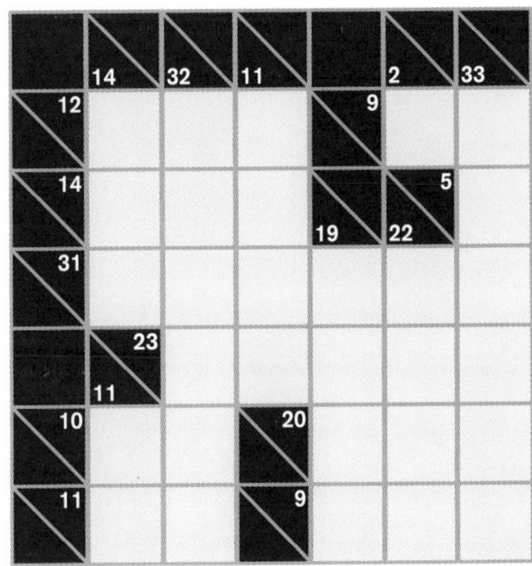

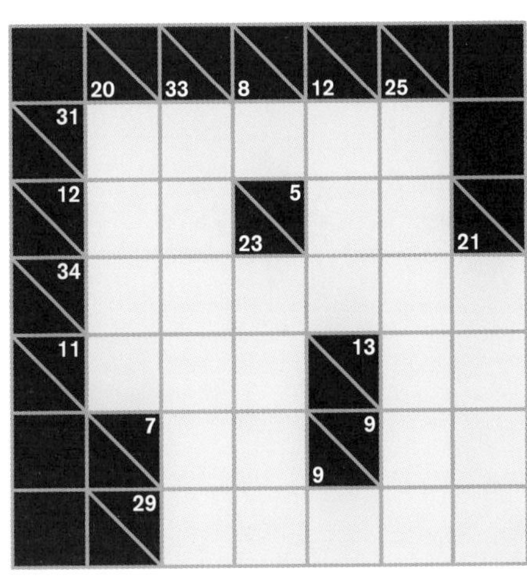

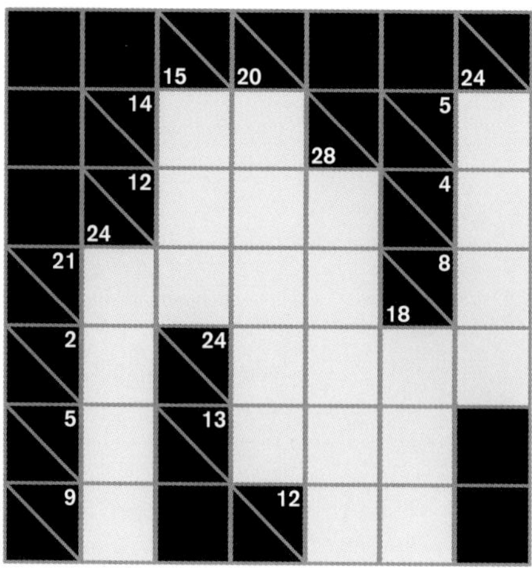

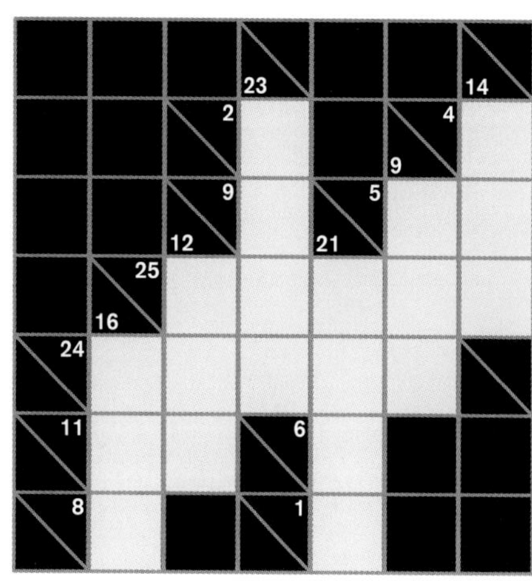

179

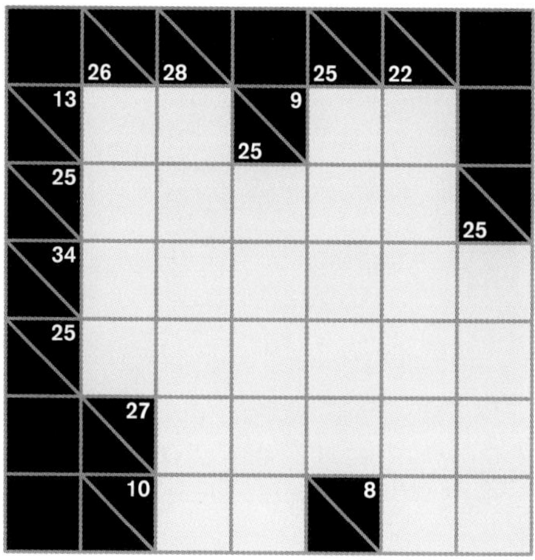

177

180

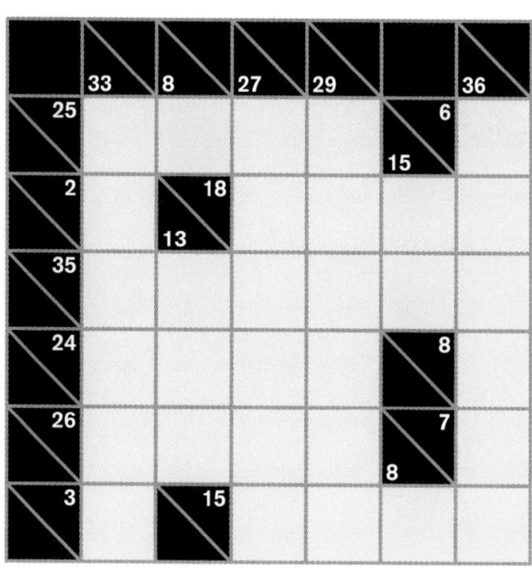

Mark potential values for the squares in the corners of the boxes so you can clearly see all possibilities.

181

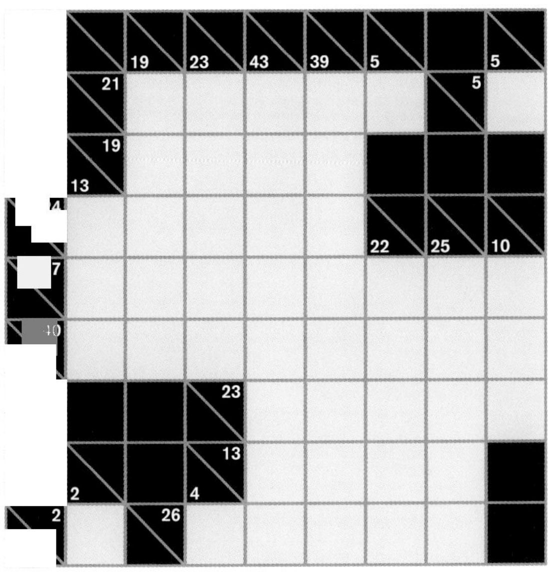

183

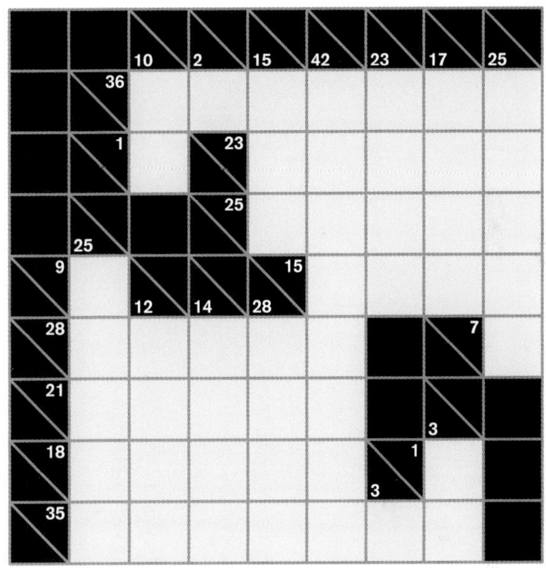

182

184

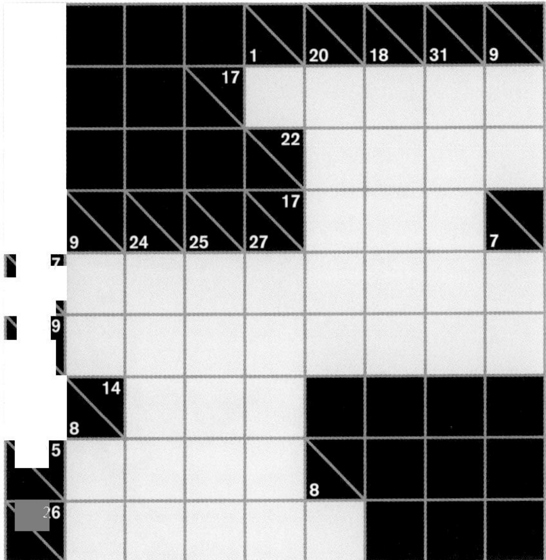

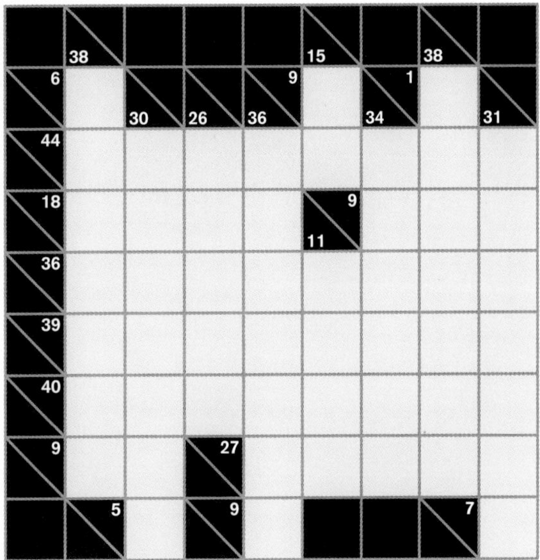

185

186

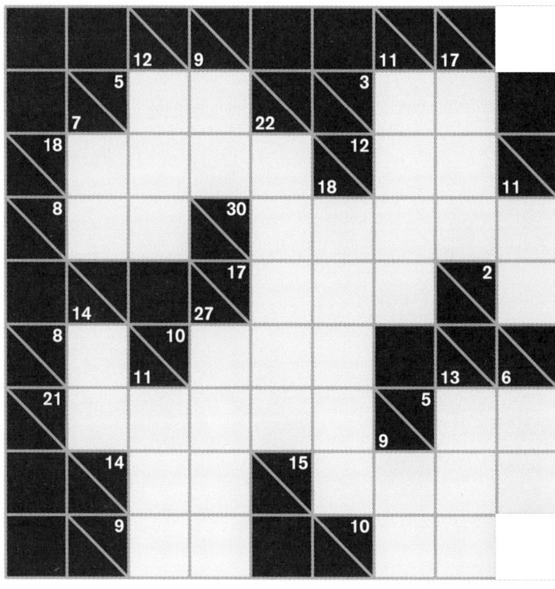

187

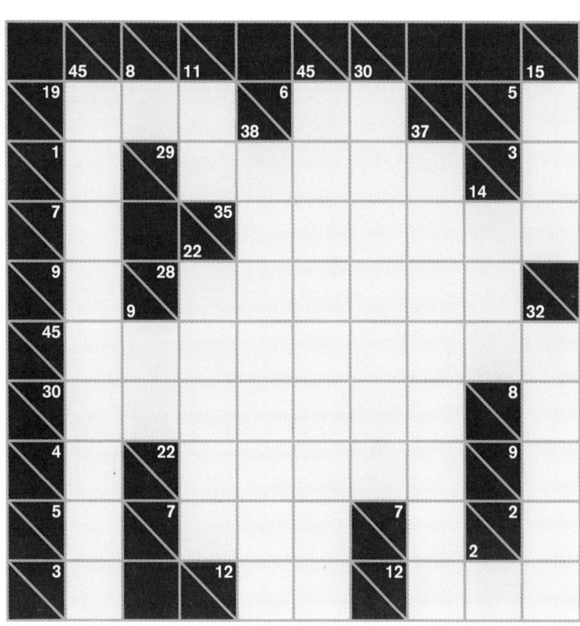

A useful tip for doing all kinds of mental arithmetic calculations is to break the number down into simpler constituent parts, perform the calculation and then add up the resulting answers.

188

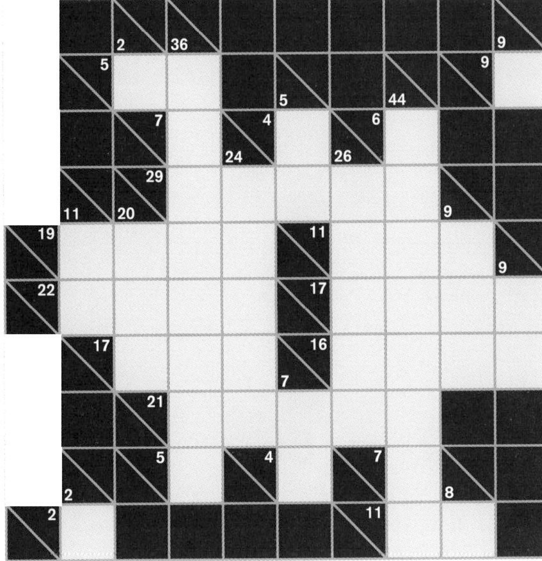

189

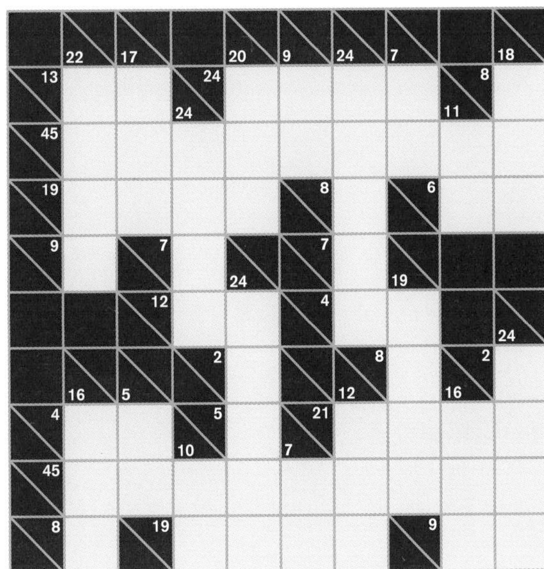

Remember that working out all of the possible combinations for each clue will make it easier and prevent duplication.

190

MORE GRIDS AND SQUARES

Use addition, subtraction and multiplication to complete the sums in these matrices. Refer to page 172-173 for a reminder.

191

In these two puzzles each calculation contains addition, subtraction and multiplication. The number in each dark blue square is the sum of the four numbers at its corners.

4		6		5		11	=	30
	15		27		39			
3							=	61
	30		42		56			
8							=	121
	45		57		69			
9							=	384
=		=		=		=		
81		79		59		64		

192 

9		4		14		8	=	30
	28		36		45			
8							=	23
	54		63		72			
21							=	133
	81		90		99			
19							=	464
=		=		=		=		
40		163		651		493		

You need to use numerical skills on an everyday basis. You'll find even simple adding up is easier once you have tackled number grids like these.

193

Every row and column in the grid contains an instance of addition, subtraction and multiplication. The answer to each line is a different number from 21 to 30 inclusive.

Juggling how often the different mathematical signs occur in the grid will help narrow down your options.

7			+	3		12	=	
−						x		
	+			3			=	
		−						
8	−	9			x	3	=	27
+		+		x		−		
5						4	=	
=		=		=		=		
		25						

18		21		30	x		=	
		+		−		x		
	x		−	27	+	9	=	
x								
7		10	x			8	=	43
				+		+		
		3	+			4	=	
=		=		=		=		
		48		50				

194

In this grid the answer to each line is a different number from 41 to 50 inclusive.

MAGIC SQUARES

In these grid-based puzzles, all the rows, columns and corner-to-corner lines should add up to the same number. The instructions to each individual puzzle provide further guidance.

195

Transfer four numbers from the left-hand grid to the right-hand grid, and vice versa, to produce two Magic Squares in which each row, column and corner-to-corner line totals 65.

23	6	19	2	15
4	12	3	8	16
25	18	1	14	22
11	24	7	20	25
17	4	13	21	9

17	5	25	20	13
16	23	14	8	3
11	7	1	10	21
2	24	18	9	12
19	6	22	5	15

196

At first glance, this might not appear to be a Magic Square puzzle, but it is. Can you work out the reasoning, and then select the missing tile from the available options?

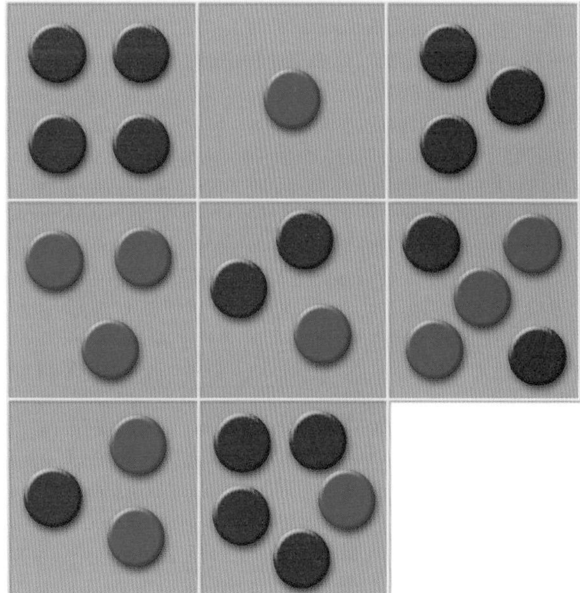

A

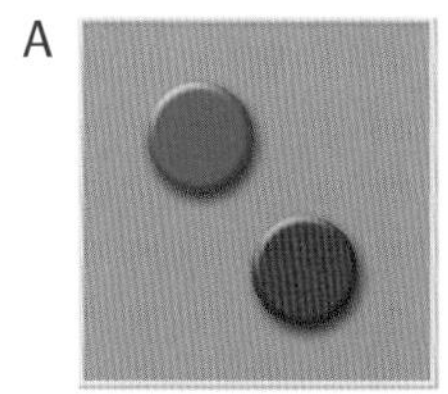

B

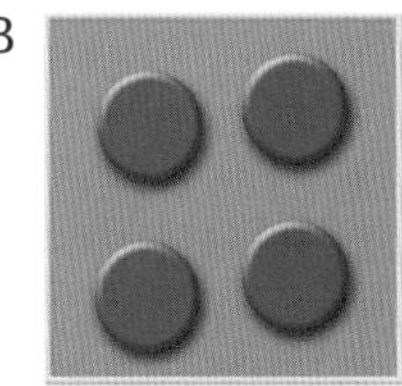

C

D

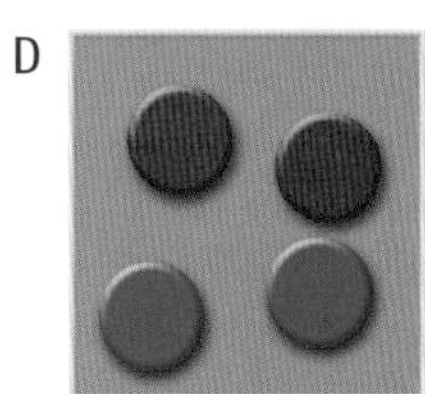

E

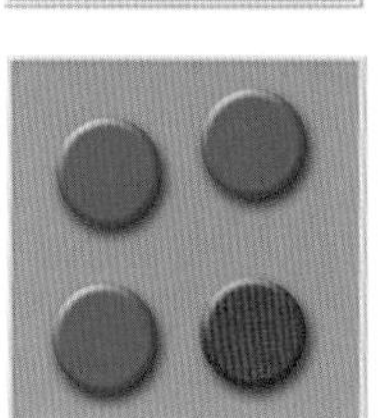

F

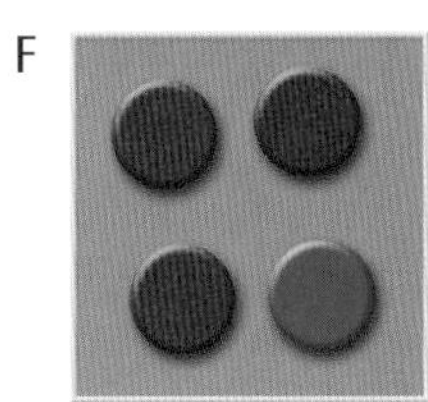

1		62		5		58	
56	15	49	48	19	44	20	9
55		25		38		18	10
11	22	36		31		43	
53	42	32		35		23	
13		37		26		41	52
14	45	16	17	46	21	50	51
57		3		60		7	

197 ★★

Insert the remaining numbers from 1–64 to produce a triple Magic Square, whereby the outer 8x8 grid is a Magic 260, the inner 6x6 is a Magic 195 and the inner 4x4 core is a Magic 130.

198 ★★

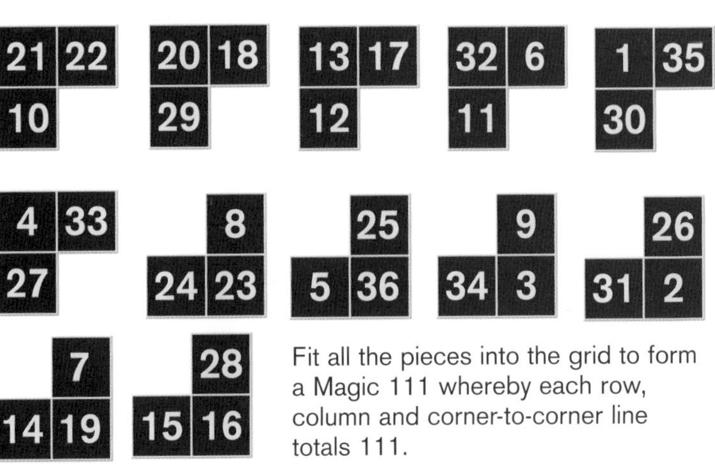

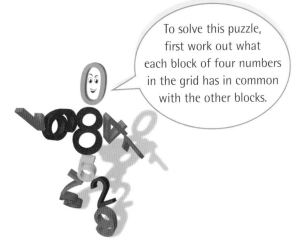

Fit all the pieces into the grid to form a Magic 111 whereby each row, column and corner-to-corner line totals 111.

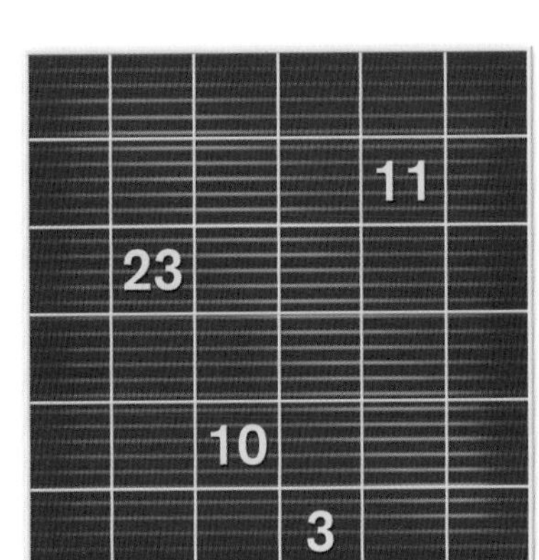

				11	
	23				
		10			
			3		

199 ★★

Insert the remaining numbers from 1–64 into the grid to produce a Magic 260.

To solve this puzzle, first work out what each block of four numbers in the grid has in common with the other blocks.

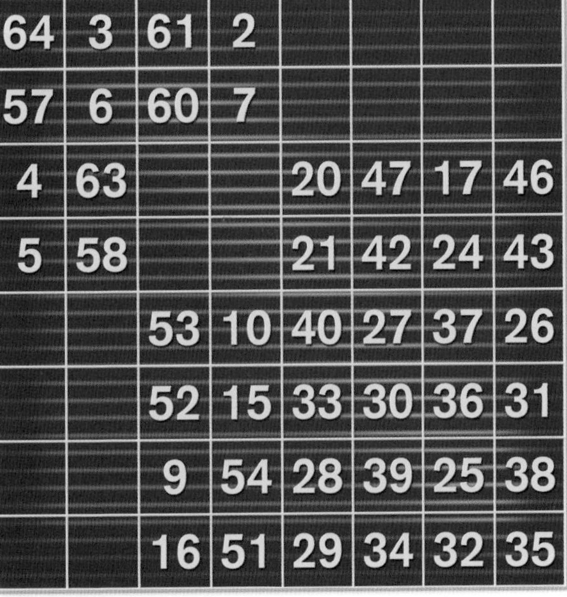

64	3	61	2				
57	6	60	7				
4	63			20	47	17	46
5	58			21	42	24	43
		53	10	40	27	37	26
		52	15	33	30	36	31
		9	54	28	39	25	38
		16	51	29	34	32	35

NUMBER CROSSWORD

This crossword will put your arithmetical skills to the test. Solve the sums and write your answers into the grid in number form.

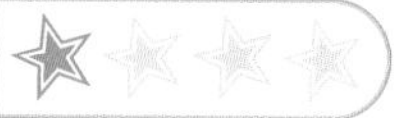

Work out the answers to the clues and insert them into the grid as you would words in a crossword. To test your arithmetical skills to the maximum, try and complete the entire crossword without the aid of a calculator.

Across

6. 805,223.5 x 8
7. (501 x 34) + (100 x 100)
9. Next in series: 99,675; 100,926; 102,177
10. 9 across + 17 across
11. 3,142,158 ÷ 6
13. (256 x 12) + (256 x 18)
15. 6,248 x 112.5%
17. 669,714 ÷ 3
20. 32,576 + 49,986 + 23,071
21. 921,152 - 137,788 - 29,005
22. 356,202 ÷ 7
23. 77,201.75 x (4 x 4)

Down

1. (7119 x 12) - 1,320
2. (892,584 - 81,122) + 10 cubed
3. 6.06 x (12 x 25)
4. 1,372,936 ÷ 8
5. 1,919,191 + 19,191,919 - 16,784,624
8. Next in series: 1,333,332.9; 999,999.6; 666,666.3
12. 1,806,090 ÷ 3
14. 13,468 x 75
16. 487,487 + 378,788 + 120,114
18. 2,599,648 x 12.5%
19. 25 cubed
21. 125.5 x 56

SMART THINKING

SMART THINKING

Intelligent deductive reasoning is not limited to investigative geniuses like Sherlock Holmes – you too can train your brain to think smart.

SMART THINKING OR, MORE CORRECTLY, deductive reasoning, was the mental asset that the fictional sleuth Sherlock Holmes claimed to use in solving crimes. The image Conan Doyle paints of Holmes is of a calm, relentless logician, observing everything carefully in order to detect and interpret the all-important clues. This type of systematic thinking – the ability to maintain the view of one goal while working on the smaller goals that lead to the whole – is not only a key skill needed for solving logic puzzles, but is also thought to be one of the unique attributes of the human brain. The other essential for unravelling logic puzzles is to hone your ability to think 'out of the box' because, even with all the clues readily to hand, the answer may not be immediately obvious.

LIKE NUMBER PUZZLES, LOGIC PUZZLES make major use of the kind of thinking done by the left-hand side of the brain. Smart thinking often requires looking at sets of 'pieces' of information and assembling them in the same way you might put together a jigsaw puzzle or the parts of a flat-packed piece of furniture. You may also need to be alert to visual details, and to assess and categorize different types of factual information, whether presented as numbers or words, shapes or colours, or a mixture of all of these.

OTHER LOGICAL BRAIN PROCESSES that come into play here are decoding information (for instance working out how codes have been encrypted), detecting and using sequences and forming in your mind an idea of the concept that lies behind a puzzle. Very often you will need to test different ideas or hypotheses about how the elements of the puzzle relate to each other, but this trial-and-error process is an important part of logical reasoning.

Calm, systematic analysis and careful observation of the given information are the keys to solving logic puzzles – as well as a creative imagination.

My name is Jude Ishus, and occasionally I will be popping up in this section to offer you nuggets of advice to help you develop your brainpower.

OF THE MANY FORMS OF LOGIC PUZZLES, one of the most popular is Battleships. To identify the correct positions of all the ships in the grid you need to work logically, eliminating 'error positions' one by one. A similar type of logic applies in Nonograms, in which squares within a grid have to be shaded to complete the puzzle. One of the keys to success is working out how many blank squares appear between each group of shaded ones. When solved, the best Nonograms reveal an entertaining image of some kind. In both these types of puzzles, working out and applying a practical strategy (another type of logical thinking) is a valuable problem-solving skill.

LOGIC AND INFORMED GUESSWORK will stand you in good stead with Cipherwords which use a crossword grid but, instead of providing clues, present a completed grid in a number code. Your task is to identify which letter each number represents. As with crosswords, each number/letter code gives you an additional piece of information towards the total. Once you have a few letters in an answer, you can then make an educated guess about the solution. Then compare the numbers for the blank squares with others in the grid to see whether your solution fits. Good tips for solving Cipherwords: 'e' is the most common letter in English; double 'e' and double 'o' are the most common repeated letters; and 'q' is almost always followed by a 'u'.

THEMED 'STORIES' ARE THE STARTING POINT for logic grids, in which the object is to record, from a variety of statements, not only which are true but how they relate to one other. Often the logic required is that of eliminating which statements are incorrect and so, by inference, arriving at the truth. Working systematically, writing down the possible solutions before you come to you final conclusions, is a good way to boost your powers of logic. To paraphrase Sherlock Holmes, 'once you have eliminated the impossible, what you are left with, no matter how improbable, must be the solution'.

EVERYONE LOVES RIDDLES, and to solve them lateral thinking is usually more helpful than pure logic. Visual riddles or rebuses demand spatial reasoning combined with word and number play, bringing both hemispheres of the brain into action. Spatial logic, and the power of predictive imagination, are essential for snooker table puzzles which ask you to predict the path of a ball, while in 'matchstick play', compilers make cryptic use of shapes and numbers to test your brain power.

DEVELOPING YOUR ABILITY TO THINK SMART and use the many different aspects of logic of which the brain is capable are the keys to success in everyday life, not least because it helps you solve practical problems. What's more, it can help you to benefit from being able to anticipate possible hurdles to progress well in advance.

MATCHSTICK PUZZLES

By using a bit of logic, lateral thinking and visual planning, you should be able to strike up a winning formula with these.

Adding it up

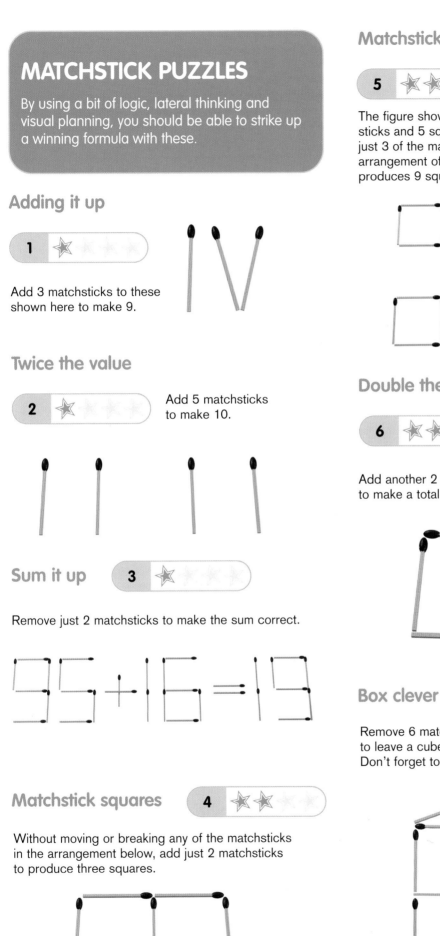

Add 3 matchsticks to these shown here to make 9.

Twice the value

Add 5 matchsticks to make 10.

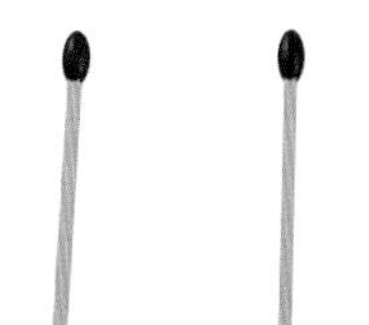

Sum it up

Remove just 2 matchsticks to make the sum correct.

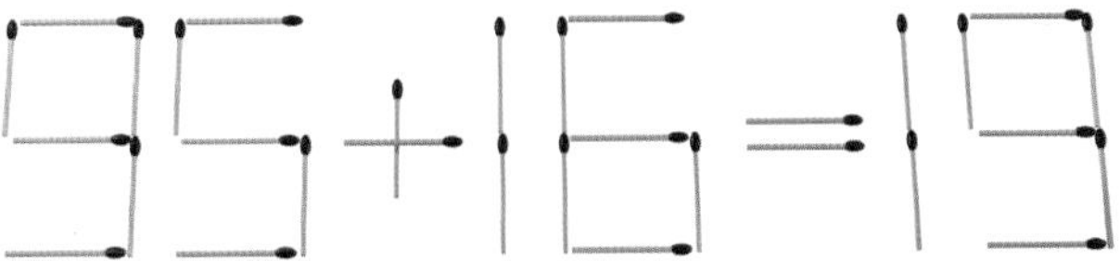

Matchstick squares

Without moving or breaking any of the matchsticks in the arrangement below, add just 2 matchsticks to produce three squares.

Matchstick maths

The figure shown here consists of 20 matchsticks and 5 squares. Alter the position of just 3 of the matchsticks to form a new arrangement of the 20 matchsticks that produces 9 squares.

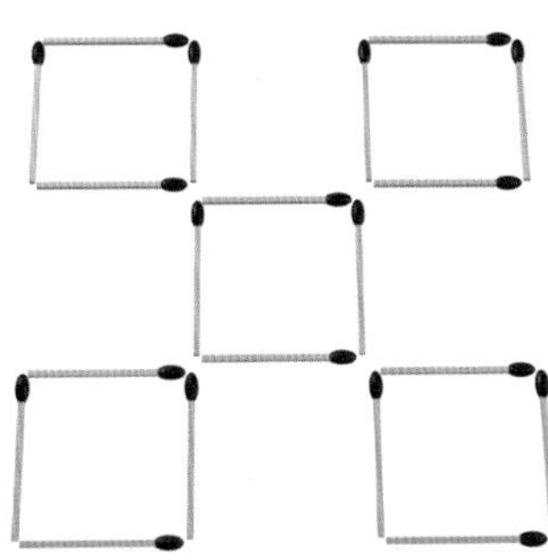

Double the fun

Add another 2 matches to this diagram to make a total of 2 squares.

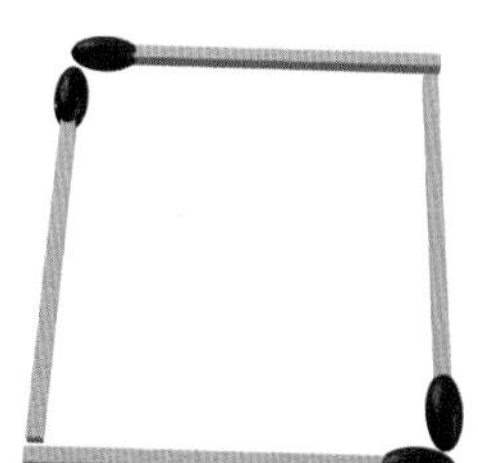

Box clever

Remove 6 matches from this arrangement to leave a cube.
Don't forget to think laterally.

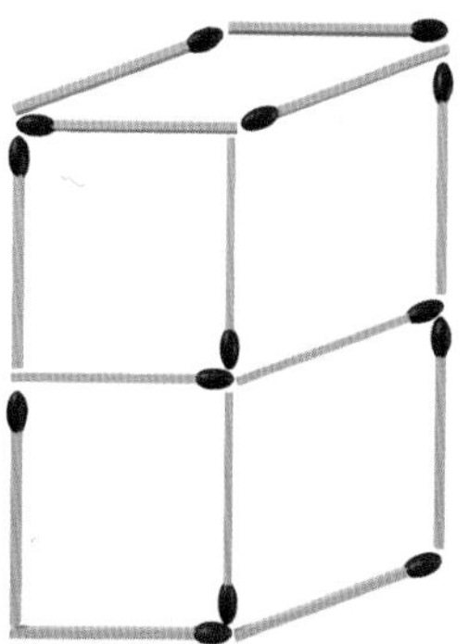

BATTLESHIPS

The grids represent sections of ocean in which a fleet of ships is hiding. The fleet is detailed alongside each puzzle (**see key**). The digits down the right-hand side and below the grid, indicate the number of grid squares that are occupied by vessels in the corresponding rows and columns. We have started you off by showing you parts of some of the ships; use this information to locate them all. All the ships lie in one row or column, (that is, they are not diagonal) and no ships occupy adjacent squares, even diagonally.

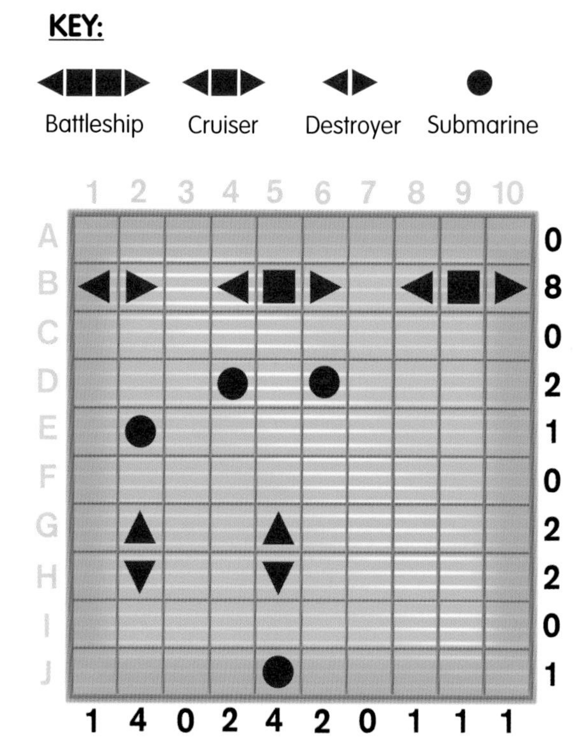

9

The fleet consists of: 1 cruiser, 2 destroyer and 3 submarines.

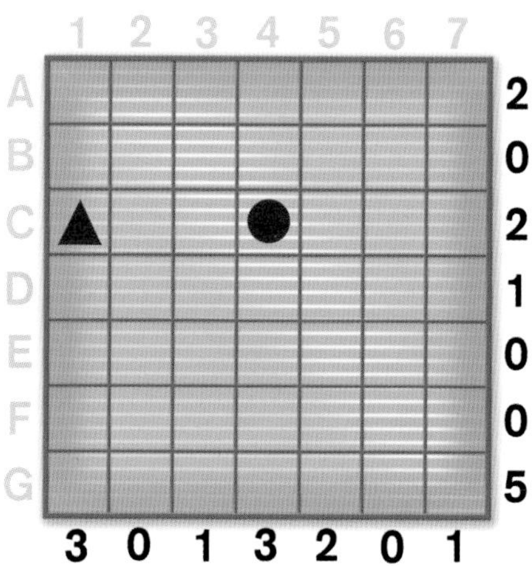

8

The fleet consists of: 1 cruiser, 2 destroyers and 4 submarines.

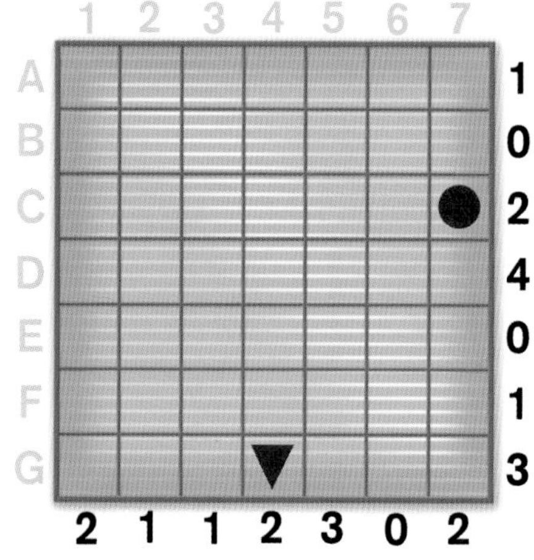

10

The fleet consists of: 1 cruiser, 2 destroy and 3 submarines

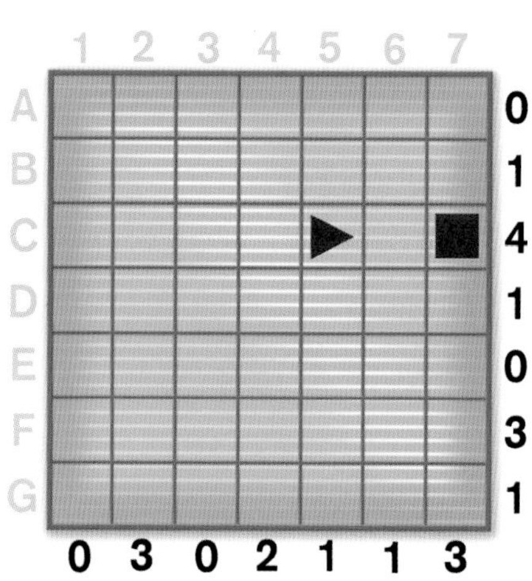

SMART THINKING

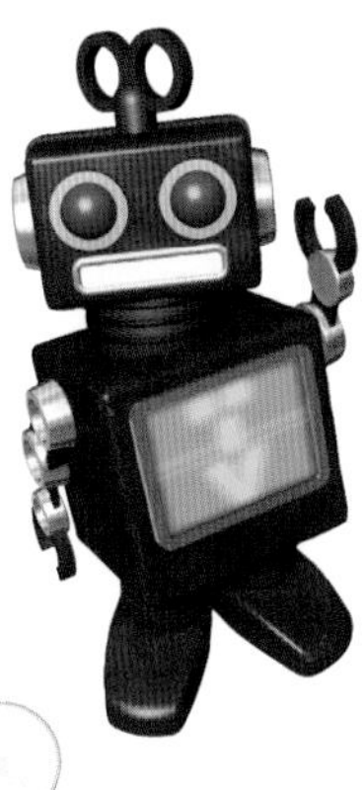

A row with a 0 tells you that it is all sea, while a solid red square indicates the middle section of a ship. That makes it easier to try to position the larger ships first.

11

The fleet consists of: 1 battleship, 2 cruisers, 3 destroyers and 5 submarines.

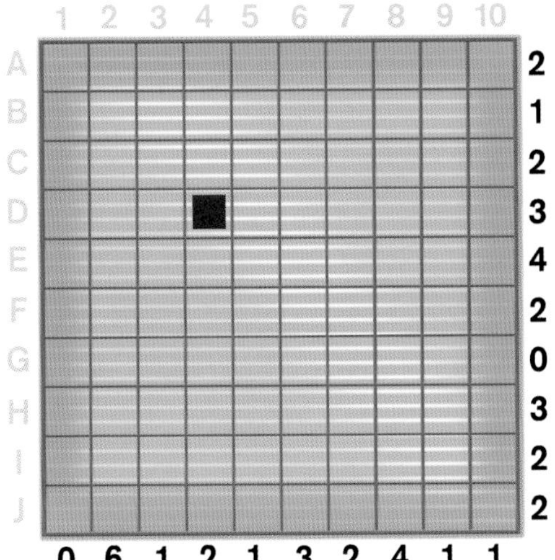

12

The fleet consists of: 1 battleship, 2 cruisers, 3 destroyers and 4 submarines.

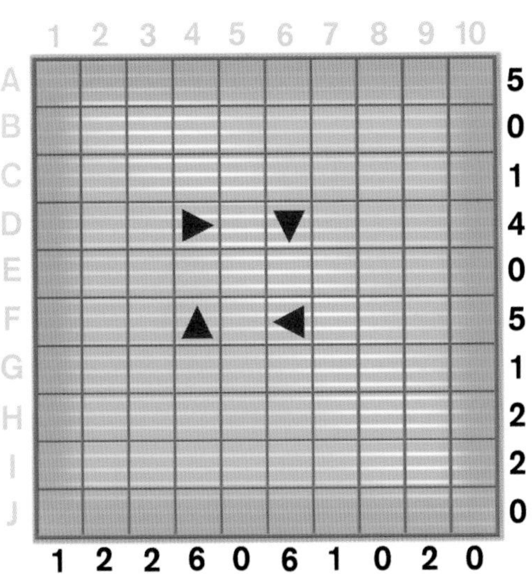

13

The fleet consists of: 1 battleship, 2 cruisers, 3 destroyers and 4 submarines.

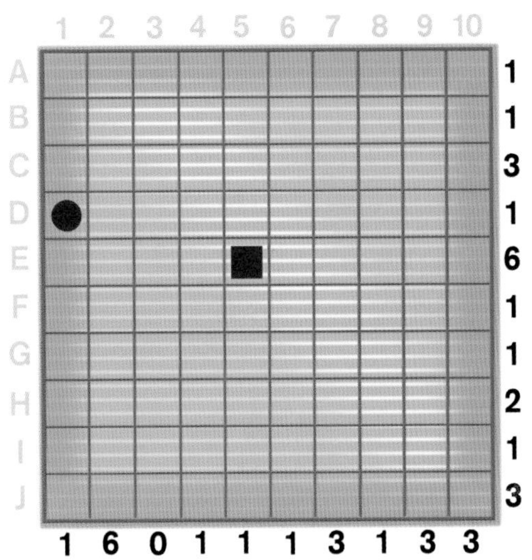

14

The fleet consists of: 1 battleship, 2 cruisers, 3 destroyers and 4 submarines.

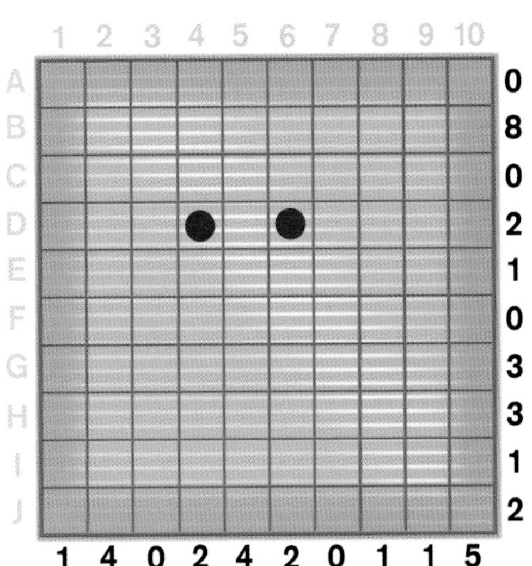

HEXAGON BATTLESHIPS

The principal of Battleships remains the same – but we've just given them an extra twist! Follow the direction of the arrows to work out the row that matches the relevant number, then solve the puzzle.

16 ★★★

The fleet consists of: 1 battleship, 2 cruisers, 3 destroyers and 4 submarines.

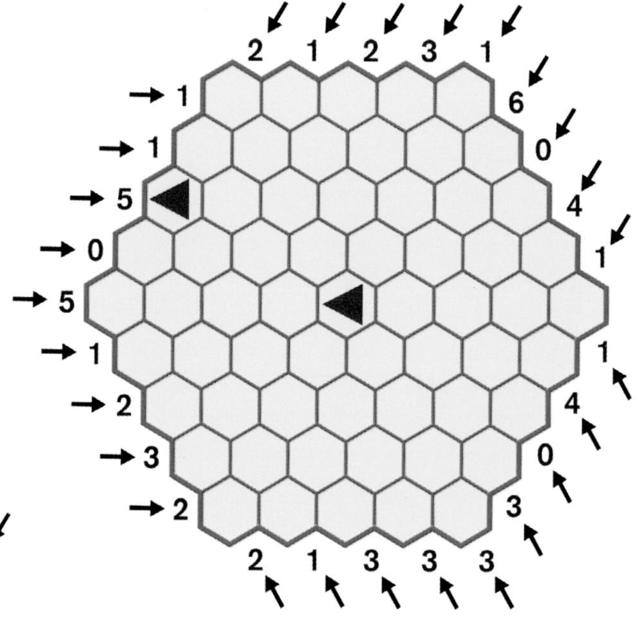

15 ★★★

The fleet consists of: 1 battleship, 2 cruisers, 3 destroyers and 4 submarines.

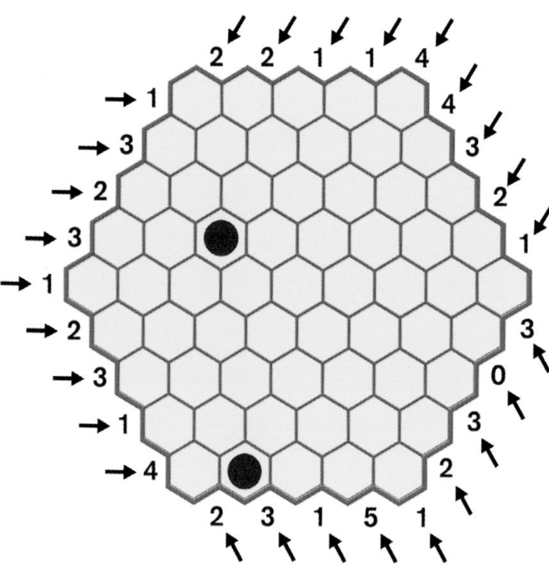

17 ★★★★

The fleet consists of: 1 aircraft carrier, 2 battleships, 3 cruisers, 4 destroyers and 5 submarines.

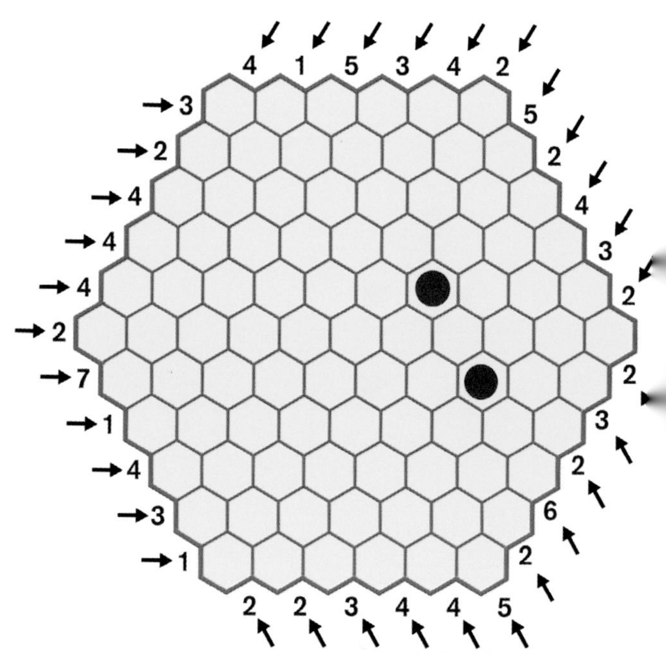

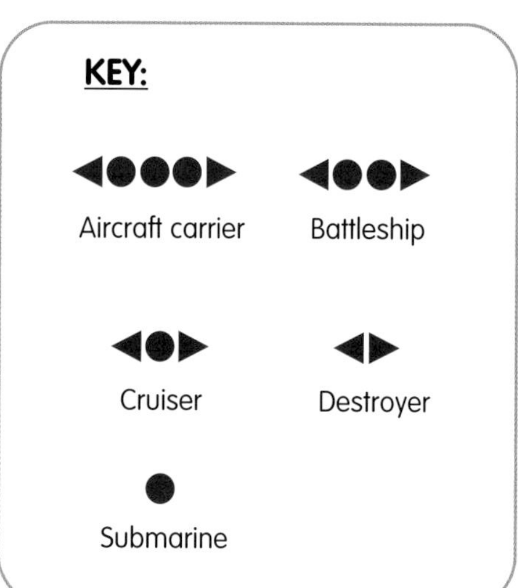

LOGIC PUZZLES

The word 'logic' comes from the Greek *logos,* meaning word, speech or reason. Some of us arrive at solutions via the detective route, by looking at the evidence or information available and weighing up the options. Others are more instinctive. Both kinds of thinkers will find plenty to challenge them in the logic puzzles on the following pages, which will improve your powers of both analysis and reasoning.

18 

Riddle me this

Without my first I'm culture mad
My first three show I'm not so bad.

Odd letters mean to delve into
First, second, last is money due.

Drop off my last, and that's not all
The whole word means to have a ball.

Guess what

Take off my first I am a stag
The second's gone, pulled by a nag

Without my fourth is something said
Losing the last she makes the bed

Odd letters sleep upon your lap
The whole reveals an outline map.

A real belter!

On a 747 there are five seats together in each row in the centre of the plane. Each seat has one buckle and one clasp of a seat-belt. However, the three passengers not occupying an aisle seat can use a buckle from the left and a clasp from the right or vice versa. Assuming the passengers 'belt-up' by picking one clasp and one buckle randomly, what is the probability of all five passengers 'belting-up' correctly?

21 

Weigh it up

You are given 12 balls and are told that one of them is lighter or heavier than the others. You have a set of scales (but no weights) and have three weighings to establish which ball is the odd one out and whether it is heavier or lighter than the others. How is this done?

PICTORIAL REBUSES

In these puzzles words are represented by combinations of pictures. A creative mix of words and visual trickery, they are sometimes straightforward and occasionally frustrating. Use lateral thinking if you are struggling – it helps to think 'outside the box'.

22 

Say what you see: what am I?

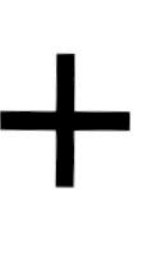

23 

Name the opera depicted here.

24  

What am I?

25  

What phrase is depicted below?

26 

Which familiar phrase is illustrated here?

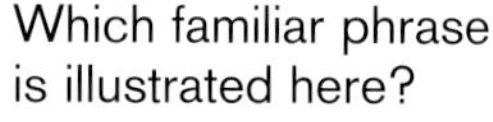

LITERAL REBUSES

These puzzles are similar to pictorial rebuses except they use a combination of words arranged in an unusual way, or with a graphic device added, in order to indicate a well-known phrase. For example, the answer to **THE & EEEE** is **'The Andes'**.

27 ★

GENE RATION

28 ★

tHE haNd

29

NOOS

30

BILLED

31 ★★

SCR EEN

32

D (K) / W

33 ★★★

B (S H) E

34 ★★★

SH OT

35 ★★★

IQE2

36 ★★★

37 ★★★★

HE ID

38 ★★★★

X÷

RIDDLES

It is said that the earliest riddles were presented as ancient oracles. In ancient times, riddles were mainly about the sun, moon, rainbows and the wind. One of the great Greek poets, Homer, supposedly died of humiliation because he could not answer a riddle.

What am I?

39  

My first is in heaven, and also in hell.
My second's in goodbye, but not in farewell.
My third is in front, but not in behind.
My fourth is in coarse, but not in refined.
My fifth is in ear, and also in eye.
So tell me now, please, what creature am I?

Water riddle

40  

My first is in angry, but never in calm.
My second's in dairy, and also in farm.
My third is in active,
but never in idle.
My fourth is in harness,
but not in a bridle.
My fifth is in mother,
as well as in daughter.
What might I be, that you
see on the water?

Holes everywhere

41  

I have holes on my top and my bottom.
I have holes on my left and my right.
I even have holes in my middle,
yet I still hold water.
What am I?

Condemned?

42  

A murderer is condemned to death. He has to choose between three rooms. The first is full of raging fires, the second is full of assassins with loaded guns, and the third is full of lions that haven't eaten in three years. Which room is safest for him?

Guess what?

43 

My first is in earlier, also in later.
My second's in tyrant, but not in dictator.
My third is in break, but not in repair.
My fourth is in circle, but never in square.
My fifth is in deep, but not in profound.
My whole travels with you,
quite close to the ground.
What am I?

Conundrum

44    

What gets wetter the more it dries?

Weight loss

45  

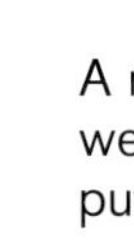

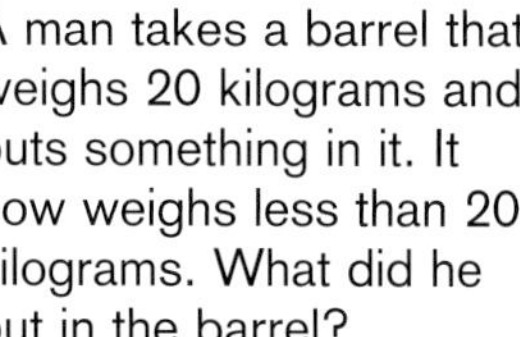

A man takes a barrel that weighs 20 kilograms and puts something in it. It now weighs less than 20 kilograms. What did he put in the barrel?

Heartless? 46 ★★

My first is in wages as well as in earning.
My second's in fire, but never in burning.
My third is in sun, and also in rain.
My fourth is in pleasure, but never in pain.
My fifth's in dimension, and also in size.
My sixth is in mince as well as in pies.
My seventh's in soul, but not found in heart.
My whole is a book which is really the start.

The name game 47 ★★

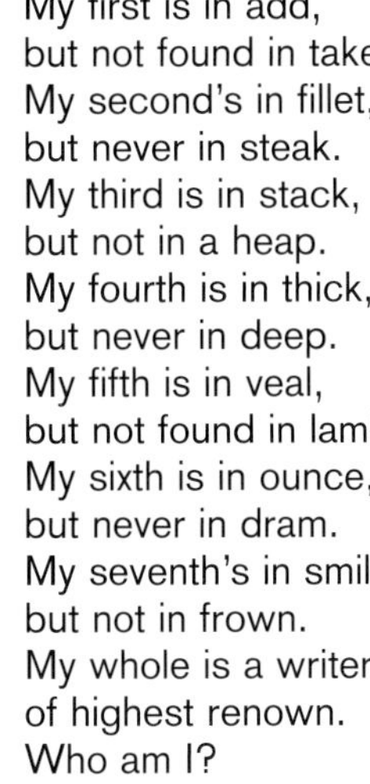

My first is in add,
but not found in take.
My second's in fillet,
but never in steak.
My third is in stack,
but not in a heap.
My fourth is in thick,
but never in deep.
My fifth is in veal,
but not found in lamb.
My sixth is in ounce,
but never in dram.
My seventh's in smile,
but not in frown.
My whole is a writer
of highest renown.
Who am I?

Family affairs 48 ★

Four people are eating dinner together when one of them remarks: 'Do you realize that around this table, there is a mother, a father, a brother, a sister, a son, a daughter, a niece, a nephew, an aunt, an uncle and a couple of cousins?' If everyone is related by blood (with no unusual marriages) how is this possible?

Court report 49 ★

A dozen royals gathered round, entertained by two who clowned. Each king there had servants ten, though none of them were common men. The lowest servant sometimes might, defeat the king in a fair fight. A weapon stout, a priceless jewel, the beat of life, a farmer's tool. What are we talking about here?

Shot in the dark 50 ★

In your sock drawer you have six pairs of blue socks, five pairs of brown socks and three pairs of black socks. In complete darkness, what's the smallest number of socks you have to take out to be sure of having a matching pair?

Secret state 51 ★

My first is in people, but not in a crowd.
My second's in shower, but never in cloud.
My third is in apple, but not found in pie.
My fourth is in purchase, but never in buy.
My fifth is in Peter, but not found in Paul.
My whole is a state that's desired by all.

Perfect pair 52 ★

Two girls are born to the same mother on the same afternoon, within the same hour, in the same year, and yet they're not twins. How can this be?

Transparent 53 ★

There is an ancient invention, still used in some parts of the world today, that allows people to see through walls. What is it?

Cryptic colour

My first, fourth and sixth letters make a number.
My sixth, third and second make a part of the body.
My first, fifth, second and sixth make a monster.
My second, third, fifth and sixth make a fierce anger.
My first, second, fifth, third and fourth make an instrument.
What colour am I?

Riddle me this

My first is in ready, and also in able.
My second's in barn, but not in a stable.
My third is in heavy, but never in light.
My fourth's in this morning, but not in tonight.
My fifth is in movement, but not in delay.
My sixth is in wander, but not in astray.
My seventh is in minute, but not found in hour.
Now, can you tell me the name of this flower?

Mystery traveller

It can pass through doors. It can travel great distances, even round the world. But all the time, it stays in a corner. What is it?

Kidnapped

This is a true story from Taiwan. A rich man's son was kidnapped. The ransom note told him to take a valuable diamond to a phone booth in the middle of a public park. Plainclothes police officers surrounded the park, intending to follow the criminal or his messenger. The rich man arrived at the phone booth and followed instructions – but the police were powerless to prevent the diamond from leaving the park and reaching the crafty villain. What happened?

Pond life

There are two ducks
in front of two other ducks.
There are two ducks
behind two other ducks.
There are two ducks
beside two other ducks.
What's the smallest number of ducks described here?

Take a chance

Can you solve this rather unusual riddle?

My first is in smelling, but not in laborious.
My second's in laborious, but not in smelling.
My third is in smelling, but not in laborious.
My fourth's in laborious, but not in smelling.
My fifth is in smelling, **and** in laborious.
My sixth is in smelling, but not in laborious.
My seventh's in laborious, but not in smelling.
What's the betting you can't guess what I am?

Angry words

Think of words ending in -gry. Angry and hungry are two of them. There are only three words in the English language. What is the third word? It's something you use every day. If you read the riddle carefully, you'll find the answer within it.

You may not need
any hints at this stage but
I would suggest a pen and paper
to work out the riddles on this
last, more difficult, section.

CRYPTOGRAMS

Cryptograms are short messages in which certain letters have been replaced by other letters, or are jumbled up to cause confusion. See if you can decipher the codes in the puzzles that follow to become a true cryptographer.

Find the plans

Special Agent Hardy used his skeleton key to let himself into the house where he knew the secret plans were hidden. His partner, Agent Laurel, had left a coded note describing their location. Hardy found the note and read:

YDUT SEHT NITE PRAC EHTR EDNU

Using all the skills he had learnt at Special Agent School, Hardy decoded the message, retrieved the plans and made his getaway. Where were they hidden?

Simple code

Simon Simple, the Berlin-based superspy, received this innocent-looking telegram from Control, apparently about two tourists. He immediately went out and bought an airline ticket. Why? Where to? What was the coded message Simple deciphered from this telegram?

Terry and Kath expect to have eight nights in Germany. Help them find lodgings in good hotels. They talk of returning on Monday evening.

Message for 007

James Bond would approve of the sentiment of this phrase, which has been encoded with a simple cipher. Can you decode it?

NKXG CPF NGV FKG

Hidden message

Find a short hidden message in this list of words:

cabbage fiasco never spring rustle sonata tidings bureau lateral corona towel bikini object soften seldom picnic office shouted enigma adverb recall device animal shriek esteem oyster

Military intelligence

When the following coded message arrived from HQ, Major Rhodes wasted no time in deciphering it and planning what to do.

WEZWI LLJAT TAXCK ATQSU NSKET TOZMO RRQOW

How did the code work, and what did the message tell the major?

SMART THINKING

Cryptogram

Here is a well-known proverb written in a simple cipher.
How quickly can you crack the code?
(It might help if you ask some friends to help you.)

LAMY GAMCR LAJE KIFGS VOQJ

Crack the code

Can you decipher this hidden message?

TIIRALES HSSELYAY

(When you discover the answer,
you may disagree with the statement!)

Cryptic numbers

The following observation by Albert Einstein has been encoded using numbers for letters. You don't need to know anything about Einstein, but you need to apply logic and lateral thinking to work out how the code works:

**269663 946 427 63837 6233 2
6478253 427 63837 87433
26984464 639.**

To get started with deciphering, try to find single letters and letter combinations that might represent those that are common in the English language. For example, the letters 'E', 'I' or 'A', and the combinations ' TH ', 'AND', 'OF' or 'ING'.

NON-GRID PUZZLES

Although each of the following puzzles presents a different type of challenge, you don't need special knowledge to solve them. They simply require an ability to work clearly and analytically through the clues you are given, following common sense reasoning, step by step, through to its conclusion.

Switched on?

In the bank of lights shown below:

Switch A turns lights 1 and 2 on/off or off/on

Switch B turns lights 2 and 4 on/off or off/on

Switch C turns lights 1 and 3 on/off or off/on

Switch D turns lights 3 and 4 on/off or off/on

Switches C, B A and D are thrown in turn with the result that Figure 1 becomes Figure 2. Which one of the switches, therefore, must not be working?

Figure 1 Figure 2

= ON

= OFF

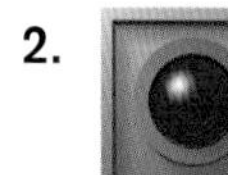

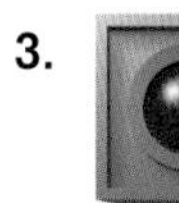

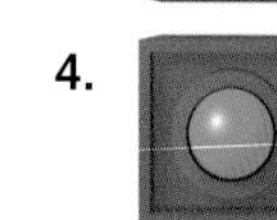

1. 1.
2. 2.
3. 3.
4. 4.

Tricky letters

E4 O6 R3

C9 L5 G7 I8 P1

What letter/number combination is missing?

Breadwinner

You are preparing toast for three people, who require just one slice of toast each.

You have a toaster which, although it holds two slices of bread at the same time only toasts one side of each of the two slices of bread at a time.

It takes just one minute to toast one side of a slice of bread.

What is the fastest time in which it is possible to toast the three slices of bread on both sides, and how would you do it?

Missing three

The numbers 4-16 have already been placed into the square almost, but not quite, at random.

Following just two simple rules, where would you place the numbers 1,2 and 3 in the square?

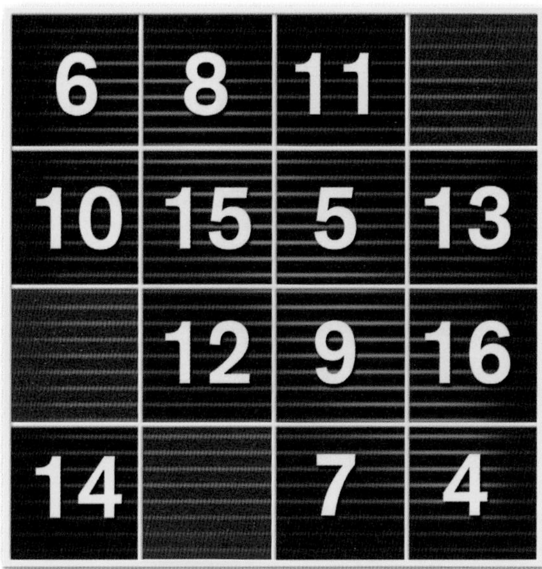

Think of different ways of moving, altering or substituting letters in some kind of pattern. Doing this will exercise your visual skills as well as your verbal and numerical logic skills – skills that are all useful for tasks like map reading.

Level pegging

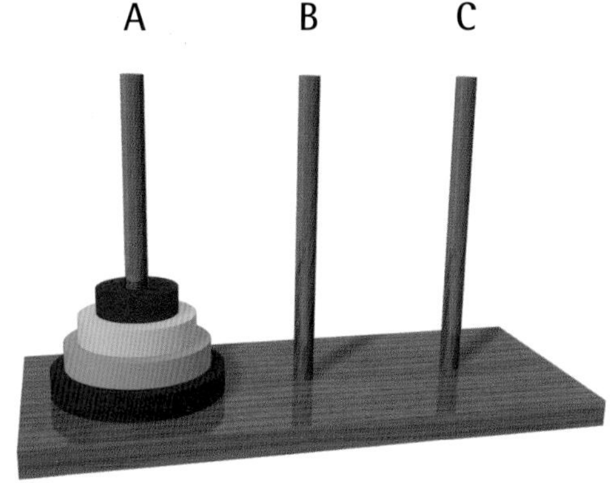

Transfer all of the discs from Peg A to Peg B following these rules:

• You may take discs off a peg one at a time only and put each disc on another peg, but never in such a way that a disc is put on top of a smaller disc.

• You must finish with the four discs in the same position on Peg B as they are now shown on Peg A.

• The transfer can be achieved in 15 moves. Can you figure out how?

Ground manoeuvres

74

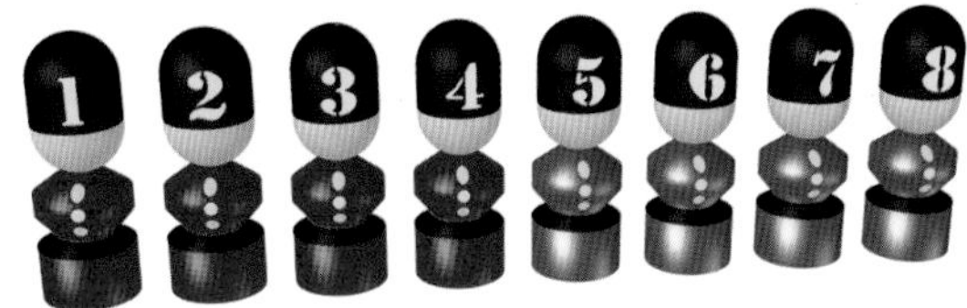

Eight soldiers line up on parade in a straight row, four in red uniforms followed by four in blue uniforms (RRRRBBBB). You must move the soldiers two at a time and in four such manoeuvres assemble the eight soldiers so that they are still in a straight row; however, they must be in alternate blue and red uniforms (BRBRBRBR).

How can this be done?

SNOOKER PUZZLES

In each of the puzzles below you are playing the white cue ball. What is the minimum number of cushions you will have to play off in order to sink the black ball without hitting any of the red balls first? Assume that the angle at which the white ball strikes the cushions is the same angle at which it leaves it.

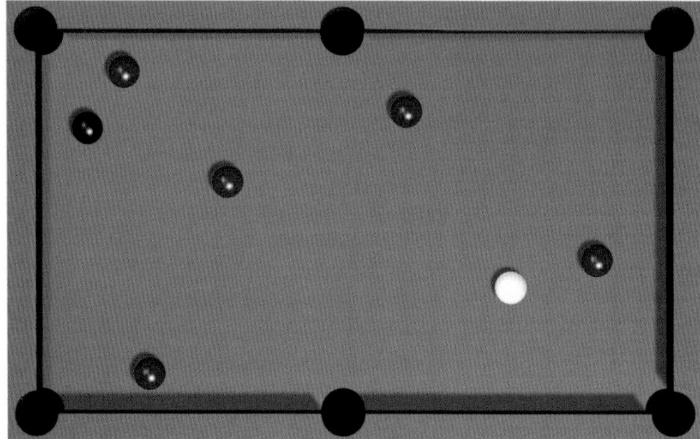

76

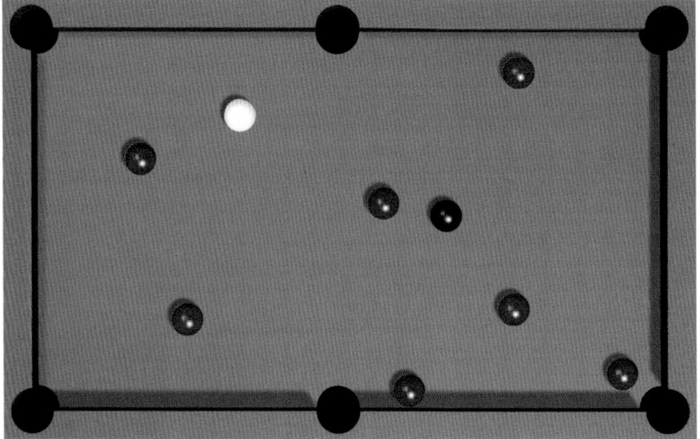

77

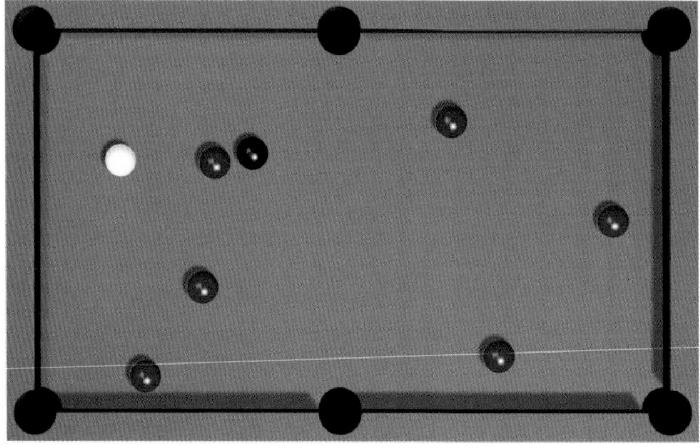

These puzzles test your aptitude for visual logic and your ability in spatial reasoning – a key skill for creative and strategic thinkers.

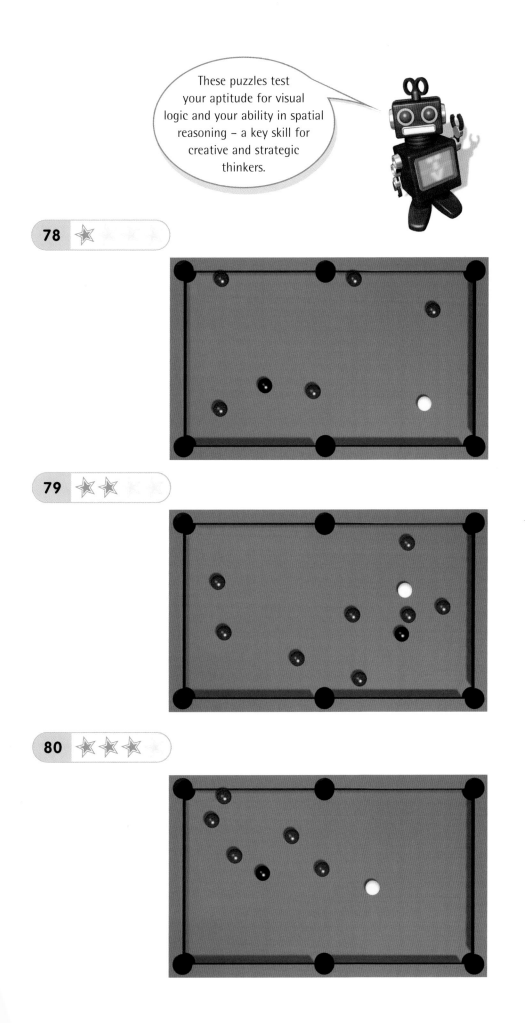

78 ★

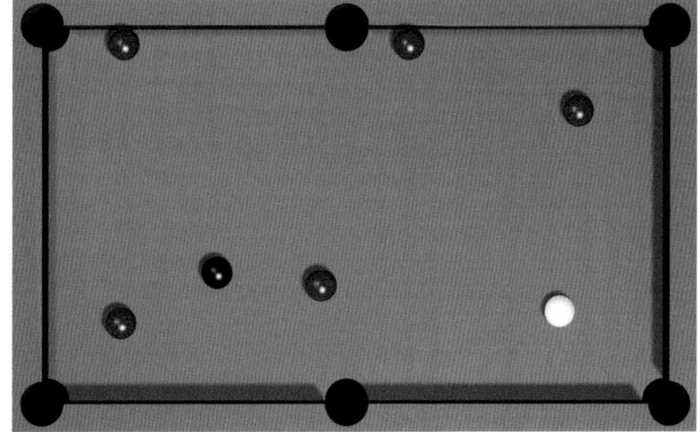

79 ★★

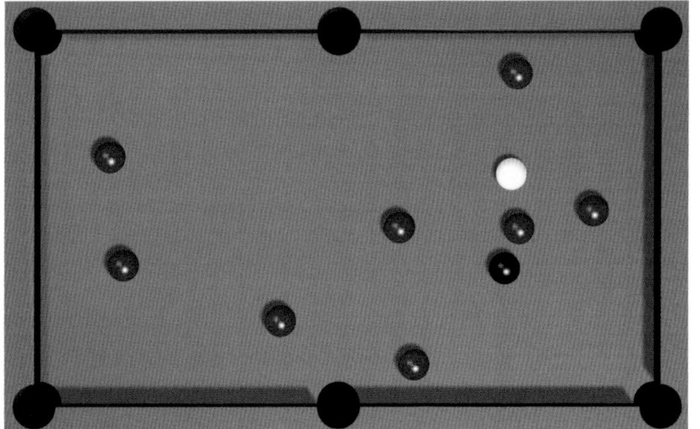

80 ★★★

SMART THINKING

MINESWEEPER

Each number in the grid shows the number of mines in adjacent squares, including those connected diagonally. No mine can be horizontally, vertically or diagonally adjacent to any other, and no mine can appear in the same square as a number. Can you work out where the mines are laid? One has been placed to help you.

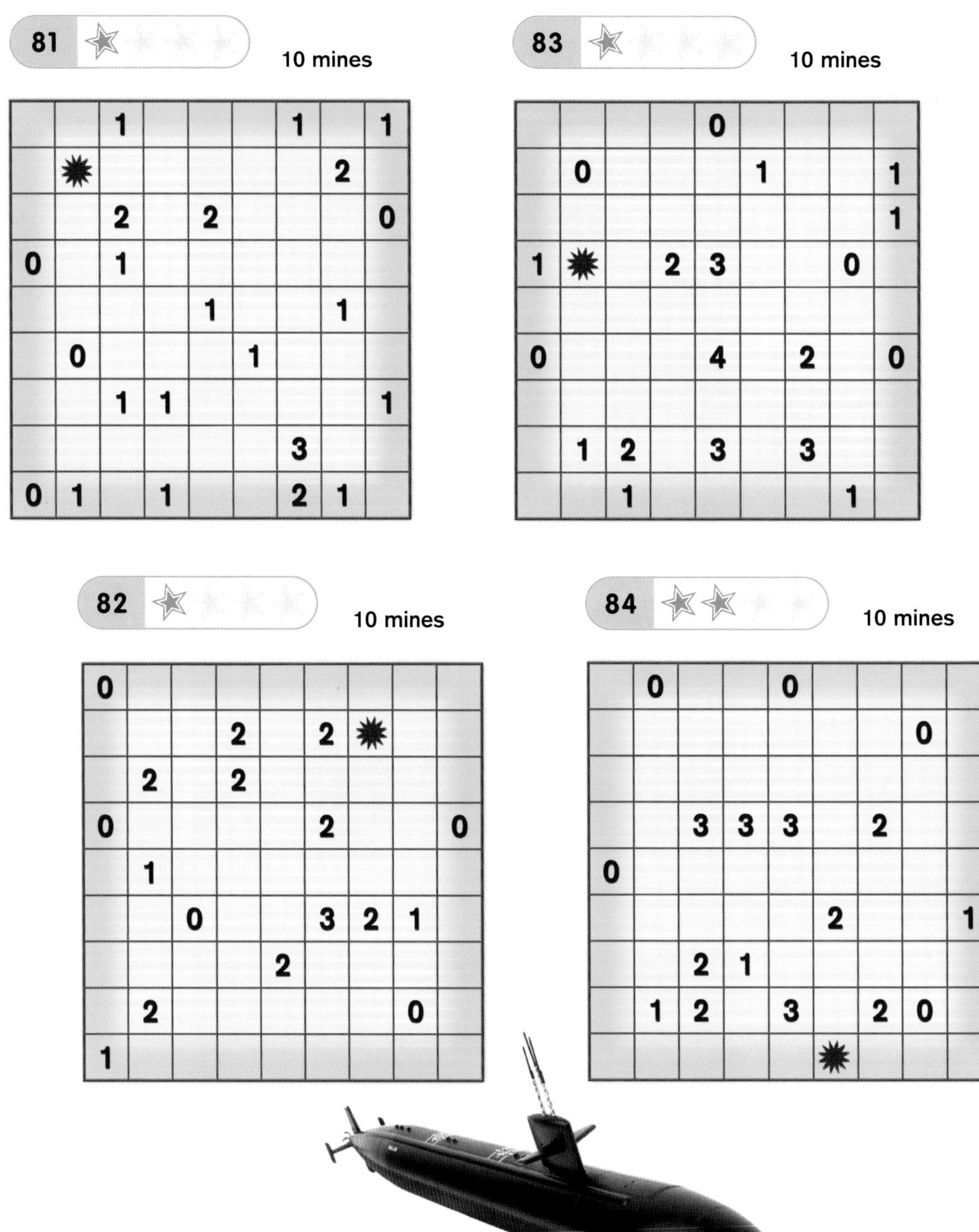

81 ★ — 10 mines

		1				1		1
	✱						2	
		2		2				0
0		1						
				1			1	
	0				1			
		1	1					1
						3		
0	1		1			2	1	

83 ★ — 10 mines

				0				
	0				1			1
								1
1	✱		2	3			0	
0				4		2		0
	1	2		3		3		
		1					1	

82 ★ — 10 mines

0								
			2		2	✱		
	2		2					
0					2			0
	1							
		0			3	2	1	
				2				
	2						0	
1								

84 ★★ — 10 mines

	0			0				
							0	
		3	3	3		2		
0								
					2			1
		2	1					
	1	2		3		2	0	
					✱			

10 mines

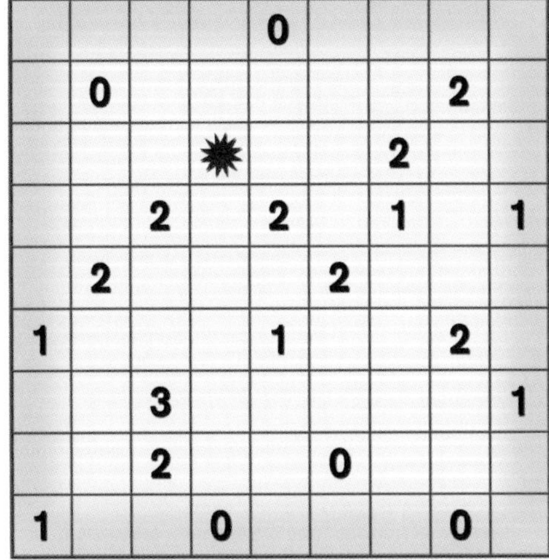

				0				
	0						2	
			✹			2		
		2		2		1		1
	2				2			
1				1			2	
		3						1
		2			0			
1			0				0	

86

15 mines

1					✹			1
			1					
	1					1		2
1			2		2		1	
		1						
	2				3		1	
2								1
		1	2					
			1	1		2		

15 mines

1			1	1		1	1	
		2						1
2								
1	✹					1	1	
	1		1					1
1		1		1				
	1					3		
2			2					
	1	1						

15 mines

				1				
	✹	2		3		3	1	
	1							
			2					2
		2		2		1		
	2		2				2	
	1				1			
		2			2			
1				1		1		1

89

15 mines

	2		1				1	
1								
			3		3			✹
1	2							1
			2		3		2	
		1						
	2				3	3		
	2		2					
1				2				

15 mines

1								1
		1		1			3	
	2	1	1		1			
				2			2	
	2		1				1	
				2		2	2	1
1		2						
	1	1		1	2		3	
	1							1

LOGIC GRIDS

The key to solving these puzzles is to first work out the facts that are known for sure from the information provided. Then deduce the rest of the information from there.

91 New people

	Battersea	Islington	Paddington	8 years	11 years	16 years	Meadow View	Rose Cottage	White Gates
Alan Bradley									
Mavis Norton									
Walter Young									
Meadow View									
Rose Cottage									
White Gates									
8 years									
11 years									
16 years									

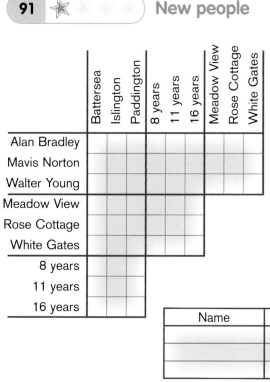

Tackfield St Andrew is a pretty Suffolk village whose inhabitants are very conservative – they still refer to a number of retired Londoners who moved there years ago as 'the new people'. From the clues below, work out where in London each of 'the new people' came from originally, how long they've lived in the village, and the name of each one's home there.

Clues

1. Walter Young, who lives at Meadow View, is not the former Londoner who used to live and work in Islington.
2. The person whose ex-home was just behind Paddington railway station has lived in Tackfield St Andrew longer than Alan Bradley.
3. The resident of White Gates has lived in the village for more than eight years.
4. One of the 'new people' has actually been living at Rose Cottage for 16 years.

Name	Area	Period	House

92 Ton up

	Elder	Grey	Senior	Mulbury	Plighwood	Wishingwell	1985	1990	1995
Daisy									
Henry									
Margaret									
1985									
1990									
1995									
Mulbury									
Plighwood									
Wishingwell									

This month, three residents of the Hawthorn Meadow old folk's home in Storbury will be receiving congratulations from the Queen for reaching the grand old age of 100. From the clues below, can you work out each centenarian's full name, the nearby village where they lived before coming to Hawthorn Meadow, and the date they moved into the home?

Clues

1. The resident called Senior moved to Hawthorn Meadow in a later year than the person who used to live in Mulbury.
2. Henry is an ex-farm worker who lived all his life in Wishingwell until he moved to Hawthorn Meadow.
3. For most of her working life, Margaret Grey ran a village post office.
4. It was in 1995 that the person surnamed Elder, who isn't Daisy, moved into the home.

First name	Surname	Village	Year

93 Firework night

	Pinwheel Gdns	Rockett Road	Squibb Street	7:00 pm	7:15 pm	7:30 pm	Barbecue	Curry	Fish and chips
Bill Cobb									
Mick North									
Steve Tibbs									
Barbecue									
Curry									
Fish and chips									
7:00 pm									
7:15 pm									
7:30 pm									

Three of the firefighters from Barchester Fire Station each put on a fireworks display for their own and the neighbours' children with a meal to follow. From the clues below, can you work out where each man lives, the time that his party started, and what kind of food they enjoyed?

Clues

1. Mick North's fireworks party started earlier than the one put on by the firefighter who lives in Pinwheel Gardens.
2. The guests at the fireworks party in Squibb Street finished up with a barbecue.
3. Bill Cobb lives in one of the new houses in Rockett Road.
4. The fireworks display which began at 7:00 pm ended at about 8:30, when all those present had fish and chips.

Firefighter	Address	Start	Meal

94 Witchfinder General

In the mid-17th century, Matthew Hopkins, the so-called 'Witchfinder General', was responsible for the deaths of many supposed witches and warlocks in East Anglia, including three from villages close to Storbury. From the clues below, can you work out each woman's name, nickname, the village from which she came and when she was convicted of witchcraft?

	'Granny Noggs'	'Mother Blue'	'Red Biddy'	Gammonham	Hillside	Lychgate	1647	1648	1649
Alice Noggs									
Clara Pinch									
Edith Rudge									
1647									
1648									
1649									
Gammonham									
Hillside									
Lychgate									

Clues

1. Not unnaturally, Alice Noggs was known as 'Granny Noggs'.
2. The witch from Gammonham was dragged before a court by Matthew Hopkins in 1647.
3. 'Mother Bluenose' wasn't the woman tried as a witch in 1648, nor did she come from the village of Lychgate, which wasn't where Clara Pinch lived all her life.
4. It was in 1649 that the Witchfinder General 'proved' that 'Red Biddy' was a witch in league with the Devil; Edith Rudge was tried in a later year than the woman from Hillside.

Testing your ability to read, digest and apply information, these puzzles give your logical thinking processes a good workout.

Real name	Nickname	Village	Year

95 Telephonic communication

These days almost everybody has a mobile phone, but back in the 1920s there were just four telephones on the local exchange for the Shropshire village of Ringwell. From the clues below, can you work out the full name and address of the subscriber assigned each number?

Clues

1. Reginald Haughton's telephone number was one less than Mr Sloman's, which wasn't Ringwell 4.
2. Lionel, whose phone number was Ringwell 3, wasn't the local squire who lived at the Manor House.
3. Ringwell 4 was the phone number for Holly Farm.
4. Mr Digby's phone number fell numerically between Frederick's and the one for the local pub, the King's Head.

	Alfred	Frederick	Lionel	Reginald	Digby	Haughton	Morley	Sloman	Holly Farm	King's Head	Manor House	Post Office Stores
Ringwell 1												
Ringwell 2												
Ringwell 3												
Ringwell 4												
Holly Farm												
King's Head												
Manor House												
Post Office Stores												
Digby												
Haughton												
Morley												
Sloman												

Phone number	First name	Surname	Address

96 Circus of spies

During the Second World War, Department AX of the British Secret Service infiltrated spies into Occupied Europe in a number of ingenious ways. In one of the most imaginative schemes, four agents were supplied with false identities as performers in a touring circus from neutral Portugal. From the clues given, work out each man's real name, his Department AX ID number, and the false name and occupation which he was assigned?

Clues

1. Algy Blake's departmental ID number was between those of the man who was given the false name 'Manuel Silva' and the one who had to pose as the circus' strong man.
2. The agent assigned the identity of juggler 'Jose Braga' had a higher identity number than Mark Niles.
3. Agent AX33 went into Occupied Europe pretending to be a clown.
4. Paul Rouse was issued with identification papers in the name of 'Anibal Gomes'.
5. Jack Keane's departmental ID number was one below that of the man who, having been recruited from the ranks of the Household Cavalry, was sent into Europe, without any additional training, posing as a trick rider.

	AX31	AX32	AX33	AX34	'Anibal Gomes'	'Jose Braga'	'Manuel Silva'	'Teofilo Mendes'	Clown	Juggler	Strong man	Trick rider
Algy Blake												
Jack Keane												
Mark Niles												
Paul Rouse												
Clown												
Juggler												
Strong man												
Trick rider												
'Anibal Gomes'												
'Jose Braga'												
'Manuel Silva'												
'Teofilo Mendes'												

Real name	ID number	False name	Occupation

97 ★★ The reviewer

The weekly *Northchester Bugle* features reviews of the plays staged at the city's Trafford Theatre, by a critic known only as The Reviewer. From the clues given, can you work out which play was reviewed in each of last month's issues, who it was performed by, and what The Reviewer thought of it?

Clues

1. Shakespeare's *The Tempest* was reviewed the week after the performance by the White Rose Theatre Company (WRTC), which wasn't the production that The Reviewer described as 'workmanlike'.
2. It was the Northchester Amateur Dramatic Society (NADS) whose production of Dylan Thomas' *Under Milk Wood* came under The Reviewer's critical eye.
3. On the 28th, The Reviewer reviewed a play called *Greybeard*, by local dramatist Wilfred Ramsbottom.
4. It was on an even-numbered day of the month that *The Bugle* featured The Reviewer's notice about the Cloggers' Theatre Company (CTC) production, which he thought was 'terrible'.
5. The production which The Reviewer decided was 'good in parts', was reviewed earlier than the performance of Agatha Christie's whodunnit The Hollow.

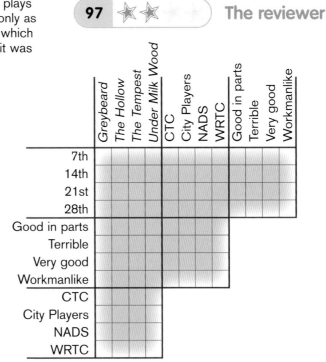

	Greybeard	*The Hollow*	*The Tempest*	*Under Milk Wood*	CTC	City Players	NADS	WRTC	Good in parts	Terrible	Very good	Workmanlike
7th												
14th												
21st												
28th												
Good in parts												
Terrible												
Very good												
Workmanlike												
CTC												
City Players												
NADS												
WRTC												

Date	Play	Company	Opinion

98 ★★ Coded

An agent of the General Intelligence Agency engaged in the interdepartmental rivalry which occupies almost as much of the GIA's efforts as actual intelligence work, acquired an encrypted list of the operations being mounted by the Special Intelligence Agency. It listed the agent in charge, the force at his command and its objective; though when he decrypted it, he ended up with just a list of their codenames. From the clues below, can you work out the codenames of each operation, its commander, his forces and their objective?

Clues

1. Operation Muskdeer isn't the one intended to accomplish Cowslip; it's not Astatine who has been put in charge of Taskforce Gamma.
2. Hafnium is the agent-in-charge for Operation Badger.
3. The codename of the operation assigned to Mercury and his Taskforce Omicron is one letter shorter than that of the operation whose objective is Lavender.
4. Petunia is the aim of Operation Porcupine.
5. The codename of the operation being undertaken by Taskforce Lambda to achieve Orchid ends in the same letter as the one assigned to the operation being headed up by Thorium.

	Agent-in-Charge: Astatine	Hafnium	Mercury	Thorium	Taskforce: Gamma	Lambda	Omicron	Theta	Objective: Cowslip	Lavender	Orchid	Petunia
Operation: Badger												
Gazelle												
Muskdeer												
Porcupine												
Objective: Cowslip												
Lavender												
Orchid												
Petunia												
Taskforce: Gamma												
Lambda												
Omicron												
Theta												

Operation	Agent-in-Charge	Taskforce	Objective

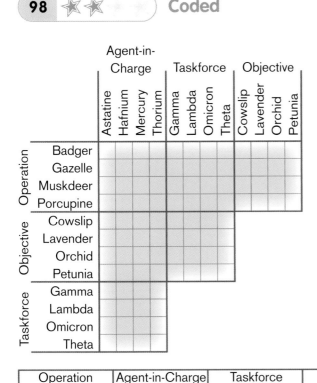

99 ★★★ The last word

As their train comes to a halt at a London terminus, five commuters contentedly fold up their daily newspapers, having just completed their respective crosswords. From the following information, can you discover the newspaper favoured by each commuter, the number of the final clue solved by each, and the answer word concerned?

Clues

1. The final word entered in one crossword – but not that in the *Independent* or *Guardian* – was 3 across BAGATELLE; the answer completing the *Independent* crossword was not 4 down or EXPONENT.
2. Paddy Tunn has not just completed the *Guardian* crossword, but his final answer had a lower clue number than that of Lou Waters.
3. Lou Waters' last answer was PEDESTAL, while the *Times* reader's last clue was numbered two higher than the one with the answer MOTLEY.
4. The final answer inserted in the *Daily Express* crossword was 7 across.
5. Mary Lebone's last clue was 5 down.
6. Vic Tourier reads the *Daily Telegraph*.

	Daily Express	*Daily Telegraph*	*Guardian*	*Independent*	*Times*	3 across	4 down	5 down	6 across	7 across	BAGATELLE	EXPONENT	MOTLEY	PEDESTAL	RELISH
Mary Lebone															
Canon Street															
Vic Tourier															
Paddy Tunn															
Lou Waters															
BAGATELLE															
EXPONENT															
MOTLEY															
PEDESTAL															
RELISH															
3 across															
4 down															
5 down															
6 across															
7 across															

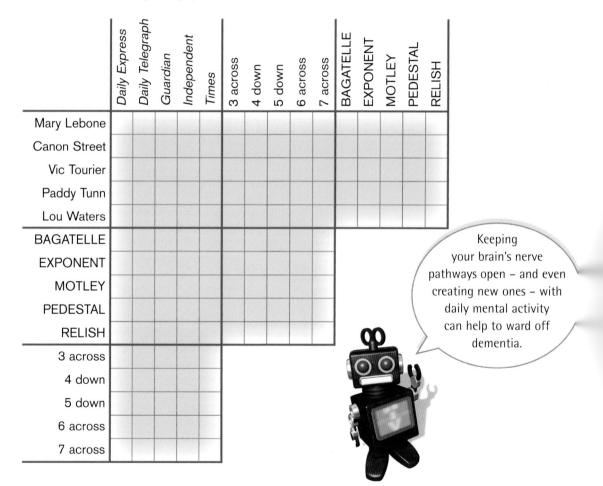

Keeping your brain's nerve pathways open – and even creating new ones – with daily mental activity can help to ward off dementia.

Commuter	Paper	Clue	Answer

100 ★★★★ All done?

At an auction sale, six regular attenders, each bearing an identification paddle with a number, were seated in the positions numbered 1 to 6 in the front row, from left to right. During the sale, each bought one lot. From the clues given below, can you name the six, say which lot each successfully bid for, and work out the number on his or her paddle?

Clues

1. Marvin made the next of our featured bids after the client with paddle 130, who was somewhere to his left.
2. Edward is next but one to the right of the holder of paddle 149; the latter is not Alistair, who is not in seat 1.
3. Lot 17 was knocked down to Philip; the paddle he displayed when the hammer fell bore an even number.
4. Tarquin's identification paddle bore the number next lower than that waved by the buyer of lot 53.
5. The holder of paddle 193 bought a later lot than the occupant of seat 1, but not the next of our featured six.
6. One client displayed paddle 128 after making a successful bid for lot 60; this was not Connor, who had seat 5 at the sale.
7. The owner of paddle 114 was in seat 3, while lot 6 was knocked down to the buyer in seat 4, whose paddle was not numbered 161.
8. An odd-numbered lot was bought by the client in seat 2.

	Alistair	Connor	Edward	Marvin	Philip	Tarquin	Lot 6	Lot 17	Lot 21	Lot 44	Lot 53	Lot 60	Paddle 114	Paddle 128	Paddle 130	Paddle 149	Paddle 161	Paddle 193
1																		
2																		
3																		
4																		
5																		
6																		
Paddle 114																		
Paddle 128																		
Paddle 130																		
Paddle 149																		
Paddle 161																		
Paddle 193																		
Lot 6																		
Lot 17																		
Lot 21																		
Lot 44																		
Lot 53																		
Lot 60																		

	1	2	3	4	5	6
Name:						
Lot number:						
Paddle:						

NONOGRAMS

The aim of a nonogram is to reveal a hidden picture in the grid provided. As you work out which squares on the grid should be shaded in, you will see an image emerge.

How to complete a nonogram

The numbers by each row or column tell you how many squares in that line should be shaded. For example, 2, 1, 3, tells you that from left to right (or top to bottom) there is a group of two shaded squares, followed by one on its own, then another three shaded squares. Shaded blocks on the same line must have at least one white square between them. However, there is no clue as to how many white squares come before the first shaded block.

Occasionally it will be obvious; for instance, if the grid is ten squares across and one of the rows features a block of six shaded squares, you can be 100 per cent certain that the centre two blocks on the line will need shading. You may also find it helpful to put a dot in squares you definitely know to be empty.

Example: 2, 1, 3

Beat this

101 

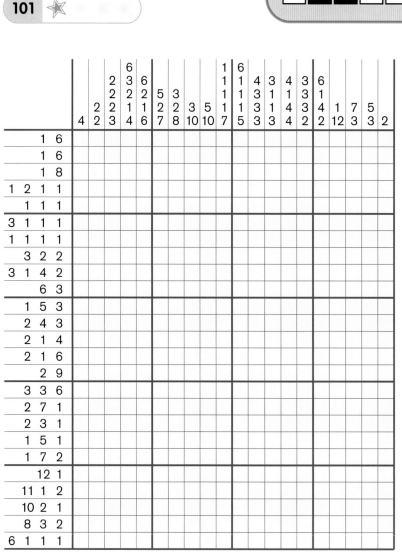

Column	Clue
1	4
2	2 2
3	2 2 2 3
4	6 3 2 1 4
5	6 2 1 6
6	5 2 7
7	3 2 8
8	3 10
9	5 10
10	1 1 1 1 7
11	6 1 1 1 5
12	4 3 3 3
13	3 1 1 3
14	4 1 4 4
15	3 3 3 2
16	6 1 4 2
17	1 12
18	7 3
19	5 3
20	2

Row clues (top to bottom):

Row	Clue
1	1 6
2	1 6
3	1 8
4	1 2 1 1
5	1 1 1
6	3 1 1 1
7	1 1 1 1
8	3 2 2
9	3 1 4 2
10	6 3
11	1 5 3
12	2 4 3
13	2 1 4
14	2 1 6
15	2 9
16	3 3 6
17	2 7 1
18	2 3 1
19	1 5 1
20	1 7 2
21	12 1
22	11 1 2
23	10 2 1
24	8 3 2
25	6 1 1 1

Nonograms test your ability to think logically and to apply supplied information to determine a puzzle's solution. These skills come in useful when reading particularly clever whodunnit novels or playing detective board games.

Shady youngsters

102 ★★

1. 3 6
2. 1 1 3 2 1
3. 1 2 1 2 2 1
4. 3 2 1 2 2 2 1
5. 1 1 1 1 2 3 2 1
6. 1 2 1 6 2 2 2
7. 1 1 3 1 2 2 1
8. 2 1 3 2 1 3
9. 2 1 2 1 2 2 2 2
10. 3 1 2 1 1 2 2 2
11. 1 2 7 2 3 2 2
12. 1 1 2 1 5 2 3
13. 2 2 1 2 1 3 2 3
14. 2 2 1 3 1 3 3
15. 4 1 3 1 2 5
16. 1 5 1 2 1 1 2 2 3
17. 3 4 2 2 4 1 4 2
18. 1 2 3 4 2 1 2 4 2
19. 1 2 2 1 1 1 1 2 2 1
20. 2 2 2 3 3 3 1 1
21. 2 3 2 4 2
22. 2 3 2 2 2
23. 13 2 2
24. 9 4 7
25. 22

Row clues (top to bottom):

1. 6
2. 1 3
3. 3 2
4. 4 1
5. 8 2 1
6. 3 4 3
7. 2 3 2
8. 8 2
9. 7 2
10. 5 2
11. 4 2 2
12. 1 1 4
13. 1 1 1 1 3
14. 1 1 1 1 3
15. 1 7 3
16. 1 2 3 2 2
17. 4 6 1 1 1 2
18. 1 2 2 1 1 1 1 1
19. 3 4 2 4 1 1
20. 4 1 5 1 2 1
21. 1 2 2 3 3
22. 1 2 2 2
23. 5 1 1 2
24. 2 3 3 4 2
25. 3 12 2 1
26. 1 3 6 4 1
27. 1 4 5 1 1
28. 2 12 2 1
29. 4 6 4 2
30. 5 6 2
31. 14 2
32. 8 3 2
33. 3 5 7
34. 5 4 5
35. 5 2

SMART THINKING

Hopping mad

103 

1. 2 8
2. 1 3 4
3. 10 2 3
4. 2 4
5. 4 9
6. 11
7. 15
8. 2 20
9. 1 2 15 6
10. 1 1 8 7 7
11. 1 13 5 9
12. 16 4 9
13. 4 7 2 2 9
14. 4 2 6 2 2 5 3
15. 2 6 5 2 1 5 2
16. 1 1 6 3 1 1 2 3 1 2
17. 2 4 2 1 4 2 2
18. 2 4 6 5 1
19. 1 1 5 6
20. 2 1 4 8
21. 5 1 1 1 1 4 2
22. 2 1 1 1
23. 9 1 1
24. 1 3
25. 2

Row clues (top to bottom):

1. 1
2. 1 1 1
3. 1 1 1 3 3 1 1
4. 3 1 1 1 2 1 1 1 1
5. 3 1 1 1 1 1 3
6. 2 2 4 1 1
7. 1 6 3
8. 1 3 2 2
9. 1 7 1
10. 1 3 5 1
11. 4 4
12. 4 2
13. 5 1
14. 7 1 2
15. 7 3
16. 8 1 1
17. 11 1 1
18. 3 2 4 2
19. 3 2 3 1 1
20. 4 2 1 1 3
21. 5 2 2 1
22. 7 2 4
23. 1 8 2 3
24. 2 9 3
25. 2 8 6
26. 2 6 5
27. 1 5 5 2 2
28. 1 4 7 3
29. 1 12 4
30. 2 13 4
31. 15 4
32. 13 6
33. 4 7 5
34. 9
35. 8

Pretty in pink

104 ★★★

1. 9 3
2. 8 3
3. 8 3
4. 8 2
5. 10 2 1
6. 2 7 3
7. 2 5 3 7 1
8. 2 24 3
9. 2 4 13 2 1
10. 2 12 4
11. 2 4 2 4 4
12. 2 3 2 6 4
13. 2 3 2 11 2 1
14. 2 2 2 5 7 3
15. 2 2 5 9 1
16. 2 2 4 3
17. 2 1 4 2 1
18. 3 3 1 1 2
19. 3 4 4 4
20. 3 6 2 4
21. 4 12 6 1
22. 4 3 3 2 2 1
23. 1 5 6 2 1 3
24. 1 11 3 2 1 1 2
25. 2 7 2 3 3 1 1
26. 2 2 7 2 1
27. 2 2 4 1 2
28. 1 1 2 1 3 3
29. 1 1 2 2 2 1
30. 1 4 2 1

Row clues (top to bottom):

1. 3 3
2. 3
3. 8 1
4. 12
5. 4 5 1 1
6. 3 4 1
7. 2 5 4
8. 2 7 3
9. 2 7 3
10. 9 4 3
11. 8 5 2 2
12. 7 4 5 2
13. 11 8 2
14. 6 3 11 2
15. 17 3 2
16. 16 2 2
17. 3 1 9 1 2
18. 2 7 1 1
19. 2 2 2 1 1
20. 1 2 1 1 1
21. 1 2 1 1 2
22. 2 1 1 1
23. 2 2 2 2
24. 2 2 1 2
25. 2 1 2 2
26. 1 1 2 2
27. 1 1 2 2
28. 1 2 1 2
29. 1 2 2 1 1
30. 2 1 1 1
31. 2 1 2 5
32. 1 1 1 1 4
33. 1 1 5 3
34. 1 1 4 3
35. 1 1 1 2
36. 1 1 1 1
37. 6 7 9 5
38. 6 7 2 5 2 3
39. 3 3 3 3 3 2 2
40. 1 5 6 4 2

SMART THINKING

April showers

105 ★★★★

Column	Clue
1	3 1
2	4 1
3	5 4 1 1
4	1 6 1 2 1 3 1
5	6 1 2 2 1
6	8 1 2 3 3
7	8 1 2 2 5 2
8	10 3 2 2 1
9	10 1 2 2
10	11 2 1 4
11	12 1 1 2 2
12	12 2 2 2 1 1 2
13	14 8 4 2 1 3
14	10 2 3 1 1 2 5 2 3
15	8 2 3 1 1 1 7 2 13
16	6 3 4 2 11 9 4
17	5 5 4 1 1 2 1 9 9 4
18	5 6 5 1 1 1 10 9 4
19	4 7 5 2 1 22 4
20	4 8 5 1 5 12 4
21	3 8 6 4 1 11 4
22	3 9 7 4 4 11 4
23	2 9 12 8 7 7
24	2 11 7 12 7 4
25	2 11 3 16 7
26	2 12 19 5 1 1
27	27 10 8 1
28	17 8 9 10 1
29	17 9 12 2
30	18 5 1 13 1
31	2 13 4 1 13 1
32	2 12 2 14 4
33	2 11 2 1 12 2
34	4 9 1 1 2 7 1
35	5 8 1 2 1 2 7 3
36	6 7 1 1 4 4 7 1
37	8 4 13 7 1
38	10 1 1 2 5 7 1
39	14 1 2 7
40	13 1 1 1 1 7 1
41	12 1 1 2 4 1 2 1
42	11 1 1 2 12 1
43	1 1 11 1 2 2 3 12 1
44	10 16 11 1
45	10 17 8 2
46	9 1 2 8 2
47	1 1 8 1 2 2 3 4
48	7 1 1 2 1
49	4 1 1 2 2
50	1 1 1 3

Row clues (top to bottom):

Row	Clue
1	3
2	13 1
3	1 20
4	13 8
5	13 7 3
6	13 10 4 1 1
7	14 13 5
8	14 14 5
9	14 16 6
10	15 17 6
11	14 18 7 1
12	14 19 7
13	8 20 8
14	6 21 8
15	5 13 8
16	2 8 11 9
17	11 10 8
18	13 1 8 9
19	1 14 2 5 9
20	3 7 2 3 10
21	1 4 3 13
22	3 3 3 3 6
23	1 2 2 3 1 5
24	2 2 1 3 1 4
25	1 1 4 3 3
26	1 1 4 1 1 2
27	2 1 3 2 2
28	1 3 1 3 7 5
29	1 2 1 3 1 2
30	2 1 6 3 5
31	6 1 8 4 10
32	1 1 9 5 2
33	4 2 1 11 5 3
34	2 1 6 1 9 2 2 5
35	1 1 6 1 8 1 1 11
36	1 2 8 7 1 3
37	1 1 2 9 10 1 5
38	2 3 7 8 1 9
39	2 6 6 2 11
40	2 5 4 2 3
41	2 5 1 3 2
42	2 2 3 4 2
43	6 2 7
44	2 8 3
45	15 5
46	15 7
47	18 10
48	1 26 4
49	1 1 11 14 4
50	1 2 1 11 14 4
51	8 12 18
52	12 8 12 4
53	8 9 4
54	9 6 5
55	1 9 4
56	2 1 1
57	6 10 1 1
58	12 1 1 1 1
59	14 1 2 1 3 2
60	14 13 11

SMART THINKING

CRYPTOCROSS

A cryptogram is a coded message in which each letter of the alphabet has been substituted for another.

This is what has happened in the crossword below. Every letter has been substituted for another at random. For example, you will see from the key that all the alphabet letter E's have been replaced by the code letter S, and all the alphabet letter I's are represented by the code letter O. Each of the 26 letters of the alphabet is used at least once.

106 ★★★★

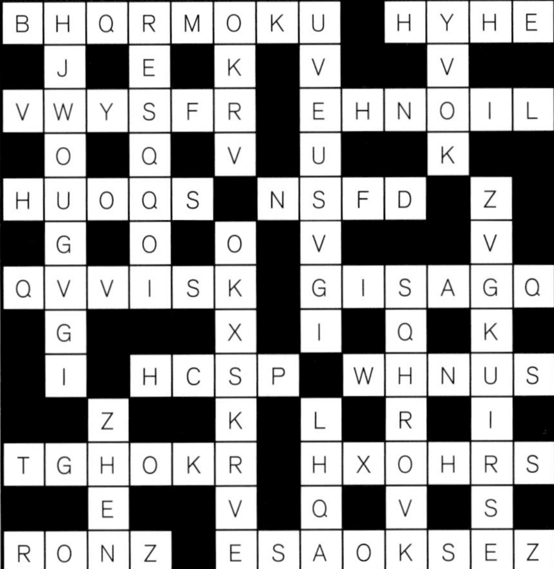

B	H	Q	R	M	O	K	U		H	Y	H	E
	J		E		K		V			V		
V	W	Y	S	F	R		E	H	N	O	I	L
	O		Q		V		U			K		
H	U	O	Q	S		N	S	F	D		Z	
	G		O		O		V				V	
Q	V	V	I	S	K		G	I	S	A	G	Q
	G				X		I		Q		K	
	I		H	C	S	P		W	H	N	U	S
		Z			K		L		R		I	
T	G	H	O	K	R		H	X	O	H	R	S
		E			V		Q		V		S	
R	O	N	Z		E	S	A	O	K	S	E	Z

Can you decode the crossword and enter all the correct words in the grid below?

To keep your brain at full stretch, try making up your own clues to a crossword. Work back from the solution to think of the clue.

A	B	C	D	E	F	G	H	I	J	K	L	M
				S				O				
N	**O**	**P**	**Q**	**R**	**S**	**T**	**U**	**V**	**W**	**X**	**Y**	**Z**

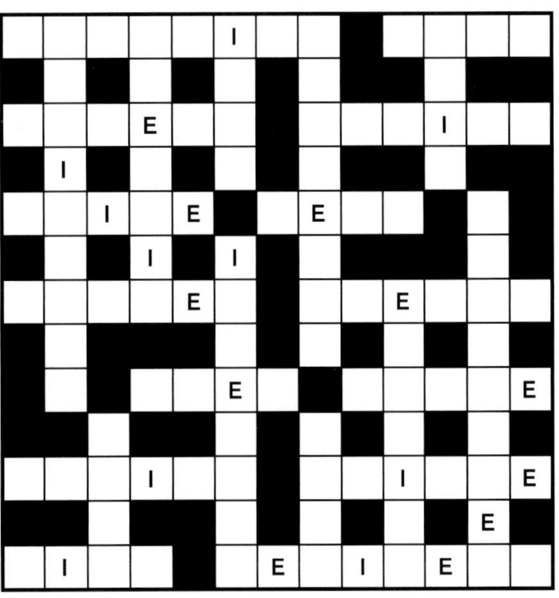

KICKSELF

Kickself puzzles are made up of questions that usually have obvious answers – but if you don't work it out, you will want to kick yourself when you see the solution.

Hull, on the east coast of England, is 128 miles away from Liverpool, which is on the west coast of England.

One day, the Trans-Pennine Express, which makes just one 10-minute stop, leaves Hull for Liverpool. At exactly the same time, another express train, which makes three 5-minute stops, leaves Liverpool for Hull.

The Hull to Liverpool train travels at an average speed of 80 mph and the Liverpool to Hull train travels at an average speed of 75 mph.

Which train will be farthest from Hull when they meet?

In my closet all but five of my ties are striped, all but five are plain brown, all but five are plain red, all but five are plain green, all but five are polka dot and all but five are plain black.

How many ties do I have in my closet?

What letter is missing?

What do the following have in common?

Duke Ellington

The New Testament

A car park

The game of Scrabble

A crocodile

In the year 2002 Christmas Day was on a Wednesday. One week later New Year's Day was also on a Wednesday, because New Year's Day always comes exactly seven days after Christmas Day.

In the year 2022 why will Christmas Day and New Year's Day fall on different days of the week?

ECN EUQ ESE SRE ???

What three letters come next?

Is it:

a. VOC
b. VER
c. EWE
d. ENO

NO WRY NOODLE

Use all 11 letters of the phrase above to spell out one word only.

SMART THINKING

What is the missing figure in this sequence?

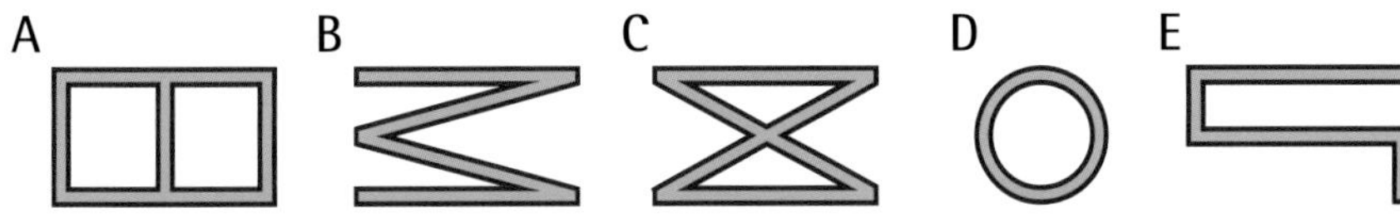

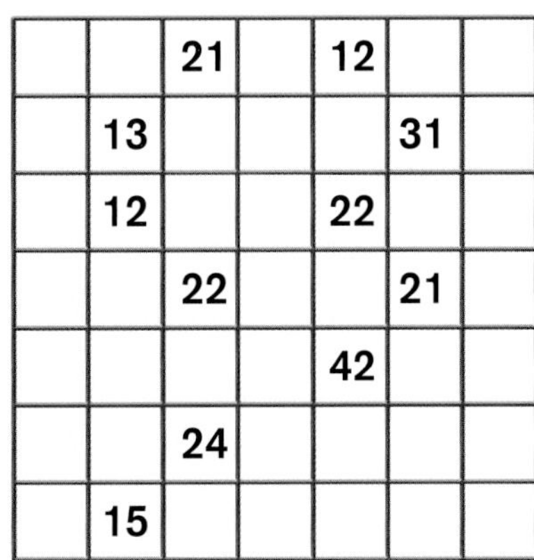

		21		12		
	13				31	
	12			22		
		22			21	
				42		
		24				
	15					

Following the rules and logic of the example above, replace the dot in each square below with the correct number.

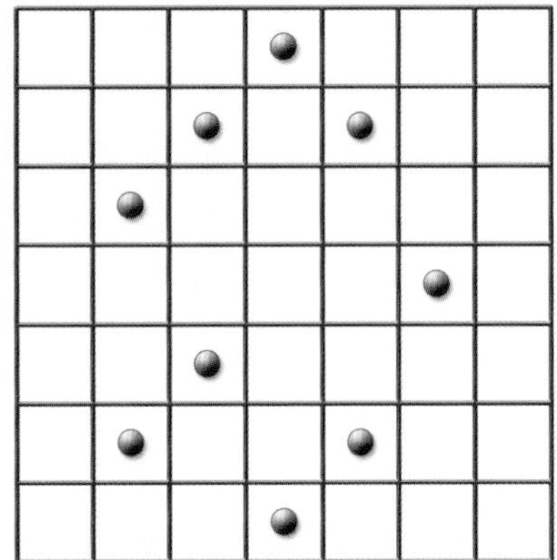

Which is the word in the missing square?

CALM	HOPE	ONLY
OVEN	SEEK	EACH
ONYX	NEXT	?

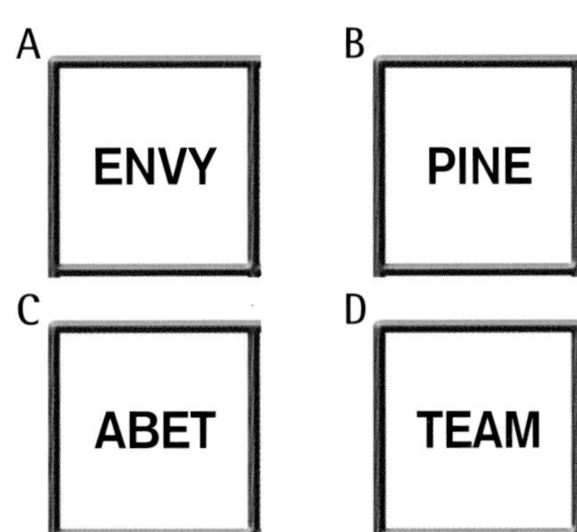

How is it possible to take away nine of the fourteen captain's chairs and leave just two?

Re-orientate the letter blocks above to form a six-letter word in the English language.

DICE GAMES

In the puzzles on these and the following pages, your challenge is to work out which of the given dice could be accurately formed from the template provided in each example.

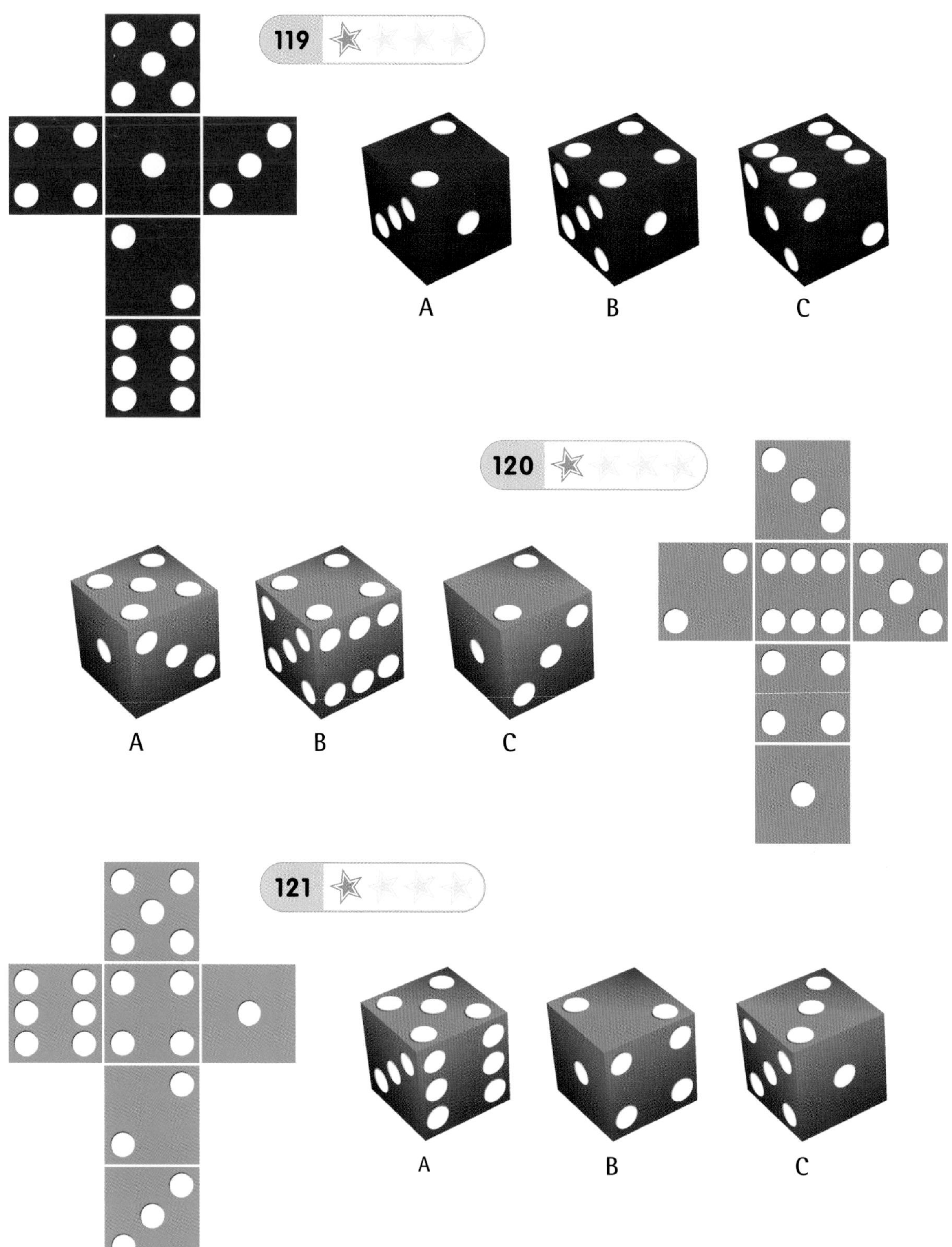

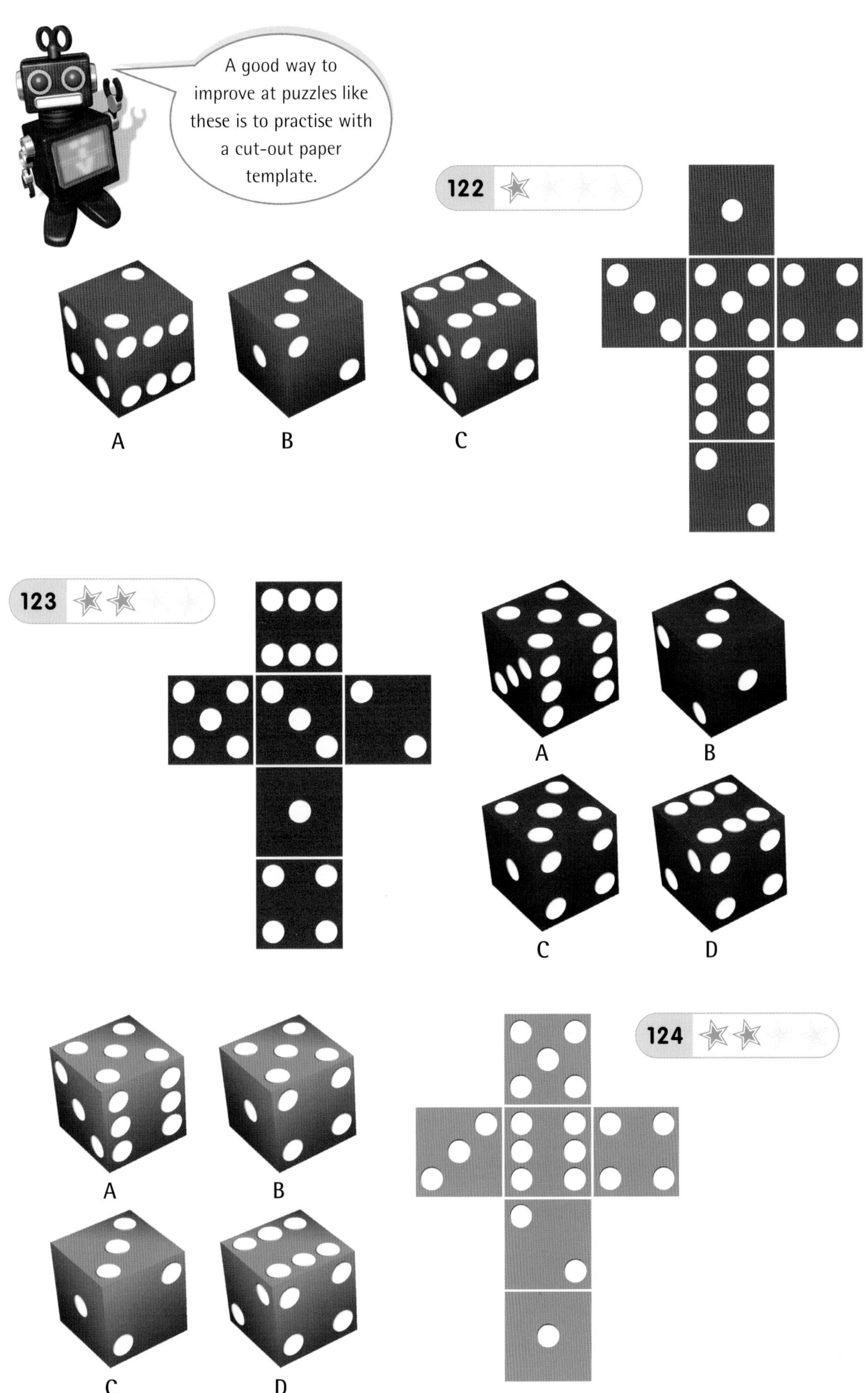
A good way to improve at puzzles like these is to practise with a cut-out paper template.
122
A
B
C
123
A
B
C
D
A
B
C
D
124

125
A
B
C
D
126
A
B
C
D
127
A
B
C
D
E

128

A B C D E

129

A B C D E F

130

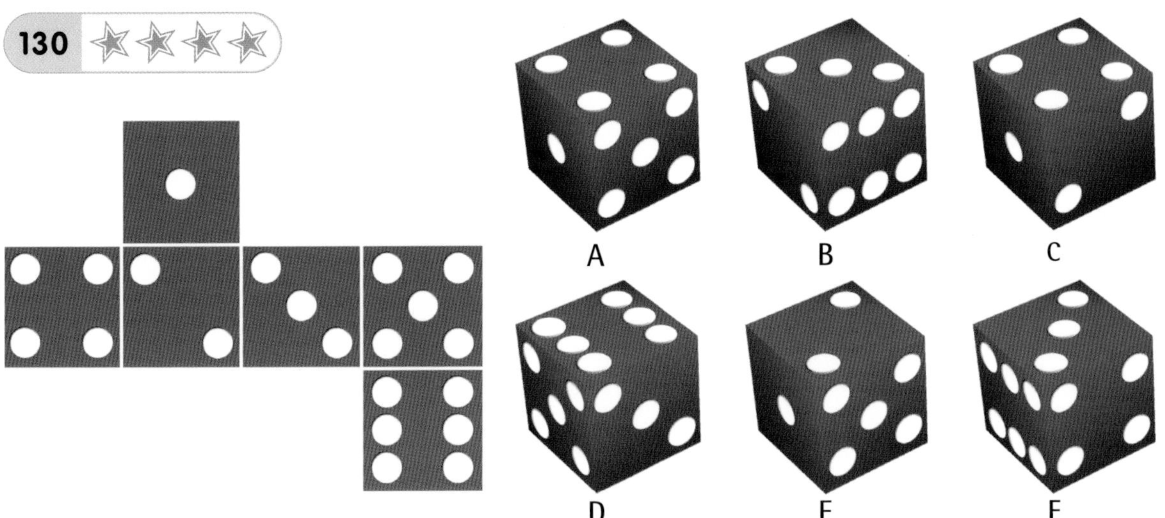

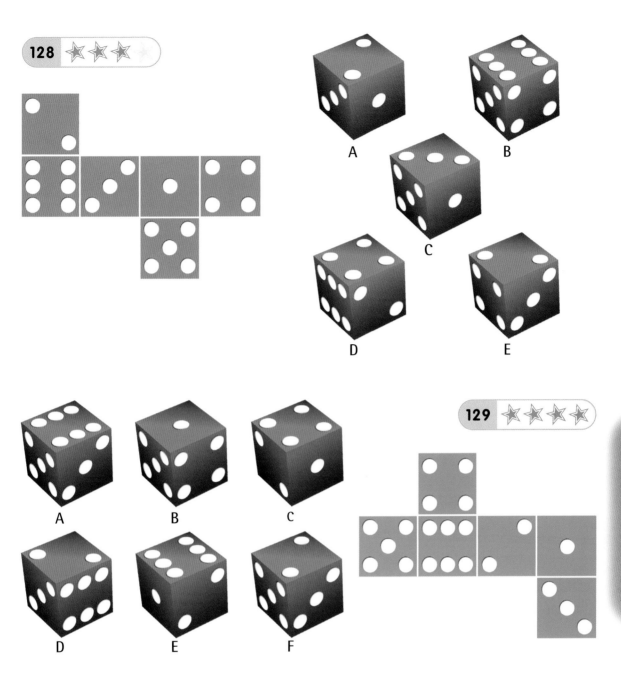

SMART THINKING

CODES/CRYPTOGRAMS

In cryptography a message is disguised using codes and ciphers. A cryptogram is the coded message, and cryptoanalysis is the breaking of the code or cipher without the key.

The puzzles in this section use cipher codes whereby numbers have been used to disguise a message, phrase or quotation.

131 

Crack the code

In the following list, numbers have been allocated to letters in accordance with their position in the alphabet: A = 1, B = 2, C = 3, D = 4, E = 5 etc.

However, to make the cryptoanalysis much more difficult word boundaries have been eliminated, for example, the word CIPHER, in which the position of the letters in the alphabet is 3 – 9 – 16 – 8 – 5 – 18, would appear as 39168518.

Can you decode the five names below, and then choose which is the odd one out?

1. 31531151819161149512 (2 words)
2. 1615135181149114
3. 38982118211
4. 1991135195
5. 413819821144

132 

Hidden message

Pay careful attention to the instructions when decoding the following message.

61, 24, 42, 12 61, 14,
49, 53, 40, 25, 66, 38, 32

CRYPTOPHONES:

Decipher the codes shown below the telephone face to solve the puzzles that follow. Each number represents one of the letters shown with it on the telephone dial. A number does not necessarily represent the same letter each time.

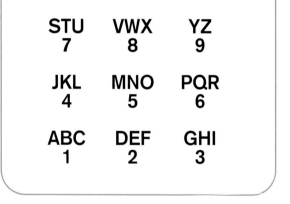

STU 7	VWX 8	YZ 9
JKL 4	MNO 5	PQR 6
ABC 1	DEF 2	GHI 3

133 

Use the cryptophone code to find a familiar saying.

1277 73353 73512 743122 16212

134 

Use the same code again to find a phrase.

1673231314 357244332512

135 

Decipher this cryptophone code to reveal a quotation.

665161773517355 37 732 73322 52 7352

136 The Polybius Cipher

A	B	C	D	E
F	G	H	I	J
K	L	M	N	O
P	Q	R	S	T
U	V	W	X	Y

This code was invented by a Greek writer Polybius in the 2nd century BC.

With the aid of the grid opposite, can you decode the quotation below?

11 13, 35, 34, 44, 24, 14, 15, 43, 11, 45, 15
41, 15, 43, 44, 35, 34 24, 44
44, 35, 33, 15, 35, 34, 15 53, 23, 35 13, 11, 34
41, 32, 11, 55 45, 23, 15 12, 11, 22, 41, 24, 41, 15, 44
12, 51, 45 14, 35, 15, 44, 34, ' 45

137 Multi-choice

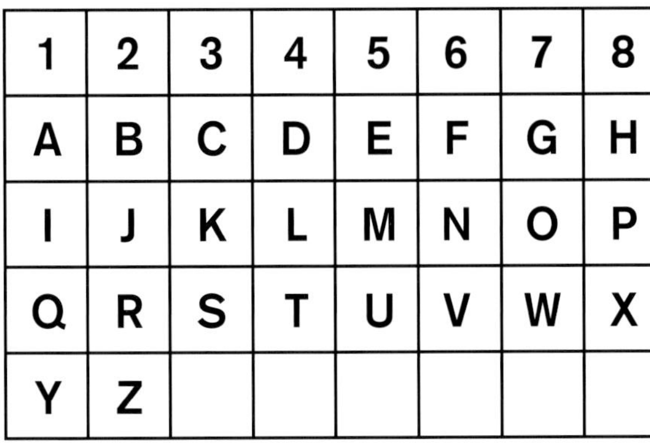

1	2	3	4	5	6	7	8
A	B	C	D	E	F	G	H
I	J	K	L	M	N	O	P
Q	R	S	T	U	V	W	X
Y	Z						

Cryptophones are made difficult by their multiple options at each stage. Use a process of elimination to rule out unlikely options.

Each number provides a choice of either three or four letters in accordance with the above table.

Now decode the following words of wisdom:

A. 485 8121478 13 1 5134521753 25134

B. 485 78415134 827341153 4814 75 4165 16 485
2534 76 144 87331245 772443, 164 485 853315134
65123 4813 13 4255 126167 315312

138 Number cruncher

Figure out this puzzle to find a secret message. You will need to work out how each number relates to a letter's position in the alphabet.

969 445, 100, 189, 209, 559 767, 143, 113 478, 826, 915, 794

CIPHERWORDS

In these puzzles, you have to work out which letter of the alphabet is represented by each number. Repeat the starter letters throughout the puzzle wherever they are given. This should give enough clues to the identity of the other letters to enable you to guess at likely words. The finished grid will resemble a normal crossword solution.

139 ★★

Study the four letters provided in the grid, and use them to deduce which numbers represent the rest of the letters in the alphabet.

Remember that the most common letter in the English language is E so it will probably occur most often in the grid.

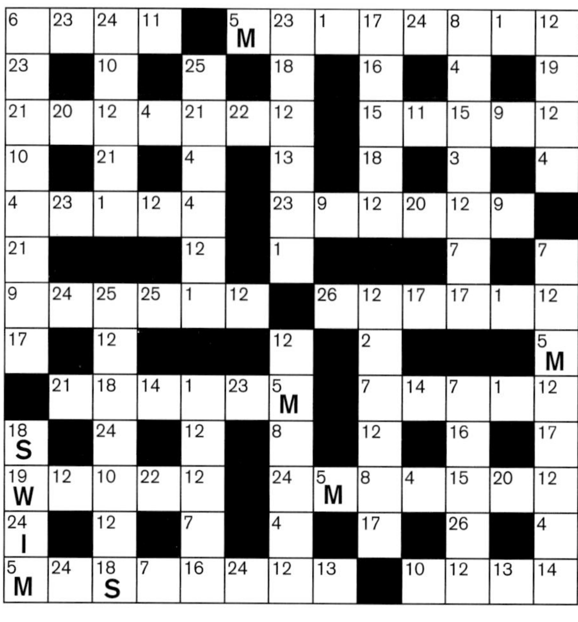

6	23	24	11		5 M	23	1	17	24	8	1	12
23		10		25		18		16		4		19
21	20	12	4	21	22	12		15	11	15	9	12
10		21		4		13		18		3		4
4	23	1	12	4		23	9	12	20	12	9	
21				12		1				7		7
9	24	25	25	1	12		26	12	17	17	1	12
17		12				12		2				5 M
	21	18	14	1	23	5 M		7	14	7	1	12
18 S		24		12		8		12		16		17
19 W	12	10	22	12		24	5 M	8	4	15	20	12
24 I		12		7		4		17		26		4
5 M	24	18 S	7	16	24	12	13		10	12	13	14

1	2	3	4	5 M	6	7	8	9	10	11	12	13
14	15	16	17	18 S	19 W	20	21	22	23	24 I	25	26

140 ★★★

Having fewer letters to start off with makes this puzzle much harder. Use the same method as before to decide where the rest of letters go – you will need to use careful thinking and your full word power to complete this grid.

16	6	8	14	5	15	13		19	9	25	9	4
18		15		15		22		16		16		16
13	22	20	14	9	2	13		8	15	23	9	12
12		14		12		19		9		7		21
2	13	23	16	12		20	9	12	5	15	13	2
				13		2				12		13
10	9	1	1	8	13		21	17	12	13	4	10
13		13				21		16				
11	13	9	12	11	15	8		8	15	25	24	3
8		8		14		13		10 D		17		14
9	6	16	18	13		13	20	14 I	21	16	10	13
2		15		12		18		23 N		24		8
13	21	21	9	3		13	26	26	17	13	9	10

1	2	3	4	5	6	7	8	9	10 D	11	12	13
14 I	15	16	17	18	19	20	21	22	23 N	24	25	26

141 ★★★☆

You may need to use trial and error in attempting this Cipherword as only two letters have been provided to start you off.

	26		22		15	■	9 U		12		12	
11	14	26	26	3	26	■	11 S	26	26	11	6	22
■	18	■	26	■	25	■	10	■	26	■	19	■
24	9	16	20	■	4	15	26	14	2	4	19	7
■	1	■	■	■	5	■	13	■	13	■	25	■
23	10	4	23	8	26	14	■	24	18	8	26	13
■	■	■	18	■	13	■	13	■	18	■	■	■
11	20	26	14	15	■	2	26	21	2	4	25	26
■	13	■	17	■	6	■	5	■	■	■	4	■
11	26	17	9	26	14	23	26	■	16	6	3	26
■	19	■	26	■	1	■	13	■	4	■	6	■
5	26	11	11	26	25	■	11	26	14	2	13	7
■	13	■	2	■	26	■	26	■	21	■	15	■

1	2	3	4	5	6	7	8	9 U	10	11 S	12	13
14	15	16	17	18	19	20	21	22	23	24	25	26

142 ★★★★

With only one letter as a guide, you should only try and tackle this puzzle when you have completed one of the previous Cipherwords.

8	26	15	8	■	4	1	17	1	4	18	19	25
2	■	19	■	10	■	21	■	14	■	12	■	1
18	11	6	1	1	9	1	■	1	14	26	25	1
12	■	9	■	18	■	4	■	4	■	16	■	13
26	16	1	4	3	■	15	19	3 T	1	19	6	■
3	■	■	■	1	■	1	■	■	■	22	■	1
19	23	17	1	4	24	■	19	16	3	8	1	21
25	■	1	■	■	■	9	■	1	■	■	■	12
■	22	8	1	11	6	1	■	19	20	7	6	25
1	■	26	■	6	■	19	■	4	■	25	■	2
22	2	22	2	19	■	25	26	24	4	19	4	5
8	■	25	■	13	■	2	■	5	■	13	■	1
2	21	1	25	1	3	3	1	■	10	1	1	4

1	2	3 T	4	5	6	7	8	9	10	11	12	13
14	15	16	17	18	19	20	21	22	23	24	25	26

Keep in mind common word-endings and letters that often go together – for example if you have a **G** as the last letter of a word, it is probable that the word ends in **ING**. Similarly, a **Q** is almost always followed by the letter **U**.

FILL INS

Position the words listed into the correct spaces in the matrix. Once you have selected the appropriate clue by length, you should be able to work out the words that bisect it.

143 

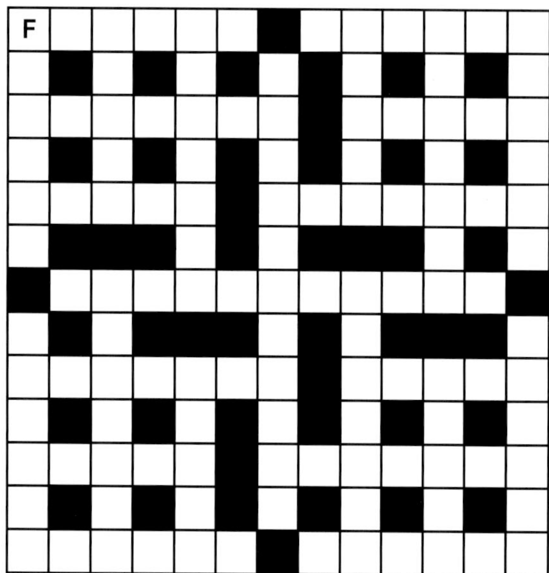

Solve these puzzles by fitting the words supplied into their correct position. The words are sorted by length and are in alphabetical order. One or two letters have been inserted to get you started.

5 letter words
Build
Dodge
Donor
Exalt
Gleam
Lager
Lupin
Yield

6 letter words
Animal
Bamboo
Facade
Folder
Letter
Opener
Ordeal
Symbol

7 letter words
Abandon
Achieve
Blatant
Capable
Chalice
Dolphin
Embargo
Radiate

11 letter words
Accommodate
Detrimental

144 

3 letter words
Axe
Ban
Emu
Era
Inn
Odd
Peg
Use

5 letter words
Adage
Aisle
Argue
Avoid
Binge
Chase
Ethos
Exact
Habit
Image
Nadir
Niece

7 letter words
Amateur
Arbiter
Chemist
Cistern
Emerald
Lattice
Message
Nemesis
Nuclear
Overlap
Perhaps
Plaster
Prattle
Radiate
Tactile
Trapper

9 letter words
Expectant
Probation
Senseless
Surrender

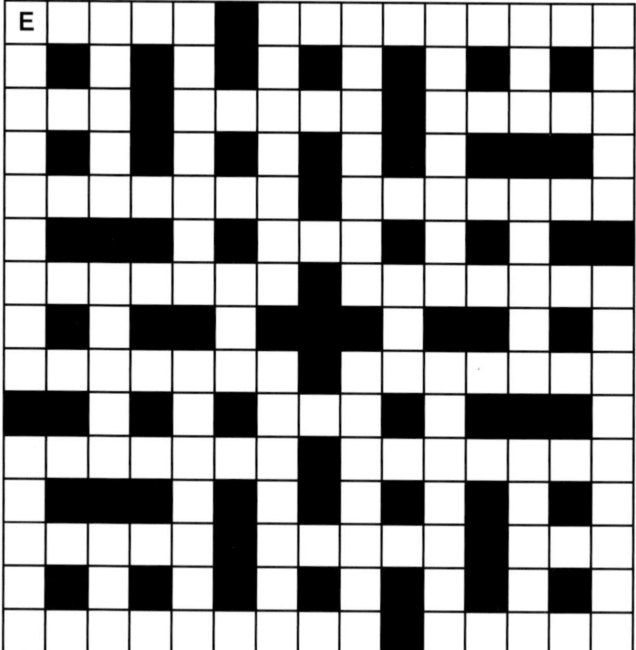

SMART THINKING

145 ★★

This fill in puzzle is harder because you only have 3-letter and 5-letter words to choose from. So pick carefully. We have added a couple of starters to set you off.

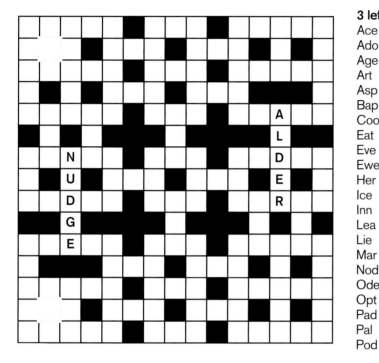

3 letter words
Ace
Ado
Age
Art
Asp
Bap
Coo
Eat
Eve
Ewe
Her
Ice
Inn
Lea
Lie
Mar
Nod
Ode
Opt
Pad
Pal
Pod
Ray
Roe
Saw
See
Sob
Spa
Sun
Tie
Try
Via

5 letter words
~~Alder~~
Alien
Angel
Argue
Aspen
Bathe
Beard
Beret
Chaos
Cramp
Dingo
Ditty
Flash
Fleet
Hedge
Leafy
Manor
Nervy
~~Nudge~~
Paper
Plant
Pleat
Reign
Repel
Robin
Ruddy
Sedan
Split
Stone
Tango
Tense
World

146 ★★★★

This is a harder version that uses numbers instead of letters. Solve the puzzle in a similar way by fitting the numbers supplied into their correct position in the diagram. The numbers are sorted by length and are in ascending order.

3 figures
141
172
207
213
259
379
405
412
413
491
512
523
588
647
651
657
675
733
742
788
821
824
833
843
852
861
952
975

4 figures
1759
2284
3575
6134

5 figures
47320
54784
80287
87879

6 figures
458485
541032
543254
862314
867325
876510
893285
893291

7 figures
2375192
7225129
7235678
7525182

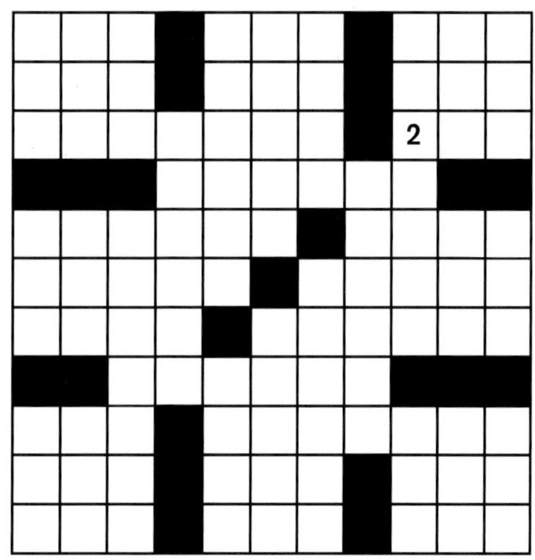

SMART THINKING

LATERAL THINKING

The term 'lateral thinking' was coined by its creator and pioneer, Dr Edward de Bono, and is a system for creative problem solving. The word 'lateral' means *of, or relating to, either side, away from the median axis.* These puzzles are designed to exercise your powers of lateral thinking, and encourage creative thought to find solutions that may not seem apparent at first glance.

147

Column A	Column B
CALL	**HOUSE**
SUIT	**KIN**
WALK	**LEG**
GUT	**TIRED**

Which word above is in the wrong column?

148

My sister Susan recently met an old school chum. 'Gosh', she said, 'I haven't seen you since we were at University together, must be about 10 years'. 'Yes', said her friend, 'since that time I have opened up my own fashion store, and I also got married'. 'Congratulations', said my sister, 'was it to anyone I know'. 'No, I don't believe so', said her friend, 'but this is my son, who is now eight years old'. 'Hello', said my sister, 'and what is your name?' 'I am named after my father', replied the boy. 'Then I think your name must be Peter' said my sister.

How did she know?

149

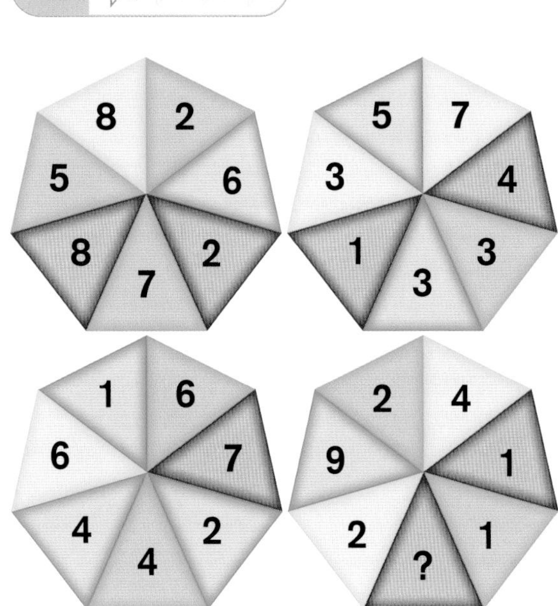

What number should replace the question mark?

150

How much does my cat Tinkerbell weigh if it weighs 2 kilograms plus half its own weight?

151

Four explorers deep in the jungle have to cross a rope bridge in the middle of a moonless night. Unfortunately the bridge is only strong enough to support two people at a time. Because deep in the jungle on a moonless night it is pitch black, the explorers need a torch to guide them, otherwise there is every likelihood they would lose their footing and plunge to their deaths in the ravine below. However, between them they have only one torch.

Young Jane can cross the ravine in two minutes, her brother Gordon can cross in three minutes, their father Paul can cross in five minutes, but old Colonel Montegue can only hobble across in 15 minutes.

What is the quickest time in which it is possible for all four to reach the other side?

152

Place a marble into a bottle, then seal the bottle by putting a cork in the opening at the top.

How is it possible to get the marble out of the bottle without pulling out the cork or breaking the bottle?

153

	5829614	is to	**8642159**
and	**7231569**	is to	**6213579**
therefore	**9241638**	is to	**???????**

154

Fill in the missing letters in the two related sequences below.

T E N T D T T S F ? R C

H ? I E S A E O A E I A

155

Philarmonus, Vaudemont, Florentius, Placentio, Hysterica

Apart from all being Shakespearian characters, what do the names above all have in common, and which name below has the same thing in common with them?

Leonatus, Edmundsbury, Cavaleiro, Calpurnia

156

12			13		
		21	23		22
12			13		
	11				12
32	31		33		32
		11		?	

What two-figure number should replace the question mark?

157

S O E N S Y ?

What letter completes the sequence above?

161

What are the missing letters in this sequence?

aa, ee, ii, ee, ii, ??, ee

158

    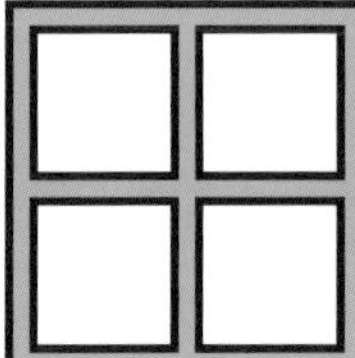

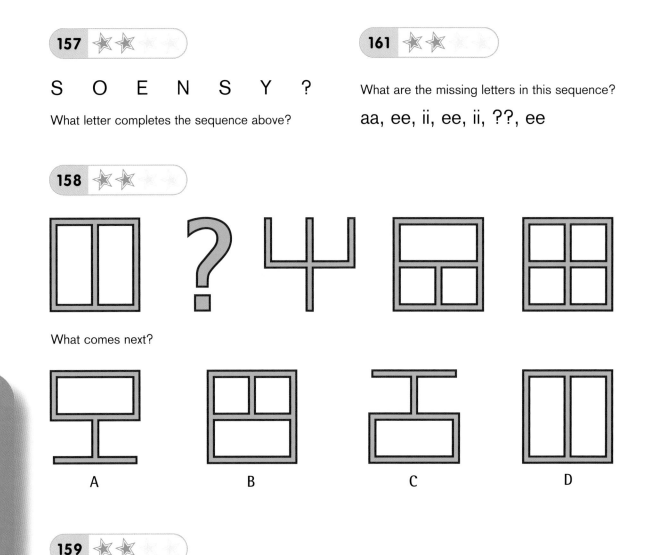

What comes next?

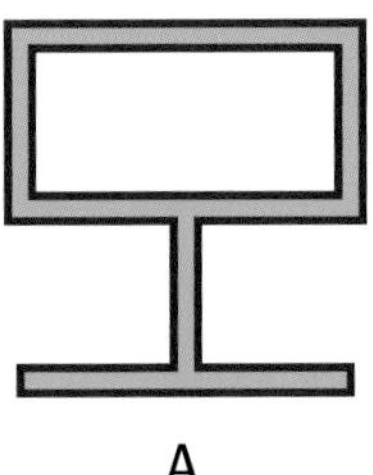

A

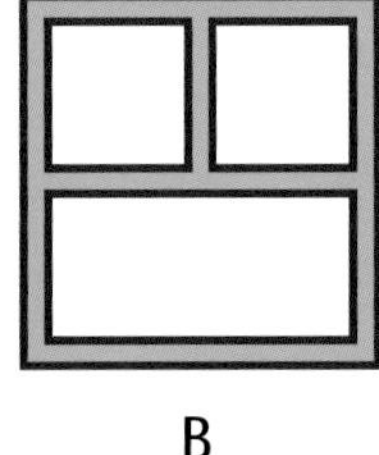

B

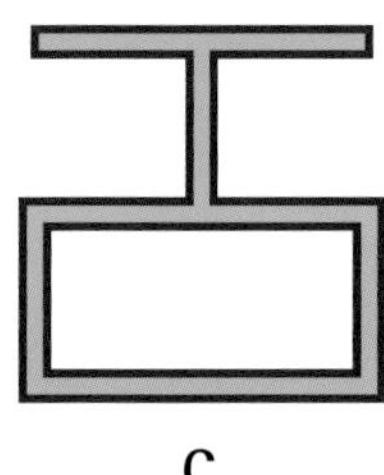

C

D

SMART THINKING

159

Mother has baked a cake for her daughter's 18th birthday party which she is about to share out between the five people present.

The cake measures 22.5 cm on each side. There is a layer of cream around the top perimeter and all the sides are covered in a layer of marzipan.

Mother must divide up the cake into five equal and fair portions. How does she go about doing this to everyone's satisfaction?

160

What phrase is contained in the array of words to the right?

MASK	AMID	KEEN	EDGE
ABLE	LOST	STAR	SHOW
PLEA	LAND	TIDY	PAST
DRUM	ZONE	LATE	EAST

What number should replace the question mark?

2	2	3	2	1	3
2	2	1	3	1	6
1	3	2	2	2	5
2	1	4	3	2	7
3	2	3	9	11	?

aqueduct, obstacle, incubate, headlong, outweigh, boastful, shortage, ?

What comes next?

mistaken, sandwich, yourself, optimize or gridlock?

aghast	raisin
knight	dowager
spin	this
totem	idea
end	?

What word below is missing?

ace, leg, jug, fan, yet

alkaline, twilight, carefree, forestry, positive, singular, tungsten, Einstein, ????????, temerity.

What word below is missing?

Shanghai
Brisbane
Calcutta
Istanbul
Santiago

166

LOG
PET
ELF
TRY
ARM
SKI
GAP
SHE
CAT
???
PEN
TIN
TOP
ORB
ONE

What word below is missing?

WET, PET, TIP, CAR, OLD ?

LATERAL THINKING SITUATIONS

These puzzles combine puzzling and storytelling. Basic clues to the answers are provided, but you need to fill in the rest of the details to find the solutions. You will need to use both logic and imagination – our solutions are in the Answers section starting on page 341, but you may dream up your own feasible explanations.

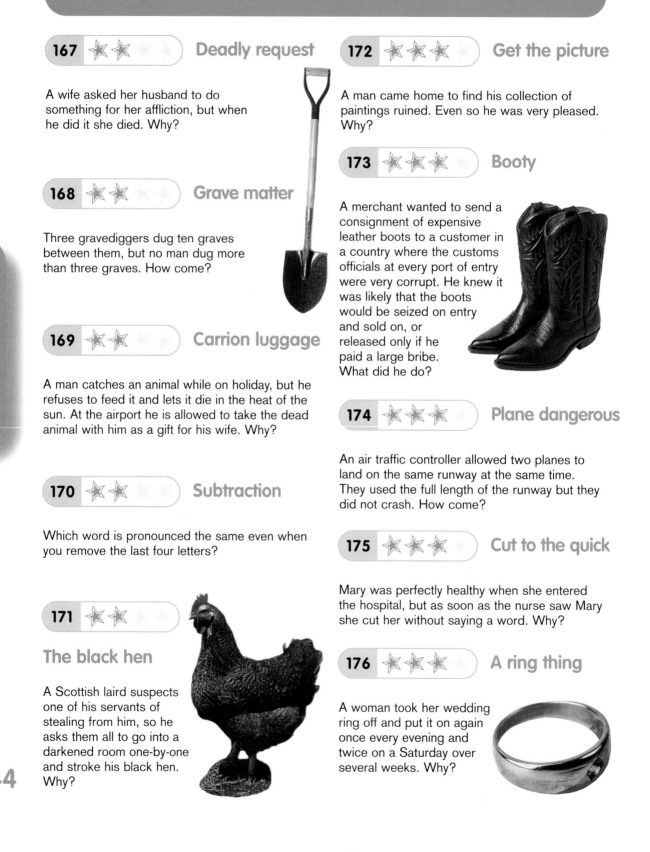

167 Deadly request

A wife asked her husband to do something for her affliction, but when he did it she died. Why?

168 Grave matter

Three gravediggers dug ten graves between them, but no man dug more than three graves. How come?

169 Carrion luggage

A man catches an animal while on holiday, but he refuses to feed it and lets it die in the heat of the sun. At the airport he is allowed to take the dead animal with him as a gift for his wife. Why?

170 Subtraction

Which word is pronounced the same even when you remove the last four letters?

171 The black hen

A Scottish laird suspects one of his servants of stealing from him, so he asks them all to go into a darkened room one-by-one and stroke his black hen. Why?

172 Get the picture

A man came home to find his collection of paintings ruined. Even so he was very pleased. Why?

173 Booty

A merchant wanted to send a consignment of expensive leather boots to a customer in a country where the customs officials at every port of entry were very corrupt. He knew it was likely that the boots would be seized on entry and sold on, or released only if he paid a large bribe. What did he do?

174 Plane dangerous

An air traffic controller allowed two planes to land on the same runway at the same time. They used the full length of the runway but they did not crash. How come?

175 Cut to the quick

Mary was perfectly healthy when she entered the hospital, but as soon as the nurse saw Mary she cut her without saying a word. Why?

176 A ring thing

A woman took her wedding ring off and put it on again once every evening and twice on a Saturday over several weeks. Why?

MISCELLANEOUS LOGIC PUZZLES

All the puzzles on this and the following pages can be solved by using logical analysis. Consider all the evidence you have been given before reaching your conclusion.

The squashed fly

Two trains are heading towards one another from 100 miles apart on a single track. The first is travelling at 60 mph, and the second at 40 mph. A fly starts at the front of the first train and flies to the second and then back to the first, then back to the second, and so on. Eventually there is a terrible crash and our fly is squashed. If the fly can fly at 50 mph, how far does he fly before the crash?

Coloured order

Bigmouth Bertha had been given a bag of jawbreakers by her mother in order to stop her chattering. The bag contained nine coloured sweets: three red, three yellow and three green. Bertha removed three sweets from the bag, one at a time. Her brother, Boring Bernard, who was a collector of insignificant detail, noted the following four facts in his diary:

1. A yellow sweet was not taken out later than a green one, and vice-versa.
2. Only if a yellow was removed later than a red one was a green taken earlier than a red.
3. A green was not taken earlier than a red, and vice-versa.
4. The first sweet was a different colour from both the second and third.

What colour were the three sweets in the order of their removal?

On report

Can you punctuate the following sentence so that it makes perfect sense:

Smith where Jones had had had had had had had had had had had the teacher's approval.

Averages

On average, two out of seventy-two people get 2, two out of seventy-two people get 12, and twelve out of seventy-two people get 7. No-one ever gets only 1 and no-one ever gets 17. What on earth am I talking about?

A Hollywood murder

Inspector Lestrade enters the dining room. A body lies in the middle of the room. Four other people were in the room when the lights went out. Each of them makes a statement.

Alice: 'I know who killed her.'
Benny: 'I killed her.'
Carol: 'Benny killed her.'
Donald: 'It wasn't Benny or Carol.'

Background enquiries reveal that all the suspects are totally untrustworthy, so Lestrade correctly perceives that they are all lying. Who was the murderer?

A taxing road problem

There are four farmers, named Able, Baker, Charlie and Dog, who live up a dirt road leading off State Highway 1. They are located one, two, three and four miles, respectively, from the highway. The county offers to pave the road up to Dog's place, if the farmers will pay the cost of it, which the county reckons to be $4,800. So the boys get together at Jimmy's Bar, and Dog proposes that they all pay a quarter of the cost. The others know that he is a sly old Dog and so they're a bit skeptical. If you are Able, propose a reasonable allocation of the costs.

183

Three boxes

Charlene's parents have bought her some birthday presents, but have hidden them in one of three boxes. They have told her that both statements are true on one of the boxes, both statements are false on one of the boxes, and on the third box one statement is true and one is false, but she doesn't know what order the boxes are in. Which box contains the presents?

The presents are not in this box.
They are in the red box.

The presents are not in the yellow box.
They are in the blue box.

The presents are not in this box.
They are in the yellow box.

The deranged secretary

My secretary, Mrs. Flubbit, has done it again. She has taken all my letters and put each one into the wrong envelope. So now I have to open up all the envelopes to find out what is in each. Surely, when I have opened all but one of the envelopes, I can deduce what is in the last one. Or can I do better? How many envelopes do I have to open before I can work out what is in each of the remaining envelopes?

Truth and treasures

Scatterbrain the Treasurer had forgotten how many gold, silver and bronze coins were in the town vaults. So, rather than spend the rest of his life counting the cash, he decided to ask the three guards, one for each type of coin, how many coins were in their charge. Now, the guards were the uncooperative sort, and the best Scatterbrain could get from each one was a statement about the number of coins in the other two vaults.

Dimwit, who was guarding the gold, said, '3,000 silver and 5,000 bronze'; Thickplank, in charge of the silver, said, '3,000 gold and 5,000 bronze' and Beefbrain, who was protecting the bronze, said, '4,000 gold and 3,000 silver'. To make matters worse, only one guard was being truthful, each of the others stating at least one false amount.

If there were 12,000 coins in total, how were they distributed?

A Middle Eastern muddle

An Arab sheikh had three sons. He died, and in his will he left his oil wells to be divided among them. The eldest son was to receive half of them, the second son one third and the youngest son one seventh. When they went to divide the wells, they discovered that there were 41 wells. Since there is no satisfactory way to divide a well, they were puzzled as to how to proceed. They called on their uncle Omar, who was wise but poor – he owned only one well.
How did he solve the problem?

Superheroes

Superheroes, A, B, C and D attend a conference during a lull in global crime. They wear labels A, B, C and D in order not to confuse each other.

'Do you realize,' says A to C, 'each one of us has the wrong label. What's more, if we two swapped with each other it wouldn't improve matters.'
'Is that so?' A asked the man wearing D.
'He's right', said D to the man wearing A.
Who was wearing which label?

Word riddle #1

Walking beneath me as you pass through,
Or a small land with an Everglade view,

I'm useful to have where landmarks are shown,
Notes by the seven with concordant tone.

One in a million will let you see
A vital secret when you have me

189

Word riddle #2

My first is in peckish, but isn't in rice
My second's in staccato, but isn't in twice

My third is in giant, but is far from sight
My fourth is in almond and also in blight

My fifth is in China and also in game
What is this Eastern creature's name?

190

The baffled brewer

Burper the Brewer was scratching his head. He had just received an order for three barrels of beer: one to contain 19 litres, another to contain 10 litres, and the third to contain 7 litres. Now, he had the correct total quantity in three equal-sized barrels. However, the barrels were all half full. His problem was to produce the correct quantities in the three barrels. To help him he had three measuring jugs having capacities of three litres, two litres and one litre. Since Burper was clearly in a fix, he needed help – so he telephoned his Mom, who gave the following advice:

'Each measuring jug must be used once only to transfer a full jug of beer from one barrel to another. Furthermore, each barrel must be involved in at least two transfer operations, such that on each occasion there is either a gain or a loss of beer.'

It is clear that Burper's mother didn't simplify the procedure! But if we do follow her advice, what are the operations required?

191

Library logo

These seven books have been placed in alphabetical order by title; however, they should have been ordered by author. When correctly positioned, *Cruel Cake Recipes* is somewhere to the left of *Grandma the Polevaulter*, which is three places to the right of *Desert Pub Crawl*. *Baking a Brick* is an even number of places to the right of *Evenings in the Bath*, and *Faking a Heart Attack* is two places away from *After Dinner Insults*. Exactly three books are currently correctly positioned. What is the correct order?

192

The wine bearers

You have been invited to a banquet at the local Puzzler's Association. As guest of honour, it is your duty to pour the wine. Naturally, this task is not as simple as it might at first appear. You are presented with two containers, one which holds 15 glasses-worth of wine and one which holds 16 glasses-worth. There are no measurement marks on either of the containers. There is also a main barrel which holds a large amount of wine. The wine must be poured into eight glasses from a container that is, at the time, holding exactly the right amount of wine. You can pour wine into and out of your containers and the barrel until the objective is reached; what is the shortest number of steps in which this can be achieved?

193

The family next door

A family moves in next door to you. You make the movers a cup of coffee, and while chatting to you, they say: 'You will like your new neighbours – they have two children just like you.' Later that evening, you go next door to invite the neighbours over for a drink. A polite little girl answers, but says, 'Mommy and Daddy are assembling a bed at the moment, so they can't come to the door. They will call on you in an hour, though.' You return to your house and speculate whether the family has two girls, or a boy and a girl. What are the percentages of each possibility?

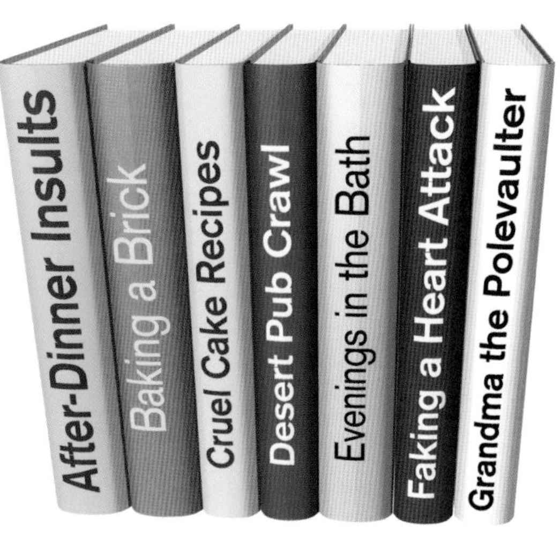

194

Long and short

Two candles are lit at the same moment. One is 5 cm long and the other is 3 cm longer. The long one burns twice as fast as the short one.

How short is the long one when it is as long as the short one, and how long is the short one when the long one is no longer?

195

Byzantine salesmanship

A Genovese merchant was dying, so he called his nine sons to his side. He gave the eldest 90 pearls, the next eldest 80 pearls, and so on down to the youngest son, who received 10 pearls. He instructs them to go and sell them in the markets at Padua and Venice, and to divide his fortune proportionally to the amount they earn. The sons go to Padua, and being fair-minded, they all resolve to sell their pearls at the same price. They each sell some of their pearls, then take the remainder to Venice. Again they all resolve to sell their pearls at the same price. Despite these complications, at the end they find they have all earned the same amount. How did this happen?

196

Four wise men

Four friends, Mr. White, Mr. Black, Mr. Brown and Mr. Green, met up in their local bar on Christmas Eve to exchange gifts. Each man had one gift of a coloured shirt to give to one of the others, and each person received one shirt. The bartender, when trying to recall the incident, could only remember the following facts:

1. No man gave or received a shirt that was the same colour as his name.
2. Mr. White gave a black shirt.
3. Mr. Green gave his gift to Mr. Black.
4. The shirt colours were the same as the friends' names.

Can you help the bartender sort out who gave what to whom?

197

A carol conundrum

I attended a Christmas carol service recently and sang six carols from a book containing a hundred or so festive songs, split into three groups of two carols each. The carols were each numbered in the book with a two-digit number which contained no zero. When we took a hot chocolate break after each couple of carols, I noticed that in each set of two, one carol was an integer multiple of the other. Furthermore, each pair contained one common digit, and if this digit was removed, the ratio of the two remaining single digit numbers was the same as before. What were the three pairs of numbers?

198

Strange relations in Much Puzzling

My village, Much Puzzling, has a baker, a brewer and a butcher. The other day I was talking to the baker's wife and she remarked that these three jobs were held by a Mr. Baker, a Mr. Brewer and a Mr. Butcher, but, of course, no man held the job corresponding to his surname.

'Surely everyone knows that – even a newcomer like myself!' I responded. Then she continued, 'But I bet you don't know what Mrs. Brewer told me just the other day. You see, each of the men married the sister of one of the other men. And no man married a woman of the same name as his occupation!'

What was the butcher's wife's maiden name?

To come to a conclusion when presented with given facts and figures requires judgment, deduction and reasoning. Often the key is that you have to add a critical piece of information to solve the puzzle.

Quigley

There are five tribes of knaves, each with its own special costume. One of the knaves is named Quigley, and your task is to find him.

You have asked directions and some of the knaves have responded by pointing along the path of what they claim is the shortest route (involving the fewest paths, knave to knave) leading to Quigley. Before he answered, each knave phoned the Department of Information (DOI) for an instruction on whether to indicate a true or false direction. However, you know a spy in the department who tells you what the instruction was. If the instruction was to give a false direction, a question mark has been placed just over the knave concerned.

The various tribes have strange habits. The tribe of ZOMBIES never replies at all, and does not give directions. Members of the tribe of TRUTHFUL KNAVES always indicate the true shortest route to Quigley, no matter what the DOI instruction is. Members of the tribe of LYING KNAVES always indicate a false direction, whatever the instruction is. Members of the tribe of CONFORMISTS always

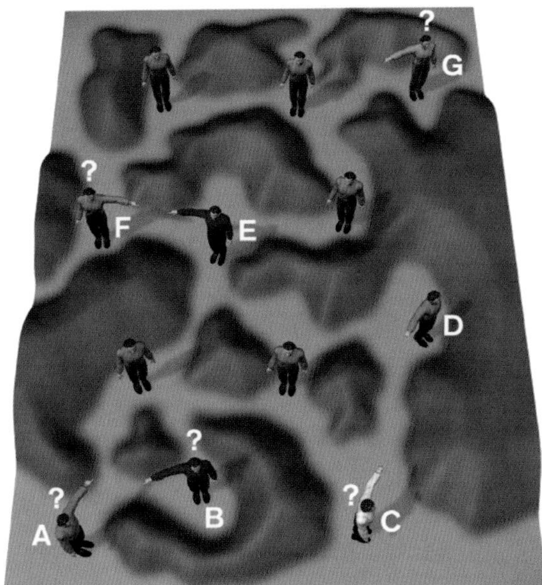

follow the DOI instruction, and members of the tribe of DISSIDENTS always do the precise opposite to what they are told by the DOI.

You know one important fact – Quigley is a LYING KNAVE – so he will always direct you away from himself. To help you the knaves have been lettered, except for the ZOMBIES who are useless. Of course, part of your problem is to discover what costumes the tribes are wearing today.

Five dart ton

The stall at the visiting fairground had a strange-looking dartboard which consisted of just a grid containing twelve numbers, as shown below. To win a prize, the attendant explained, you had to throw five darts, each into a different square, so the total scored would come to exactly 100. I decided to give it a try.

Being a mathematician, I calculated that there were only eight ways in which this difficult feat could be achieved. I paid my fee and threw my first dart, which landed in a scoring area. However, as soon as it landed, I knew that I had reduced my chance of winning to only one of the eight possibilities. What was the score of my first dart?

26	8	42	34
21	33	6	22
27	19	38	16

Share and share alike

Jessica and her friends like to eat big lunches. One day Jessica brought four sandwiches and Amy brought five. Samantha totally forgot to bring her lunch but she still joined Jessica and Amy, and the girls shared the available sandwiches equally. After eating, Samantha said, 'Thanks a million. I've got to go, but here's some money to pay for the sandwiches.' She left $3 and ran off. Jessica said, 'Let me see, I brought four sandwiches and you brought five, so I get four-ninths of $3, which is four-thirds of one dollar, which is $1.33, near enough.' Amy said, 'Ummm, I'm not sure that's fair.' Who is right?

Weighing the evidence

You are given 12 balls and are told that one of them is lighter or heavier than the others. You have a set of scales (but no weights) and have only three weighings to establish which ball is the odd one out and whether it is heavier or lighter than the others. How is this done?

Telephone trickery

Dad was looking rather pleased with himself and I asked him why. 'I've just got a job overseas, all expenses paid. Tom just rang and told me.'
'Good for you, Dad', I said, 'Where are you going?'
'Funny you should ask', said Dad, 'but while Tom was telling me over the telephone, I noticed something unusual.'
'Another one of your teasers, Dad?' I asked.
'I suppose it is', he replied. 'You know we've got this old-fashioned telephone with the letters on the dial as well as the numbers?'
'Yes', I responded.
'Well', Dad continued, 'If you substitute the numbers on the telephone dial for each of the letters in the country that I'm off to, they form a perfect square.'
I took a peep at our telephone dial, and soon realized that it would take me a while to figure it out. Can you?

Inflation

The numbers 1 to 20 appear on the five balloons below, four numbers on each balloon. However, only two of the numbers are visible from this angle. Determine the hidden numbers on each balloon so that the totals on every balloon are the same.

The witch's pudding

Winnie the Witch had a habit of living in people's broom cupboards, where she would experiment with her vile concoctions. On one occasion she had five ingredients ready to put in a pudding. The volume of dishwater was one half of the cauldron volume, the brandy was one third, the snow was one quarter, the crushed pig's ear was one fifth and the sheep droppings were one sixth. The brandy was added later than the crushed pig's ear, but earlier than the dishwater. The snow was added two places after the sheep droppings. Of course, the cauldron spilled over. In what order were the ingredients added?

206

An Easter brainteaser

It's Easter morning in Toyland, the sun is shining, the birds are singing, daffodils are everywhere and winter is simply ages away. In one particular street, near the Lemonade River, there are five candy cottages in a row. Each cottage is a different flavour. In each candy cottage lives one child, and each child has been given an Easter gift. In addition, each child owns a game and a model. From the following clues, answer these two questions:

a. Who has been given a box of chocolates?
b. Who owns a model airplane?

Clues:

1. Sandy lives in Strawberry Cottage.
2. Lime Cottage is to the right of the Vanilla Cottage.
3. Julie is playing with a tank.
4. An Easter bonnet has been given to the child in Lime Cottage.
5. An Easter egg has been given to Leslie.
6. The child playing Ludo also owns a model bus.
7. The child in Lemon Cottage is playing backgammon.
8. The child in the middle cottage has been given a chocolate bunny.
9. John lives in the first cottage.
10. The child with the train set lives next to the child playing tiddlywinks.
11. The child playing with the boat lives next to the child playing backgammon.
12. The child trying to puzzle out solitaire also has a bag of jelly beans.
13. Andy is playing chess.
14. John lives next door to Banana Cottage.

WORD CHALLENGES

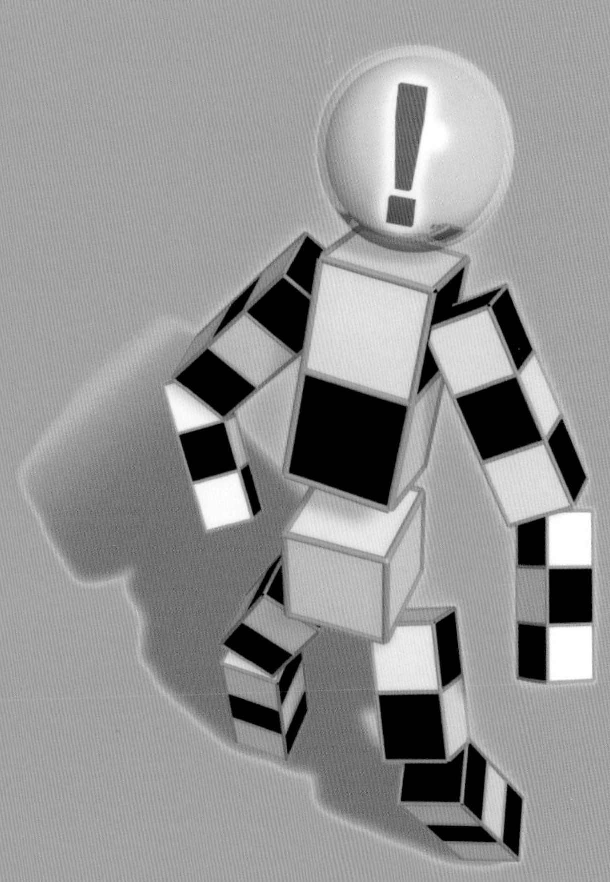

WORD CHALLENGES

'To get the right word in the right place is a rare achievement' (Mark Twain), which is why so many of us revel in solving real brainteasing word puzzles.

AS YOUR PUZZLING SKILLS IMPROVE, or if you are already adept at word puzzles, you will be ready for more demanding word play. To solve these 'word challenges', particularly more difficult cryptic crosswords, you will need a wide vocabulary (and the desire to expand it) a good general knowledge, and the ability to think 'outside the box'. A penchant for puns and jokes, the staples of cryptic crossword compilers, is an additional asset.

TO HELP WITH WORD CHALLENGES, acquire a dictionary containing not only less common words but also abbreviations and colloquialisms. Many puzzlers prefer dictionaries that also include the names of key people and places. It is also handy to have a thesaurus, a reference book that offers words with similar or opposed meanings grouped by themes, and possibly a book of crossword lists that contains names of everything from birds and musical instruments to lakes and rivers, Presidents and Prime Ministers. You will also find a world atlas helpful, and a dictionary of quotations. If you don't possess an encyclopedia, the Internet is another useful source of facts.

MANY HARDER PUZZLES NOT ONLY make more demands on your vocabulary but also require knowledge of such subjects as musical terminology, the names of characters in Shakespeare plays, and the capital cities of obscure countries. Or you may need to find the name of a bird or an insect, a planet or constellation. Other types of clues in cryptic puzzles also require the ability to think laterally. So the clue 'Eight letters in liquid form. (5)' translates to the answer 'water'. The eight letters are 'H to O', the liquid's formula.

To solve more difficult puzzles, apply all the hints that have already been offered to help with simpler puzzles.

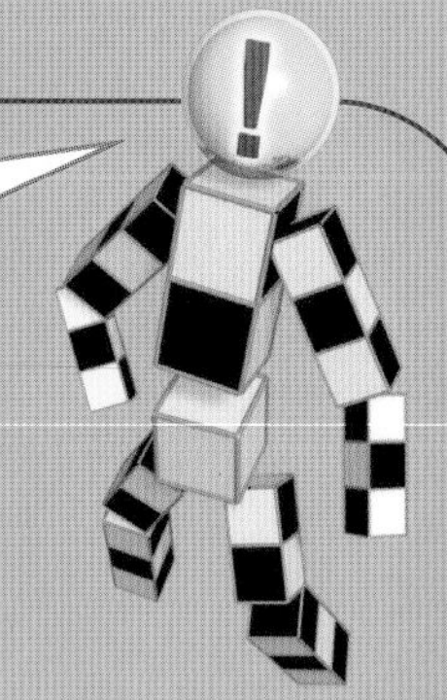

Hello again,
Mr. Spellman here. If you've made it this far, you must be ready for some really cunning conundrums. But I'll give you advice whenever I can.

A RIGOROUS VOCABULARY TEST IS PRESENTED in word challenges that require you to find as many words of three or more letters in a longer word such as 'cheating'. Most people can easily get to 20 words, but find 40 difficult and 60 virtually impossible. But, apart from thumbing the dictionary, there are techniques that can help. If you are methodical, you can start with the letter 'a' and see what three letter words you can build using two more letters. You'll find one word is 'act', and when you add 'ing' to the end it gives a second word. To get a different view of the letters (also useful for solving anagrams) write them at random on a piece of paper and look at the different patterns that emerge.

WHEN TACKLING WORD CHALLENGES it is often easier to deduce a word's ending before you find its beginning. It may be possible, for instance, to work out that a word ends in '...ing', '...ive', '...ment' or '...ance'. When answers are two words long, and only one of the pair is immediately obvious, fill it into the grid. That will help you to solve other clues until the complete answer reveals itself. This may also help give your conscious brain a rest and a chance to change perspective. It is surprising how often clues that seem impossible can be easily solved if you return to a puzzle after an hour's break.

WHEN YOU START ON MORE DIFFICULT CROSSWORDS and word puzzles there is no harm in using all the help you can get to find solutions, since practice will improve your skills immeasurably. As well as books there are some handy Websites you can consult. Type 'word finder' into a search engine such as Google or Yahoo! and in the search results you will see some word finder links. You can then enter the letters you know and use symbols such as asterisks and question marks to indicate those you are missing. Similar programs linked through other Websites also solve anagrams. To get those elusive solutions, you can also buy crossword solver books and electronic machines, similar to hand-held calculators, that work in a similar way to the Web-based programs.

BUT WHATEVER HELP YOU EMPLOY, to improve your solving skills you still need to use your brain to work out why your solution is correct. If the answer is a word, place or person you've never heard of, you should also check its meaning, location or identity in the dictionary, atlas or encyclopedia. Only by doing this will you actually boost your vocabulary and general knowledge. This is far from cheating; it is a totally legitimate way of stretching your brain.

WORD LADDERS

These word ladders work in the same way as those on pages 28 and 29 – they're just a little more tricky.

Turn TART into DISH

Turn FOOL into SAGE

Turn FREE into TRAP

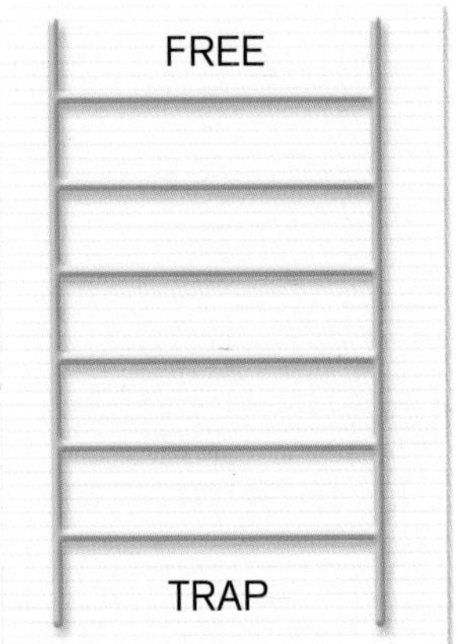

Turn FRESH into STALE

WORDSEARCHES AND WORD SCRAMBLES

The puzzles on these pages work in precisely the same way as those on pages 22-27, but they have been designed to stretch your puzzling powers just that little bit further.

5 ★★★ African adventure

Can you find 30 African countries in this jumbo wordsearch?

ALGERIA	EGYPT	LIBYA	NIGERIA	SWAZILAND
ANGOLA	ETHIOPIA	MADAGASCAR	SENEGAL	TANZANIA
BOTSWANA	GAMBIA	MALAWI	SIERRA LEONE	TUNISIA
CAMEROON	GHANA	MOROCCO	SOMALIA	UGANDA
CHAD	KENYA	MOZAMBIQUE	SOUTH AFRICA	ZAMBIA
CONGO	LESOTHO	NAMIBIA	SUDAN	ZIMBABWE

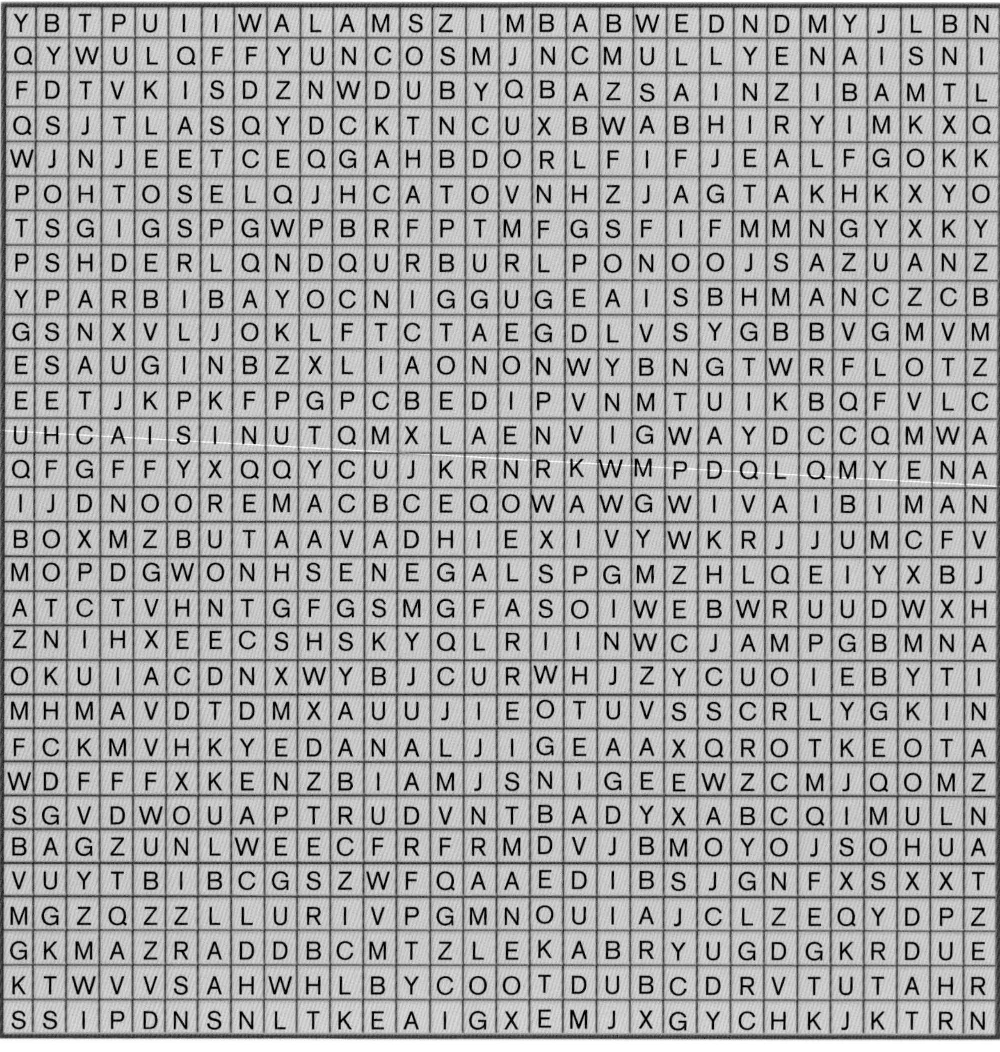

Y B T P U I I W A L A M S Z I M B A B W E D N D M Y J L B N
Q Y W U L Q F F Y U N C O S M J N C M U L L Y E N A I S N I
F D T V K I S D Z N W D U B Y Q B A Z S A I N Z I B A M T L
Q S J T L A S Q Y D C K T N C U X B W A B H I R Y I M K X Q
W J N J E E T C E Q G A H B D O R L F I F J E A L F G O K K
P O H T O S E L Q J H C A T O V N H Z J A G T A K H K X Y O
T S G I G S P G W P B R F P T M F G S F I F M M N G Y X K Y
P S H D E R L Q N D Q U R B U R L P O N O O J S A Z U A N Z
Y P A R B I B A Y O C N I G G U G E A I S B H M A N C Z C B
G S N X V L J O K L F T C T A E G D L V S Y G B B V G M V M
E S A U G I N B Z X L I A O N O N W Y B N G T W R F L O T Z
E E T J K P K F P G P C B E D I P V N M T U I K B Q F V L C
U H C A I S I N U T Q M X L A E N V I G W A Y D C C Q M W A
Q F G F F Y X Q Q Y C U J K R N R K W M P D Q L Q M Y E N A
I J D N O O R E M A C B C E Q O W A W G W I V A I B I M A N
B O X M Z B U T A A V A D H I E X I V Y W K R J J U M C F V
M O P D G W O N H S E N E G A L S P G M Z H L Q E I Y X B J
A T C T V H N T G F G S M G F A S O I W E B W R U U D W X H
Z N I H X E E C S H S K Y Q L R I I N W C J A M P G B M N A
O K U I A C D N X W Y B J C U R W H J Z Y C U O I E B Y T I
M H M A V D T D M X A U U J I E O T U V S S C R L Y G K I N
F C K M V H K Y E D A N A L J I G E A A X Q R O T K E O T A
W D F F F X K E N Z B I A M J S N I G E E W Z C M J Q O M Z
S G V D W O U A P T R U D V N T B A D Y X A B C Q I M U L N
B A G Z U N L W E E C F R F R M D V J B M O Y O J S O H U A
V U Y T B I B C G S Z W F Q A A E D I B S J G N F X S X X T
M G Z Q Z Z L L U R I V P G M N O U I A J C L Z E Q Y D P Z
G K M A Z R A D D B C M T Z L E K A B R Y U G D G K R D U E
K T W V V S A H W H L B Y C O O T D U B C D R V T U T A H R
S S I P D N S N L T K E A I G X E M J X G Y C H K J K T R N

United States

ARIZONA
CALIFORNIA
CONNECTICUT
GEORGIA
HAWAII
IDAHO
INDIANA
KANSAS
KENTUCKY
MAINE
MARYLAND
MASSACHUSETTS
MISSISSIPPI
NEBRASKA
NEW YORK
OHIO
PENNSYLVANIA
SOUTH CAROLINA
UTAH
WASHINGTON
WEST VIRGINIA

Take a trip around America and find the names of 20 of the 50 states in this tricky wordsearch. Which listed state doesnt appear?

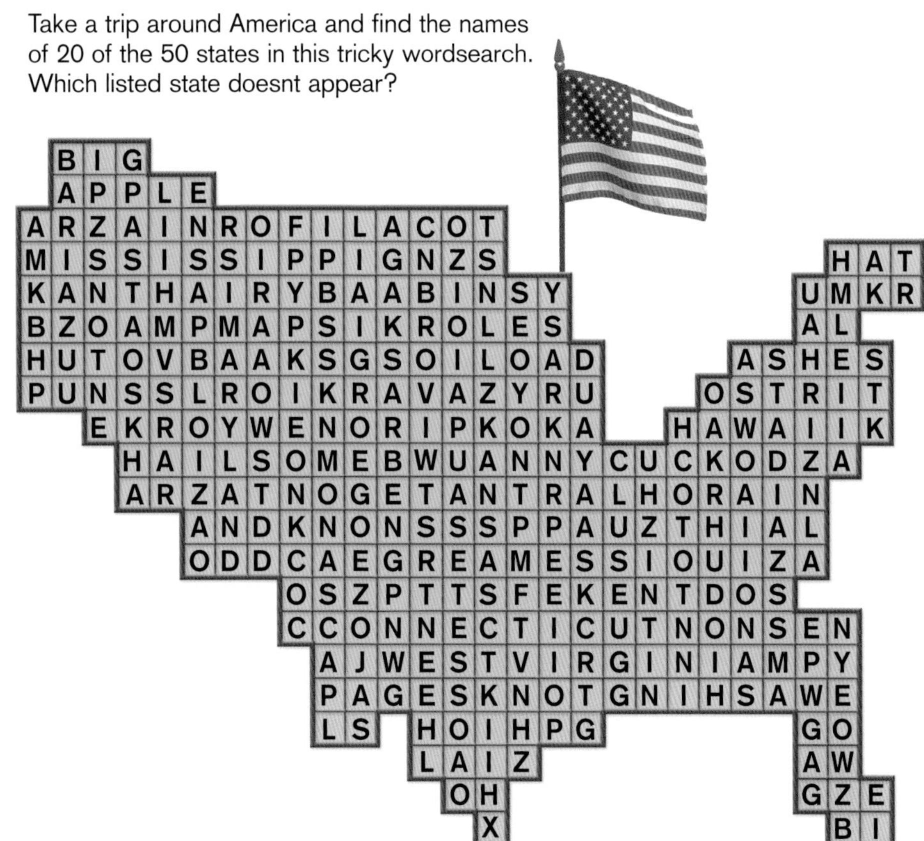

Heavenly bodies

7

AQUARIUS
ARIES
CANCER
CAPRICORN
CYGNUS
GEMINI
IO
JUPITER
LEO
LIBRA
MARS
MERCURY
MOON
NEPTUNE
ORION
PISCES
SAGITTARIUS
SATURN
SCORPIO
TAURUS
URANUS
URSA MAJOR
VENUS
VIRGO

Complete this astral puzzle by uncovering the listed words in the star grid.

For basic word searches, go to page 21

8  V words

Starting from the central square, spell out six 8-letter words and one 7-letter word, all beginnning with the letter V. Apart from the V, each letter should be used once.

M	I	T	B	G	E	R
L	C	A	R	A	T	Y
I	A	E	O	Y	O	I
T	R	E	V	E	L	C
A	R	O	O	I	R	U
C	T	A	C	T	N	L
I	Y	L	I	S	T	E

10  One word 3

What is the longest word that can be found in this grid by working from square to square in any direction? You may start anywhere you like, but each letter can only be used once.

W	S	V	R	X
T	H	E	Y	F
I	M	D	U	L
C	O	Q	B	J
P	G	N	A	K

9 Complete the quotations

Complete the quotations on the right with eleven words, all of which can be found within the grid below. Each letter may be used more than once, but not in the same word.

Y	N	O	I	T	B	E	A
A	T	U	I	I	M	L	C
I	N	S	G	U	L	A	E
L	V	E	R	D	S	P	T
Q	I	S	E	N	S	N	D
N	U	N	O	L	L	I	K
A	D	E	I	M	A	N	M
A	R	T	T	I	C	X	E

1. The trouble with some women is they get all ________ about nothing – and then they marry him. **Cher**

2. I'm tough, ________ and I know exactly what I want. **Madonna**

3. In the beginning, the _______ was created. This made a lot of people very angry, and has been widely regarded as a bad idea. **Douglas Adams**

4. Houston, ________ Base here. The eagle has landed. **Buzz Aldrin**

5. I took a speed-reading course and read War and Peace in twenty minutes. It involves ________. **Woody Allen**

6. If God wanted us to bend over he'd put ________ on the floor. **Joan Rivers**

7. I feel like a ________ tonight – but one at a time. **Mae West**

8. Happiness in ________ people is the rarest thing I know. **Ernest Hemingway**

9. I've been on a ________, but never on time. **Marilyn Monroe**

10. I love ________, it's people I can't stand. **Charles Schultz**

11. All we are saying is give _______ a chance. **John Lennon**

WORD BLOCK-INS

The following are more difficult versions of the Word A Day puzzles on page 32. The convention is the same but the skill level certainly isn't.

11 Block-in 1

Here are some clues:
Row 5: Read out loud (6).
Line 11: 25 year anniversary (6).

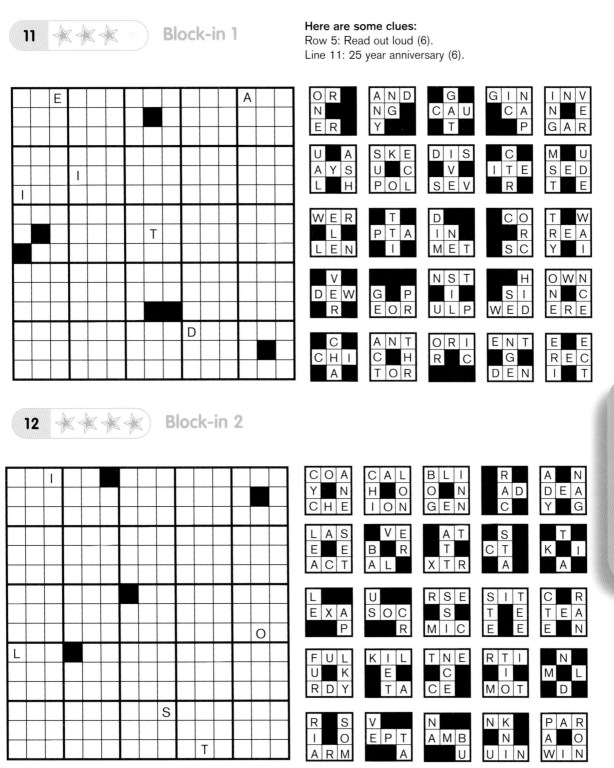

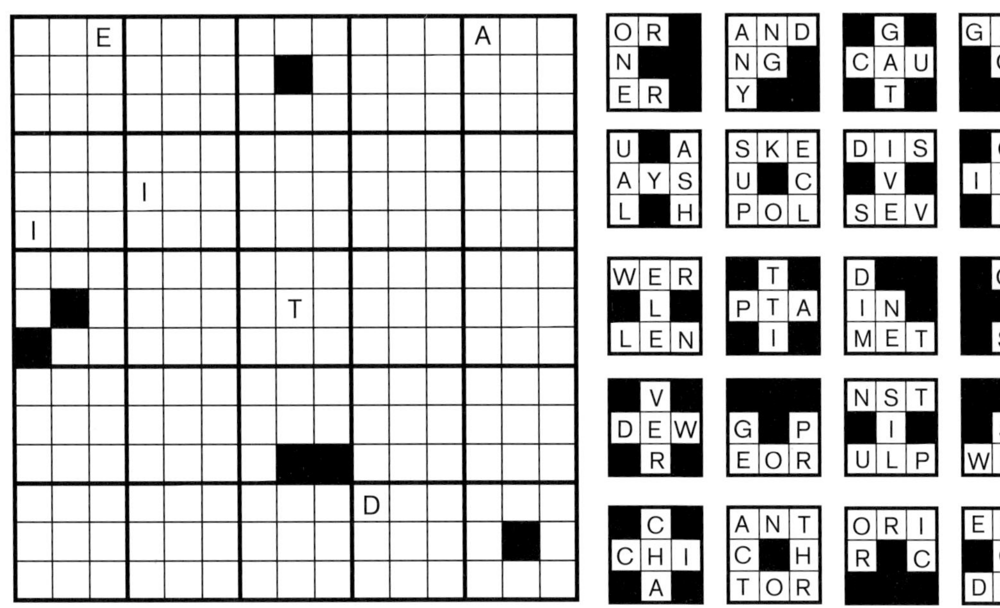

12 Block-in 2

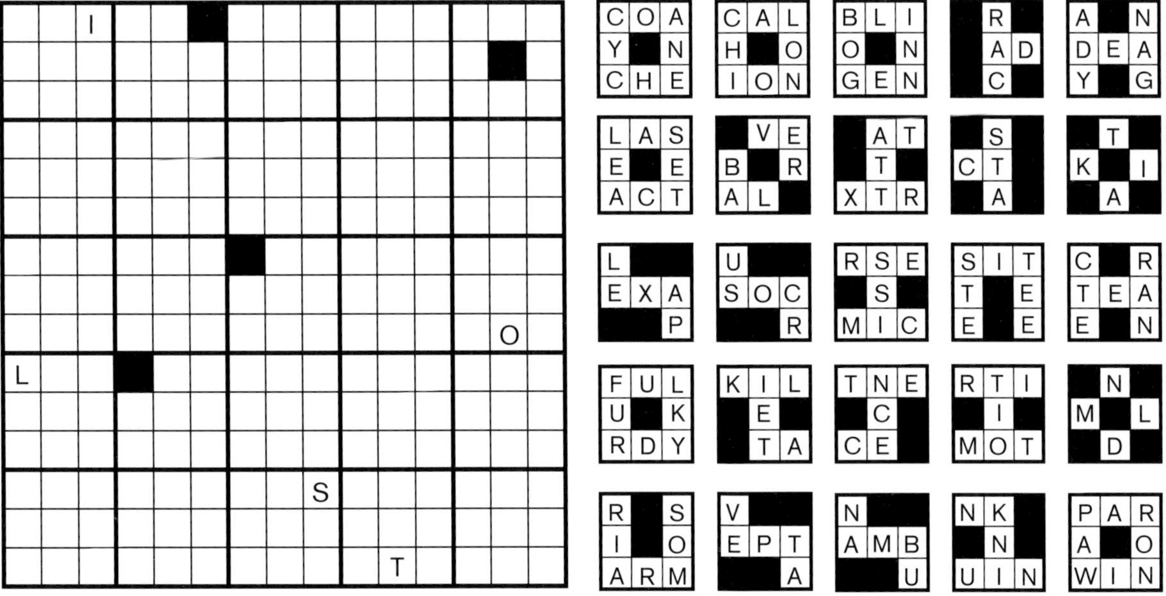

WORD CHALLENGES

CONCISE CROSSWORDS

The following are more difficult versions of the A Word A Day puzzles on page 34. We haven't apportioned any time constraints, but if you're here then you're improving.

13

Across

1. Concede defeat (6)
4. Enclose in paper (4)
8. Drag heavily (3)
9. Sifts, strains (7)
10. Free from obstruction (5)
11. Handled roughly (5)
13. Rash, hurried (5)
15. Pieces of computer data (5)
17. Gives stage cues (7)
19. Small hotel or pub (3)
20. Rice wine (4)
21. Course of a meal (6)

Down

1. Ancient object (5)
2. Small seals in rings (7)
3. Achieve a great deal (2,3)
5. Grain used for American whiskey (3)
6. Assumed an identity (5)
7. Peal (of thunder) (4)
12. More amusing (7)
13. Wishes, expects (5)
14. Short shrill barks (4)
15. Ship's non-commissioned officer (5)
16. Have the feeling that (5)
18. Acorn tree (3)

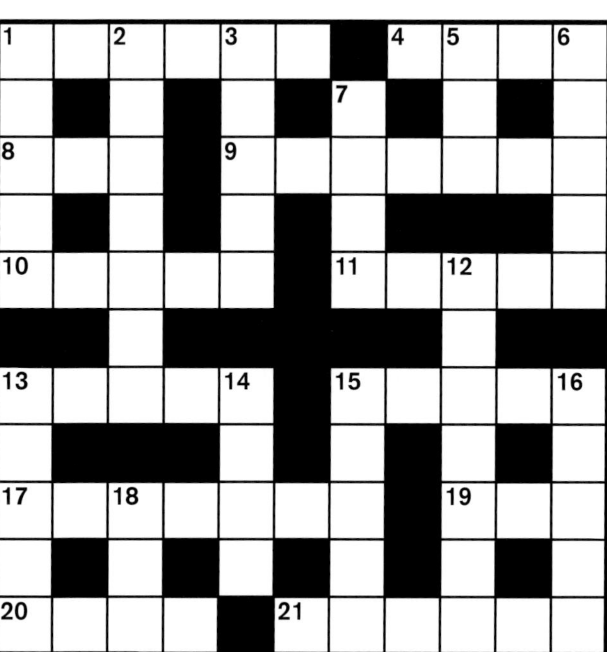

14

Across

7. Ape or historian? (6)
8. Informal language (5)
9. American composer (5,7)
13. The A of W. A. Mozart (7)
17. Symbol of socialism (3,4)
21. Lowest possible temperature (8,4)
24. Rind used as a vessel (5)
25. Artificial (6)

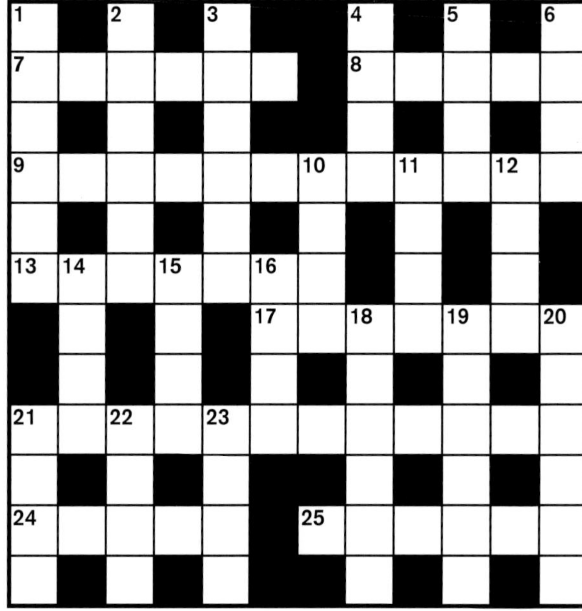

Down

1. Large lizard (6) 2. Peninsula (6) 3. Room for sitters waiting (6) 4. Please reply (to my invitation) (1,1,1,1) 5. Molten rock (4) 6. Got older (4) 10. English river (4) 11. Organ of photosynthesis (4) 12. Type of star (4) 14. Biblical half-brother of Ben-ammi (4) 15. Founder of Carthage or modern singer? (4) 16. Form of Hindustani (4) 18. Chaperone (6) 19. German songs (6) 20. Type of delivery from a spin bowler in cricket (6) 21. Jason's ship (4) 22. Male horse kept for breeding (4) 23. Outdoor swimming pool (4)

15

Across

1. Tangible substance (8) **5**. Mathematical sign (4) **8**. Sudden alarm (5) **11**. Granny Smith? (5) **15**. Novel about the First World War (3,5,2,3,7,5) **16**. Twist? (5) **17**. Commercial exchange (5) **18**. Released (5) **19**. Most unattractive (7) **20**. Flightless birds (5) **22**. Cherished desire (5) **24**. Draw magnetically? (7) **26**. TV detective or code man? (5) **27**. Zulu warriors (4) **28**. Henry Ford thought it was 'more or less a bunk' (7) **29**. Animal with much to do in December (8) **34**. 'The cruellest month', said TS Eliot (5) **35**. Passenger-carrying vessel (5) **36**. Permitted (7) **38**. There must be some mistake here! (5) **40**. Einstein's proposal that matter causes space to curve (7,6,2,10) **44**. William who was the Conqueror's son (5) **46**. Books of maps (7) **48**. Former name of mountainous republic (5) **50**. Publication (5) **51**. ——— *Rock* by Graham Greene (8) **52**. The person to get in touch with (7) **53**. Shaft on which wheel rotates (4) **57**. Freshwater fish (5) **59**. *The* ——— *Boy* by Terence Rattigan (7) **60**. Type of sword (5) **62**. Josiah, the English potter (5) **63**. Time before night (7) **65**. Pipeline or planet? (5) **67**. Big jet (5) **69**. Cowboy's rope (5) **70**. Pattern of depression in winter (8,9,8) **71**. Garb (5) **72**. Alloy (5) **73**. Elegant hotel (4) **74**. Protect from harm (8)

Down

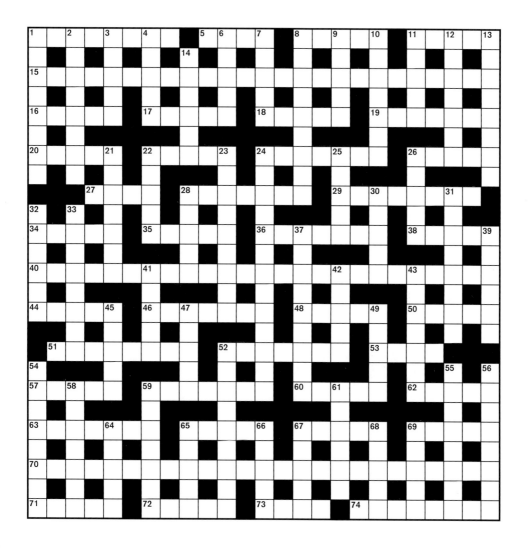

1. Wanders (8) **2**. Showing natural aptitude (8) **3**. Way from A to B (5) **4**. Representative (5) **6**. Unit of capacity (5) **7**. Ledge (5) **8**. Before long (9) **9**. Famous (5) **10**. Administrative division in Methodism (7) **11**. Terrible (5) **12**. Trailblazer (7) **13**. Authorized (8) **14**. Roman poet (6) **21**. Test-piece of embroidery (7) **22**. Training exercise (5) **23**. Edible fungi (9) **24**. Film set in the Vietnam war (10,3) **25**. Pointer (5) **26**. Minute fly (5) **28**. Intuitive feeling (5) **30**. Ghandi's country (5) **31**. Furthest back in time (8) **32**. Long-tailed monkey (6) **33**. Move from one soccer team to another (8) **37**. Coastal rescue vessels (9) **39**. Verses (6) **41**. Smallest amount (5) **42**. White heron (5) **43**. Hanging bits of frozen water (7) **45**. Faculty of vision (5) **47**. Fabric (5) **49**. Astound (5) **52**. What a rainbow is (9) **54**. Emphasized (8) **55**. Think about (8) **56**. Facility (8) **58**. Perform surgery (7) **59**. North American dwellings (7) **61**. Unusually large (6) **64**. English actor Jeremy (5) **65**. Stage of development (5) **66**. Award consisting of a gold-plated statuette (5) **67**. Supporting beam (5) **68**. Twig of willow tree (5) **69**. Big cats (5)

Across

1. Desk with a computer and other equipment (11) **7**. Plaster of lime, cement and gravel (9) **13**. Laughing wild dogs (6) **14**. Group of islands in Polynesia (5) **15**. Pouched Australian animal (8) **16**. Observer (9) **17**. Spanish city famous for sword-making (6) **18**. Large-scale biblical or historical film, perhaps (4) **20**. Particular type of diving equipment (5) **21**. Nero or Napoleon, for example (7) **23**. Pulled for influence (7) **27**. Style of trouser-leg (8-3) **29**. Amphibian, Latin name *Bufo marinus* (5,4) **31**. Nicholas _____, 16th-century Protestant bishop and martyr (6) **33**. Electronic device used by a percussionist (4,3) **34**. Withdrawal of labour (6) **35**. Another name for Pyracantha (9) **37**. Non-track athletics (5,6) **40**. Word-joining strokes (7) **41**. UK music trend of the 1990s (7) **42**. Pack tightly (5) **46**. Without the power of speech (4) **48**. _____ *Head*, East Sussex landmark (6) **49**. Pins and balls table game (9) **52**. Variety of egg-nog (8) **53**. Face shield attached to a helmet (5) **54**. Collection of short stories by Isaac Asimov (1,5) **55**. Combination of ideas to form a theory (9) **56**. Permanent molars at the back of the jaw (6,5)

Down

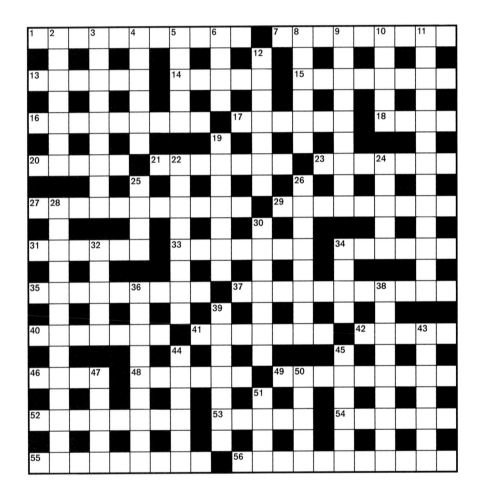

2. Pertaining to an international quadrennial sporting event (7) **3**. Largest hooded snake (4,5) **4**. Of a central Italian region (6) **5**. Italian Poet 1544-95 (5) **6**. Electrical resistance units (4) **8**. Location of The Ring of Brodgar (6) **9**. Highly explosive compound (9) **10**. Irish county south of Galway (5) **11**. Man's comfortable short coat for after-dinner wear (7,6) **12**. Russian-born author of *The Defence* and *Bend Sinister* (7) **19**. Bright star in the constellation Leo (7) **22**. Bullfighters who kill the animal (8) **24**. Entomb (5) **25**. ______ **Pop**, singer synonymous with punk rock (4) **26**. Very hot curry (8) **28**. Church feast after Pentecost (7,6) **30**. Supports for broken limbs (7) **32**. Bloodsucking worm, once used in medicine (5) **34**. Canal constructed by Ferdinand de Lesseps (4) **36**. Parking device on a car (9) **38**. Steak cut between two ribs (9) **39**. Collection of public records (7) **43**. Radioactive material produced by nuclear explosions (7) **44**. Rum and lime cocktail (9) **45**. Trademark tranquillizer (6) **47**. _____ *on the Landscape* , novel by Tom Sharpe (5) **50**. Strong, bitter tasting (5) **51**. Town in Piedmont, famous for its sparkling wine (4)

17

Across

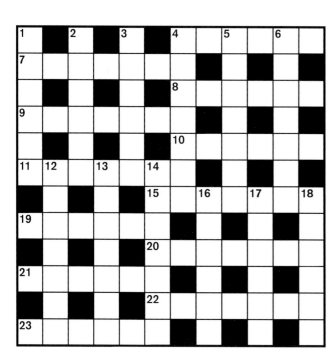

4. Slogan to rally support (3,3)
7. Compress (7)
8. Discombobulate (6)
9. Apprehends (7)
10. Sport (6)
11. Crêpe (7)
15. She gave Theseus a thread (7)
19. Relating to a particular gland (6)
20. Material from animal skin (7)
21. Socialize informally (6)
22. View (7)
23. Malodorous (6)

Down

1. Endeavours (6)
2. Mineral used in some watches (6)
3. High-living group (3,3)
4. Noah, the American lexicographer (7)
5. Balkan republic (7)
6. Native of Moscow maybe (7)
12. Clothes for identification (7)
13. Everlasting (7)
14. High chest of drawers (7)
16. Sloping typeface (6)
17. Flowering plant (6)
18. Like knight looking for adventure (6)

18

Across

1. God of wine (7) **5.** Indian statesman known as 'Pandit' (5) **8.** Fear of spiders (13) **9.** Singer once married to Sonny (4) **10.** An unsegmented cylindrical worm (8) **12.** Union for actors (6) **13.** Fabric given a puckered effect by chemical treatment (6) **16.** Sullen and unsociable (8) **17.** The season of Pentecost as a festival (4) **19.** Spanish Jesuit missionary (7,6) **20.** Element with atomic number 86 (5) **21.** Water tank (7)

Down

1. Vivien Leigh's role in *A Streetcar Named Desire* (7)
2. Thick steak named after a French statesman (13)
3. Ditch acting as a barrier at the end of garden (2-2)
4. Bram, author of *Dracula* (6)
5. Native American Indians (8)
6. The option of taking what is offered or nothing at all (7,6)
7. Edict of a Russian Czar (5)
11. Member of ancient civilization (8)
14. The alimentary canal (7)
15. A word once used to mean 'medicine' (6)
16. One who plays a sort of small flute (5)
18. First name of Danish storyteller (4)

WORD CHALLENGES

For more standard Cryptic Crosswords go to page 38

Across

1. Risky experience coming by river (9)
8. Untidy state of officers' room (4)
9. I'm to resolve dispute that's instant (9)
10. Jewel seen in shop alcove (4)
13. Penny put down for material (5)
15. Is map queried regularly when flawed (6)
16. I will interrupt unacceptable thought (6)
17. Little room has outsize fiddles (6)
19. Heartless grandee unexpectedly settled (6)
20. Soft part of fruit damaged shelf (5)
21. Gradually move to the border (4)
24. Charge for commercial assignment (9)
25. Is familiar, we hear, with wine's bouquet (4)
26. Roman officer in counter-revolution (9)

Down

2. Lady re-arranges Dutch cheese (4)
3. Flat in Stevenage (4)
4. Small amount of pudding (6)
5. Keep alien during wet weather (6)
6. Couple involved in deeds mix-up hadn't a hope (9)
7. Daughter in seaplane crash at coastal pavement (9) **11.** Villain sees crimes upset social worker (9) **12.** Express regret for new sepia logo (9) **13.** Check before producing soft top (5) **14.** Money essential for baker (5) **18.** Winter vehicle left in marsh grass (6) **19.** Foolish person first to give support (6) **22.** Person taking advantage of devious ruse (4) **23.** Some weirdo documents former inhabitant of Mauritius (4)

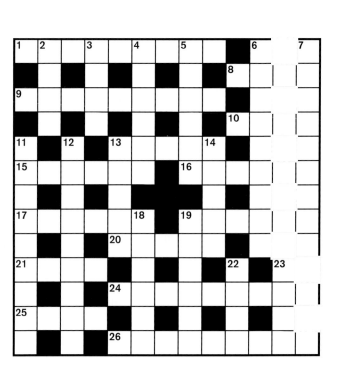

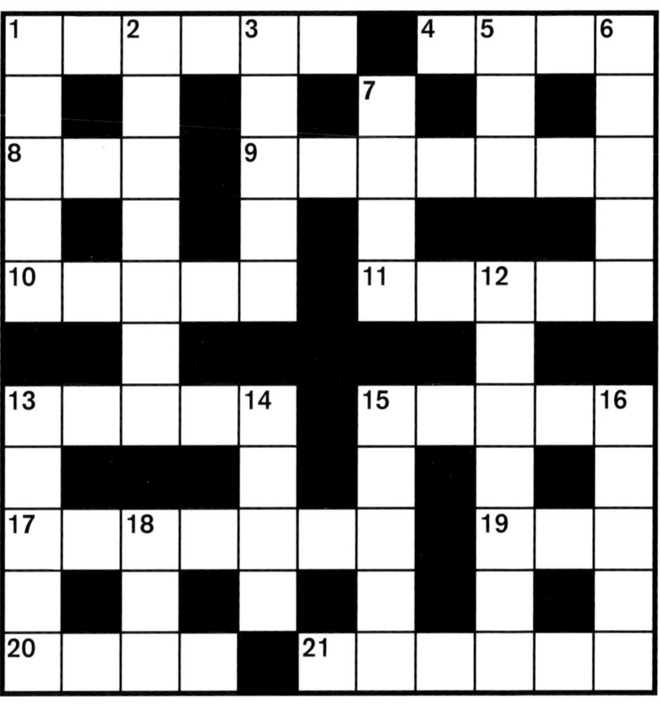

Across

1. Return prize for furniture compartment (6)
4. Trade was ruined by parking (4)
8. I will shortly get poorly (3)
9. Barely cooked part of Welsh dish (7)
10. Ambassador taking part in maiden voyage (5)
11. Month for troop movement (5)
13. Original tree, by the way (5)
15. Hoard of money, it's said (5)
17. Fish left in straw hat (7)
19. Label visible centre stage (3)
20. Eastern place of iniquity, or paradise? (4)
21. Aim, that is, for a soccer player (6)

Down

1. Verdi arrangement shows power (5) **2.** Finished everywhere (3-4) **3.** Relay organized in good time (5) **5.** Internet trap (3) **6.** Surfacing substance for sports field (5) **7.** Some played rumba instrument (4) **12.** Article about poetry reading (7) **13.** Lie concerning roughage (5) **14.** A little portrait at eminent gallery (4) **15.** Vehicle to move freight (5) **16.** Hound beheaded bird (5) **18.** Raw mineral found in forest (3)

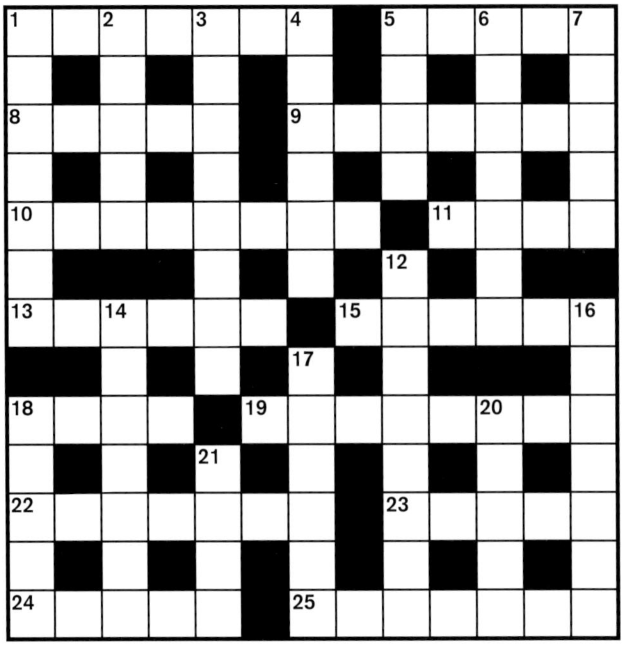

Across

1. Music and wine bring harmony (7)
5. Guide one into snippet of land (5)
8. Young herring parts cooked (5)
9. Rushed back with speed to tell tales (7)
10. One handling stage drama in front of hill (8)
11. Reasonable-sounding charge (4)
13. Obligation to hold back gym lesson for stand-in (6)
15. Mourn mental aberration (6)
18. Pen made of silver in extremes of climate (4)
19. Good man leaving *Eastenders*, turning to song (8)
22. D – a blind alley (4,3)
23. To survive in Essex is tough! (5)
24. Teach to process trout (5)
25. Man, for example, taken in by crazy fool (7)

Down

1. Ponders about answer (7) **2.** Super new prize-money (5) **3.** Dismissed sheds for pariahs (8) **4.** Loudspeaker – it starts to irritate (6) **5.** Leave car quietly on vessel (4) **6.** Gradual loss of stormy lake, over a period (7) **7.** Subject of article on yours truly (5) **12.** Slapdash tailoring left creases (8) **14.** Get in touch with insect parade (7) **16.** Indulged, being given medical help (7) **17.** Hardly ever upset models (6) **18.** Bounder and French trainee (5) **20.** Sprightly American soldier covered in beer (5) **21.** Conference or two, say (4)

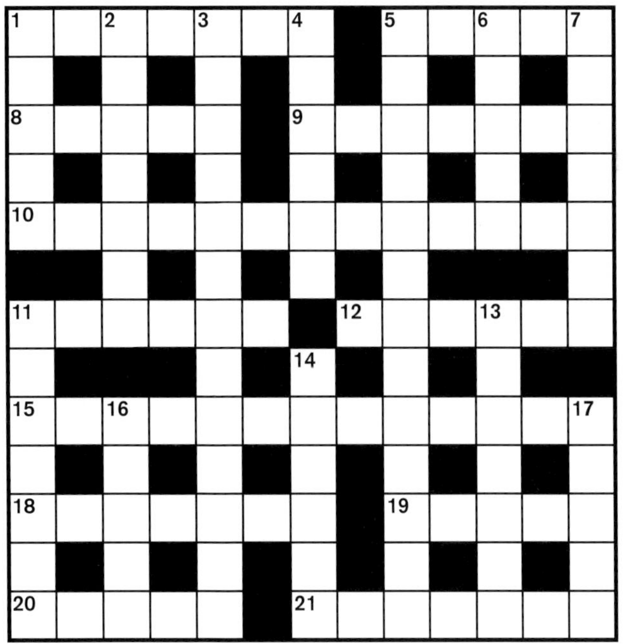

Across

1. Opportunist steals crane behind church (7)
5. Foreign Office coppers provide target (5)
8. Starts rising in sunny eastern resort (5)
9. Give the Middle Eastern ruler a fruit (7)
10. Feign ignorance at the scoring of undeniable (4,1,5,3)
11. Seen an adder? It's the season (6)
12. Step back after being in control of frozen land (6)
15. Fool had blends distributed to relatives (5,3,5)
18. Eavesdrop on city man; it's his nightmare (7)
19. Dig to expose buried note (5)
20. Song for late admission of returning leg – ridiculous (5)
21. Former lover can find edges of chart lost (7)

Down

1. Scream training on vault (5) **2.** Confuse a horse with a sheep (7) **3.** Geese catch toe when making dairy product (7,6) **4.** Actress Jane is heard to swish (6) **5.** Fling round one executive, essential in office (6,7) **6.** It's fashionable to break up (5) **7.** Alarm at finding fish in little drink (5,2) **11.** Flexible sleeping arrangement, so brilliant in the sixties said journalist (4,3) **13.** Roy and Don down from city of London suburb (7) **14.** Misleading of international body to model symbol of rememberance (6) **16.** Man changed grade (5) **17.** Lived to notice scar (5)

23

When rearranged, the letters in the blue squares will give the name of one of the world's oceans

Across

6. The Rome term produces a measure of heat (11)
7. Participate in the French string era (6)
8. Shoots at backstop (4)
9. From the pond, find red or green snails at first (5)
11. Request calm (5)
13. Arrest unruly set at Maidenhead (4)
14. Spot the poster (6)
16. Sheer away from partner Stan (11)

Down

1. Part of the face excavated from ditch in ancient site (4)
2. Old cooker men put in art display (11)
3. Light sensitive receptors divert the traffic (5)
4. Met pure rate of movement, measured by 6 (11)
5. 1960s musician said to have six legs (6)
10. Official statement concerning revolution (6)
12. Snatches photograph (5)
15. Staff find where the raspberry grows (4)

24

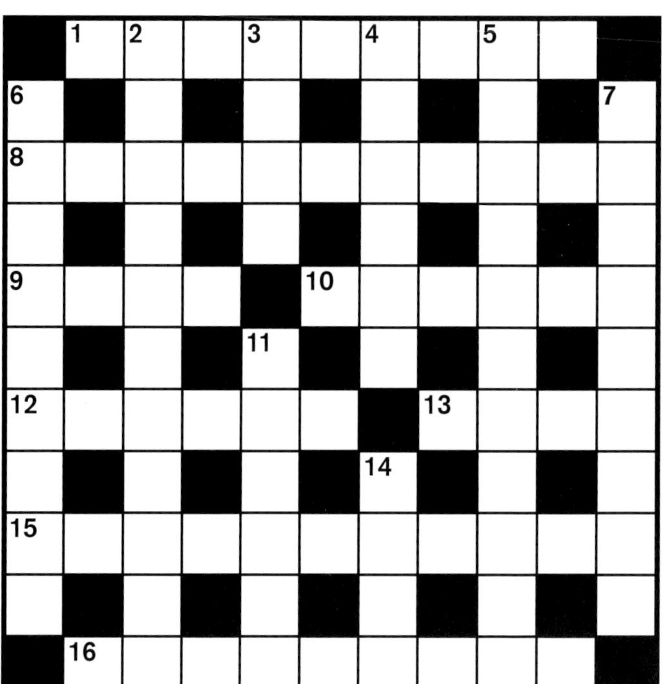

Across

1. Go with the hands to register West Indian points (9)
8. Snaps at soft, hot love symbols (11)
9. Band of titanium for the queen (4)
10. The setting of locks to catch chair dodgers (6)
12. Breathe in, and laugh before the French (6)
13. The thread of a story (4)
15. It's sweet to feed baby by scented climber (11)
16. Quick – see trophy repaired (3,6)

Down

2. Free to vary the money for small expenses (5,6)
3. Cut the corn (4)
4. Fighting over tool in Poland (6)
5. Excellent trade – you can buy it all here (11)
6. Emphasize the mark on the lamp (9)
7. Damaged, ousted and bewildered (9)
11. Over-act before it won't work (4,2)
14. Obtain eight, maybe from a dice (4)

Across

1. Have need of engineers and some paper (7)
5. Laity disrupted the country (5)
8. Stop eating around the end of June? Quite the reverse (5)
9. Student got peer agitated (7)
10. Grace ill, unfortunately – having a bad reaction to food, perhaps (8)
11. In Emma I detect someone to help with the cleaning (4)
13. Naturist in dust storm (6)
15. Modern centre redeveloped (6)
18. Bragged about the sailors (4)
19. Left with expert – may be moved (8)
22. Weighty number almost stir (7)
23. Hear nobleman when we sleep? (5)
24. Abandon the trench (5)
25. Person voting for German prince (7)

Down

1. Doesn't join in the chorus (7) **2.** Does this bird show a yellow streak? (5) **3.** Concern shown for money that's accrued (8) **4.** Liveliness of eccentric priest (6) **5.** New lido – an object of admiration (4) **6.** Mean to declare date of birth (7) **7.** First of you lied about harvest (5) **12.** Fine lots of words? (8) **14.** Lowest form of river vermin (7) **16.** Loudspeaker point to sway round (7) **17.** Mix us up some pudding (6) **18.** Could possibly be obscure (5) **20.** In scrap, make a move for a racist! (5) **21.** Shop turned out to be upper class (4)

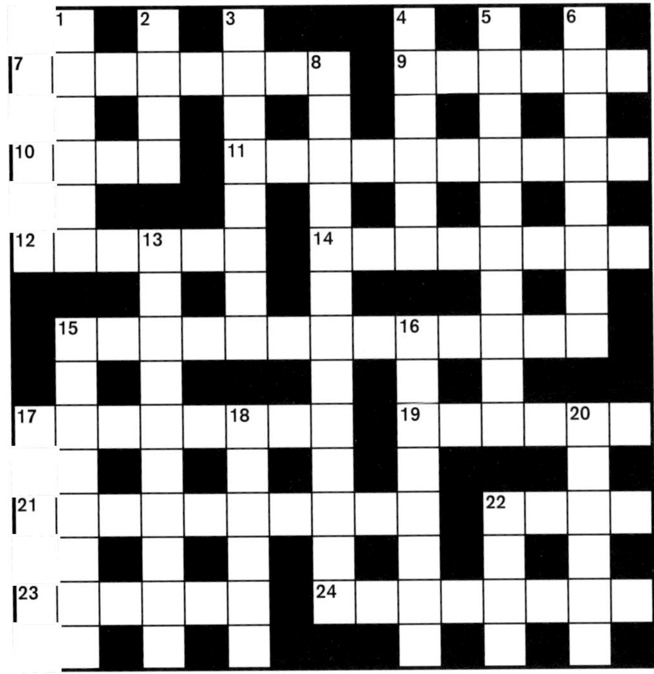

Across

7. People in authority play the trumpet perhaps (3,5)
9. Crazy bird (6)
10. Condescend to speak to Hamlet (4)
11. To converse wildly over temporary insurance arrangements (5,5)
12. Blubber before the whip of a prosperous man (3,3)
14. It's typical for little Andrew to be in France (8)
15. Art movement concerning apple tree hair (3-10)
17. City finds Britain initiates the cause of trouble (8)
19. Begins it, before you say 'in position'(2,4)
21. Young lady recovered from unproductive spell at cricket (6,4)
22. Scottish reformer makes a noise at the door (4)
23. Allow insect to attack (3,3)
24. Not to worry about lack of substance (2,6)

Down

1. Solo piece performed in season at arena... (6) **2.** ...with instrument of love in honour (4) **3.** Cat cult practised in India (8) **4.** Sharp knife, perhaps redundant during 21 (6) **5.** Physical movements of a cobra troubled with spasms (10) **6.** Bridle at losing right to hold one who is lazy (4,4) **8.** Wonderful feeling for event requires hard pull between two poles (7,6) **13.** Perhaps Wensleydale will lift the depressed (7,3) **15.** Eats even steak, if chewed (8) **16.** Witticisms point to pig and sheep (8) **18.** Listen; a noise that exasperates (6) **20.** Tool required by king whilst wearing a towel (6) **22.** Look at Elizabethan holding a shrew (4)

ACROSTICS

As before (see pages 42-43) place the answers to the given clues in the grids provided. The convention is the same as before but of course these will be more creatively tricky.

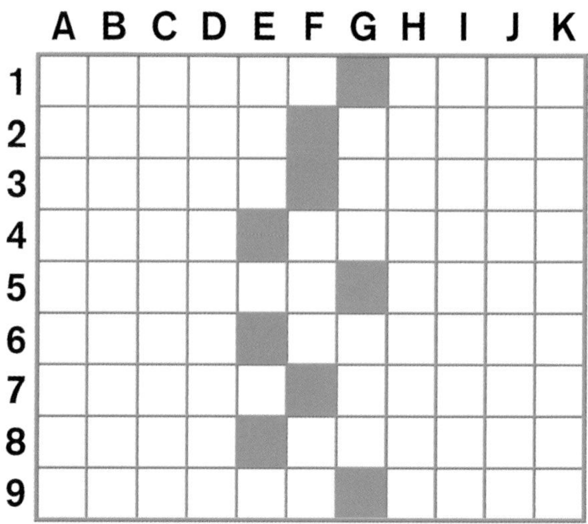

Solve the clues in the main grid row by row, then transfer the relevant letters to form a quote below. Column A will spell out its author.

Row 1: Younger • Open up
Row 2: Command • Sag
Row 3: Robbery • Panache
Row 4: Require • Be present
Row 5: Sharp twist • Lofty
Row 6: As well • Oily
Row 7: Not old • Shore
Row 8: Small cut • Harm
Row 9: Sufficient • Feeble

QUOTE:
8C; 1K; 1B;2H; 5I; 6F; 8K/3C; 6C/7G; 3K; 8B; 9B; 7E/3G; 5E; 7I; 1F; 4I; 2C/4G; 2J/8F; 2D; 6I; 5H; 7K/8G 1I; 2G/3D; 8I; 4D; 1J; 5K; 1D; 7D; 9E/9D; 2K/9J; 4J; 6K; 9H; 4F; 3I

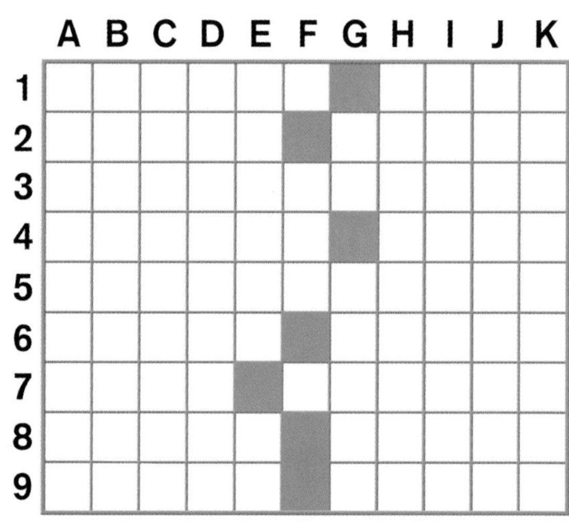

Solve the clues in the main grid row by row, then transfer the relevant letters to form a quote below. Column A will spell out its author.

Row 1: Emotional • Flavoursome
Row 2: Loathe • Power
Row 3: Rural areas
Row 4: Little fish • Spring forth
Row 5: Look into
Row 6: Door lock • Pure (diamonds)
Row 7: Tranquil period • Copper alloy
Row 8: Append • Broadcasting (2,3)
Row 9: Specialist position • Tendon

QUOTE:
5F; 6E; 9E/9K; 1D; 3D; 3J/4E; 8B/1J; 4K; 8I; 6H; 1F; 5K/2H; 3H/7F; 7D; 3B; 4F; 8D; 9I; 4H/3E; 2J; 7G; 8G; 6J; 5H; 2C/6C; 1K; 3I; 4J/9C; 1B; 8H; 6K; 9H; 1E; 5D; 5B; 2K

29

Solve the clues in the main grid row by row, then transfer the relevant letters to form a quote below. Column A will spell out its author.

Row 1:	Calm fears	• Magnate
Row 2:	Plump	• Listen
Row 3:	Average	• Arab chief (spelling var.)
Row 4:	Pocket knife	
Row 5:	Tiny amount	• Indifferent
Row 6:	Foul-smelling	• Detective
Row 7:	Impervious to light	• Large book
Row 8:	Following	• Instinctive
Row 9:	Leaping insect	

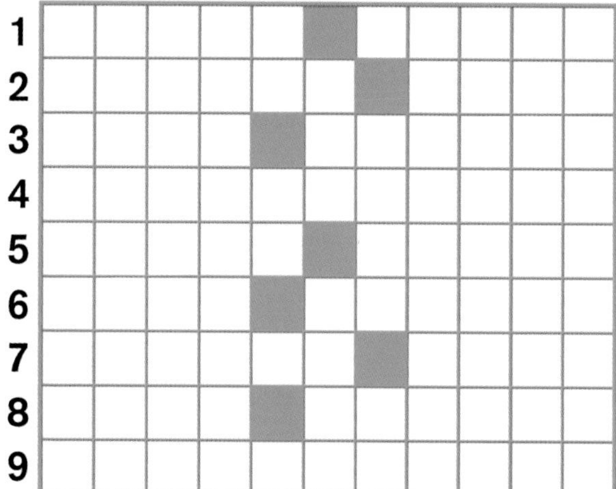

QUOTE:
4F; 9G; 7E; 6F; 2C; 1H; 8G/7H; 2J; 3C; 2E; 7D; 6I; 3I; 4H; 1K; 4C; 8D; 1E/4G; 9C; 5J; 3H/9F; 7K; 9K; 5K/4D; 3G; 9J/5E; 7C; 1I; 5H; 3B/2H; 8I; 9D/6G; 5C; 6C; 2F; 8K; 4J

If some of the solutions are missing or proving troublesome, remember that you can still solve the main vertical solution with a bit of ingenuity

30

	A	B	C	D	E	F	G	H	I	J	K
1											
2											
3											
4											
5											
6											
7											
8											
9											
10											
11											

Solve the clues in the main grid row by row, then transfer the relevant letters to form a quote below. Column A will spell out its author.

Row 1: Bile storing organ (4,7)
Row 2: Terracotta, for example
Row 3: Ready to wear (3-3-5)
Row 4: Doubt
Row 5: Relating to good eating
Row 6: Unrestrained
Row 7: A stream, for example
Row 8: Red tape
Row 9: Regrettable
Row 10: Competition riding
Row 11: Entertainment of guests

QUOTE:
9K; 6F; 3I; 5E; 8K; 10D; 2E; 4D; 9E; 8D/11F; 3E; 1G; 4H/3K; 8C; 7K; 2F; 1I; 7G; 10G/3G; 6C; 5J; 2J; 11C/1D; 2K; 7C/9J; 11K; 4E; 6G; 9H; 6K; 7J/3C; 1J; 5B; 8H

 For more standard Anagrams go to page **44**

More Hollywood who's who

The names of five international film stars, past and present, are hidden in each puzzle below. Can you find them?

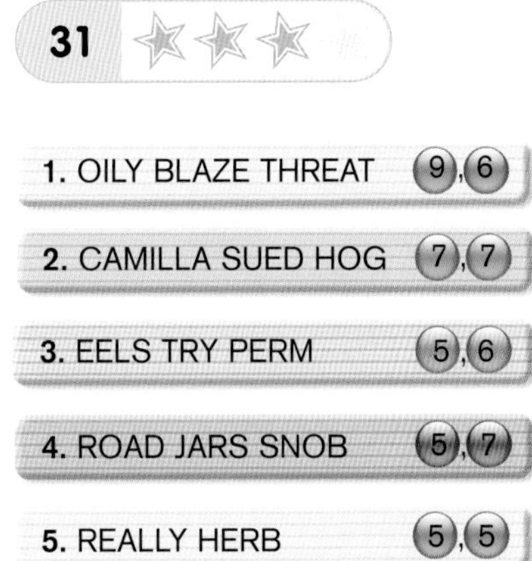

31
1. OILY BLAZE THREAT (9),(6)
2. CAMILLA SUED HOG (7),(7)
3. EELS TRY PERM (5),(6)
4. ROAD JARS SNOB (5),(7)
5. REALLY HERB (5),(5)

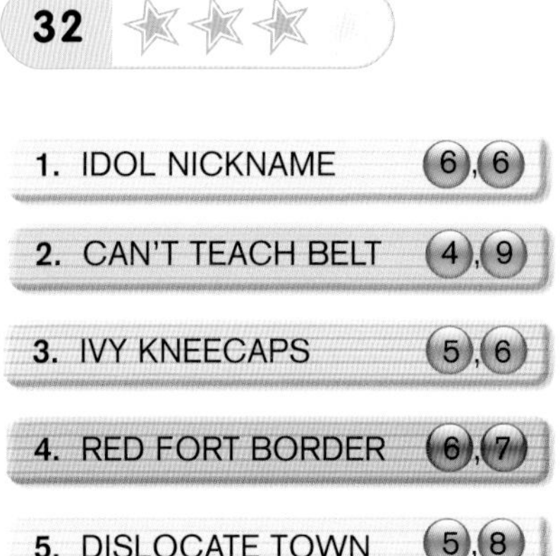

32
1. IDOL NICKNAME (6),(6)
2. CAN'T TEACH BELT (4),(9)
3. IVY KNEECAPS (5),(6)
4. RED FORT BORDER (6),(7)
5. DISLOCATE TOWN (5),(8)

Multi-syllabic mix up

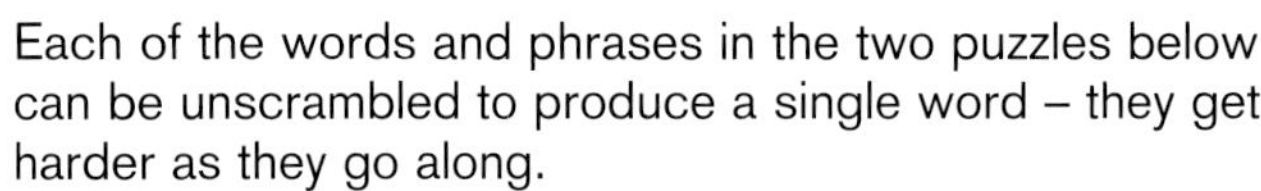
Each of the words and phrases in the two puzzles below can be unscrambled to produce a single word – they get harder as they go along.

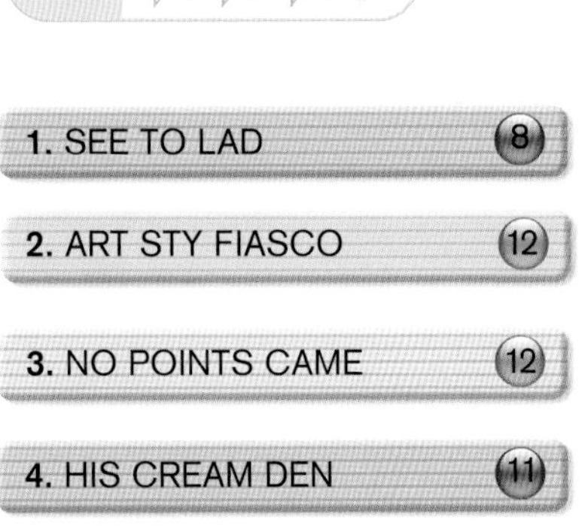

33
1. SEE TO LAD (8)
2. ART STY FIASCO (12)
3. NO POINTS CAME (12)
4. HIS CREAM DEN (11)

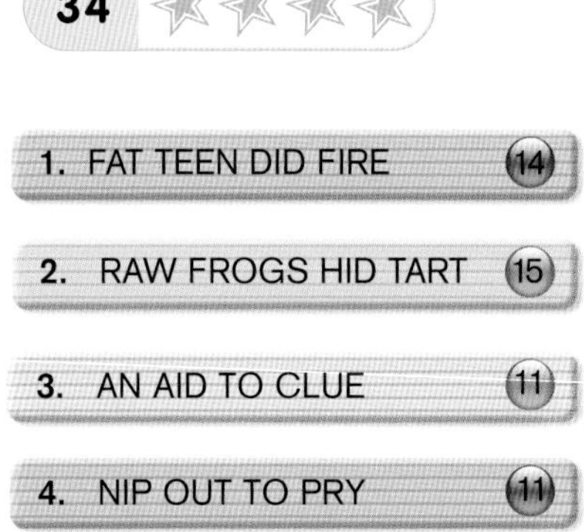

34
1. FAT TEEN DID FIRE (14)
2. RAW FROGS HID TART (15)
3. AN AID TO CLUE (11)
4. NIP OUT TO PRY (11)

Where in the world?

Can you find the four places hidden in each puzzle featured here? Each two-word phrase can be unscrambled to make the name of a country.

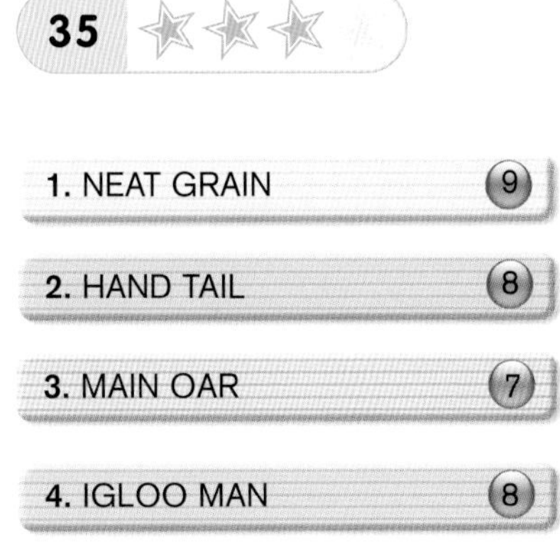

35
1. NEAT GRAIN (9)
2. HAND TAIL (8)
3. MAIN OAR (7)
4. IGLOO MAN (8)

36
1. OCEAN MAID (9)
2. VISA LONE (8)
3. GABLE HANDS (10)
4. NAGS EEL (7)

DEFINITIONS

Test your word power and knowledge with these teasers. There is only one correct answer to the given definition and the remainder are designed to confuse you. This selection is more difficult than those on pages 46-47 – glad you made it here!

37

Can you see the truth amid a cloud of deception and red herrings? Don't be distracted by the false definitions below – they're just to put you off. Which is the true definition?

1. **GYRE**
a bird of prey
b to spin round
c gypsy scarf
d to stroll

2. **ENTRECHAT**
a ballet step
b small cat
c conversation
d secret

3. **FIBULA**
a asteroid
b thin fibre
c untruth
d leg bone

4. **MAZURKA**
a Czech beer
b Polish dance
c Hungarian stew
d Albanian peasant

5. **SCRIMMAGE**
a scrum
b land tax
c carving
d writing-paper

6. **DIURNAL**
a daily
b weekly
c monthly
d yearly

7. **OSPREY**
a type of shark
b porcupine
c bird of prey
d small lizard

8. **TOR**
a Norse god
b injury
c barrel
d hill

9. **CONSOMMÉ**
a bound together
b clear soup
c consumed with jealousy
d costume jewellery

10. **SCABBARD**
a sheath
b foxglove
c breastplate
d shellfish

11. **LARRUP**
a thrash
b crash
c dash
d brash

12. **BOWLINE**
a ship's prow
b type of knot
c archery range
d shoelace

13. **PRECLUDE**
a in advance
b remember
c prevent
d musical introduction

14. **CORROBOREE**
a Indian funeral
b Caribbean restaurant
c Aboriginal festival
d Brazilian bandana

15. **INDOMITABLE**
a careless
b resolute
c crucial
d idle

38

You may have heard or read these words before – but not very often. They're all fairly obscure, gathered from the darker corners of the dictionary. How many do you recognize?

1. **STASIS**
a pale blue flower
b state of equilibrium
c orbit of a comet
d three-dimensional figure

2. **EMICATE**
a sparkle
b dissolve
c reject
d depart

3. **SUBFUSC**
a fungus
b mirror
c sombre
d shallow

4. **TOPE**
a corner
b drink
c figure of speech
d African antelope

5. **POTAMOLOGY**
a study of potatoes
b study of poisons
c study of rivers
d study of caves

6. **EPITHALAMIUM**
a tombstone
b stratum of rock
c bone in the ear
d wedding song

7. **MOPOKE**
a Australian bird
b Eskimo sledge
c Zulu compound
d Celtic parliament

8. **ECAUDATE**
a furnishing fabric
b dictatorial
c tailless
d mild laxative

9. **LEK**
a Albanian currency
b Danish farm
c Russian bomber
d Moroccan platter

10. **LOBSCOUSE**
a ignorant fellow
b small donkey
c eye complaint
d sailors' stew

11. **IRENIC**
a sarcastic
b peaceful
c from the south
d transparent

12. **DECLIVITY**
a downward slope
b downright refusal
c compound interest
d vigorous action

13. **MERGANSER**
a type of seaweed
b inheritance agreement
c diving bird
d Welsh magician

14. **THORIUM**
a Viking breastplate
b radioactive metal
c Egyptian god
d medieval ditch

15. **WIDDERSHINS**
a bone-marrow soup
b graveyard wall
c topsy-turvy
d counter-clockwise

WORD CIRCLES

In these word circles no starter letters are provided. The answers read clockwise round the circle and the end of each word overlaps the start of the next by one or more letters.

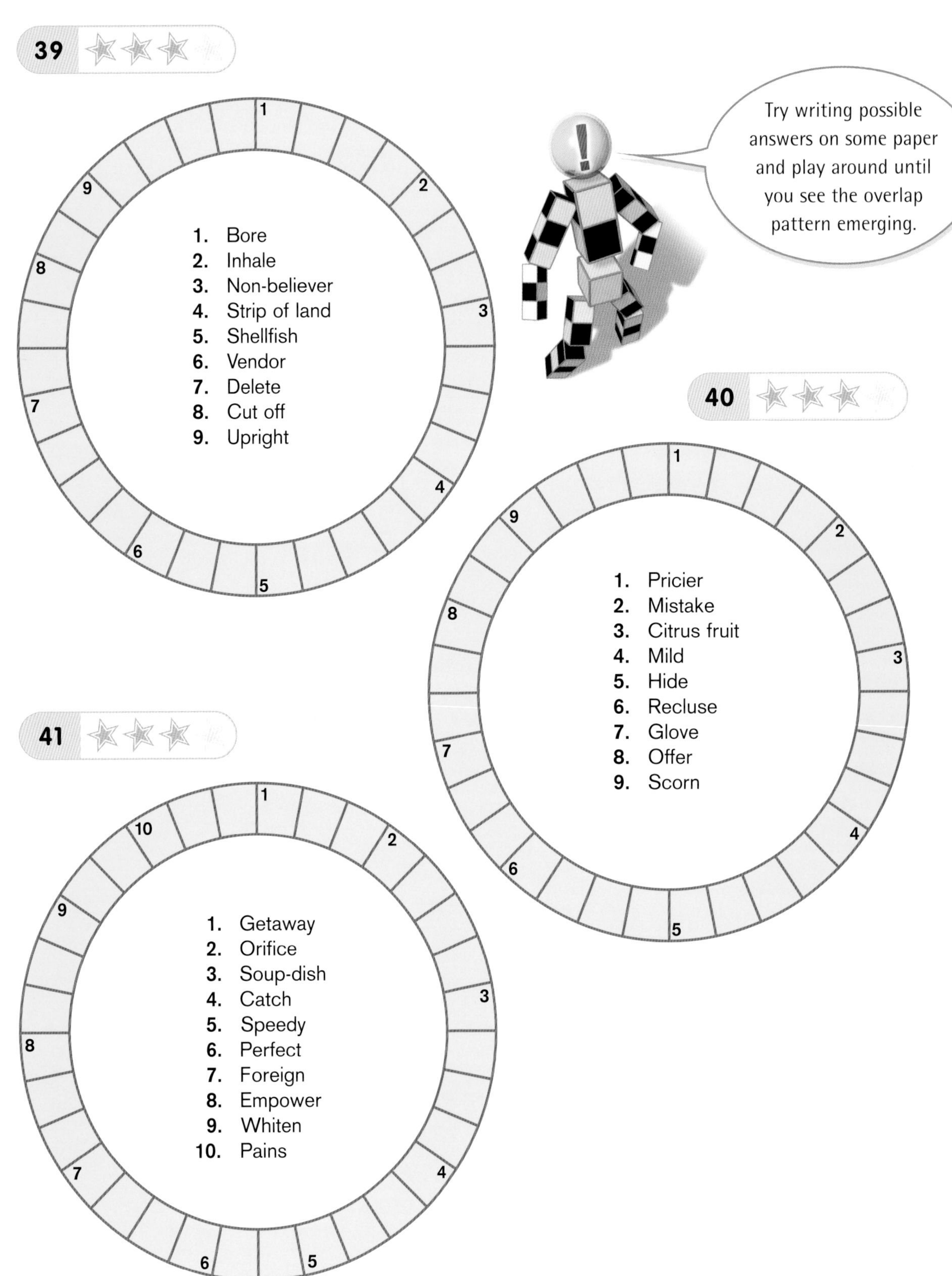

39
1. Bore
2. Inhale
3. Non-believer
4. Strip of land
5. Shellfish
6. Vendor
7. Delete
8. Cut off
9. Upright
Try writing possible answers on some paper and play around until you see the overlap pattern emerging.
40
1. Pricier
2. Mistake
3. Citrus fruit
4. Mild
5. Hide
6. Recluse
7. Glove
8. Offer
9. Scorn
41
1. Getaway
2. Orifice
3. Soup-dish
4. Catch
5. Speedy
6. Perfect
7. Foreign
8. Empower
9. Whiten
10. Pains

WORD CHALLENGES

ANAGRAMS

Mix up a word or phrase and you have an anagram. Each of the following sets of phrases can be unscrambled to produce a name or phrase on the theme of soccer or space travel. Don't get too distracted by the initial phrase and think laterally.

Soccer crazy!

Here are eight anagrams of the names of famous soccer players. They may be British or international players from the past and present. The numbers refer to the word arrangement of the solution.

42

1. NEW DIALS (5,3)
2. NARCOTIC ENA (4,7)
3. ALSO DRIVE LOADS (7,7)
4. RODEO MAD AGAIN (5,8)

43

1. MADE AS DIVAN (5,6)
2. HALF SLINKY JEMIMA'S BODY (5,5,11)
3. GRANT REVERSED (6,7)
4. RIVIERA CAP KIT (7,6)

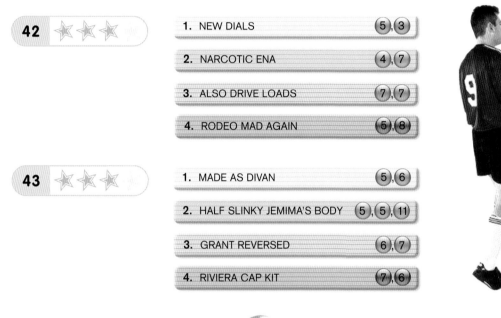

Space & space travel

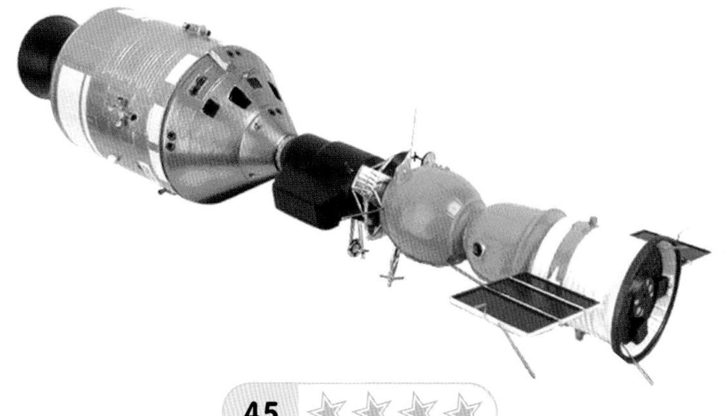

Here are eight anagrams of words or terms on the subject of space and space travel. The numbers refer to the word arrangement of the solution.

44

1. BURN A CABLE (4,6)
2. DARK JON BELL (7,4)
3. GRAIN AIR GUY (4,7)
4. A CAPRI ALE HUNT (5,8)

45

1. LO, MESSY RATS (5,6)
2. SCENT AN ANTI PARASITE LOTION (13,5,7)
3. UNLOCK THE RACER (6,8)
4. A LOW MONK (4,4)

WORD OPPOSITES WITH MISSING CONSONANTS

Your task here is to find an opposite for each of the words in the left-hand column. For instance, the opposite of 'tedious' could be 'exciting' or 'thrilling'. To point you in the right direction, we've given you some letters – but to make it harder, we've removed all the consonants, and sometimes some of the vowels too.

46 

Difficulty	- I - - - I - I - -
Victorious	- E - E - - E -
Quit	- E - - E - E - E
Introvert	- - - I - I - I - - I - -
Civilized	- A - - A - - A -

47 

Genuine	- - - I - I - I - -
Spartan	- U - U - - - U -
Cheerful	- O - O - O - -
Disrespect	- E - E - E - - E
Recalcitrant	- A - A - - A - - -

LANGUAGE EQUATIONS

These puzzles combine math, logic, lateral thinking and general knowledge. You may have already tried this type of puzzle on page 50 – these are harder.

48

Add some initials to a number and you have a language equation. Here are five cryptic phrases for you to decipher:

4 H O T A

6 W O K H T E

5 S O A P

7 D S

8 L O A S

49

Can you decipher the film titles represented by these five word equations?

2001: A S O

12 A M

101 D

7 B F 7 B

T 39 S

50

Can you make sense of these phrases, which all consist of a multiple of 10 and some initials?

10 = E I T D

20 = F O I A P

40 = D I L

60 = Y D W A

90 = D I A R A

MISSING LINKS

Can you think sideways? To solve these missing-words puzzles, you need to be able to jump laterally from one verbal association to another. Find the missing word that completes a phrase with the first word, and starts a quite different one with the second.

51

1. cross .... place
2. street .... relief
3. real .... tax
4. life .... boat
5. swimming .... table
6. break .... hall
7. chair .... room
8. water .... rope
9. film .... cut
10. power .... master

52

1. roaring .... winds
2. high .... beaten
3. saw .... ache
4. turn .... staff
5. cartridge .... chain
6. stone .... reckoning
7. slow .... sickness
8. turning .... blank
9. rear .... rail
10. push .... hole

WORD CHALLENGES

ALPHA DICE

If you have skipped the earlier easier versions of these puzzless then turn to page 52 where simpler versions await you.The principle is the same. In every case the initial blue squares form another word.

1						
2						
3						
4						
5						
6						
7						
8						
9						
10						

Clues

1. European capital
2. Sudden
3. Almost
4. Japanese garment
5. Part of the eye
6. Idealized place
7. Seasoning
8. Award
9. Hole in the tooth
10. Annual

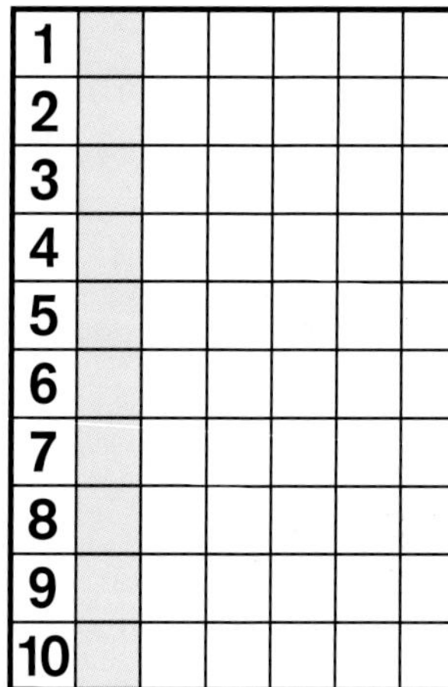

Clues

1. A dozen
2. Wild cat of Latin America
3. Log
4. Vegetable
5. Intimidate
6. Edible pulse
7. Rainbow colour
8. Large seabird
9. Capital of Cuba
10. Jungle hero

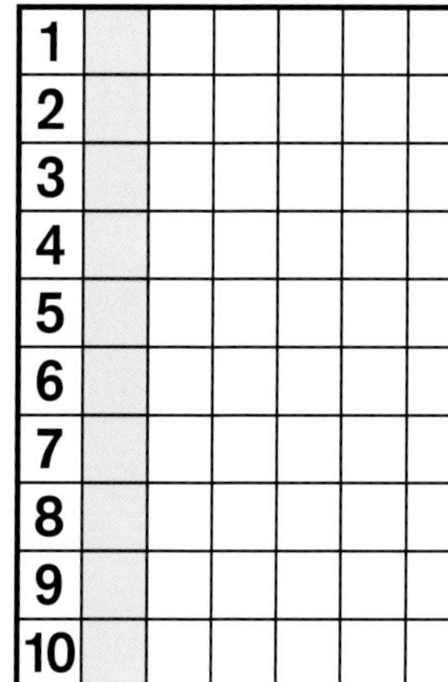

Clues

1. Container for beer
2. Hold up
3. Type of apple
4. Small stones or pebbles
5. Spring festival
6. Dairy product
7. The East
8. Flowering shrub
9. Wealth
10. Fairground car

WORD CHALLENGES

PROOFREADING

Check your spelling and punctuation skills with these proofreading exercises, that are packed full of literal errors and commonly misspelled words.

 56 

Personal letter

Dear Chris

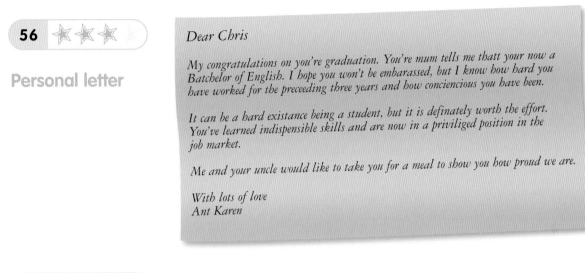

My congratulations on you're graduation. You're mum tells me thatt your now a Batchelor of English. I hope you won't be embarassed, but I know how hard you have worked for the preceeding three years and how conciencious you have been.

It can be a hard existance being a student, but it is definately worth the effort. You've learned indispensible skills and are now in a priviliged position in the job market.

Me and your uncle would like to take you for a meal to show you how proud we are.

With lots of love
Ant Karen

57 

Fictional story paragraph

A weary night had become the first day of the new milennium. The Inspecter reached across the table and snatched the notbook from her hands. It was full of notes written in miniscule handwriting – did it contain evidence of a dangerous liason. The suspect was a large bulky woman and the chair was scarcly large enough to acomodate her. At first it was hard to guauge her reaction. He studied the picture from the moniter. He thought she fits the identafication perfectly. And in that moment he glimpsed the wierd and amazing truth. 'Your witholding the truth from me' he said. Hed made the conection at last. 'Your harrassing me,' she said. She became rigid all over, so much so that she didnt turn her head at the rythmic clanging of the bell.

58 

Lifestyle article

Escaping the 9 to five

After a long week of dischord at work, marked only by ever more bizare demands from the boss, what could be nicer than that quintesentially British pastime of a quick escape to the tranquillity of the countryside. The affect of drawing the first few breathes of rural air into your lungs is enough to calm even the most comitted city dweller.
But we shouldnt be decieved about the reality of the rural idyl. Sadly as the roads try to cope with the haemorhage of urban types heading towards greener pastures. alluding the crowds is becoming even harder. In todays countryside, even if you get to sip a daquiri on you're verrandah, to the ernest strains of cooeing doves, your almost certain to be acompanied by the incesant drone of four-by-fours on the nearby moterway.

MONOGRAMS

Find the answer to each puzzle by moving around the circle following the red lines. If the letter is four letters away or less it is found by tracing around the circumference. In the event of double letters, the letter in question is visited just once.

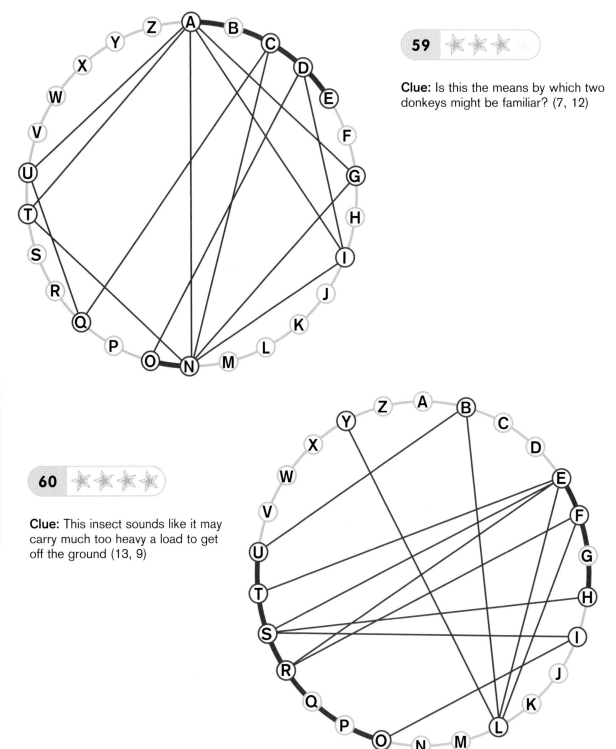

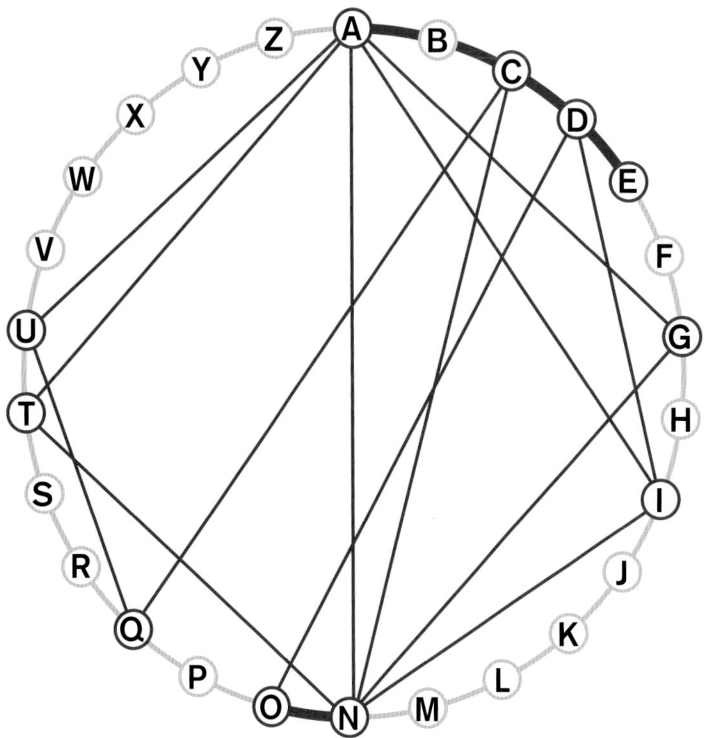

Clue: Is this the means by which two donkeys might be familiar? (7, 12)

Clue: This insect sounds like it may carry much too heavy a load to get off the ground (13, 9)

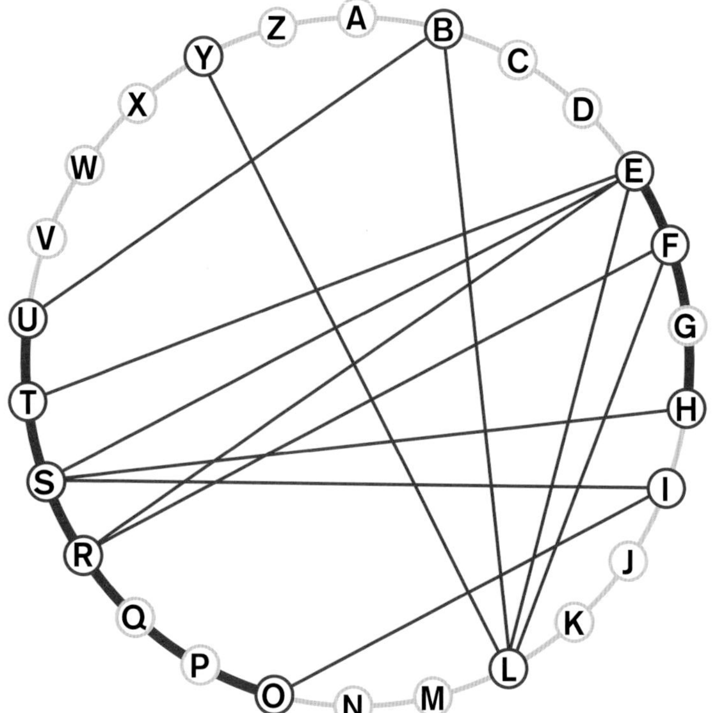

WORD CHALLENGES

HETERONYMS

As with previous heteronyms, the clues below will lead you to identically spelt words with different sounds and meanings. However, this time some of the answers may have different presentations, perhaps with spaces and hyphens. For example, **'resign' (to quit)** and **'re-sign' (to sign again)**.

61 Problem pairs

1. Miscellaneous / dehydrate naturally
2. Recoil / disadvantage
3. Prominent / incapable
4. Prisoner / find guilty
5. Not excessive or extreme / to preside over
6. Computer terminal / to comfort
7. Document giving permission / to allow

Heteronyms are an excellent way of increasing your vocabulary. They also help to keep a check on your spelling.

62 Horrible heteronyms

These two apparently unconnected phrases are clues to a pair of heteronyms – one string of letters that can be broken up into two quite different sets of words. What are they?

American volcano / sets up magnifying equipment

For simpler Palindromes go to page **60-61**

Back and forth 1

63 ★★★

Can you make sense of these palindromes? A gift for words and a logical mind is all you need to fill in the missing letters to make each of them read the same forwards and backwards.

1. Political Americans engage in stellar fun performance:
   S*A* **MY B* D**O*R*T***

2. Clever gent creates a renowned waterway:
   A *A*, * PN * C*N*L, P*N**A**

3. Perhaps romancers turn against each other:
   W*N'* *O*E **V**T **W**

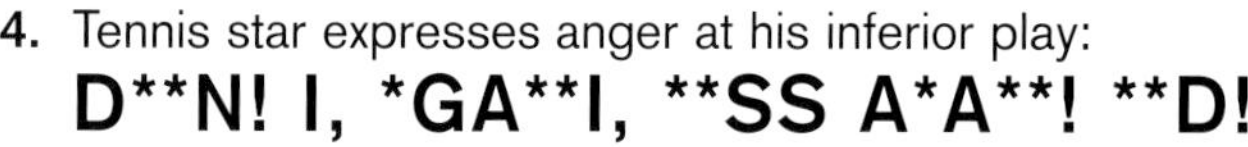

4. Tennis star expresses anger at his inferior play:
   DN! I, *GA**I, **SS A*A**! **D!**

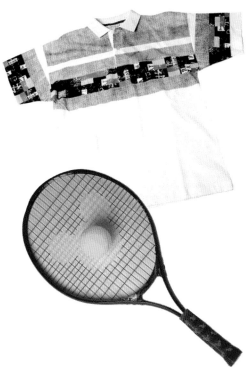

Back and forth 2

64 ★★★★

Use the cryptic clues as a guide to deciphering these palindromic phrases. The answers are longer and fewer letters have been provided.

1. Perhaps a father's explanation of what casual speech signifies:
   O, ***N* ** * *IL, **N**

2. Greedy man's advice on Italian food:
   '* * L**A **G; *O ***G * ****M***

3. Three girls share a message:
   M** **T* ****H *E* ***R**'* ****G****

4. Old, esteemed man reflects on his past actions:
   ****V**** N**, * **V* *N.**
   *** **D * ** ** ***L, * ***D**, ***R?**

WORD CHALLENGES

WORD CENTRES

The words in the following lists have something in common – they can all be found hidden away in the middle of longer words. Supply the missing letters indicated by the asterisks and uncover the longer words.

Five in the middle

Use your word knowledge and powers of common sense to work out full-length words of seven, nine and 11 letters.

1. *HASTE*
2. *RAVER*
3. **STILE**
4. **SOLVE**
5. ***PRESS***
6. ***COURT***

In the English language, the single letter that appears most often at the beginning of a word is T followed by A, O, S, I, W, H, C and B; and at the end the most common is E followed by S, D, T, N, R, Y and O.

Four in the middle

Can you identify these 10-letter words from their centres?

1. ***ITEM***
2. ***ENDS***
3. ***EVER***
4. ***POND***
5. ***BUST***
6. ***CELL***
7. ***GRIM***
8. ***FUND***

For simpler Word Squares go to page 64

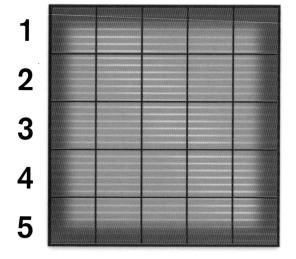

1

2

3

4

5

1. Exams
2. Additional
3. Rob
4. Characteristic
5. Seasoned

68

1. Dish of mixed vegetables
2. Maxim
3. Tag
4. Representative
5. Greek character

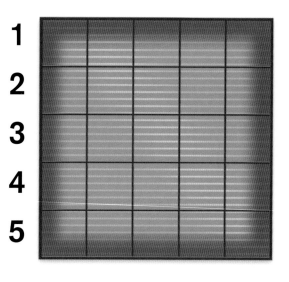

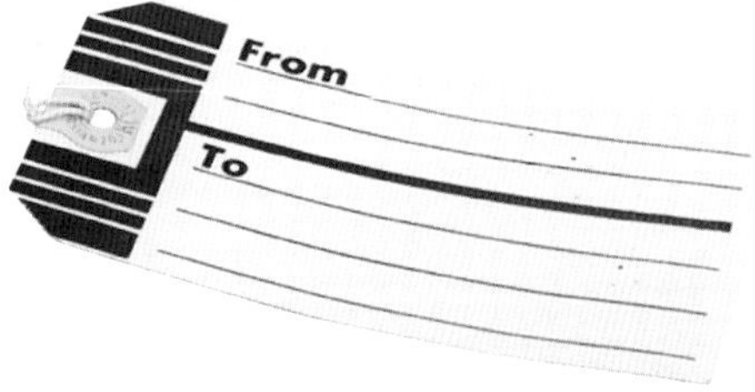

1

2

3

4

5

WORD CHALLENGES

1

2

3

4

5

69

1. Sample
2. African plants and their juice
3. Pieces of furniture
4. To annoy unkindly
5. English county

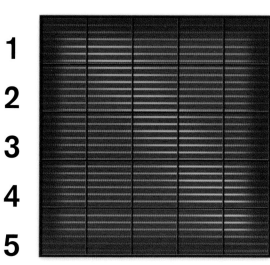

CIPHERWORDS

These puzzles are crosswords with a twist. The aim is to determine which letter of the alphabet belongs in each cell of the grid. The numbers 1-26 serve as ciphers for those letters, and cells with the same numbers will always contain the same letters.

A few letters have been provided as a guide to start you off. Using your word knowledge and powers of logic, work out which numbers represent the rest of the letters in the alphabet.

70 ★★★

■	20	15	14	12	15	19	■	18	14	25
7	■	16	■	2	■	2	■	22	■	14
14	18	18	15	12	■	23	22	11	13	9
16	■	13	■	13	■	19	■	13	■	2
24	2	12	10	■	21 F	2	18	17	14	12
■	■	■	14	■	15 U	■	15	■	■	■
12	2	21	17	13	12	■	8	14	26	13
15	■	16	■	6	■	7	■	3	■	1
19	2	22	3	13	■	2	12	14	19	2
4	■	9	■	18	■	16	■	9	■	19
2	12	17	■	17	12	14	5	13	16	■

1	2	3	4	5	6	7	8	9	10	11	12	13
14	15 U	16	17	18	19	20	21 F	22	23	24	25	26

A B C D E ~~F~~ G H I J K L M N O P Q R S T ~~U~~ V W X Y Z

71 ★★★

■	3	18	17	7	21	15	1	18	9	23	13	■
18	■	6	■	15	■	22	■	24	■	22	■	20
24	19	6	■	15	22	25	23	9	19	24	22	1
4	■	7	■	18	■	9	■	23	■	16	■	22
18	17	21	9	3	9	24	12	■	15 F	22 A	21	2
3	■	■	■	9	■	12	■	1	■	21	■	7
23	13	25	19	19	24	■	5	22	24	6	22	1
9	■	7	■	24	■	16	■	10	■	■	■	7
15	22	9	21	■	15	19	26	9	24	7	3	3
9	■	1	■	17	■	11	■	24	■	22	■	3
7	23	9	8	18	7	23	23	7	■	12	7	1
6	■	6	■	24	■	19	■	3	■	1	■	13
■	11	14	9	23	7	11	22	3	14	7	6	■

1	2	3	4	5	6	7	8	9	10	11	12	13
14	15 F	16	17	18	19	20	21	22 A	23	24	25	26

~~A~~ B C D E ~~F~~ G H I J K L M N O P Q R S T U V X Y Z

Cross off each letter as you put it in the grid to help you keep track of the letters left to use.

For simpler Novelty Crosswords go to page 68

This crossword will test your word knowledge and vocabulary. Each answer is a word that can fit either in front of or behind both words in the clue to form completely new words or phrases. For example, if the clue is 'Family; House' then the answer is 'Tree' (family tree, tree house).

Across

7. Post; Oil (4)
8. Month; Roman (8)
9. Card; Parade (8)
10. Head; Home (4)
11. Wood; Hole (6)
13. Fore; Gun (6)
15. Bare; Worm (6)
17. Pad; Artist (6)
18. Mate; Cap (4)
20. Mile; Aero (8)
22. Civil; Flight (8)
23. Bird; Rib (4)

Down

1. Club; Board (8)
2. Fire; Air (4)
3. Stations; Legal (6)
4. Record; Card (6)
5. Concealed; Fee (8)
6. Sea; Drum (4)
12. Guitar; Oven (8)
14. Rate; Stock (8)
16. Tap; Belly (6)
17. Deal; Mile (6)
19. Hand; Boat (4)
21. Perfect; Cubic (4)

73 ★★★★

Christmas has come early for cryptic crossword lovers with this novelty tree-shaped puzzle.

Happy Crossmas!

Across

1. Music bursting onto the scene (3)
3. Expressed pain as we ran around the tree (5)
4. A puzzle about the vehicle (5)
7. Lara beats an unusual material (9)
9. Money made thanks to chess players (7)
12. Does he possibly have the weight of the world on his shoulders? (4-7)
18. Unofficial dispenser of Australian justice? (8,5)
19. Seedy type that can open doors? (6)
22. Sound voiced by boy and worker (6)
27. Down below, there's a good deal to be had! (7,8)
28. Be a sport on slippery ground (5)
29. Rare angel fish? (5)

Down

1. A saying to show that Rob has lost heart (7)
2. Cheap snacks? (7)
5. An undesirable on the landscape, perhaps (4)
6. Heard to ruminate on the street (4)
8. Say farewell to a crazy idea at university (5)
10. Choice of the non-choosy (3)
11. Hair-stylist living in Los Angeles (3)
12. Prepare for a double impact? (5)
13. Belief in the animal to a degree (5)
14. Push the boat out? (5)
15. Smooths things over for golfers (5)
16. Word making a comeback before heading for a watery demise (5)
17. Unoriginal contribution to television programming (5)
19. Top secret meat is counterfeit (4)
20. Language where actions speak louder than words (4)
21. Chief support of water supply by river (8)
23. A witness, on paper (8)
24. Mary fears they're up for a fight (4)
25. Prepare to hit the right note (4)
26. Curtail a rebel brigade (7)

For simpler Arrow Words go to page **66-67**

74 ★★★

These Arrow Words are completed using the same method as before – but this time the clues have been made harder so as to test your word power and get your brain really ticking over.

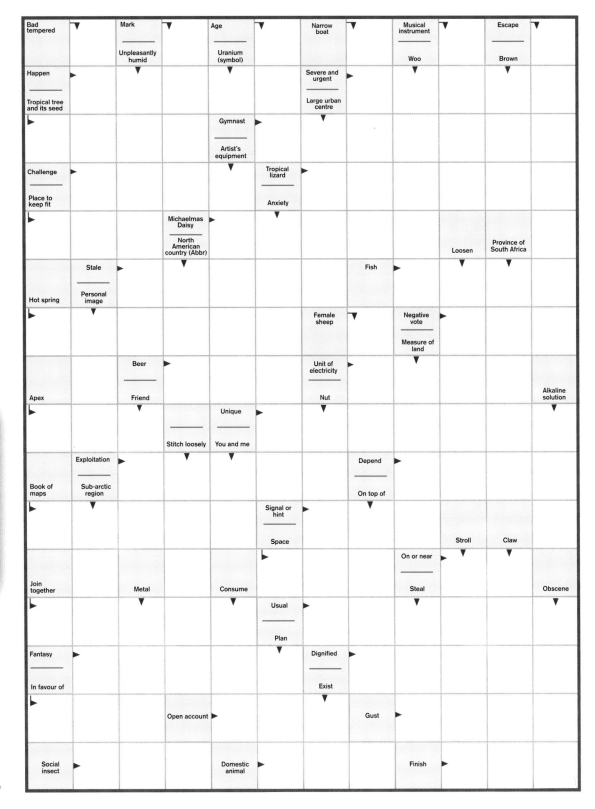

Bad tempered		Mark / Unpleasantly humid		Age / Uranium (symbol)		Narrow boat		Musical instrument / Woo		Escape / Brown	
Happen / Tropical tree and its seed						Severe and urgent / Large urban centre					
				Gymnast / Artist's equipment							
Challenge / Place to keep fit					Tropical lizard / Anxiety						
			Michaelmas Daisy / North American country (Abbr)						Loosen	Province of South Africa	
Hot spring	Stale / Personal image						Fish				
						Female sheep		Negative vote / Measure of land			
Apex		Beer / Friend				Unit of electricity / Nut					Alkaline solution
			Stitch loosely	Unique / You and me							
Book of maps	Exploitation / Sub-arctic region						Depend / On top of				
					Signal or hint / Space				Stroll	Claw	
Join together		Metal		Consume				On or near / Steal			Obscene
					Usual / Plan						
Fantasy / In favour of						Dignified / Exist					
			Open account				Gust				
Social insect				Domestic animal				Finish			

75 ★★★★

If you find puzzles like these tricky, try some of the earlier Arrow Words before attempting this harder one.

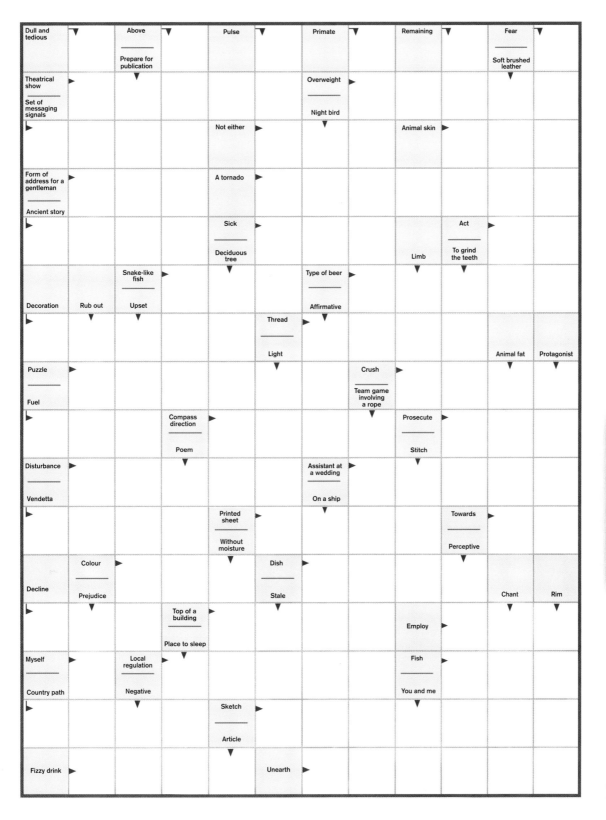

Dull and tedious

Above / Prepare for publication

Pulse

Primate

Remaining

Fear / Soft brushed leather

Theatrical show / Set of messaging signals

Overweight / Night bird

Not either

Animal skin

Form of address for a gentleman / Ancient story

A tornado

Sick / Deciduous tree

Limb

Act / To grind the teeth

Decoration

Rub out

Snake-like fish / Upset

Type of beer / Affirmative

Thread / Light

Animal fat

Protagonist

Puzzle / Fuel

Crush / Team game involving a rope

Compass direction / Poem

Prosecute / Stitch

Disturbance / Vendetta

Assistant at a wedding / On a ship

Printed sheet / Without moisture

Towards / Perceptive

Decline

Colour / Prejudice

Dish / Stale

Chant

Rim

Top of a building / Place to sleep

Employ

Myself / Country path

Local regulation / Negative

Fish / You and me

Sketch / Article

Fizzy drink

Unearth

ANAGRAMMED SYNONYMS

The following two puzzles consists of a group of three words. Your task is to find two of the three that can be paired to form an anagram of another word, which in turn, is a synonym of the remaining word.

EXAMPLE:

LEG - MEEK - NET

The words LEG and NET are an anagram of GENTLE, which is a synonym of the word MEEK.

76 ★★★

1. ONCE - EDIT - SEND
2. REFUGE - PLOT - STUB

It may help to think of a synonym for each word before trying to unscramble the anagrams.

77 ★★★

1. TIE - SPIN - TROUPE
2. FAULT - VARY - CUTE
3. LENIENT - MIX - GRIM

For easier Disc wheels, go to page **74**

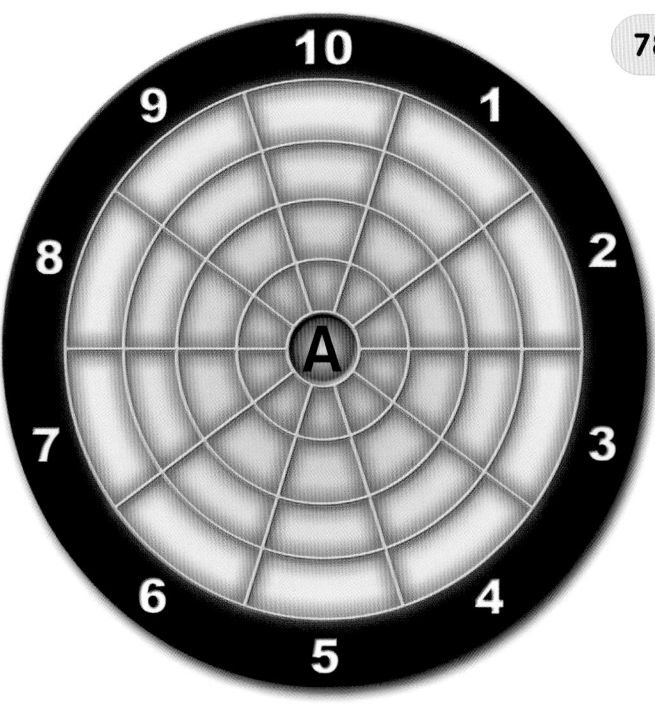

78 ★★★ **Disc wheels**

The answers to the questions are all five-letter words ending with the letter A in the centre. The initial letters when read clockwise from 1 will give a form of disguise.

1. Punctuation mark
2. Market place of ancient Athens
3. Craze
4. Japanese city
5. Extreme
6. The vegetation of a region
7. South American mammal
8. Scent
9. Greek character
10. Heather

WORD RINGS

These are like regular anagrams but made a little different by wrapping the letters around a ring in a random order. In addition to the main anagram, using the letters in the ring, see how many words of three letters or more you can find.

For easier Word rings go to page **75**

79

81

THREE-DIMENSIONAL CRYPTIC CROSSWORD

To keep you on your toes, this cryptic crossword has an extra twist – you have to make your solutions work over three planes instead of one. As well as testing your word and deduction skills, it keeps your visual and spatial awareness up to speed.

83 ★★★

Across

1. Submit strongbox with missing lid (5)
4. Sways in moments of agitation (5)
10. Careless and wanting, we hear (3)
11. Frown at point on hood (5)
12. Dock confused pet on uppermost platform (3,4)
13. Take a look and say 'Where's the summit?' (4)
14. Interpret what he priced strangely (8)
16. Pastry found in city den (6)
17. Lent cool pun to argument about hayfever indicator (6,5)
20. Calamity for 501s showing in autumn (8)
22. Exhaust one cab (4)
24. Give fuel back (3)
25. Bellini's heroine struggles with Roman (5)
26. Beg stewed rice from frozen sea-goer (7)
27. Gasp about one colour (5)
28. Faded from being overworked in gym (5)
29. Mean rump steak cooked at leisure spot (9,4)
32. Half expect love is usually volatile (9)
35. Type of anger that is right inside (3)
36. Immature bug hidden right in viscous rock (5)
37. Swinging but no, not whilst yawning (6)
39. Arthur's man loses biblical chap to the spear (5)
40. Top knight takes drug by the barrel load (3)
42. Whipped up rodent troubles, finally contained (6)
44. Crank ties up net – it's for hitting balls over (6,6)
47. Tired, so look round shelter (6)
49. Died well, as at the end of lives (6)
51. Poor Tina – fathered by a timid person (5-7)
55. Try to follow author of verse (6)
59. Grey envelope containing part of a needle (3)
61. Fabric from which half London and all New York is made (5)
62. Eggs, carried via car all around (6)
64. Wear down queen with a long poem (5)
65. Request from Nigella's kitchen (3)
66. No real rooster will turn up eventually (6,2,5)
67. A race from northern islands lost king to lawyers (9)

Down

2. Fail to conceal ox model called 'Bush' (7)
3. Simple, as you can see if you look here (4)
5. Loop the loop: medication taken up with sweet (8)
6. Black stuff on which soccer is played (5)
7. Back trouble CD is damaged and passed over (7,4)
8. Protection for bay in midst of disturbance (5)
9. Trainees re-lay pine carpets (11)
15. Circulation problems end nap, idleness results (4,3,7)
18. Female star badly delaying lad (7,4)
19. Be away with stubble! (5)
21. Notice a true/false identifying mark (9)
23. An erroneous stratagem, I judge (10)
29. Saying that a team gets nothing to a thousand (5)
30. Follows Monsieur with love of money (4)
31. One thousand and one wishes start with the birds (5)
33. Beat vegetable (5)
34. One trade is best (5)
38. Falls badly, again over artist (7)
41. Former havens for international sales (7)
43. Employ half an excuse (3)
45. Religious notion undermines nationalism at first (3)
46. King with computing equipment (3)
48. Heard solver makes jumpers? (3)
49. Prepare for pinafore, maybe (5)
50. Let nothing rise above the door (6)
52. Legendary headmaster ran about, being elderly (6)
53. It's still above, and hot above also (5)
54. Discharge from jet flying around city (5)
56. To be serious, consume fat (5)
57. Singer to follow a student (4)
58. The bosses sound uninteresting (5)
60. Raises sore points in the circus (4)
62. Looks good... stop filming 'Ecstasy'! (4)
63. Study a red box (4)
65. Part of church shown in cheap sepia prints (4)

THEMED ANAGRAMS

In each of these puzzles you are provided with a list of words. Try to arrange the words in pairs so that each pair forms an anagram relating to the specified theme. For example, if the theme was **fruit** and the words **plane** and **pipe** appeared in the list, they could be combined to form an anagram of **pineapple**.

Theme: flowers

84

RISE	WEEDS	AEON	ROMP	MICE
BIG	LIES	OFFAL	LAST	DID

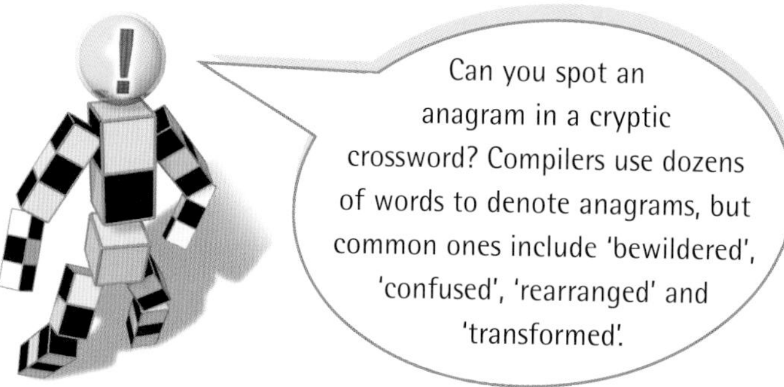

Can you spot an anagram in a cryptic crossword? Compilers use dozens of words to denote anagrams, but common ones include 'bewildered', 'confused', 'rearranged' and 'transformed'.

Theme: birds

85

BRIGADE	BRICK	REST	WIT	ANT	ATLAS	ELK
RUG	GALA	BALD	GOLF	GIRLS	MAIN	ROBS

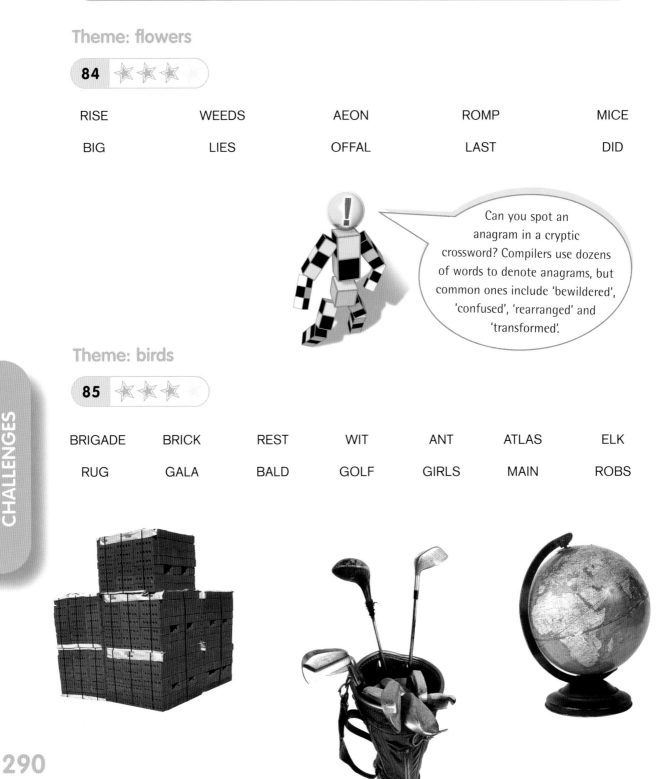

CROSS-ALPHABET

Complete the crosswords below by using all 26 letters of the alphabet once only.

86 ★★★

Insert the answers to the clues into the grid using the word lengths as a guide – the clues are given in no particular order.

bend the head in submission (3)

to act or vote for another person (5)

cry of the duck (5)

tarboosh (3)

danced or bopped in a lively manner (5)

an informal term for mother (2)

unpleasant to look at (9)

R N I

87 ★★★★

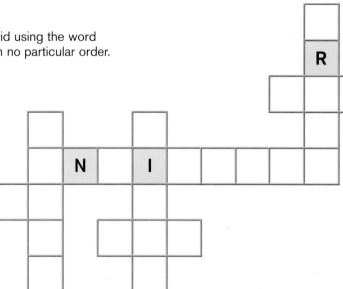

In this puzzle, use each letter of the alphabet just once each to complete the grid.

a lifting device (4)

to have existence (2)

examine someone's knowledge about something (4)

solemn promise (3)

irresponsibly frivolous (7)

a sudden uncontrollable attack, as of giggling or coughing (8)

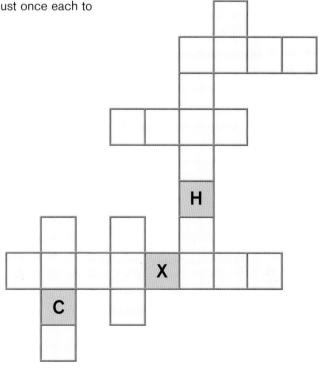

to parry off (4)

H X C

For previous Enigmagrams go to page 82

88 Clothes

Four eight-letter words have been scrambled. Solve the anagrams and then use the highlighted letters in each to make a new eight-letter word.

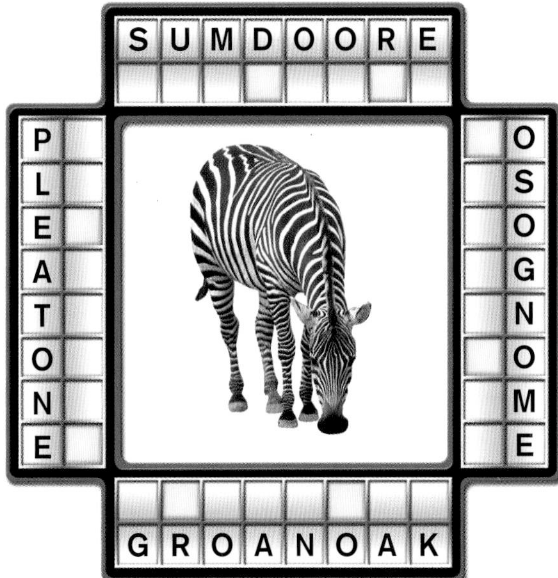

89 Animals

Solve the four anagrams to discover animals hiding within.

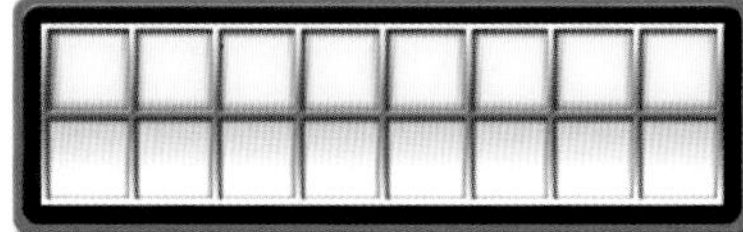

90 Flowers

Find the four eight-letter plant names that have been jumbled up. Then solve the anagram, made up of the highlighted letters, to make a new eight-letter plant name.

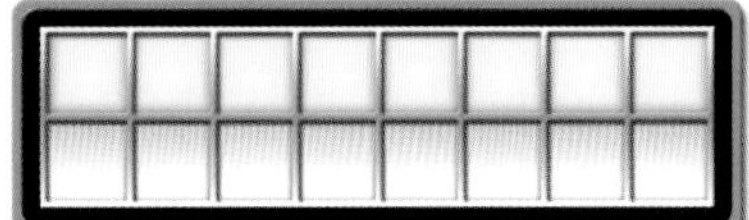

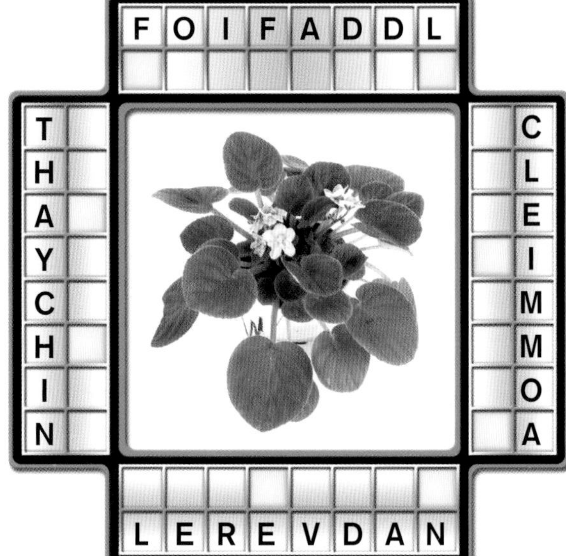

91 Sports

When solved, these anagrams reveal sporting terms. Once completed, use the highlighted letters to make a fifth twelve-letter sporting term.

Solving anagrams uses both verbal and spatial reasoning, therefore both the left and the right side of the brain benefit from these kinds of puzzles.

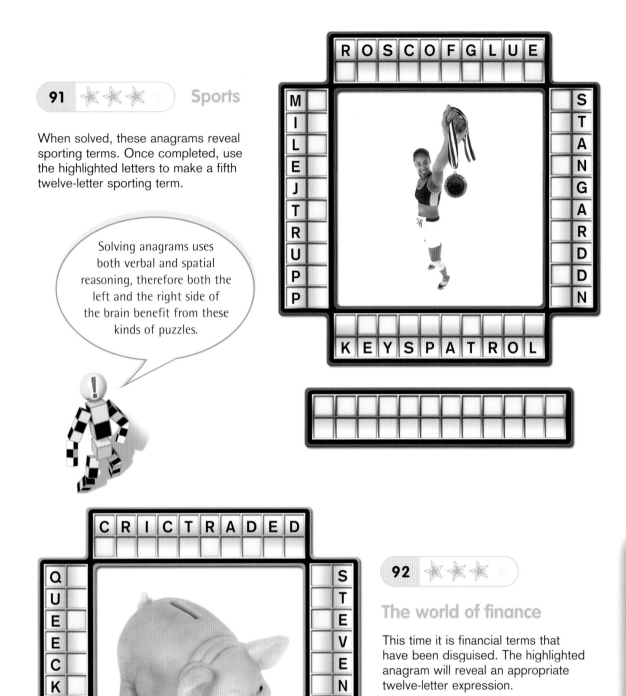

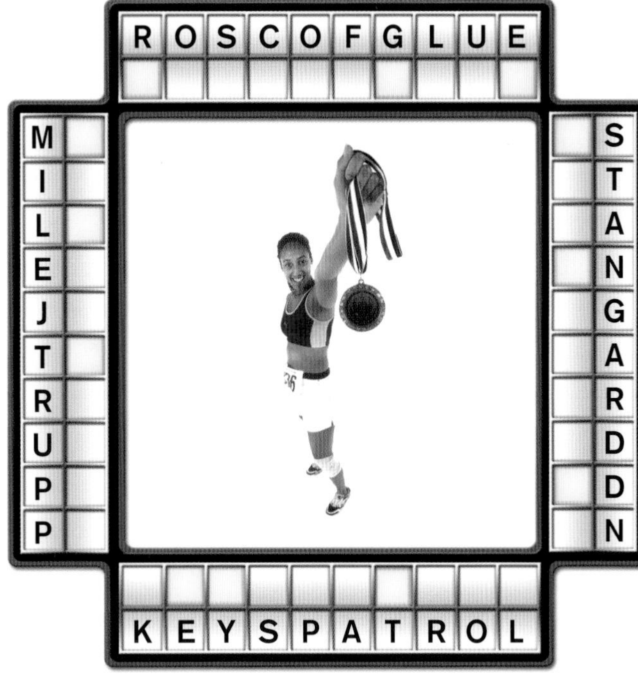

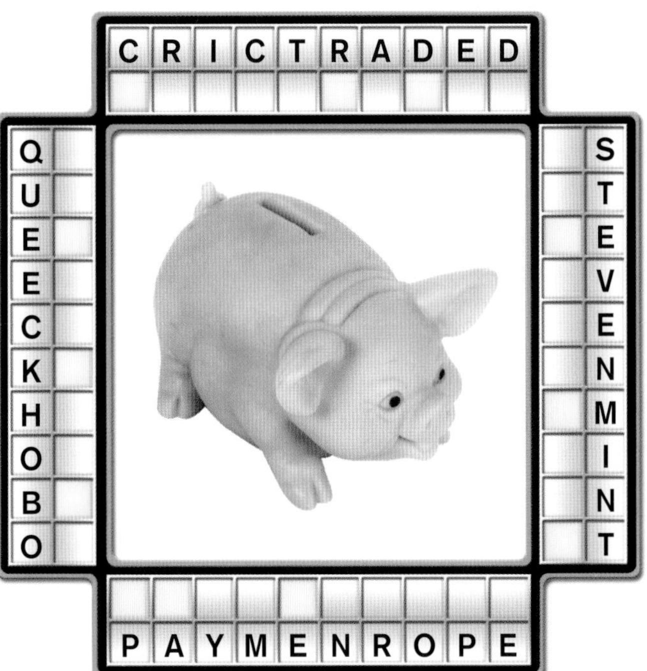

92 The world of finance

This time it is financial terms that have been disguised. The highlighted anagram will reveal an appropriate twelve-letter expression.

WORD CHALLENGES

NETWORK

Use every letter once to find a 14-letter word in each puzzle. All successive letters in the answer must be linked by a line. For easier versions of these Network puzzles, refer back to pages 90-91.

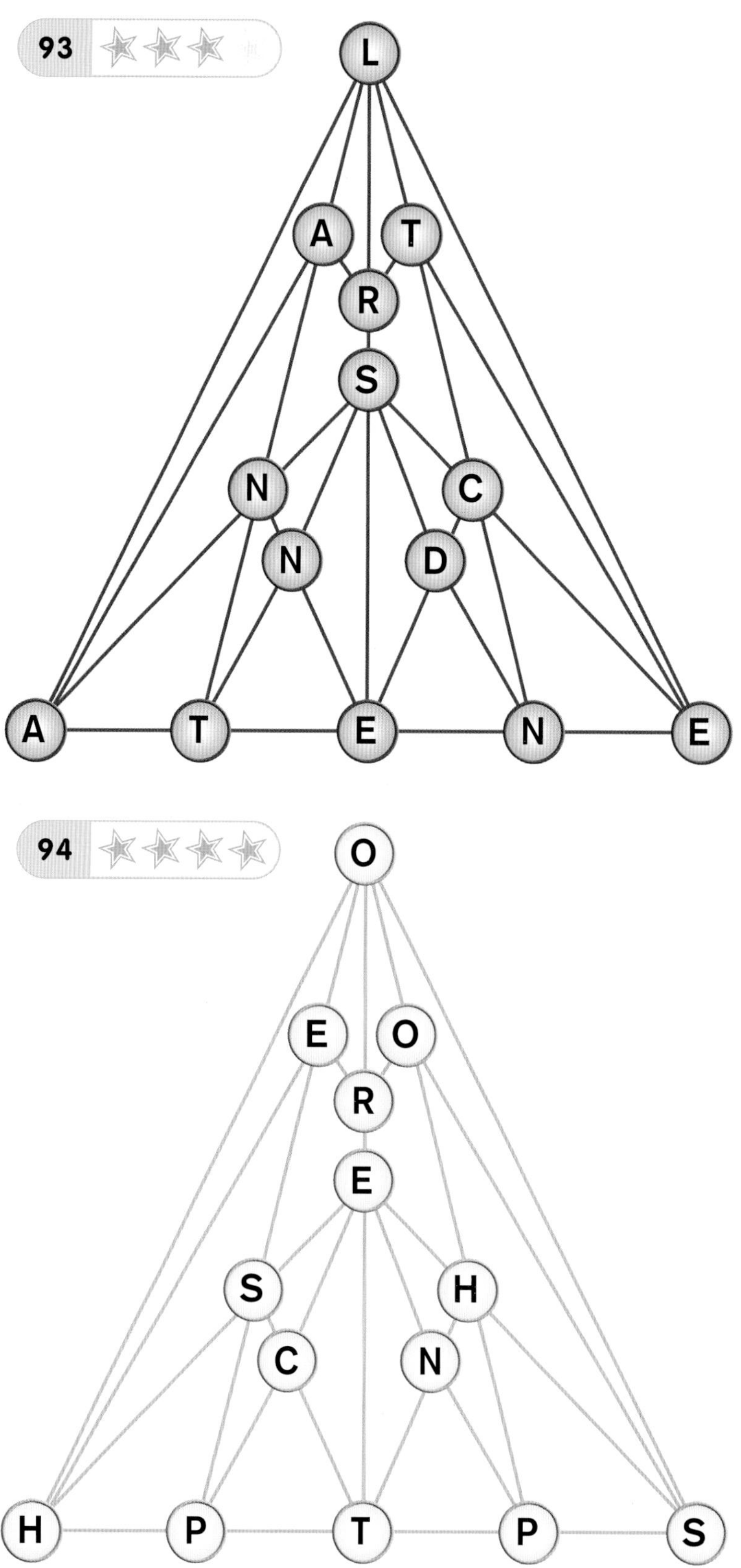

95

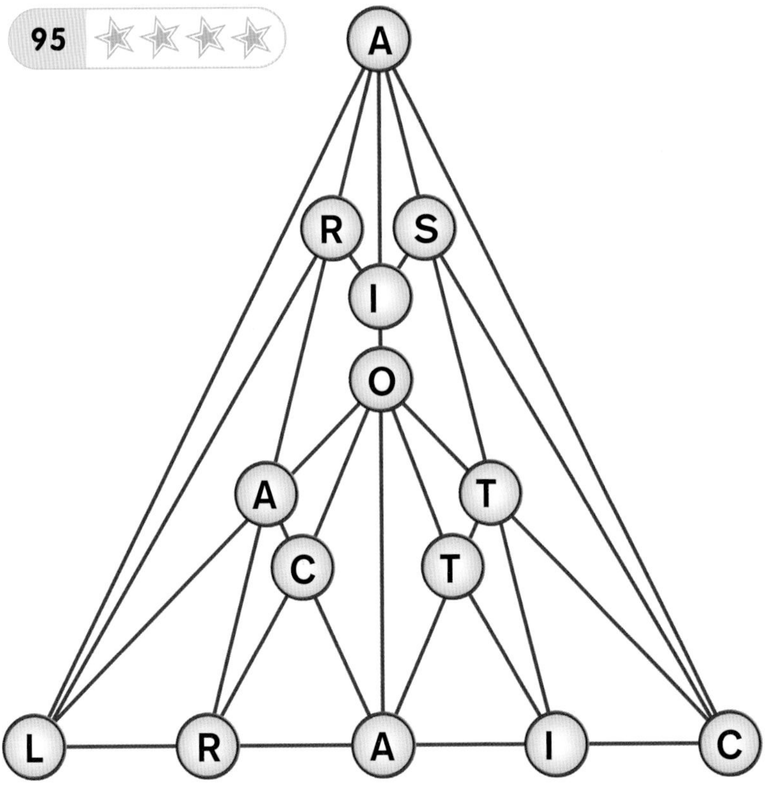

VERBOSITIES

Translate the verbose language used in these puzzles into simpler English, and uncover four well-known proverbs.

96

1. With quick and nimble motion, and with comparatively little weight that would normally exist only in the imagination, I am creating terpsichorean movement. What am I doing?

2. I am, by increments, placing further combustible material to that which is already enkindled. What am I doing?

97

1. In an endeavour to cause a subterfuge I am applying force in order to move the soft and curled hair of a ruminant of the genus *Ovis* across a particular person's oculi. What am I doing?

2. I am causing the main organ of photosynthesis and transpiration in a plant, which has been lately manifested, to make a movement in a different direction. What am I doing?

TRACKWORD

In each of the puzzles in this section, work from letter to connected letter to spell out a word. You are only allowed to use each letter once and every letter must be included.

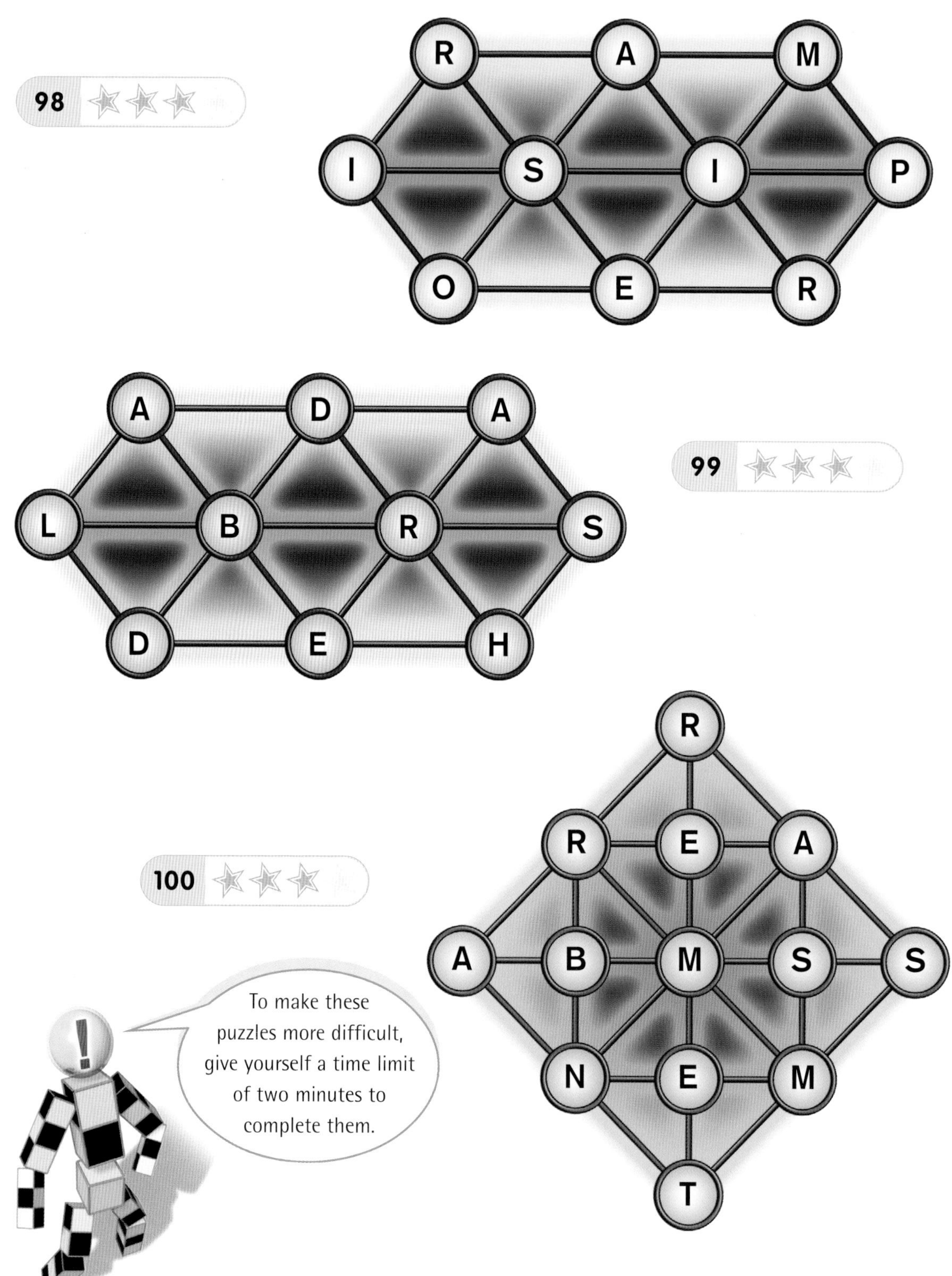

WORD CHALLENGES

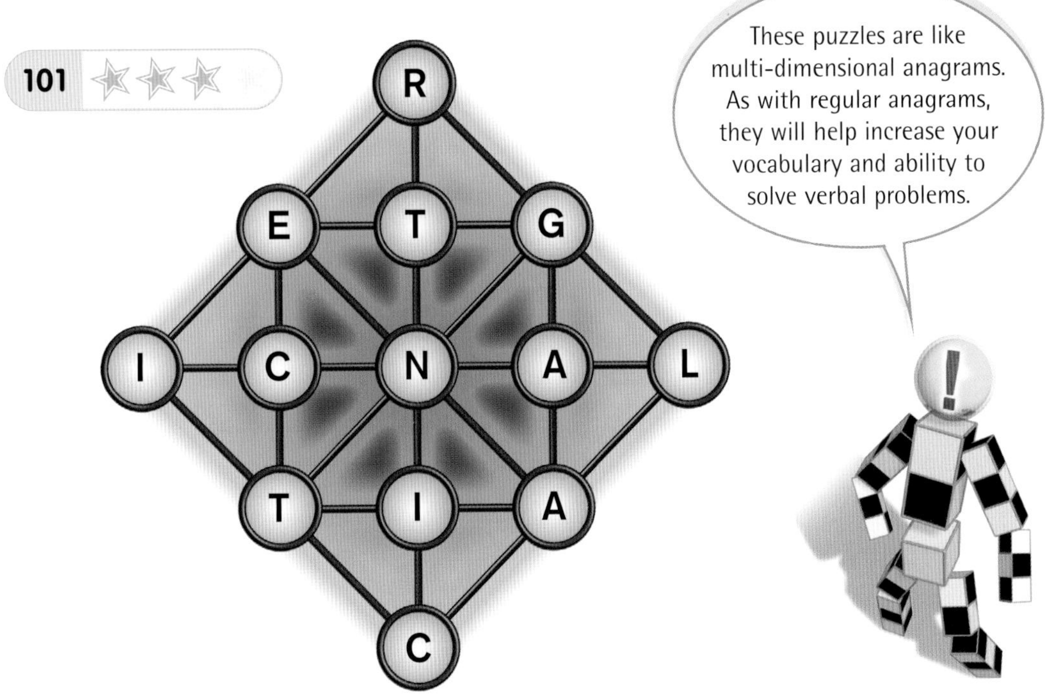

101
R
E
T
G
I
C
N
A
L
T
I
A
C
These puzzles are like multi-dimensional anagrams. As with regular anagrams, they will help increase your vocabulary and ability to solve verbal problems.
!

WORD CENTRES

The following words can all be found at the centre of longer words. Test your vocabulary by replacing the asterisks with letters to form the full-length word.

Kettle of fish

Can you identify the following words from their fishy centres?

** BASS ****
*** CHAR *
** LING **
** SOLE ***
*** TUNA **

Centre piece

Can you spot the nine-letter words from their centres?

** ANKLE **
** CHEST **
** LATER **
** MEDIA **
** SHONE **

WORD CHALLENGES

ODD WORD OUT

In each group of words below there is an odd one out. The explanations for this vary widely from puzzle to puzzle, so be sure to look at the words from every angle.

104

1. Cube
   Pyramid
   Sphere
   Dodecahedron
   Pentagon

2. Lever
   Repaid
   Deliver
   Stressed
   Retriever

3. Thames
   Seine
   Rhine
   Vistula
   Tagus

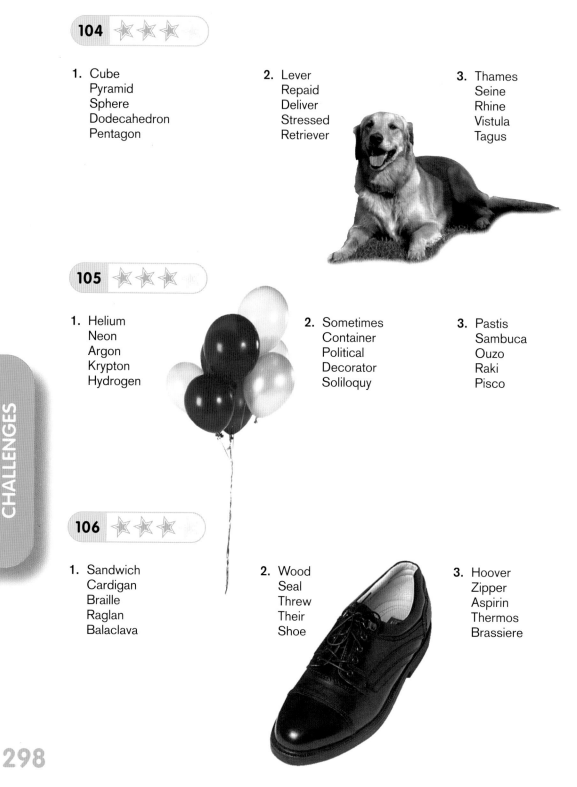

105

1. Helium
   Neon
   Argon
   Krypton
   Hydrogen

2. Sometimes
   Container
   Political
   Decorator
   Soliloquy

3. Pastis
   Sambuca
   Ouzo
   Raki
   Pisco

106

1. Sandwich
   Cardigan
   Braille
   Raglan
   Balaclava

2. Wood
   Seal
   Threw
   Their
   Shoe

3. Hoover
   Zipper
   Aspirin
   Thermos
   Brassiere

1. Paten
   Dean
   Curate
   Cardinal
   Rector

2. Skirt
   Coat
   Sock
   Sweater
   Tie

3. Apollo
   Artemis
   Ares
   Persephone
   Hephaestus

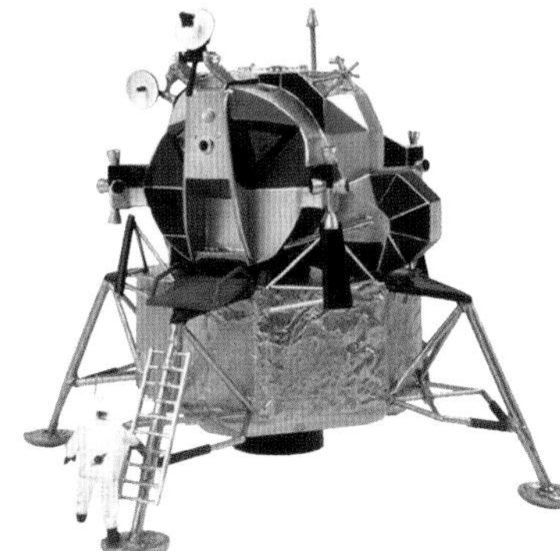

Use your general knowledge, or refer to a dictionary or atlas, to help solve these puzzles. Pay close attention to details including the specific kind of word, the length of words and the sequence to help you find the solution.

HIDDEN WORD

Somewhere within each of the following sentences is a hidden word, the letters of which are separated by spaces and by punctuation. Otherwise, the word is written as a whole. The sentences provide a cryptic clue, so study them carefully.

1. This stud enthuses over his books.
2. Hunt through these archives for documents.
3. The power of the crystal is manifest.
4. How much does he utter? Seems like not a lot.
5. My uncle averted disaster with his knife.

1. She typed antisocial comments about others' little mistakes.
2. Wanting to lose weight, he agreed to sacrifice desserts.
3. His refusal to do chores, like taking out the rubbish, irked her a lot.
4. Take a ride to Uranus via Mercury.
5. Deliberation is truth in kingship.

WORD LINKS

In each of the following puzzles, change the first word into the second word by finding a link at each stage. For example, the word **HAND** can be changed to **GLOVE** through the following steps: **HAND – OUT – FOX – GLOVE**.

The links can either produce a compound word, an hyphenated word or a two-word phrase. For example, the word **SUN** when added to **DRY** produces the word **SUNDRY**, when added to **UP** it produces the hyphenated word **SUN-UP** and when added to **CREAM** produces the phrase **SUN CREAM**.

Turn BLACK to WHITE

110

BLACK
* * I *
* A *
* * P *
* I N *
* * T
L * *
* F *
WHITE

Make NIGHT DAY

111

NIGHT
* L * *
* * U * E
* * L *
* *
* I G * *
* A * *
* * M *
DAY

Puzzles like these improve your vocabulary so that you have a much wider range of words to use when writing or speaking.

Put LETTER in POST

112

LETTER
* E * D
* * N *
* *
* * T
* A C *
* * T E *
* E *
POST

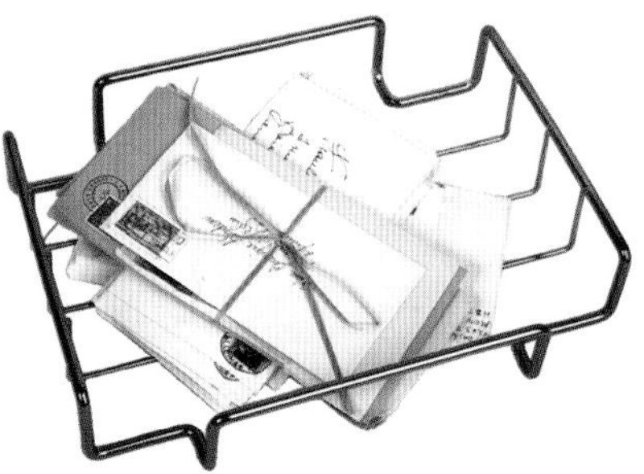

WORD CHALLENGES

Put MONEY into BANK

MONEY
*** O ***
*** * R**
*** O * ***
*** * D ***
*** H * ***
*** A ***
*** * D ***
*** ***
*** I * * ***
BANK

Put PEN to PAPER

PEN
*** N * * ***
*** * G ***
*** I S ***
*** R * C ***
*** O * ***
*** * L ***
*** U ***
*** O * S ***
*** * ***
PAPER

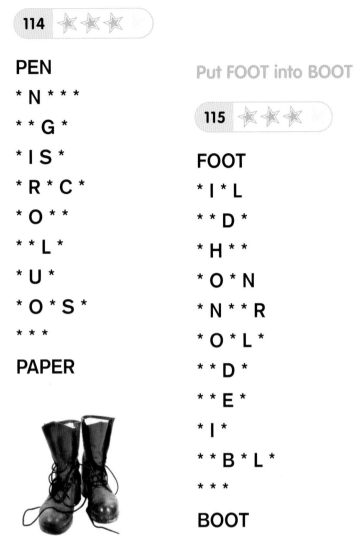

Put FOOT into BOOT

FOOT
*** I * L**
*** * D ***
*** H * ***
*** O * N**
*** N * * R**
*** O * L ***
*** * D ***
*** * E ***
*** I ***
*** * B * L ***
*** * ***
BOOT

INTERLINKS

Find a word that follows the first word in the clue and will make a new word or phrase when preceding the second word in the clue. For example, the answer to **dog.........burst** would be star – Dog **Star**, and **Star**burst.

FALL..........HAND
BIRD.........STORM
DOG.........PASTE
SCOUT.........FOLLOWER

BEACH.....COCK
KERB........FUND
WHEEL......PERSON
WHITE........STAFF

CRYPTIC WORD CENTRES

The answer to these cryptic clues are either synonyms or antonyms. As a twist, the answer is hidden within the sentence, spelt correctly from left to right. However, the letters are spread out along the sentence making the answer difficult to find.

Synonyms

1. Separately add salt to cooking.
2. Such a depressing tragedy ensued.
3. Total noted lastingly.
4. And it's really filthy!
5. Friends won't remember badges today.

1. Nervous one flounces off to avoid any chances.
2. Records reveal airship landing here first.
3. Fill your room with glowing lanterns.
4. Please use abundant grease while cleaning this axle.
5. Pot is to charge drinks.

WORD CHALLENGES

If you like cryptic crosswords, have a go at these puzzles which will test your ability to crack cryptic clues.

Antonyms

1. Scrooges never donate amounts.
2. Some quietly warn people receiving presents.
3. Goodbye, making it final.
4. There's plenty.
5. Mounting excitement completely overwhelms.

121 ★★★★

1. Armies usually return home after wars.
2. Adding software completed the database.
3. Pieces brought together.
4. Bring the principle captives inside.
5. Plenty leave their task undone whenever difficulties a

WORD PAIRS

Word pairs are two words which, when put together, form a new word or phrase. For example, **MATE** and **SHIP** can be put together to form the word **SHIPMATE**. Similarly, **GLOVES** and **KID** can be paired up to create the phrase **KID GLOVES**.

Bloomers?

122

Find the 15 pairs, three of which are bloomers, in the list of 30 words.

BEAR
CALF
CAT
CHICKEN
CHURCH
COPY
COW
CROSSING
DOG
EAGLE
ELEPHANT
FOX
GLOVE
HARE
HEART
HORSE
JACK
LION
LOVE
MARCH
MOUSE
PELICAN
POWER
RABBIT
ROSE
SLIP
SPREAD
WHITE
WIRE
WITNESS

Cover me!

124

Listed below in alphabetical order are another 30 words which can be matched up to make 15 new words or phrases, three of which will keep you covered.

BAND
BICYCLE
BOOB
BUS
CAR
CART
CHAIN
COACH
CONDUCTOR
DONKEY
FELLOW
GHOST
GUARD
HAMMER
INK
JACKET
JET
PANDA
PARTY
RIDGE
ROCKET
SALAD
SHIP
SLEDGE
TANK
TOP
TRAIN
TUBE
VAN
WAGON

Music to my ears

123

Listed below in alphabetical order are 40 words which can be matched up to make 20 new words or phrases. When you have matched them all up, can you find the three items to provide even more harmony?

BACK
BANK
BELL
BLOOD
BONE
BOUND
BRAIN
CENTRE
CHEST
CHILD
EAR
EYE
FACE
FAINT
FAIRY
FLUTE
FOOT
FUNNY
HAND
HAWK
HEAD
HEART
LIP
MOUTH
MUSCLE
NERVE
NOSE
NOTE
NUT
OFFICE
ORGAN
PAPER
RIB
ROCK
SERVICE
SPARE
TONGUE
TOOTH
TWISTER
WIG

PALINDROMIC ANAGRAMS

A palindrome is a word or phrase which reads the same backwards as forwards, such as **MADAM, RADAR,** and **MADAM I'M ADAM**.

In the following puzzles a palindromic phrase has been anagrammed, for example; **SENSE LIFELINE** is an anagram of the palindromic phrase – **SENILE FELINES.**

To help you, a number of letters have already been inserted into each answer.

125

in a den and indeed

***D *** **N* *I**

126

no men sell on moon

*O L***** ** *E***

127

I position options

, *T ** **P**I**

128

yes, surprise sunny pig

*U***, * **Y *****E* ***

129

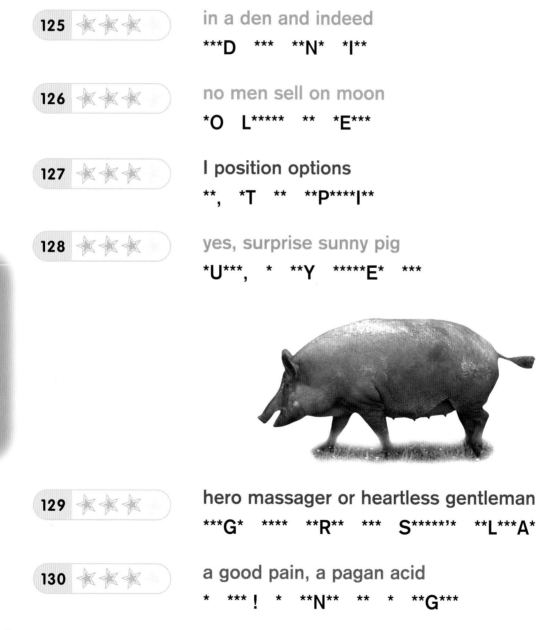

hero massager or heartless gentleman

G* * **R** *** S*****'* **L***A*

130

a good pain, a pagan acid

* *** ! * **N** ** * **G***

131

drum major or refer fraud

***D** *** * *** *F *** *U*

132

wittiest lies awaits loo

*** ** E**O*’* *****T * *** ?

133

a raw Costa Rica awaits

*** ** * **R ** * *** * S** ?

134

sniffler for sloppier gorgon

L* ? ** *, *****R *R**** ****

135

naïve love-lorn artists

T* *I ** ** ***L ****

136

rare menacers on an overactive emotion

*N**, * V*** **** **** **C* R*** ** ***N**

BLENDED SQUARES

A Magic Word square is a matrix of letters constructed in such a way that by using words of equal length, the same words can be read both horizontally and vertically, as in the 5x5 grid right.

The Blended Square puzzles in this section each consist of five connected 5x5 Magic Word squares. The clues are given in sets of five and colour-coded for each square, but they are not given in any particular order.

EXAMPLE:

T	O	A	S	T
O	R	D	E	R
A	D	O	R	E
S	E	R	V	E
T	R	E	E	S

137

Clues:

Red bordered square
1. Eskimo's domed hut.
2. Capital city of South Korea.
3. Supernatural creature of Nordic folklore.
4. Armed robbery.
5. Mountain notorious for its fearsome North Face.

Blue bordered square
1. Small light boat.
2. Cured pork.
3. Impoverished.
4. Tropical plant, also called American aloe.
5. Egg-shaped.

Yellow bordered square
1. A fabric woven with fibres from the flax plant.
2. Greek muse of love poetry.
3. A synthetic fabric.
4. Elephant or walrus tusk.
5. A point or line that remains at rest while other parts of the body are in a state of equilibrium.

Green bordered square
1. Got up.
2. Famous bath salt.
3. Large body of water.
4. The dried flesh of the coconut.
5. Identified.

Orange bordered square
1. Angry.
2. Knowing.
3. Regenerate.
4. Moshe * * * * * (1915–1981), Israeli general and statesman.
5. Lowest point, opposite to zenith.

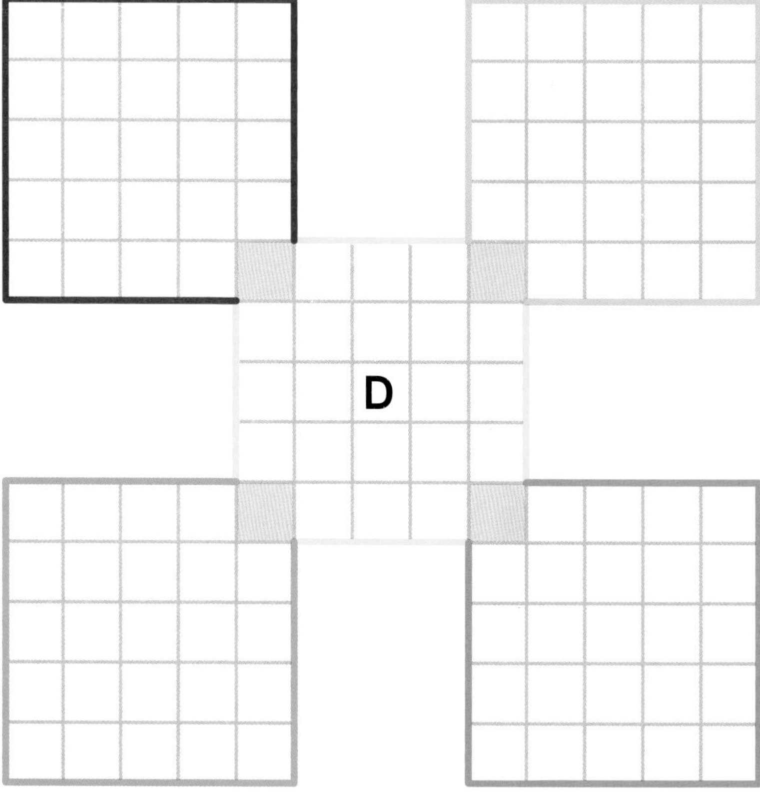

138

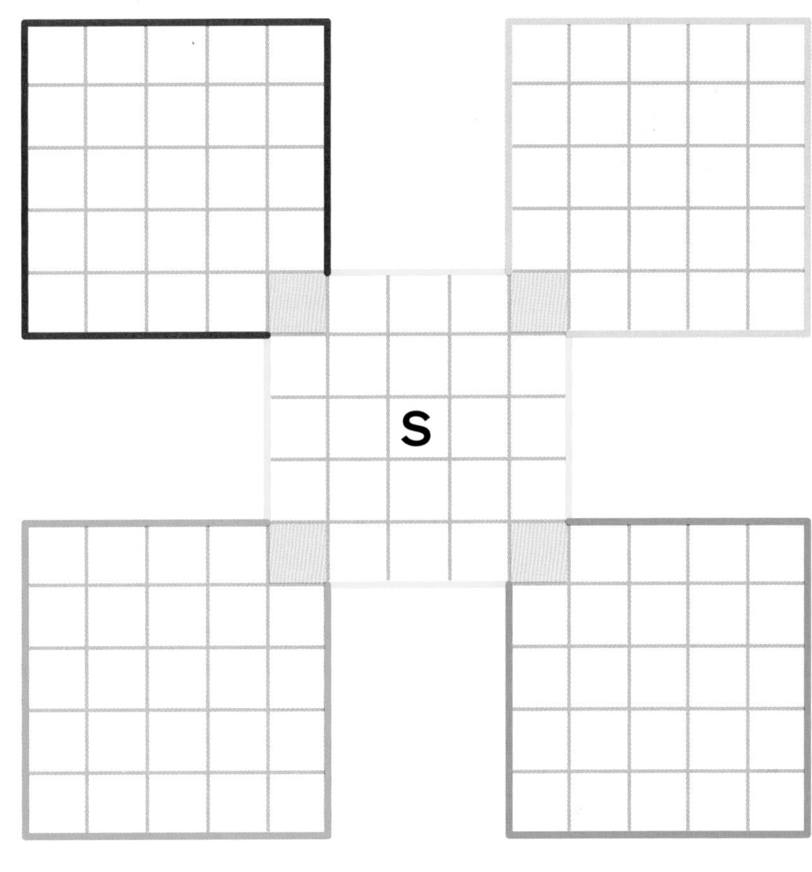

Clues:

Red bordered square

1. Exert power or authority.
2. Broadcasting medium.
3. Small European viper.
4. Creep along.
5. British Parliament house.

Blue bordered square

1. Notions.
2. Be worthy of.
3. Brief and to the point.
4. Short musical composition intended to demonstrate technical virtuosity.
5. Measuring stick.

Yellow bordered square

1. Moisten with liquid during cooking.
2. With rapid movements.
3. Wooden shoe.
4. Musical composition for eight performers.
5. Molars.

Green bordered square

1. Make suitable.
2. President of Argentina (1946–1955 and 1973–1974).
3. Burning.
4. Hold back to a later time.
5. Vogue.

Orange bordered square

1. The little wheel on a spur.
2. Musical drama.
3. Run away secretly to get married.
4. Biblical ruler of Galilee at the time of Christ.
5. Procrastinate.

Start with the central yellow grid as it has a letter provided, and work outward from there. These puzzles test both vocabulary and general knowledge.

ZOETROPE

This puzzle is inspired by the zoetrope, an old-fashioned toy with a revolving cylinder containing a series of pictures which, when rotated at speed, looks to the observer as if the subject were alive and moving.

139 ★★★

In the diagram below, the letter A on the inner wheel is set against the letter B on the outer wheel. So if you spell out the word NEE on the inner wheel, the adjacent letters on the outer wheel will produce the word OFF.

Find a four-letter word on the inner wheel that spells out another four-letter word on the outer wheel. Then, similarly, find a five-letter word and a six-letter word.

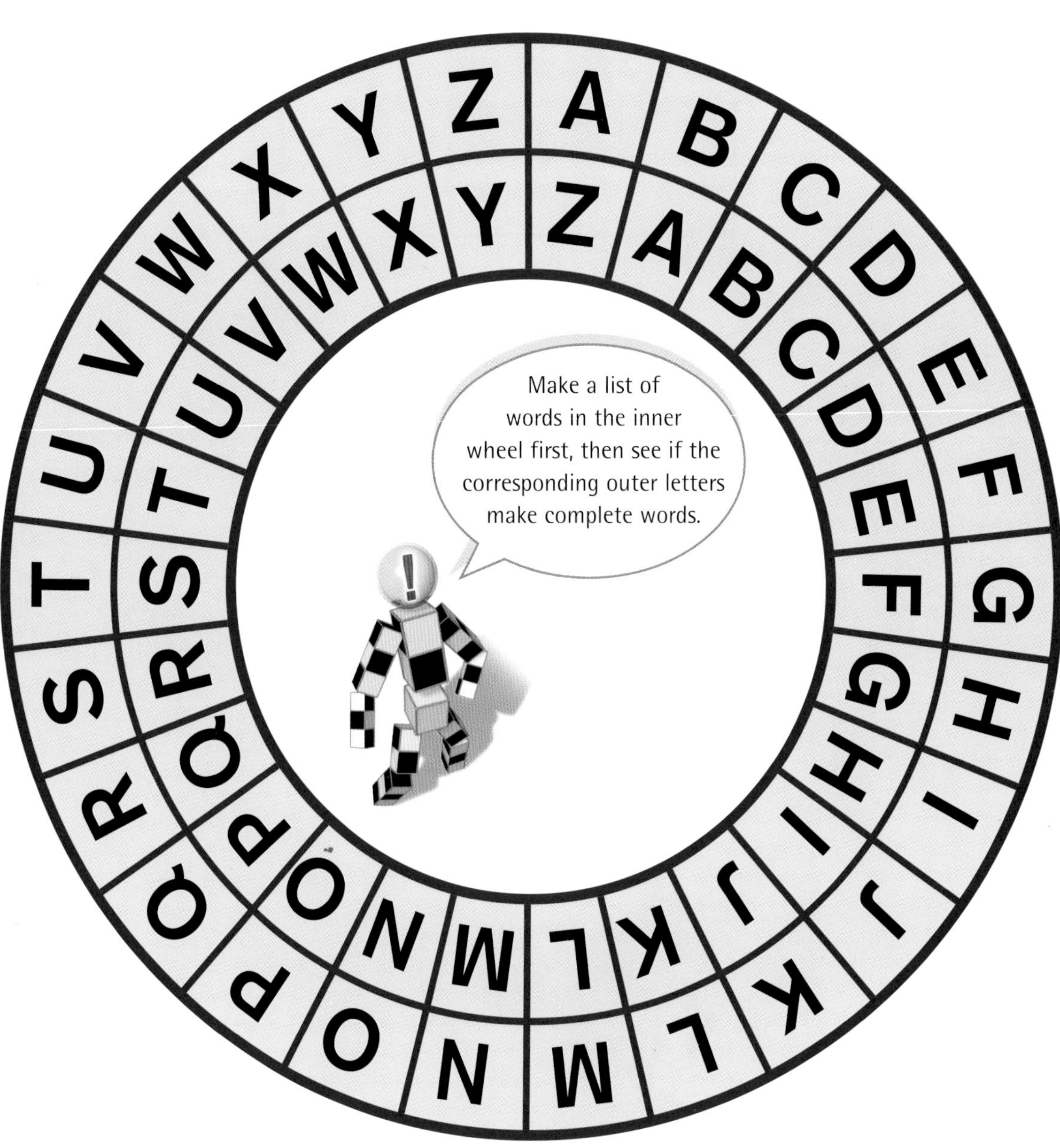

MEMORY PUZZLES

MEMORY PUZZLES

MEMORY PUZZLES

To be able to function as an individual and interact on a social level, your memory is vital. Fortunately, it is also a 'muscle' that you can exercise and develop.

WITHOUT A MEMORY IT WOULD BE IMPOSSIBLE TO LEARN anything new. And in practical terms, as well as enabling you to store information and call it up 'on demand', memory also helps you solve all kinds of problems by comparing and contrasting something you encounter for their first time with something you've come across before. It is only when memory fails that we become aware of its importance in our lives in allowing us to remember everything from the faces of our friends to PIN numbers and passwords.

THE HUMAN BRAIN STORES TWO SORTS OF MEMORIES, short-term and long-term. Short-term memory allows the temporary recall of the information that floods into it. (To understand the end of this sentence, your short-term memory remembers the beginning of it.) This form of memory has a limited capacity and is useful for remembering phone numbers or recent activity. By contrast, long-term memory stores information over days, months and years (including the letters of the alphabet and the way in which they link up to form words), retaining details that can last a life-time. These include not just facts but so-called 'active' memories such as knowing how to swim, drive a car or ride a bicycle.

EVERYTHING YOU EXPERIENCE is recorded as a memory. While long-term memory is vital to maintaining your identity and your knowledge of the world, short-term memory is a key everyday tool. For a fact to pass from short- to long-term memory depends on its importance. Fortunately, it is possible to train your brain to remember things, and so increase your long-term memory capacity.

Memory is like an athlete's muscles – a daily workout can increase both its power and strength.

I'm Mr. Mnemonic, and I'll offer you hints, tips and pieces of fun information to guide you through this section.

CHILDREN ARE GOOD AT LEARNING EVERYTHING from how to walk and talk to the names of the objects around them – although memory for facts is usually at its best during a person's school years, or just after. But whatever your age, the more you use your memory – be it factual or active, verbal or visual – the better it will be. Memory puzzles are ideal for giving your memory a workout to help keep it fit and able. And a good memory is a huge advantage once advancing years begin to take their toll on your brain power.

THE KEY TO SOLVING MEMORY PUZZLES – and hence to improving your memory – involves concentration, imagination and discipline. Many memory puzzles require you to study an image or set of images for a certain amount of time, then to recall them all or answer questions about them. While you are doing this, it is helpful to break the images down into smaller elements in order to retain as much information as possible. What colours and shapes are they? Do they have different writing or numbering on them? Where are they in relation to one another? Do certain objects share characteristics?

WHEN FACED WITH THE TASK OF READING a text from which you need to extract important facts, you must concentrate most on the small details. Are there any numbers in the article? In what order do the facts appear? Are there names of people in the text? Have you understood the relationships between the facts presented? Unless you are lucky enough to have a photographic memory, puzzles such as these can be extremely difficult.

WRITING KEY FACTS ON PAPER as you read can help your brain organize them into memorable units and, in daily life, is an excellent way of helping your memory. Another memory technique is to create associations to help you remember things. For example, names in a puzzle might be given pictorial forms. So 'Pete' could become a gardener's bag of peat fertilizer, 'Jim' a piece of gymnastic equipment, 'Mary' a party hat or noisemaker ('making merry'). In memory games in which you need to find matching pairs the trick is to work systematically, from top left to bottom right.

THERE ARE MORE GENERAL WAYS to improve your memory. Repeat facts aloud. Set yourself small memory tasks each day, such as writing down five phone numbers in the morning and seeing how many you remember by the evening. In this way, your memory gets constant workouts and becomes more fit.

VISUAL MEMORY PUZZLES

These puzzles are designed to improve your capacity for remembering objects and colours – a useful skill in everyday life.

Instant recall

Study the 10 objects below for one minute, then cover the page. How many can you remember? Do any of the colours stick in your mind? Do they help or distract you? Now see if you can also position the objects from memory.

To aid your memory, why not try to create mental links between some of the objects. For example, you could link the paper parasol to the sunglasses by thinking that the word 'sol' is French for 'sun'. Hence, para**sol** – **sun**glasses.

READ STORY – ANSWER QUESTIONS

How good is your memory? Do you take in and retain everything you read? Or do you forget the details as soon as you've finished reading? Test your powers of short-term recall with these four extracts. Read each of them once only – carefully and paying attention to details. Then turn the page and try and answer the questions without looking back. The first one is fairly easy, but they get harder. If you can correctly answer all the questions for the last extract, you may well have a photographic or eidetic memory.

An ancient love story

2

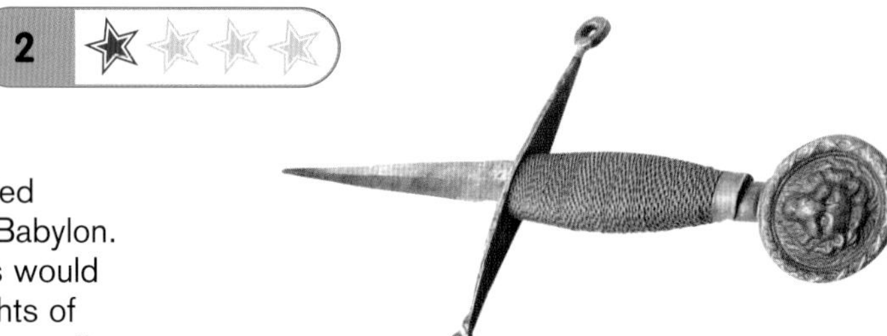

A youth called Pyramus and a maid called Thisbe lived in neighbouring houses in Babylon. They loved each other, but their parents would not allow them to marry. After many nights of whispering through a crack in the garden wall, they determined to slip away together to freedom. They agreed to meet at night by the Tomb of Ninus, under a mulberry tree full of white berries. Thisbe arrived first, but was terrified by the roar of a lioness and took flight. In her haste, she dropped her cloak, which the lioness tore to pieces with its bloody jaws. This was what Pyramus saw when he appeared a few minutes later. He felt sure that Thisbe had been devoured by a lion and that he was responsible.

In his grief, he drew his sword and plunged it into his side. Thisbe returned, hoping that the lioness was gone, and discovered her sweetheart's body. At the sound of her voice he opened his heavy eyes, then died. In despair, she killed herself with his sword. The blood of the young lovers seeped into the soil and changed the fruit of the mulberry tree from white to purple, as it is to this day.

The thwarted sleuth

The great detective pursed his thin lips and a frown furrowed his brow. Eventually he spoke: 'The owner of these spectacles is a man of just under six feet in height, who habitually wears tweed jackets. He is left-handed, balding, smokes a pipe and has seen military service in India. He lives in East London with a wife somewhat younger than himself, and two children.'

'My dear Soames!' I gasped. 'How can you possibly ascertain this by studying a pair of spectacles?'

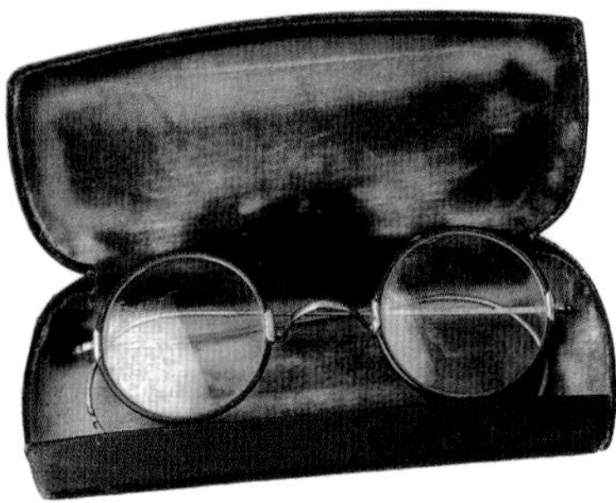

'You know my methods, Wilson.'

'You deduced it then?'

'Certainly.'

'Then I must ask you to explain—'

But I was interrupted by an urgent footfall on the stair. The estimable housekeeper Mrs. Higson opened the heavy oak door to admit a young woman in a state of some agitation. 'Forgive me... Which of you gentlemen is Mr. Shamrock Soames?' she enquired.

My colleague solemnly inclined his head and murmured: 'Pray be seated. The train journey from Winchester must have tired you. But be assured that we will find your missing dog before the day is out.'

The young lady looked puzzled. 'I am sure I do not know what you mean. I live in Marylebone. And I have never owned a dog. But I see that you have found my spectacles. I must have left them here when I delivered the laundry…'

Soames sighed and picked up his violin.

Big Ben

4

The world's most famous clock tower – properly called St. Stephen's Tower – stands 96.3 metres (316 feet) high at the north end of the Houses of Parliament in London. The clock in the tower was installed in 1858, when it was the largest in the world. The bell that strikes the hours was cast in the Whitechapel Bell Foundry and weighs 13.8 tons. It soon acquired the nickname 'Big Ben' perhaps after Sir Benjamin Hall, the Chief Commissioner of Works. Another theory is that at the time anything that was the heaviest of its kind was called 'Big Ben' after the famous prize-fighter Ben Caunt. The Westminster clock is famous for its reliability. Despite heavy bombing, it ran accurately – to within a second and a half – throughout the Blitz. But it slowed down on New Year's Eve 1962 because of a build-up of snow on the hands, and chimed the New Year 10 minutes late. The clock had its first major breakdown in 1976, when the chiming mechanism broke through metal fatigue and was not reactivated for 10 months. The clock itself stopped briefly on 30 April 1997, the day before the General Election, and again three weeks later. Its most recent lapse was on 27 May 2005, when it stopped ticking for 90 minutes, possibly due to hot weather (temperatures in London had reached 31.8°C).

Short-term memory is used to focus on things in the moment. Most people can only retain about seven items of information in their short-term memory at any given time – for example a phone number.

Stable talk

Four thoroughbred racehorses were conversing in their stable. One of them, a chestnut called Scarlet Ribbons, was boasting about his track record: 'I've won five of the ten races I've run,' he said, 'and with five different jockeys.' The three-year-old filly Antagonist was not impressed: 'Well, I've only been entered in eight races,' she said, 'but I've won six of them – including the St. Leger.' Flicking his tail contemptuously, the grey Ornamental Arch snorted: 'That's nothing. I've run in 12 races, and I've won 10, including the Derby and the 2000 Guineas!' Not to be outdone, the oldest horse in the stable, Rupert's Marbles, said: 'Wait till you reach my age. I've run in 28 races and I won all but five of them.' At this point, the horses noticed that a greyhound had been sitting there listening. 'Excuse me, guys,' he said. 'My name is Swingleton Down – perhaps you've heard of me? I don't mean to boast, but I've been entered in 40 races, and I've won 36 of them!' The horses were dumbfounded. 'Good gracious!' said Antagonist, after a hushed silence. 'That's extraordinary. A talking dog!'

An ancient love story

1. In which city did the lovers live?
2. How did they communicate at night?
3. Where did they arrange to meet?
4. Under what tree?
5. What colour were its berries originally?
6. Who arrived at the meeting-place first?
7. What did the lioness rip up?
8. How did Pyramus commit suicide?
9. Was he dead when Thisbe found him?
10. What colour did the berries turn?

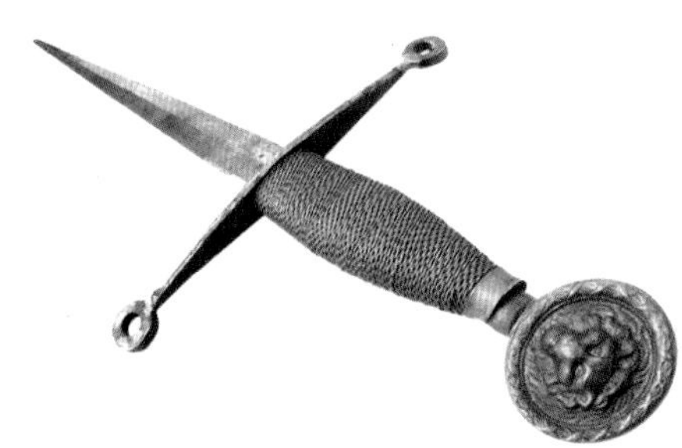

The thwarted sleuth

1. What was Soames' first name?
2. And the surname of his colleague?
3. Soames deduced that the spectacle-wearer wore – what?
4. And had done military service – where?
5. And now lived – where?
6. Who was Soames' housekeeper?
7. Where did Soames deduce the young woman had come from?
8. By what means of transport?
9. Where did the young woman actually live?
10. What had she delivered earlier?

Big Ben

1. What's the proper name of the clock tower?
2. How tall is it?
3. When was the clock installed?
4. How much does the great bell weigh?
5. Who was the Chief Commissioner of Works?
6. And who was the heavyweight boxer?
7. In which year was Big Ben late chiming the New Year?
8. What caused the chime to break in 1976?
9. What date was the General Election in 1997?
10. How long did the clock stop for in May 2005?

Stable talk

1. Which horse had won five races?
2. How many races had Antagonist run?
3. What was the name of the greyhound?
4. How many races had the filly won?
5. What was the name of the grey?
6. How many races had the greyhound run in?
7. Which horse had won the St. Leger?
8. How many races had Rupert's Marbles won?
9. Which horse had won the Derby?
10. How many races in total had the four horses won?

MEMORY PLATES

Simple memory puzzles are an easy and effective way of training your brain, which will help you to improve all your puzzling skills.

Bits 'n' bobs

6

Study this plate of 18 random objects for three minutes, then turn over the page and see how many you can remember by writing them down on a piece of paper.

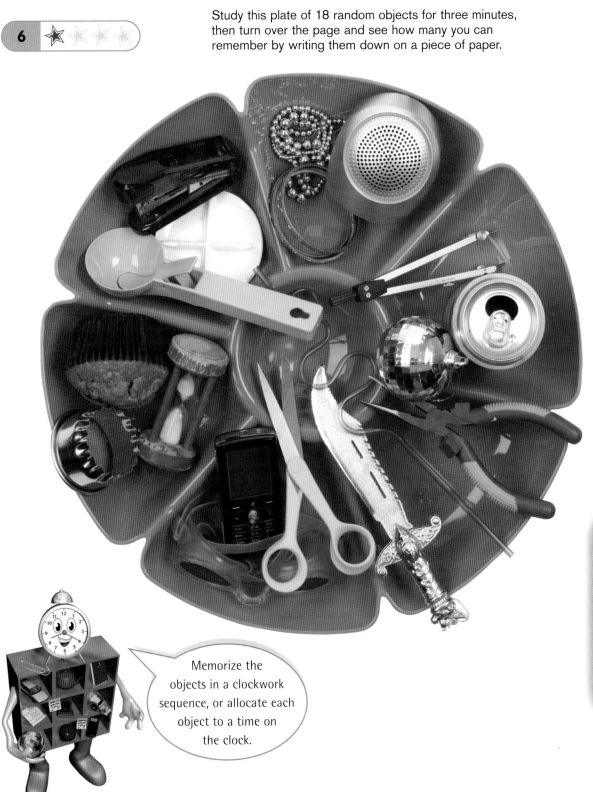

Memorize the objects in a clockwork sequence, or allocate each object to a time on the clock.

Now you see it, now you don't

7 ★★★☆

Here is an assortment of 25 unrelated objects. Again, give yourself three minutes to look at them and commit them to memory, then see how many you can recall.

Break this puzzle down by remembering the items in small groups – either in horizontal or vertical lines of five.

Memories are made of this

8 ★★★★

This time there are 32 objects arranged in random order. Is this more difficult because there are more objects, or easier because they are positioned neatly? Use the three minutes to remember as many as you can, then test yourself and see how well you do.

Another hint for helping you with these puzzles is to create mnemonics representing the objects. For example, take the first letter of each item and put them together to create words that will trigger your memory.

CHESS GAMES

These puzzles will test your powers of both recall and logic. Try to memorize the position of the pieces on the chess board, then close the book and, based on the instructions given, work out and write down the resolution of the game from memory.

White to play and get checkmate in two moves. Despite being a Queen down, white has two rooks to his advantage. But they can't do all the work by themselves.

White to play and get checkmate in two moves.

Don't be afraid to sacrifice a piece if it means you will achieve a more dominant position later in the game.

White to play and get checkmate in two moves. The immediate temptation for white is to promote his pawn on G2 to a Queen but is this wise?

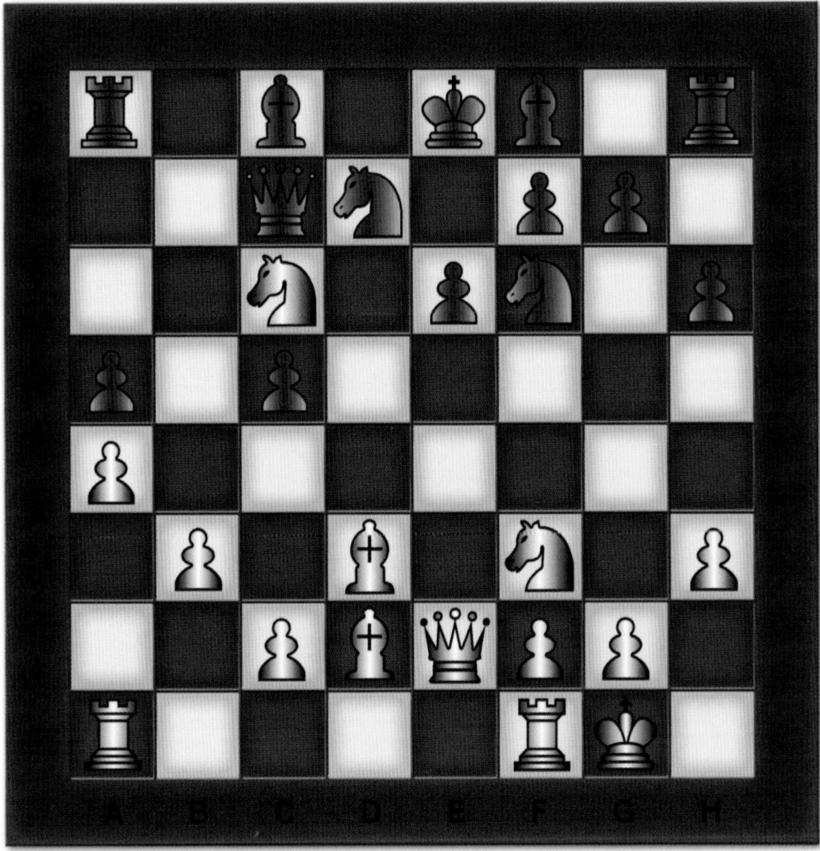

White to play and get checkmate in two moves. White can shatter his opponent's relatively cozy defensive position quickly and ruthlessly – but not without sacrifice.

White can achieve checkmate in two moves. If you can unravel the key first move of the two, there are eight different ways of getting checkmate on his next move no matter where Blue goes. Can you find all eight permutations?

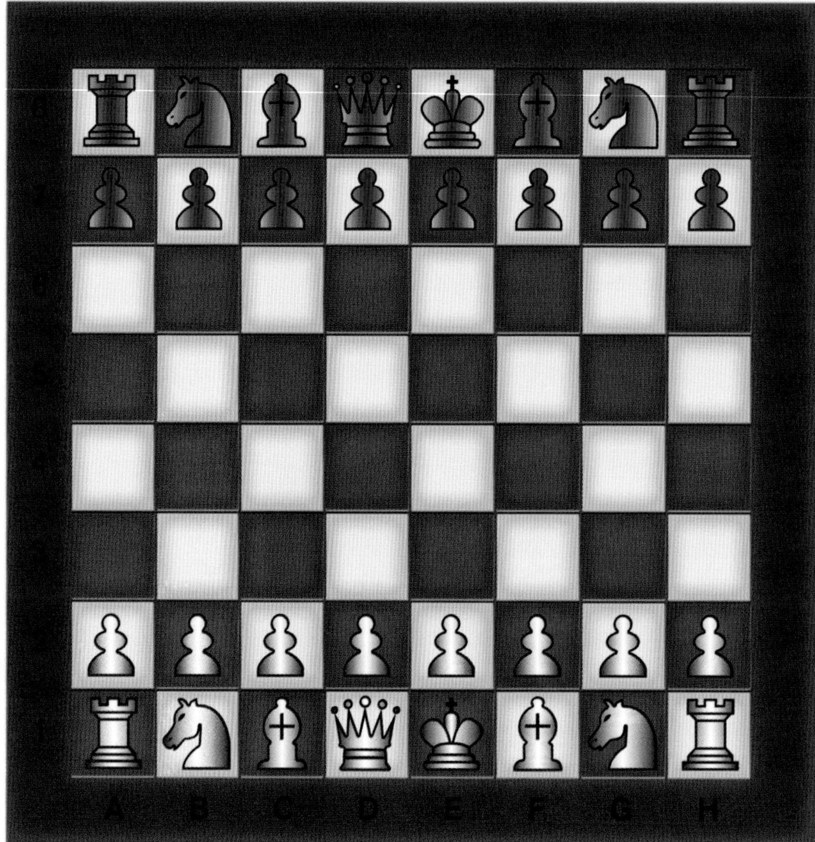

White to play. Blue can get checkmate on just his second move. You must work out the two fatal opening moves white makes to leave him unable to defend a checkmate.

Chess requires you to think several moves ahead, both of your own moves, and those of your opponent.

MEMORY PUZZLES

MEMORIZE LISTS

Test your brain to see how good it is at recalling the written word by memorizing these lists of information. You will find questions about each of them over the page.

Shopping list

Study the following shopping list for five minutes.

Bag of sugar
Tea biscuits
Can of peas
Frozen fish sticks
Strawberry cake
Pack of fresh carrots
Two dozen eggs
Lemon-flavoured yogurt
Gravy granules
Four slices of roast beef

Instructions

Read and memorize these instructions for three minutes.

Start at 5
Go left
Then down
Then right
Then to 3
Then down
Then left
Then back to 5

Memorize Lists continues on page **322**

WORD ASSOCIATION

These exercises test your ability to remember pairs of words and to form associations. Study these pairs carefully, close the book and see how many you can recall.

Carefully study the eight pairs of words for 10 minutes. Use your imagination to link each pair of words so that you will be able to remember as many as possible, as well as which word goes with which.

LEOPARD
TREE

KEYBOARD
STONE

GLUE
PEACH

CHESTNUT
PARROT

WAGON
FLAG

GHOST
CHARIOT

BRIDGE
DESK

DOMINO
SODA

This time there are 12 pairs of words to memorize in the allotted 10 minutes. Again, use as many ways as possible to link the pairs of words together so you will be able to recall them when required.

BALL
TRAMPOLINE

LADDER
HAT

PEARL
TAXI

BUGLE
CANOE

CAMERA
FISH

JOCKEY
MEDAL

BANANA
BALLOON

COFFEE
LAMP

GOAT
TABLE

TROUT
SHEEP

LIBRARY
MIRROR

SNOWMAN
VINEYARD

Word Association continues on page **322**

Memorize Lists continued from page **321**

15 Shopping list

Write out the 10 items on the shopping list you memorized. Order is not important, but attention to detail is – each item must be described correctly and in full.

Assessment

10	Exceptionally good
9	Very good
7-8	Well above average
5-6	Above average
3-4	Average

16 Instructions

Which of the following sets of instructions have you just looked at on page 321?

A

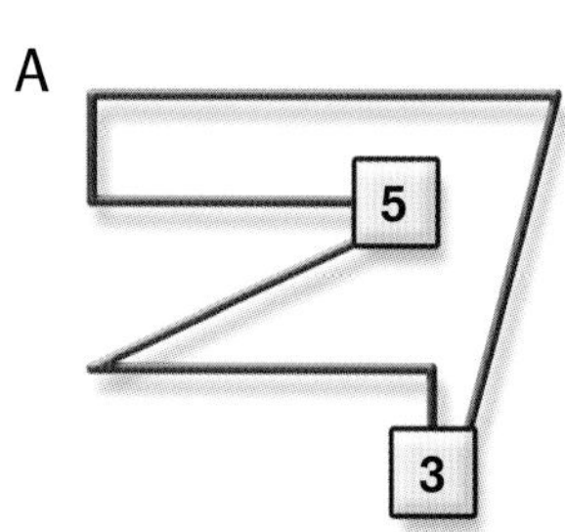

B

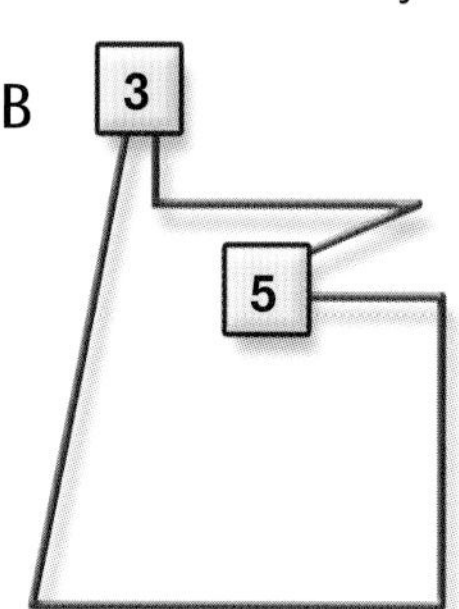

C

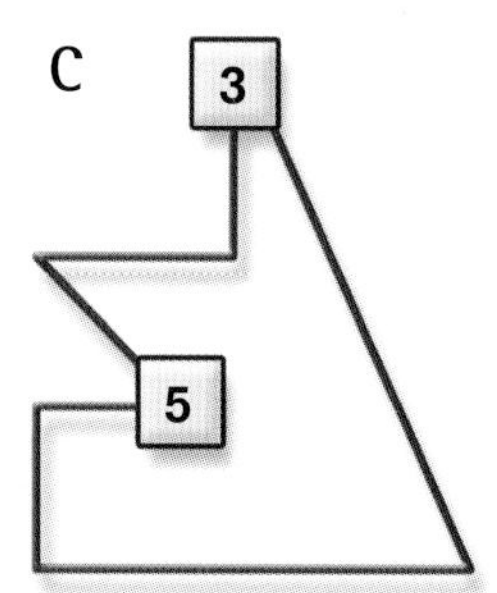

D

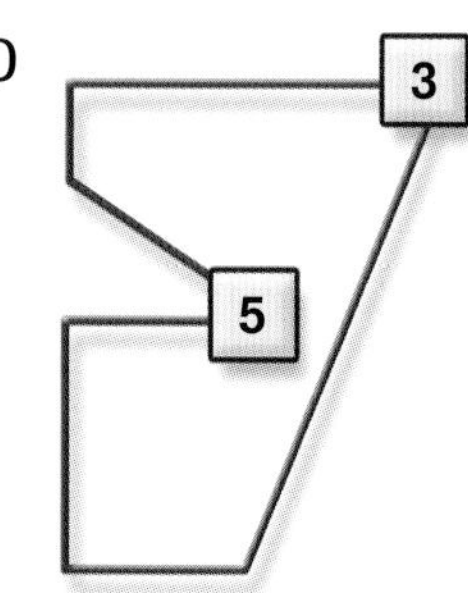

Word Association continued from page **321**

17

SODA ....
LEOPARD ....
BRIDGE ....
DOMINO ....
FLAG ....
STONE ....
PEACH ....
TREE ....
PARROT ....
GHOST ....
WAGON ....
DESK ....
GLUE ....
CHARIOT ....
CHESTNUT ....
KEYBOARD ....

Put a letter A against one pair of words, the letter B against a second pair, through to the letter H, until you have matched what you think are the original eight pairs of words.

Assessment

8 pairs correct	Exceptionally good
7	Very good
6	Well above average
5	Above average
3-4	Average

18

LAMP	**VINEYARD** ....
BALL	**CAMERA** ....
MEDAL	**TRAMPOLINE** ....
MIRROR	**BUGLE** ....
PEARL	**SNOWMAN** ....
FISH	**CANOE** ....
JOCKEY	**LIBRARY** ....
TAXI	**COFFEE** ....

Again place letters next to all the pairs that you recall from A–H. Four of the pairs have been left out of this list – can you remember which eight words are missing?

Assessment

10-12 pairs correct	Exceptionally good
9	Very good
7-8	Well above average
6	Above average
4-5	Average

MEMORIZE PATTERNS

Every part of our life relies to some extent on memory. It is what enables us to walk, study, relax, communicate and recognize our family and friends; in fact some sort of memory process is at work whatever we are doing.

Hint: The following puzzles are recognized aids to memory improvement. In order to help you memorize the diagrams, try copying them down onto paper or writing a description of them – just doing this can help you remember images better.

19

Study this for five seconds, then wait for five minutes and turn to page 324.

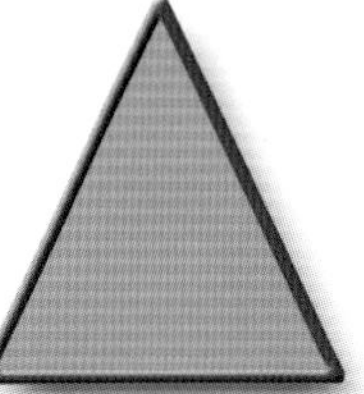

20

Take five seconds to carefully look at this picture then pause for eight minutes before turning to page 324.

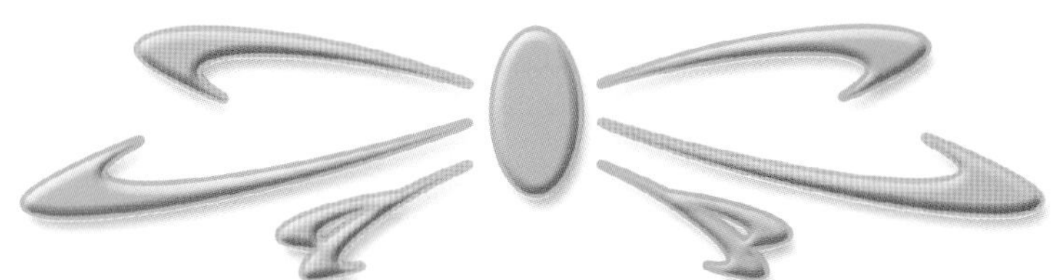

21

Again take five seconds to memorize this diagram, then wait for eight minutes and turn to page 324

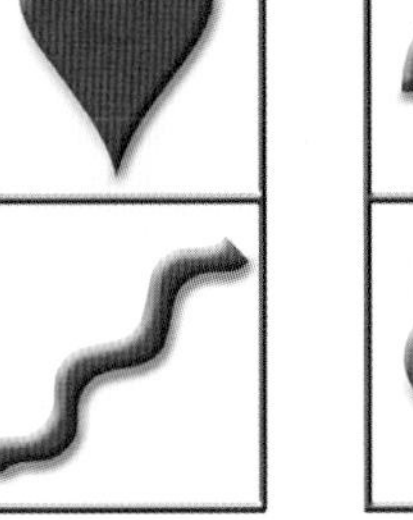
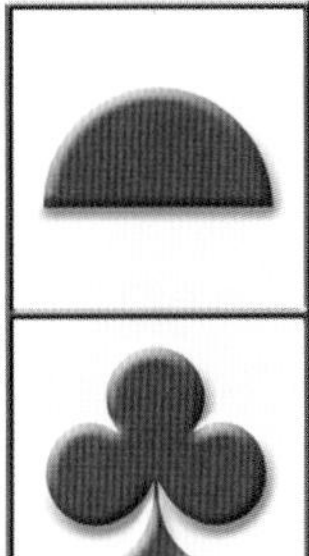
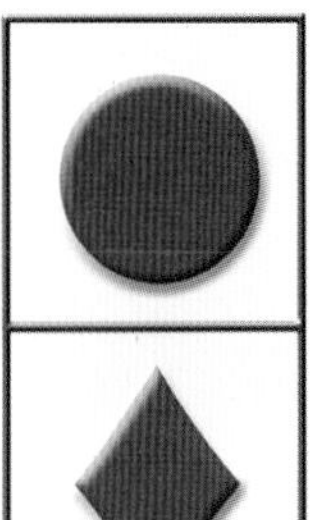

Memorize Patterns continues on page **324**

Memorize Patterns continued from page **323** 

19

Which set of three shapes did you look at five minutes ago?

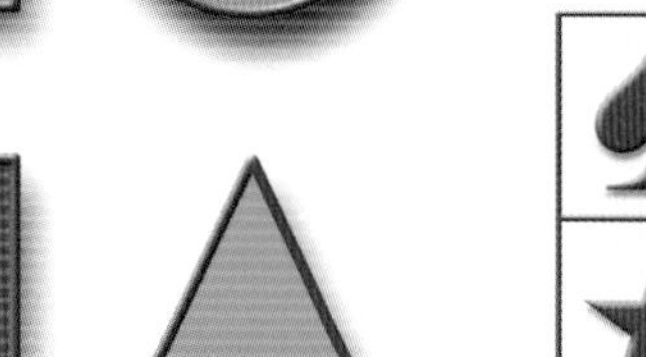

20

Which figure is exactly the same as the one you looked at eight minutes ago?

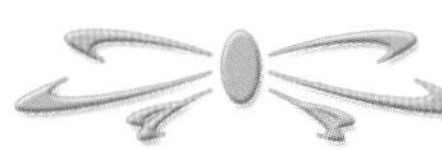
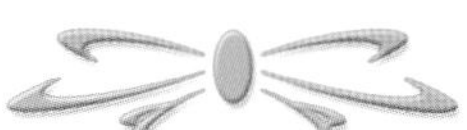

21

Which of the following images match those you memorized from the previous page?

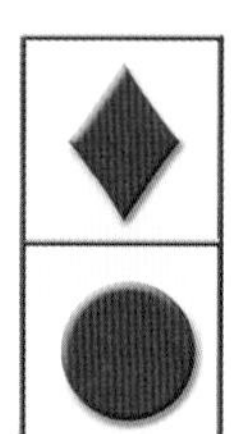

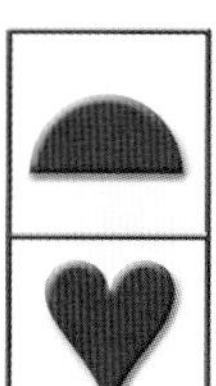

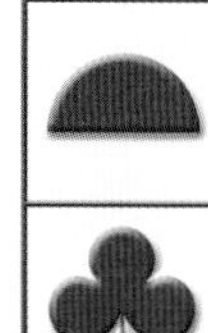
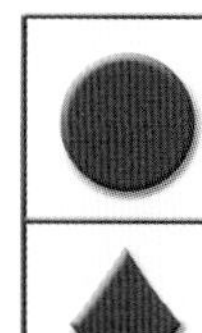
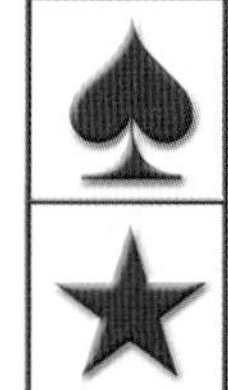

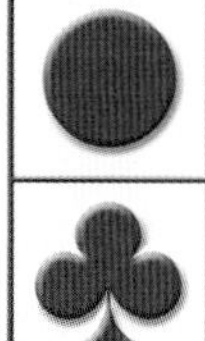
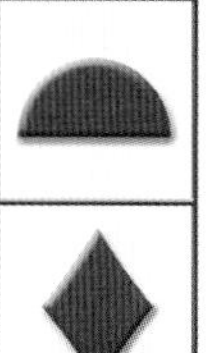
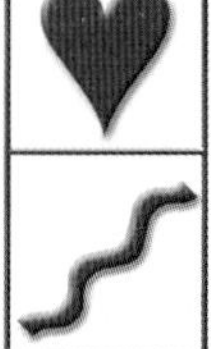
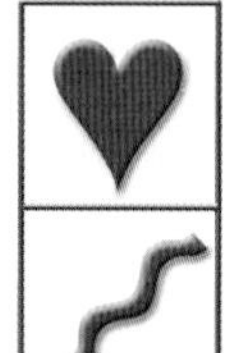
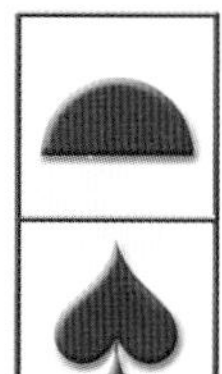
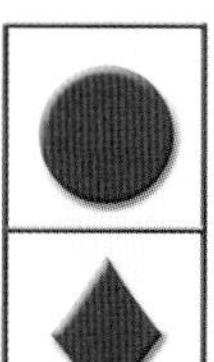
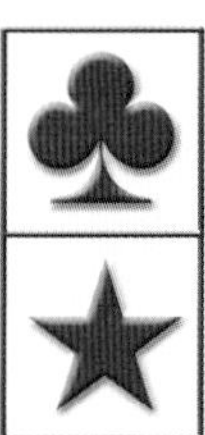

LETTER PUZZLES

Read and memorize the letter sequences in each puzzle, then follow the instructions provided to reveal the answers. If the same letter appears at the start and the end of the sequence, or two adjacent letters are the same, both are removed. The letters are referred to by their number in the sequence at any one time.

EXAMPLE:

Original sequence to memorize: GRAEMR

Instructions:

Swap 1 and 2
Swap 3 and 4

SOLUTION:

Swap 1 and 2: the sequence gives you RGAEMR – so you remove the Rs at each end to give GAEM.

Swap 3 and 4: gives you the final word – GAME.

Memorize each letter sequence for five minutes, saying it aloud if necessary, then cover it and follow the rules above as you manipulate the letters in your head. You should be left with a complete word each time.

NSAUA

Swap 1 and 5
Swap 1 and 2

RT DADS

Swap 1 and 6
Swap 4 and 5

A CD BY CB

Swap 4 and 5
Swap 1 and 2
Swap 2 and 3
Swap 5 and 6

IN GH PTP

Swap 4 and 5
Swap 6 and 7
Swap 1 and 2
Swap 5 and 6

NB ND GOBL

Swap 2 and 3
Swap 2 and 5
Swap 4 and 5

WAWA TED TN

Swap 3 and 4
Swap 4 and 5
Swap 2 and 3

MEMORY MAZES

Your memory is like a muscle – the more you use it, the more highly developed it will become. Mazes are an excellent way of improving your navigational skill and memory for routes.

Study the route through the mazes below for as long as you want, then try to recall how to get from Start to Finish in the mazes on the opposite page. Put a piece of paper over this page before starting to solve these puzzles.

MEMORY PUZZLES

28

S
F

29

F
S

30

S
F

31

F
S

NUMBER PUZZLES

Follow these simple rules to attempt the following number puzzles. At any time, the first digit in a sequence is described as digit A, the second B and so on. If the first and last numbers in the sequence are the same, they are both removed. If two adjacent numbers are the same, they are removed. The puzzle is solved when there is only one digit left.

Memorize each sequence of digits, then follow step-by-step instructions – always looking out for pairs of numbers that can be removed.

One sequence at a time, take five minutes to commit each number sequence to memory, saying them aloud if necessary, then close the book and carry out the instructions in your head, removing digits when appropriate.

3189

Swap B and C
Swap A and B
Subtract C from D

4692

Swap C and D
Swap B and C
Add A and B

23723

Swap C and D
Swap B and C

35

141352

Swap B and C
Swap B and C
Add C and D

36

6272321

Add A and B
Swap A and F
Swap D and E
Add A and B

37

98918651

Add G and H
Swap B and C

ANAGRAMS

Commit the groups of letters to memory and then try and work out the anagrams without referring back to the page. You can use the skills that you have built up doing ordinary anagrams to help solve these puzzles.

38

Read the following letter groups, then immediately cover them over. From memory, unscramble the letters to reveal a pair of linked words. Visualize the letters in your mind as clearly as possible, saying them aloud if necessary.

CARELL **GORTEF**
MYMORE **AMYLIS**

39

Read aloud the following five words until you feel confident you can remember them. Then cover them and rearrange the letters in each to give five new words. The initial letters of those words spell out the final answer.

TEAK HARE COIN SEWN LINK

40

Read the following groups of three 'words' aloud twice, then cover them over. From memory, rearrange the letters to form three words. The first word in each group is a strong clue to the other two.

TEVNIN **BYRAIN**
RACTEE **ELVERC**
SEDING **PHARS**

41

Silently read the following four words, once only. Then, from memory, rearrange the letters of each word to create four new words. The final answer is found by shuffling the first letter of the first new word, the second letter of the second new word, and so on. The answer fits the theme of all the other words in this section.

PALE NUDE LIFE FORM

To help recall the letter groups you have memorized, close your eyes and try to visualize an image of the anagrams you memorized.

CODE CRACK FROM MEMORY

These puzzles will help develop your memory by requiring you to both retain and apply information to find the answers. Memorize the codes provided, and then use them to solve the questions that follow.

Study the following code for as long as you need, then cover it up.

1 = A, 2 = B, 3 = C, etc.

Now use your memory to solve this code.

8, 1, 13, 12, 5, 20

Study this code key, then cover it.

A = B, B = C, C = D, etc.

Now, working purely from memory, solve the following code.

I, T, K, H, D, S

Memorize this code system.

% = H, $ = E, ? = R, @ = O

Now cover it, and use your memory to unravel the following code. Letters that have no equivalent in the code remain unchanged.

@ T % $ L L @

Learn this new code, then cover it.

! = P, * = L, £ = A, & = Y

Use your memorized code key to help you decipher the following hidden message.

£NT ON& £ND C*E O!£ TR£

Study the scrambled message for as long as you need, then cover it.

TIB LFT QFB SF

Use your powers of visualization to unscramble the code by taking each letter back one place in the alphabet. For example, R would become Q, L would become K and so on.

Study the following number sequence for as long as you like before covering it up. Read it aloud to help you commit it to memory.

7, 15, 2, 20, 8, 5, 20, 5

Now, in your head, turn each number into a letter, with 1 representing A, 2 representing B, 3 C and so on. As each letter appears, remove it from the words GLOBE THEATRE to reveal a famous name.

MEMORY LINE UP

How good a witness would you be? Can you remember people's faces and details of their appearance? The memory line up is based on a police identity parade, and it tests your ability to retain and recall physiological detail.

Study the first identity parade for as long as you like, then cover it over. Can you identify the person in a second parade who was also in the first – even though the photograph of them has changed?

MEMORY GRIDS

Study the grid for as long as necessary, memorizing the information in each space. Look for patterns and clues and prepare to be tested on the memory grid. When you're ready, cover the grid and answer the seven brain-stretching memory questions.

49 Animals

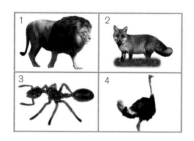

1. Which creature is underneath the lion?
2. Which creature is underneath the fox?
3. What is diagonally opposite the ant?
4. In which square is the 'king of the jungle'?
5. In which square is a word that goes in front of FUR, HOLE and TROT to make three new words?
6. Beginning with the answer to question 5, move round the grid clockwise, taking the initial letters of the four animals to give you another creature.
7. Rearrange the initial letters of the animals in this order – 1, 4, 3, 2 – to give you some food to feed them.

50 Objects

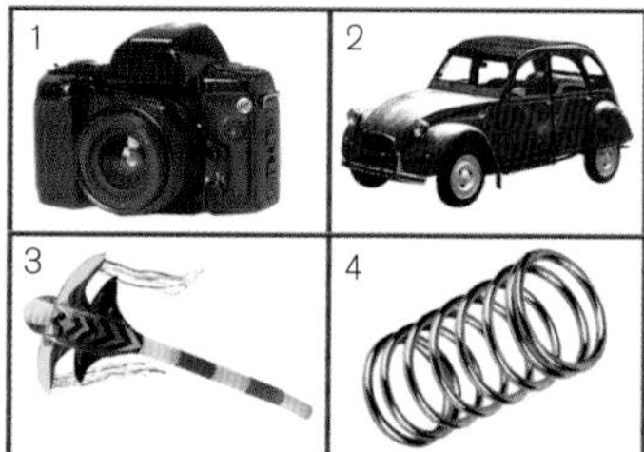

1. What's in box 4?
2. Which word can go before all four items in this grid, as well as ROOM, OFFICE and CLEVER?
3. What is diagonally opposite the SPRING?
4. Take the last letter of each item, and arrange them in the box order 2, 1, 4, 3 to make another word.
5. In which box is an object with the same initial as the one in box 1?
6. Where is the item with the same name as a bird?
7. Start at box 4, move clockwise around the grid, taking the last letter of each word to create another word.

51 Words

1 JAR	2 LIGHT
3 NURSE	4 DRESS

1. Which word is diagonally opposite NURSE?
2. What's diagonally opposite DRESS?
3. What word is underneath LIGHT?
4. In which box is a word that describes Florence Nightingale?
5. Where is the shortest word of the four?
6. Start at the answer to question 5 and work counter-clockwise round the grid. Take the last letter of each word in turn to form another word.
7. Use the answer to question 6 as a clue; what word goes before all the words in this grid to make four new words.

52 Countries

1 URUGUAY	2 RUSSIA
3 POLAND	4 EGYPT

1. Starting at box 3, move clockwise round the grid, using the initial letter of each word in turn to produce another word.
2. Where is the place that has the US in it?
3. Which country is underneath URUGUAY?
4. Which country is underneath RUSSIA?
5. What's in the box diagonally opposite EGYPT?
6. What is the only country on the continent of Africa in this grid?
7. Starting with box 3, move counter-clockwise round the grid; take the initial letters in turn to create another place name.

Famous Americans

1. Where is the man who's been Mayor of Carmel, California?
2. In which box is the woman whose surname is Ciccone?
3. Where is the partner of Stan Laurel?
4. In which box is the first man on the moon?
5. Who is between ELVIS PRESLEY and RONALD REAGAN?
6. Name the character in the middle square.
7. Starting at the top left and moving clockwise, take the first-name initial of the person in each corner of the grid to give you another famous name.

Adjectives

1. Which word is created by the initial letters of the words on the top row?
2. Which word is created by the initial letters of the words on the middle row?
3. Which word is created by the initial letters of the words on the bottom row?
4. Which word is created by the initial letters of the words in the first column, from top to bottom?
5. Do the same as in question 5 but with the words in the second column.
6. Use the same rules as in the previous two questions, but with the third column.
7. Which word is created by the initial letters of the words in the diagonal line of boxes 1, 5 and 9?

LIGHT	EXCITING	DARK
ORANGE	ACIDIC	RIPE
TASTY	ROTTEN	YELLOW

Landmarks

1. What's in the middle square?
2. In which adjacent boxes are two French landmarks?
3. Where is the only landmark that can be seen from space?
4. Which landmark is on top of another from the same country?
5. Which box features a landmark found on Pennsylvania Avenue?
6. Take the first word of the place in the box top left and the second word of the place in the box bottom middle to give you another landmark.
7. Starting at the WHITE HOUSE, move round the corner boxes counter-clockwise, taking the initial letter of each place to give you another building-related word.

HEAD	HOT	LIGHT
FACE	ARMY	SQUARE
LETTER	CURRANT	MEAT

Words

1. Where in the grid is one body part directly above another?
2. Which two words with the same initial letter appear in diagonally opposite corners?
3. Where is the shortest word in the grid?
4. Where are two edible words in adjacent squares?
5. What occupies the centre square?
6. Which word can go in front of all the words in the grid to make nine new words?
7. Take the last letters of the words in the boxes middle left, centre and middle right to give you another word that fits the theme of this grid.

Words

1. What is the word that can be put before all 16 words on this grid to form 16 new words or phrases?
2. Which word is in the bottom right-hand corner square?
3. The words in boxes 9 and 10 are opposites: what are they?
4. Put together the words in boxes 8 and 4 to make a new word.
5. Where in the grid is the first name of a recent US President?
6. What is the word in box 1?
7. Find another word that fits the theme of this grid by taking the first letter of the word in box 13; the second letter of the word in box 7; and the third letter of the word in box 11.

1 BALL	2 BELL	3 BILL	4 BAG
5 WORK	6 WRITE	7 WEAVE	8 WASH
9 ON	10 OFF	11 OUT	12 OVER
13 SHAKE	14 SAW	15 STAND	16 SOME

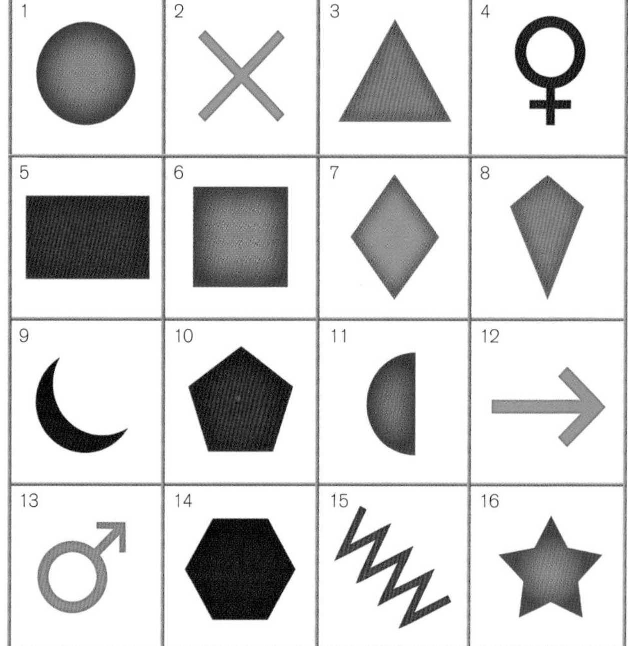

Shapes

1. Find the male and female symbols in opposite corners of the grid.
2. Find two items that fly, one on top of the other in the grid.
3. Where is the shape with the same name as a musical instrument?
4. In which direction is the arrow symbol pointing?
5. Which shape is in the bottom right-hand corner?
6. Which box contains the shape whose name is also a US Government building in Virginia?
7. Where is the symbol that is the same shape as the gird itself?

You can aid your memory by attaching the item to be remembered to an everyday item or humourous thought.

59 Objects

1. Name the four tools in the four corners of this grid.
2. Where are the two pieces of cutlery, one on top of the other?
3. Where is the implement that a Johnny Depp character had instead of hands in a famous film?
4. Where is the surname of Mickey Spillane's famous detective?
5. Which word is formed by the initial letters of the images in boxes 2, 3 and 4?
6. How many of the electrical items in the shaded central area of the grid can you remember?
7. Where is the word that goes after the image in box 15 and before the image in box 23 to make two new words?

1 PAT	2 AL	3 RYAN	4 IAN	5 SARAH
6 MAY	7 STEVEN	8 EVAN	9 PETER	10 JOHN
11 SCOTT	12 TIMOTHY	13 EVE	14 MARY	15 PAUL
16 AMY	17 BURT	18 ERROL	19 ROY	20 GEORGE
21 ANNA	22 TARQUIN	23 AISHA	24 GUY	25 BOB

60 Names

1. The initial letters of the words in the top row spell out the name of which capital city?
2. Where in the grid is Adam's other half?
3. The initials of the words in boxes 22, 23 and 24 spell a word that goes after NAME to form a new word.
4. Which two of the names in corner boxes are palindromes.
5. Which Beatle is missing from the last column?
6. Which two names in the first column are made up of the same letters?
7. The name of which month is spelt out by the initials of the names in the shaded area?

NUMBER AND SHAPE RECOGNITION

These puzzles will test your memory power by requiring you to read, process and then recall sequences of numbers and shapes.

Study the diagrams below for seven minutes and then turn to page 338.

T

R 6

A

7 N

Take seven minutes to look at this grid, then turn to page 338.

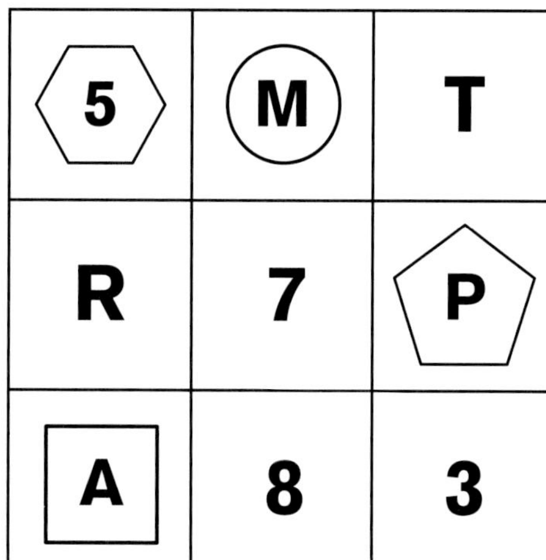

Take seven minutes to remember this sequence and then answer the questions on page 338.

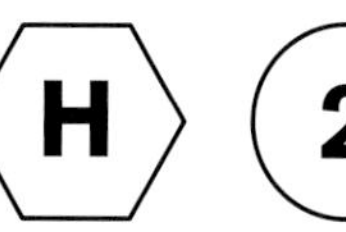

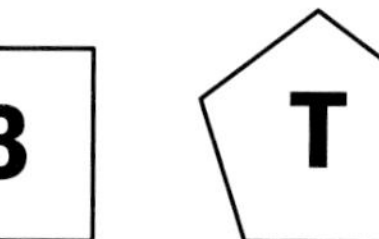

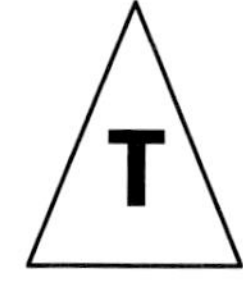

64

Study the diagram below for five minutes and then turn to page 338.

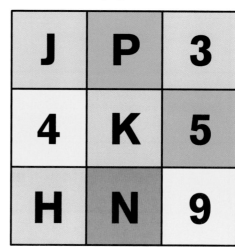

J	P	3
4	K	5
H	N	9

Try remembering the details in small groups, such as lines of shapes and figures in a grid, before trying to remember them within the larger grouping of each puzzle.

MEMORY PUZZLES

Number and Shape Recognition continues on page **338**

ATTENTION TO DETAIL

Study the circles in these four puzzles, making sure you observe all their intricacies. The questions that follow on page 338 and 339 will ask you to recall the various relationships between the numbers and symbols.

Take seven minutes to digest the information in this circle, then answer the questions on page 338.

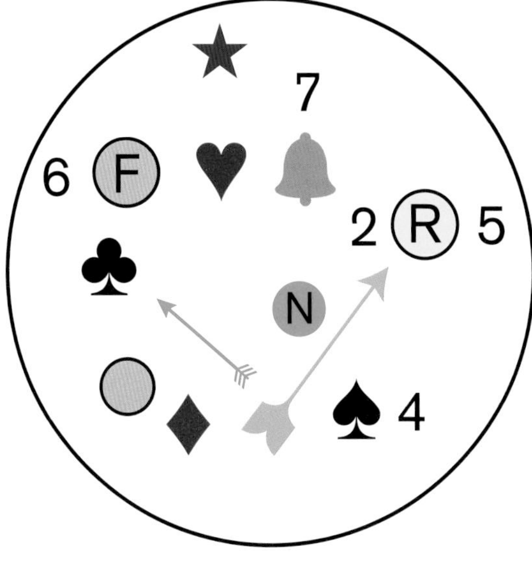

In seven minutes, memorize the numbers and symbols, then answer the questions on page 339.

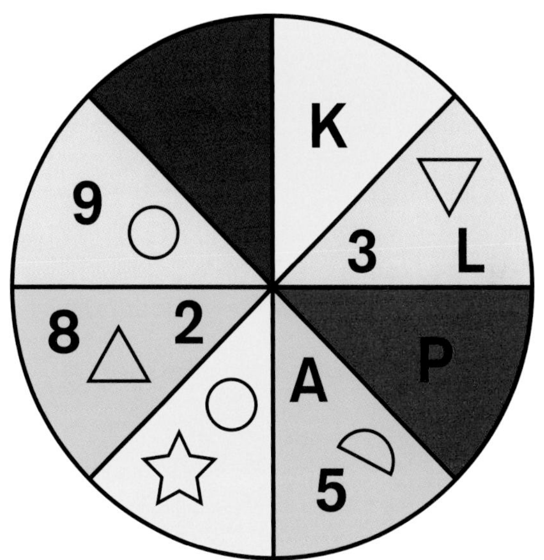

Attention to Detail continues on page **338**

Consider the set-up of the circle below for five minutes and answer the questions on page 339.

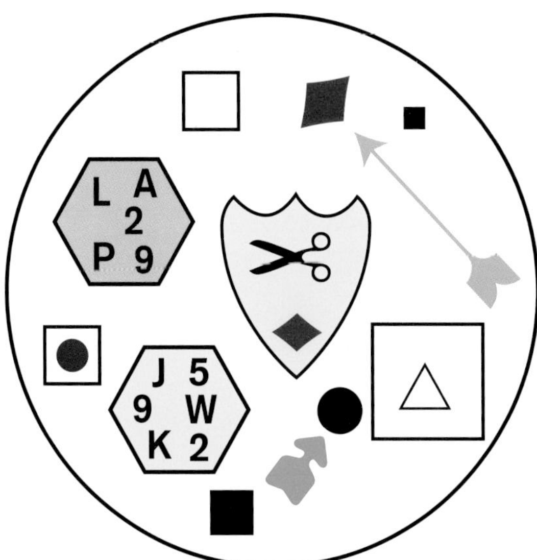

Study the diagram below for five minutes and then turn to page 339.

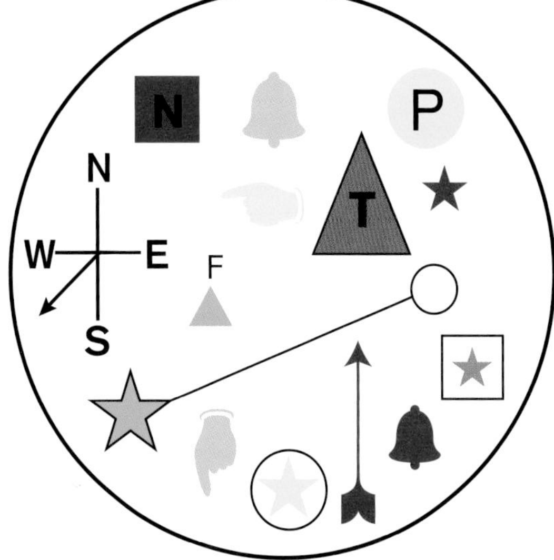

Attention to Detail continues on page **339**

Number and Shape Recognition continued from page **336** 

61

1. What is the total of the numbers in the green shapes?
   a. 11 **b.** 12 **c.** 13
2. What shape is immediately to the left of the largest circle?
   a. Hexagon **b.** Square **c.** Rectangle
3. What number appears in the yellow shape?
   a. 5 **b.** 7 **c.** 6
4. What word is spelled out by taking the letters in the first, fourth and fifth shapes in that order?
   a. MAR **b.** MAN **c.** RAM
5. Which shape is coloured blue?
   a. Large circle **b.** Square **c.** Small circle
6. Which letter/number combination is contained in the hexagon?

62

1. What letter appears in the pentagon?
   a. T **b.** A **c.** P
2. The letter A appears in what shape?
   a. Hexagon **b.** Circle **c.** Square
3. What is the total of all the odd numbers?
   a. 13 **b.** 15 **c.** 11
4. What letter/number combination appears reading across the bottom row from left to right?
   a. A7P **b.** R73 **c.** A83
5. What letter appears just above the number 3?
   a. P **b.** T **c.** R
6. What shape appears immediately above the number 7?
   a. Square **b.** Circle **c.** Hexagon

63

1. What shape is directly below the square?
   a. Triangle **b.** Circle **c.** Pentagon
2. What letter appears in the hexagon?
   a. T **b.** J **c.** H
3. What number is inside the circle?
   a. 2 **b.** 3 **c.** 4
4. Which is the only shape that appears both on the top and bottom rows?
   a. Triangle **b.** Circle **c.** Pentagon
5. Total up the numbers on the top row.
   a. 7 **b.** 6 **c.** 5
6. What number appears directly below the letter T?
   a. 4 **b.** 6 **c.** 3

64

1. How many squares are coloured green?
   a. 1 **b.** 3 **c.** 2
2. Total up the numbers in the yellow squares.
   a. 13 **b.** 12 **c.** 14
3. What is the colour of the middle square on the top row?
   a. Blue **b.** Yellow **c.** Green
4. How many squares are coloured orange?
   a. 2 **b.** 1 **c.** 3
5. What is the only number that appears in a green square?
   a. 5 **b.** 9 **c.** 3
6. What letter appears in the bottom left square?
   a. J **b.** H **c.** N

Attention to Detail continued from page **337** 

65

1. What letter appears in the blue circle?
   a. F **b.** R **c.** N
2. What number is right of the yellow circle?
   a. 5 **b.** 2 **c.** 7
3. To which symbol is the blue arrow pointing?
   a. Club **b.** Spade **c.** Heart
4. What symbol is left of the number 4?
   a. Bell **b.** Spade **c.** Star
5. What number appears above the bell?
   a. 6 **b.** 2 **c.** 7
6. What letter appears in the large pink circle?
   a. F **b.** N **c.** R

66

1. To what symbol does the green arrow point?
2. What shape is inside the largest square?
3. How many black squares appear?
4. Which three letters are in the yellow hexagon?
5. How many squares appear in total?
6. Which three letters are in the blue hexagon?
7. Which shape sits below the scissors in the yellow shield?
8. What shape is to the left of the largest square?
9. Which two numbers are in the blue hexagon?
10. What is the total of the numbers which appear in the yellow hexagon?

1. How many segments are coloured blue?
2. The number 9 is in which coloured segment?
3. What symbol is next to the star?
4. What letter appears in the red segment?
5. What colour is the only empty segment?
6. The number 3 is in which coloured segment?
7. What shape appears in two segments which are directly opposite each other?
8. What number is in a segment with a letter A?
9. What coloured segment is sandwiched between a purple and a green segment?
10. What colour segment appears directly opposite the red segment?

1. In which direction is the yellow hand pointing?
2. What letter appears above the green triangle?
3. In which direction is the blue hand pointing?
4. The letter P appears in which shape?
5. What colour is the arrow?
6. In which shape does the yellow star appear?
7. Which two figures are joined together by a connecting line?
8. To which direction is the arrow on the compass pointing?
9. What letter appears in the triangle?
10. What symbol appears immediately below the yellow circle?

WHICH FLAG?

Look at these flags for five minutes and then turn the page to answer questions about them. Your general knowledge may also be helpful here.

69

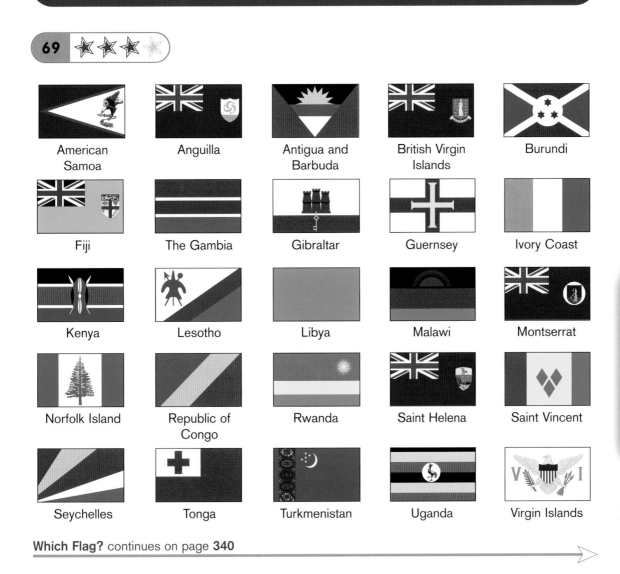

American Samoa

Anguilla

Antigua and Barbuda

British Virgin Islands

Burundi

Fiji

The Gambia

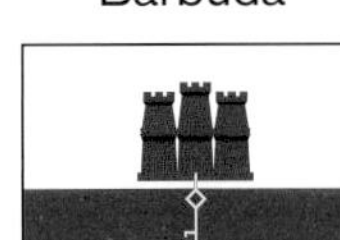
Gibraltar

Guernsey

Ivory Coast

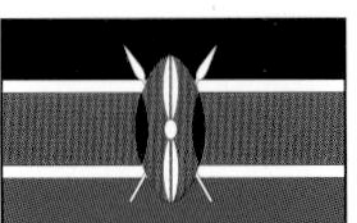
Kenya

Lesotho

Libya

Malawi

Montserrat

Norfolk Island

Republic of Congo

Rwanda

Saint Helena

Saint Vincent

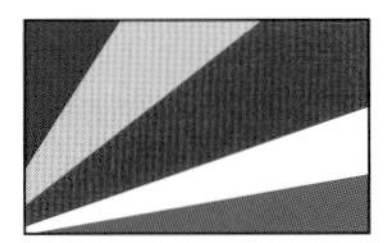
Seychelles

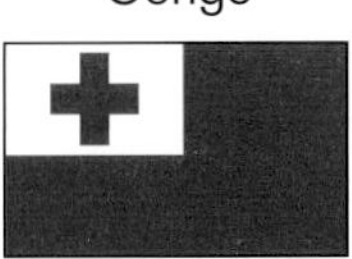
Tonga

Turkmenistan

Uganda

Virgin Islands

Which Flag? continues on page **340**

Which Flag? continued from page 337 

1. Which flag has a background of repeated black, yellow and red stripes?
2. Which flag contains a golden cross?
3. Which flag contains a red castle?
4. Which flag is red and green with a diagonal yellow stripe?
5. Which flag is first from the left on the second line down?
6. How many flags feature a Union Jack?
7. Which is the only flag to be made up of one solitary colour?
8. Which flag incorporates an inverse Swiss flag?
9. Which flag features a tree?
10. Which three colours make up the flag of The Gambia?
11. Which flag contains an eagle holding three arrows and a small branch?
12. How many different colours does the Seychelles flag contain?
13. Which is a mirror image of the Republic of Ireland flag?

ANAGRAMS FROM MEMORY

Look at each anagram for five seconds and then close the book and try to solve it from memory. The initial letters of the solutions to each anagram make up a ten-letter word.

Four-letter words

INOC
SEAT
CILE
PYSE
NABE
SURT
MEAN
RYET
WREE
ODET

Six-letter words

TRAPIVE
REUSUN
BELTOT
SAILIE
FINEUS
MATRES
KREACH
MENIMU
LESTEN
SERAGE

Eight-letter words

REECE SIX
NOT QUIET
FATE N SUN
GOOEY LID
ER CAVITY
SODA REST
LEND RAVE
GENE REIN
GENIE GEL
WROTE MAP

Ten-letter words

HONOUR AIMS
SAUNA TRIAL
PAINT ROUTE
STRAIT DIME
ISSUE ROBOT
SHOVE A WORD
ELITE TRIAL
I STUN MY OIL
GET ICE CORN
GUARD MARTY

Don't try to solve the anagrams as you memorize them – remember them as they are, then write them down on a piece of paper and unscramble them.

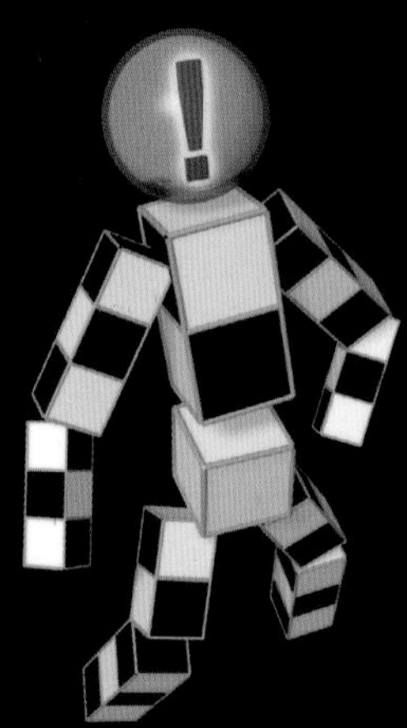

ANSWERS

ANSWERS

ANSWERS

1

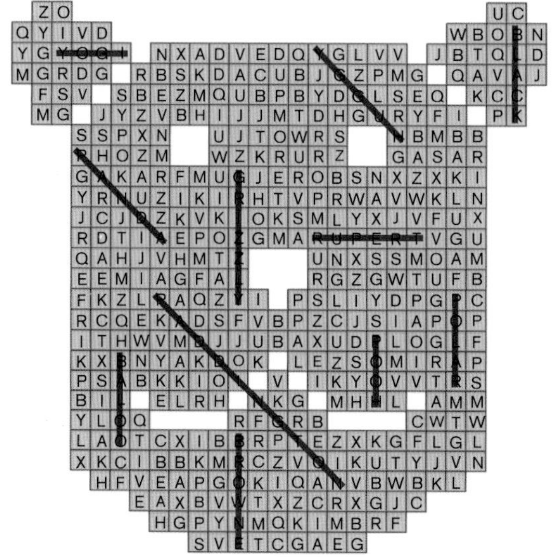

2

V W E G S S A A U A D I R M B V
E X N K I S R E P P E P O U U O
V G Y N Z S N B F S W S C I G B
M G A A M U S H R O O M S N A J
G W T S S G P K L T E A I B P T
P J O S U C B E A N S D D M E L
J D M H A A B T O W D W R T D A
S D A P A O S K S U J E M Q D S
B G T G H C T Y P M N C N Q P C
V U O Y T R D K K X Y I J S Z J
M S U Y I Z C N F U T Q G E R U
V W T B L A S A B G V G E G X I
C B K O L Y R O A A E M R I R V
L L Q B H U X W N Z C N P L G J
V S Y W J S H L G Q Y O I Q V P
E C I U J E G N A R O B N R Z B

L Y H U A G I N H G L V N W F F Q
D P B D W N E D J P Q G I U M Z D
T R T O S P D D K F Q P A R R O T
C B C G I T V V L F T M Y X B K D
E Z D X X B N Z E G N W G R D V C
S M C R C J W S M I K K I X D D M
N U P Q I U U L W P M R G I F X W
I Y Q V J O Y K T A K N V R O K K
K A V X M C X G W E O H P A P V G
C F Q U R H S O S N T G G N M S N
I B W N Z A L W Q I G E T L Q V S
T O Q W I M N C B U W L E G D I T
S U T U D S Z L K G G N C W Y M A
Y M Y M H T D F A E I K L N Z B C
O V F V S E J G R Y O T O Y X R R
I W J D B R B N J N D P P F X K A
A R A B B I T O V M K V F W D Q H

4

T R K K M U R C F L P X G Y S P R U F K
M H U J Z B O B L G O W Q D P K C R E C
O T S O R R Q H M S I Q A K L K E C D X
T E R F A Y R R E F T Y E R T N S R H P
J P I C Q G K Y A C V C E G L I F D D Q
P E L N W E Z O K F B P Y L R R X E E W
O E L S W R Z Y A E C M E I I A Q Y K Y
O I K Q E F T D P I H S L L A T B C R H
L H H A V A T Y P X L B C S E C L E A D
S M X B F Q J Z J U Z T R C R B N J Z T
Y Q P S X G J T R J S A A G M O C A O D
A K S D H F G C Y P Z F X O O J M M P N
A M T J F C A G G T Q P A H B R O U S S
T C C R J E L R H G G U C U C D C F B D
Z Z M K O F L Y V Z Q S G A C C E V A O
Y A C H T T E I A U Q B L B R U J E U I
Q H D T N L O P W C U H V I K I T B P L
S A H U Y F N C A T A M A R A N C I F S
I A P X W O J O Z P H O A Y Z I K O F B
F S F O A J S Q E B H I O C K I H R G S

5

X R C H J H G I L U Z A L S I P A L T O
E I A W O O X R P Z C W L M Y K V L U G
L G M Q A H T O P A Z B K I D K S O R Y
F Y E Q B K W V F X H T J A J M A V Q B
U Y T A X V O V G F I Y S Q Z B P M U U
U T H A W A G I Z H O X P H S Z P G O R
V X Y A U G G Z C D L A R E M E H E I E
W Y S Z X K F C P G Z A L G N L I E S E
P P T U I Z O E E N X T P R Z Q R Y E Q
S O P X C M M I A R Q I S J U Y E W B A
S D O Y T F F R R M Y V L Y R E B P H J
H I B E V N L P L W O J M Z E U F X R I
S A U N G B F J J D E C D U P K U L Q P
Z M L O N D F G A R N E T W S G W M M Q
P O G T K X S U V G V Y A S A D U T E H
F N F S Y U M N D A C V L I I Z S F E O
E D I N Q F Z X H Y L N A M B E R O B K
Q A O O K E U J U V X T G R C S P D M A
C D F O Y T K T K K A E T R G A V N B I
J K W M L O Y X G C O N C A L E Z X X F

6

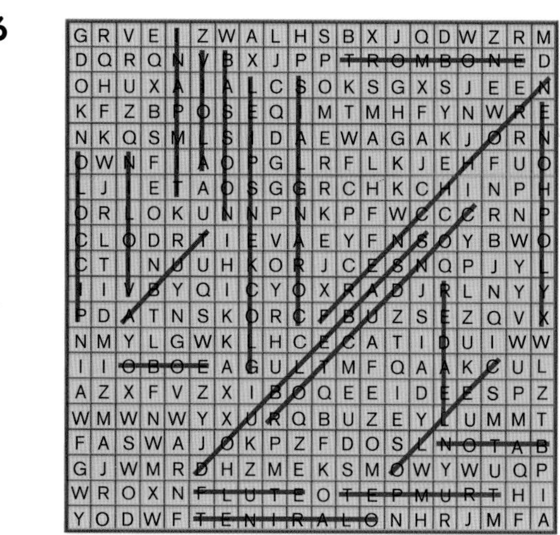

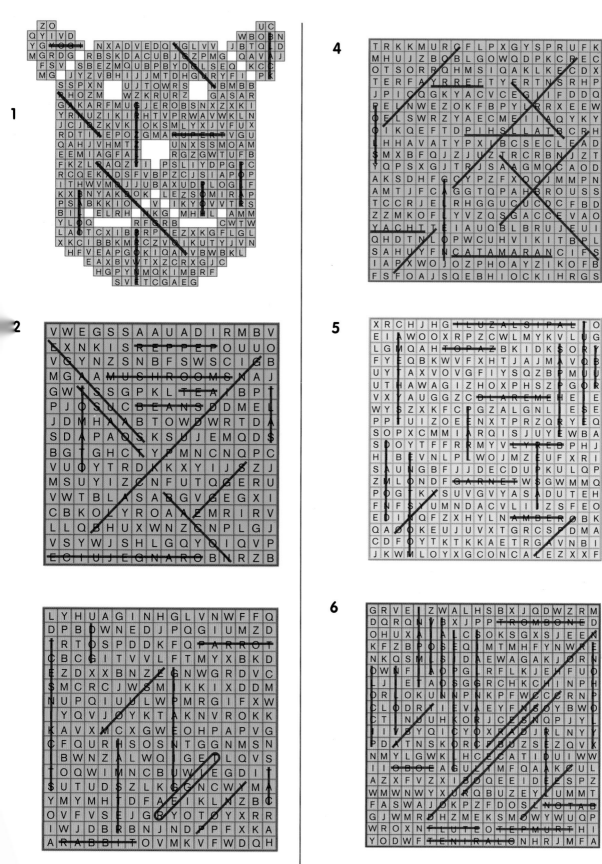

7

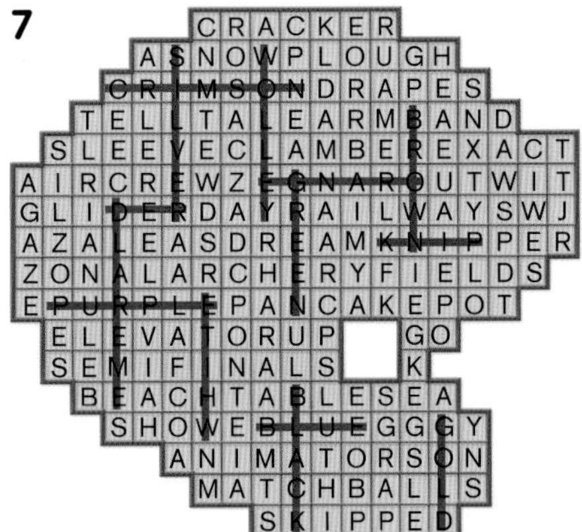

8

9

S T E R N U M T O P A Z
T H E M E L C I V A L C
I N W I N D M I L L U X
R E M A T C H I P A P T
R Y A N J S O N A T A S
U E Z X I K E Y S E C C
P R O V R U M E F T S R
A T L I L L I E S A G E
K E N N E L S A L B U M
P B A N A N A N V I L M
T R A C T O R A O R T A
P A C E E N K K E T C H

10

11

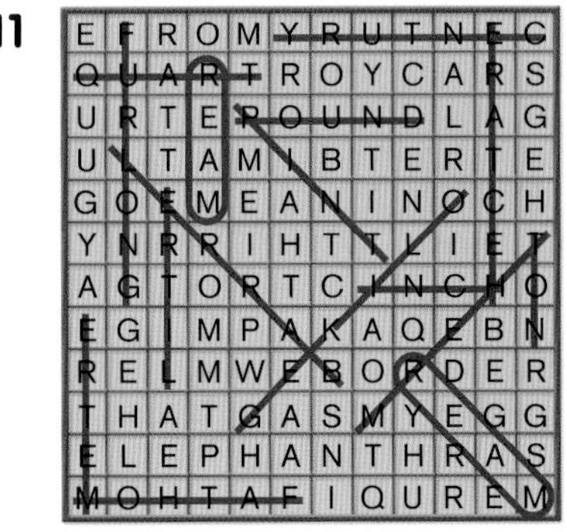

12

O B L I G A S H E L S I M N
S A R A J E V O N A S U H A
O R L A O C E L B O N E R G
A C G U Y A P S Y I E M P A
G E L L A L H O C K H E Y N
O L D A R G A H O R T J E O
G O S I R A P A N T A H N O
F N I C O R A C K E T S R Y
F A F X S Y D N Y E R G U R
M E A D E G K A M O S C O W
O G G N E V E O R L A N B O
S G D I O R R S T H I S L H
C Y S P A N I K N I S L E H
S I N K I M A Y P L E A M P

13
Read my lips

14
Positive, cheerful, hopeful, confident, expectant, buoyant

15

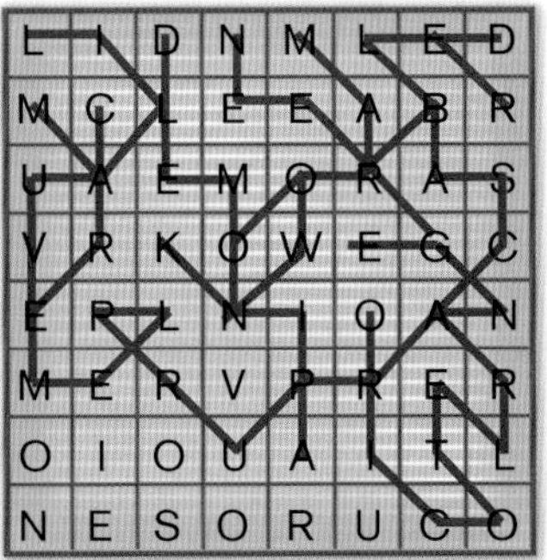

Pink, brown, green, red, purple, orange, maroon, apricot, scarlet, emerald, mauve, lilac, lemon, sable

16
Pyramid

17
Confirmed

18

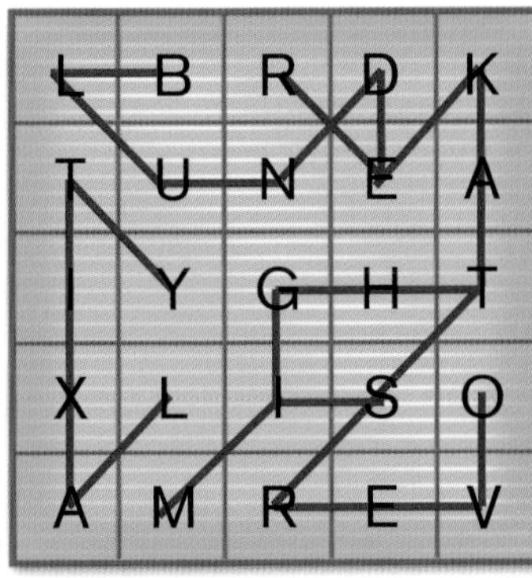

Oversight, mistake, blunder, laxity

19
With open arms.

20
Fact is stranger than fiction.

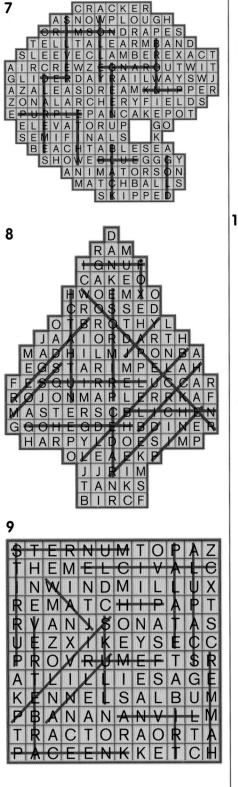

21
Florida, Maine, Idaho, Iowa, Ohio, Utah, Vermont, Texas, Oregon, New York, Delaware, Alaska, New Mexico, Montana, Alabama, Maryland.

22
PALE
PARE
PARK
DARK

23
BALL
BOLL
BOLT
COLT
COOT
FOOT

24
DOG
COG
COT
CAT

25
GAEL
GALL
GALE
PALE
PELE
PELT
CELT

26
BASS
BASE
BALE
SALE
SOLE

27
BURN
BORN
CORN
CORD
CURD
CURL
CURE

28
LA
LAD
LAID
PLAID

29
AT
ANT
PANT
PLANT

30
IN
TIN
TWIN
TWINE
TWINGE

31
AM
RAM
REAM
DREAM
DREAMY

32

	A	C	C	E	P	T		T	H	R	U	S	T	
S		E		R		H	A	Y		E		H		M
T	O	R	N	A	D	O		P	L	A	T	E	A	U
I		T		S		U	S	E		D		A		S
G	R	A	P	E	S		H		K	E	T	T	L	E
M		I		R	E	C	O	V	E	R		H		U
A	U	N	T		R		R		T		T	E	A	M
				L	I	C	E	N	C	E				
E	V	E	N		O		L		H		A	V	O	W
X		X		C	U	R	I	O	U	S		I		R
C	O	P	I	E	S		N		P	A	L	A	C	E
E		E		M		M	E	T		U		D		A
S	I	N	C	E	R	E		A	C	C	O	U	N	T
S		S		N		R	U	N		E		C		H
	C	E	N	T	R	E		K	A	R	A	T	E	

33

E	S	S	E	N	T	I	A	L		A	S	S	E	T
L		Q		O		T		I		P		E		I
S	C	U	T	T	L	E		E	M	P	E	R	O	R
E		E		I		M		U		E		V		E
W	R	E	N	C	H		S	T	A	N	D	A	R	D
H		Z		E		T		E		D		N		
E	V	E	R		T	R	A	N	S	I	S	T	O	R
R				A		E		A		X				E
E	X	P	E	R	I	M	E	N	T		S	T	O	P
		I		M		E		T		R		A		R
R	E	T	I	C	E	N	T		S	A	D	D	L	E
O		I		H		D		S		T		P		S
B	U	F	F	A	L	O		O	U	T	C	O	M	E
O		U		I		U		F		L		L		N
T	I	L	E	R		S	T	A	T	E	M	E	N	T

34

H		B		Z		N		A		L		C		L
A	W	A	K	E		E	X	P	L	O	S	I	V	E
R		N		R		C		O		V		V		A
P	E	A	C	O	C	K		S	E	E	K	I	N	G
		N						T				L		U
S	T	A	F	F		P	A	R		B	R	I	D	E
E				I		L		O		L		A		
A	D	D		G	R	A	P	P	L	E		N	I	B
		R		H		Y		H		S				A
H	E	A	R	T		G	E	E		S	Y	R	U	P
O		M				R						A		
S	H	A	M	P	O	O		S	T	E	N	C	I	L
T		T		I		U		T		V		I		E
E	X	I	S	T	E	N	C	E		I	M	A	G	E
L		C		Y		D		W		L		L		K

35
Across
1. Par
4. Pyre
8. Onus
10. Loaf
11. Poses
13. Aunt
14. Entailing
16. Wrung
17. Doers
18. Nursemaid
22. Lent
23. Serge
24. Each
25. Neon
26. Grey
27. Art

Down
1. Pope
2. Anon
3. Rust
4. Plainsmen
5. Young
6. Rang
7. Eft
9. Seaworthy
12. Sires
15. Lures
17. Dunce
18. Near
19. Area
20. Igor
21. Dent
22. Leg

36
Across
1. Tail pipes
6. Slaughter
7. Itchy feet
8. Embracing
9. Sheikhdom

Down
1. Tastiness
2. Irascible
3. Piggyback
4. Putrefied
5. Stratagem

37
Across
1. Ladies man
6. Tongs
7. Fib
8. Robe
10. Tick
13. Opt
14. Byway
16. Take stock

Down
1. Later
2. Dun
3. East
4. Mufti
5. Nib
9. Batik
11. Kayak
12. Ibis
13. Out
15. Woo

38
Across
1. Taboo
4. Orb
6. Toothless
7. Jays
8. Whey
10. Tire gauge
12. Yap
13. Erect

Down
1. Tat
2. Booby trap
3. Oche
4. Open house
5. Busby
7. Jetty
9. Ogle
11. Eat

39
Across
3. Thumb
6. Oyster
7. Uncle
8. Eponym
9. Pitch
12. Sands
15. Huddle
16. Aorta
17. Rictus
18. Freak

Down
1. Myopia
2. Stoned
3. Trump
4. Uncut
5. Beech
10. Indict
11. Callus
12. Staff
13. Nurse
14. Shark

40
Across
1. Casca
2. Basic
7. Pro
8. Humming
9. Aged
10. Isle
13. Sum
15. Airs
16. Imps
19. Scouted
21. Ego
22. Worry
23. Risky

Down
1. Cape
2. Sponger
3. Aphids
4. Bump
5. Ski
6. Cygnet
11. Suppers
12. Warsaw
14. Minder
17. Stay
18. Dory
20. Oar

41
Across
4. Riyadh
6. Lima
7. Canterbury
8. Hull
9. Brno
11. Sacramento
13. Bury
14. Athens

Down
1. Disc
2. Fauntleroy
3. Embryo
5. Heel
6. Labyrinths
8. Hiatus
10. Emma
12. Oink

42
Across
3. Burns
5. Gray
6. Wordsworth
7. Byron
9. Keats
12. Longfellow
14. Lear
15. Yeats

Down
1. Arid
2. Oath
3. Booty
4. Sewn
5. Gorge
8. Owner
10. Tools
11. Iffy
12. Lees
13. Leap

43
Across
1. Comb
3. Land
7. Dissolves
8. Writing
11. Chocolate
12. Rose
13. Peel

Down
1. Code
2. Mushrooms
4. Advantage
5. Dish
6. Control
9. Scar
10. Well

44
Across
1. Shoot
4. Stage
8. Interrupted
9. Twinkle
10. Ink
12. Six
13. Visitor
15. Distinguish
16. Egypt
17. Feast

Down
2. Handwriting
3. Oceans
5. Type
6. Greenhouses
7. Brilliant
11. Minute
14. Stop

US state:
Oregon

45

Across
1. Fair
4. Robe
7. Rig
8. Vanilla
10. Needle
12. Pail
13. Iron
15. Dragon
19. Hideous
20. Ski
21. Free
22. Noon

Down
2. Angle
3. Revel
4. Ring
5. Balsa
6. Brandish
9. Atlantis
11. Din
12. Pea
14. Order
16. Resin
17. Gusto
18. Cope

46

Across
1. Arena
4. Mason
7. Owl
8. Caravan
9. Tract
11. Hardy
12. Exact
14. Rally
16. Swallow
17. Spa
18. Let in
19. Roman

Down
1. About
2. Eel
3. Ascot
4. Marsh
5. Several
6. Nanny
10. Adamant
12. Easel
13. Talon
14. Rower
15. Yearn
17. Sum

47

Across
1. Evergreen
6. Bread
7. Vat
8. Well
10. Asks
13. Tot
14. Cacti
16. Easter egg

Down
1. Elbow
2. Ewe
3. Gods
4. Elvis
5. Net
9. Lotus
11. Sling
12. Acre
13. Tie
15. Cue

48

Across
1. Each
3. Agreed
8. Hampers
9. Duo
10. Comic strip
13. Decoration
17. Era
18. Aerosol
19. Swedes
20. Stop

Down
1. Echo
2. Cameo
4. Gas
5. Elder
6. Droops
7. Senior
11. Saturn
12. Adders
14. Crate
15. Onset
16. Clip
18. Ape

49

Across
6. Modern
7. Aunt
8. Anniversary
9. Addressed
11. Entertained
13. Bone
14. Ninety

Down
1. Mountain top
2. Remind
3. Interesting
4. Pans
5. Ingredients
10. Skinny
12. Eyes

50

Across
7. Appreciated
8. Carol
9. Euros
10. Pawn
12. Shun
15. Rifle
16. Amaze
18. Split second

Down
1. Catchphrase
2. Spur
3. Belly
4. Timer
5. Starch
6. Odds and ends
11. Waffle
13. Perth
14. Camel
17. Atom

51

Row 1: Able • Zero
Row 2: Cube • Taste
Row 3: Rent • Vast
Row 4: Oath • Value
Row 5: Beef • Make
Row 6: Away • Nanny
Row 7: Take • Half
Column A Bonus Word: Acrobat

52

Row 1: Quit • Past
Row 2: Used • Actor
Row 3: Aunt • Push
Row 4: Lamb • Fatal
Row 5: Iron • Raid
Row 6: Team • Elbow
Row 7: Yank • Sing
Column A Bonus Word: Quality

53

Row 1: Yell • Easy
Row 2: Obey • Begin
Row 3: Gear • Jail
Row 4: Hurt • Knock
Row 5: Urge • Last
Row 6: Rage • Decay
Row 7: Type • Face
Column A Bonus Word: Yoghurt

54

Row 1: Medal • Field
Row 2: Ugly • Tennis
Row 3: Smart • Faint
Row 4: Slick • Skill
Row 5: Origin • Trip
Row 6: Loaf • Bloody
Row 7: Inter • Named
Row 8: Naked • Write
Row 9: Invite • View
Column A Author: Mussolini
Quote: If I advance follow me, if I retreat kill me.

55

Row 1: Throw • Scary
Row 2: Echo • Appear
Row 3: Dainty • Stop
Row 4: Harsh • Camel
Row 5: Usher • Heart
Row 6: Grand • Theme
Row 7: Hiss • Parcel
Row 8: Empty • Whole
Row 9: Strain • Grip
Column A Author: Ted Hughes
Quote: What happens in the heart simply happens.

56

Row 1: Badge • Scarf
Row 2: Jotter • Fund
Row 3: Ocean • Often
Row 4: Rinse • Drone
Row 5: Nice • Praise
Row 6: Brave • Fluid
Row 7: Oust • Trophy
Row 8: Raffle • Shot
Row 9: Grey • Offend
Column A Author: Bjorn Borg
Quote: You have to find it. No-one else can find it for you.

57

1. Potato
2. Strawberry
3. Spinach
4. Orange
5. Tangerine
6. Lettuce
7. Courgette
8. Pineapple
9. Mushroom
10. Apricot

58

1. Al Pacino
2. Jane Fonda
3. Marlon Brando
4. Tom Hanks

59

1. Sharon Stone
2. Orson Welles
3. Russell Crowe
4. Julia Roberts

60

1. Silent (also inlets, tinsel and enlist)
2. Married
3. Orchestra
4. Sadder (also adders)

61

1. Medicine
2. Dispatch
3. Romantic
4. Competent

62

1. Sweden
2. Ireland
3. Poland
4. Germany

63

1. Belgium
2. Vietnam
3. Algeria
4. South Africa

64

1. Natalie
2. Roberta
3. Winifred
4. Angela
5. Eleanor
6. Daphne
Boy's name: Andrew

65
A single word

66
1. a
2. c
3. b
4. c
5. d
6. b
7. a
8. d
9. c
10. b
11. d
12. b
13. c
14. b
15. d

67
1. b
2. d
3. a
4. c
5. b
6. c
7. d
8. a
9. b
10. d
11. c
12. a
13. b
14. b
15. a

68
1. b
2. d
3. c
4. d
5. a
6. b
7. c
8. d
9. a
10. c
11. b
12. d
13. b
14. a
15. c

69
1. d
2. c
3. a
4. c
5. d
6. b
7. d
8. b
9. b
10. d
11. b
12. c
13. a
14. b
15. c
16. c

70
1. Guest
2. Strip
3. Police
4. Cedar
5. Argue

71
1. Diagram
2. Rampant
3. Anti
4. Item
5. Media

72
1. Remain
2. Inhuman
3. Manual
4. Almost
5. Stride
6. Demure

73
1. Cellar
2. Arrest
3. Strive
4. Vermin
5. Invade
6. Device

74
1. Sleet
2. Tunic
3. Comma
4. Awful
5. Logic
6. Chaos

75
1. Rotten
2. Tennis
3. Isolate
4. Teeth
5. Thing
6. Ingot
7. Other

76
1. Anchor
2. Horde
3. Decide
4. Dearest
5. Stain
6. Insult
7. Sultan

77
Remember
Unusual
Interested
Available
Severe

78
Diminish (or Minimise)
Monotonous
Neglected
Faraway
Orthodox

79
12 signs of the Zodiac.

80
26 letters in the alphabet.

81
7 Wonders of the World.

82
52 weeks in a year.
54 cards in a pack (including jokers).
57 Heinz varieties.

83
30 days hath September.
50 states in the USA.
60 minutes in an hour.

84
10 green bottles hanging on the wall.
24 hours from Tulsa.
50 ways to leave your lover.
76 trombones led the big parade.

85
9 symphonies by Beethoven.
9 lives of a cat.
9 planets in the Solar System.

86
1. Boy
2. House
3. Pot
4. Time
5. Date
6. Tap

87
1. Alley
2. Line
3. Handle
4. Bow
5. Tree
6. Story

88
1. Celery
2. Amazon
3. Normal
4. Yellow
5. Orange
6. Needle

First column: Canyon

89
1. Secret
2. Unlock
3. Narrow
4. Boring
5. Aflame
6. Tennis
7. Helmet
8. Inhale
9. Noodle
10. Giggle

First column: Sunbathing

90
1. Siesta
2. Handle
3. Oxygen
4. Potato
5. Warren
6. Income
7. Nausea
8. Dawdle
9. Office
10. Warmed

First column: Shop window

91
1. Coffee
2. Escape
3. Notice
4. Talent
5. Infirm
6. Murder
7. Expert
8. Tablet
9. Return
10. Employ

First column: Centimetre

92
1. Thread
2. Hurdle
3. Umpire
4. Manual
5. Bakery
6. Polish
7. Robber
8. Icicle
9. Nettle
10. Thirst

First column: Thumb print

93
1. Kipper
2. Isobel
3. Novice
4. Garlic
5. Famine
6. Italic
7. Stitch
8. Honest
9. Energy
10. Runway

First column: Kingfisher

94

Dear Chris and Mary,
We are having a **marvelous** time out here in Tenerife. The weather is **terific** and the sea feels like **its** heated! The local bars and **restaraunts** are lovely, though we're a bit **to squeemish** to try some of the more exotic **dish's**!
See you soon,
Dave and Sue

Correct spellings
marvellous; terrific; it's; restaurants; too; squeamish; dishes

95

Dear Mr. Reeman,
I write with regard to the parking ticket I **recieved** last **thursday** in the cul-de-sac leading off St. Stevens Street. My **undertsanding** is that parking **I** this area is unlimited for **dis-abled** drivers like myself. Therefore, I was **extremly** shocked to return to my vehicle to find a ticket on the windscreen. I would be **greatful** if you could please **advize** me of the regulations which apply to this **perticular** road before I forward my payment by cheque.
Yours **Sincerly**
A Hammond

Correct spellings
received; Thursday; understanding; in; disabled; extremely; grateful; advise; particular; sincerely

96

STOP PRESS!
In an **unpresidented** move last night, the former head of the **Ministery** of Transport, Sir Rupert Walker stepped down in the middle of the latest pay **despute** with the **nations** train drivers. Having stalled in **negociations** with union **representitives** for the last two weeks, **sir** Rupert decided that enough was enough. Since taking up the post, he has been almost **constently** in the newspapers for his stiff **oposition** to the various unions. A union **spokespersen** commented that modern industry **was'nt** the place for Sir **Ruperts** Victorian values. The talks will **procede** under the **guideance** of Lord Belmont.

Correct spellings
unprecedented; Ministry; dispute; nation's; negotiations; representatives; Sir; constantly; opposition; spokesperson; wasn't; Rupert's; proceed; guidance

97

The epitaphs on Roman tombstones were **addresed** to passers-by. One from the 2nd century BC describes the **qualitys** of a **dutyful** Roman wife: 'Stranger, I have only a few words to say. – This is the tomb of a **lovley women**. Her parents named her Claudia. She loved her husband with all her heart. She **beared** two sons; one she leaves here on earth, the other she has already placed under it. She was charming in **speach**, yet **pleasent** and proper in manner. She managed the house well. She **span** wool. – I have spoken. Go on your way.'

Correct spellings
addressed; qualities; dutiful; lovely; woman; bore; speech; pleasant; spun

98

An **epic thrilling swashbuckling** adventure, Curse of the Seven **Sea's** is a tale of sword fights, hidden treasure and ancient **piracey** on the waves and coastlines of **yester-year**. Following the exploits of young **sea farer**, captain Jack True, **were** taken on a journey through dangerous **straights**, **trecherous** weather and **pirate ridden** waters in a quest to return a **mistical** stolen treasure. **Shrowded** in mystery and spoken of only through whispers, True knows that the magical **treasures** healing **property's** could be his last hope of saving his loved ones, struck by a curse placed on them by the evil **warlok** Shargad. Armed with his sword, a map and a band of trusty **ship mates**, Captain Jack True sets **of** in search of hidden treasure and revenge – whatever the cost!

Correct spellings/grammar
epic, thrilling, swashbuckling; Seas; piracy; yesteryear; seafarer; we're; straits; treacherous; pirate-ridden; mystical; Shrouded; treasure's; properties; warlock; shipmates; of

99

Whole meal bread

Ingrediants:
1lb **wholmeal** flour
1 **tespoon** salt
1 teaspoon bicarbonate of **sooda**
1 teaspoon **crème** of tartar
1oz melted butter or **margerine**
1/2 pint milk, **idealy** sour or buttermilk

Method:
Heat the oven to **2000**°C/gas mark 6. Place the flour, salt and **razing** agents together in a bowl and mix thoroughly. Make a well in the mixture and **pore** in milk and melted fat. Stir in **carefuly**. Shape the dough into a **loafe** and place on a greased and **flowered** baking sheet. Brush with milk and bake for 30-**400** minutes, until browned and well-risen.

Correct spellings
Wholemeal; Ingredients; wholemeal; teaspoon; soda; cream; margarine; ideally; 200°C; raising; pour; carefully; loaf; floured; 30-40

100

Through thick and thin.

101

If you can dream it you can do it.

102

Two Gentlemen of Verona

103

Laughter is the shortest distance between two people.

104

1. Sow
2. Refuse
3. Minute
4. Desert

105

1. Entrance
2. Produce
3. Row
4. Object
5. Wound

106

Friday the Thirteenth.

107

Grandfather clock.

108

Much Ado About Nothing.

109

Lightning conductor.

110
Monkey puzzle tree.

111
Nurses run.

112
Tuna nut.

113
Gnu dung.

114
Space caps.

115
Solo gigolos.

116
Straw warts.

117
Do geese see god?

118
No lemons no melon.

119
Was it a rat I saw?

120
Ma is as selfless as I am?

121
Ah, Satan sees Natasha.

122
Panda had nap.

123
Pull up if I pull up.

124
Never odd or even.

125
Red rum, sir, is murder.

126
1. Probe
2. Theme
3. Scowl
4. Plenty
5. Aching
6. Sacred
7. Flower
8. Figure
9. Father
10. Nature

127
1. Calendar
2. Thwarted
3. Lavender
4. Progress
5. Flamenco
6. Arrested
7. Pleasant
8. Original
9. Ravenous
10. Manicure

128
1. Holiday
2. Satanic
3. Insipid
4. Embargo
5. Journal
6. Cabinet
7. Harvest
8. Nourish
9. Episode
10. Picture

129
1. Unstable
2. Improper
3. Bewilder
4. Business
5. Imminent
6. Colossal
7. Deadline
8. Withdraw
9. Sensible
10. Learning

130

131

132
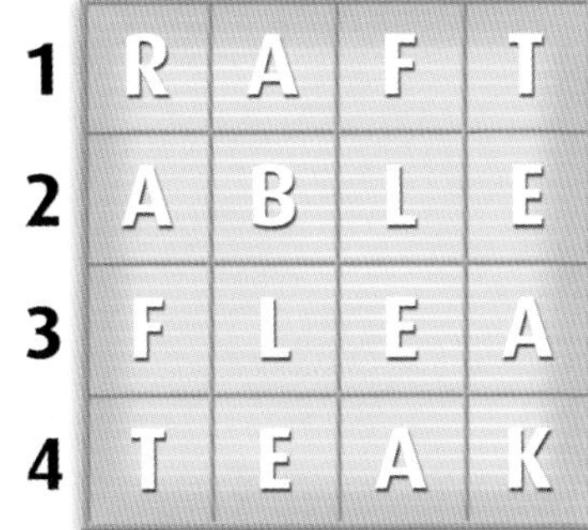

133

134

135

136

	V		C		D		S
	I	S	O	L	A	T	E
P	O	L	O		T	E	E
	L	A	N	T	E	R	N
J	A	Y		E		M	
			R	A	T		E
K	N	E	E		O	V	A
	A	U	D	I	T	O	R
B	A	R		C	A	L	L
	N	O	V	E	L	T	Y

137

	G		M		S		F
	E	L	E	C	T	O	R
P	E	A	R		E	W	E
	S	T	E	E	P	L	E
B	E	E		R			
			C	A	R	A	T
I	N	C	I	S	I	V	E
	E		D	E	N	I	M
S	A	G	E		S	A	P
	T	O	R	M	E	N	T

138

Across
1. Brainy
4. Trance
9. Rot
10. Mango
11. Yap
12. Tape
14. Kepi
16. Ale
18. Begin
19. Alert
21. Tar
24. Ride
25. Lyre
28. Now
30. Overt
31. Ode
32. Earthy
33. Adhere

Down
1. Berate
2. Apt
3. Name
5. Room
6. Nay
7. Esprit
8. Angel
13. Plead
15. Early
16. Ant
17. Ear
20. Fringe
22. Amber
23. Recede
26. Posh
27. Stud
29. War
31. Ore

139

S	U	C	C	E	S	S	■	B	O	W
A	■	R	■	S	■	H	■	A	■	E
G	R	A	S	S	■	O	A	S	I	S
■	■	W	■	A	X	E	■	I	■	T
S	I	L	L	Y	■	S	E	N	S	E
U	■	■	I	■	■	■	G	■	■	R
P	A	S	T	A	■	R	O	B	I	N
P	■	O	■	T	O	O	■	R	■	■
O	R	B	I	T	■	O	D	O	U	R
R	■	E	■	I	■	S	■	K	■	A
T	A	R	■	C	U	T	L	E	R	Y

140

P	L	A	Y	E	R	■	G	E	N	I	U	S
R	■	G	■	V	■	Z	■	A	■	T	■	U
I	M	A	G	I	N	E	■	S	T	A	I	R
N	■	I	■	L	■	B	■	Y	■	L	■	V
C	A	N	E	■	A	R	T	■	D	I	V	E
E	■	■	■	G	R	A	I	N	■	C	■	Y
■	U	P	P	E	R	■	M	O	I	S	T	■
H	■	R	■	T	A	M	E	D	■	■	■	S
A	R	E	A	■	Y	E	S	■	R	A	G	E
P	■	P	■	B	■	R	■	H	■	P	■	V
P	I	A	N	O	■	C	L	I	M	A	T	E
E	■	R	■	W	■	Y	■	D	■	R	■	R
N	E	E	D	L	E	■	S	E	T	T	E	E

141

Across
2. Bus
4. Ripon
6. Nat
8. IPod
9. Hail
12. Hitler
13. Blowup
15. Die
16. Nou
18. Taproot
21. Oslo
23. Kern
27. Burke
30. Lanka
31. Self build
35. Mute
36. Viol
37. Yom Kippur
39. In one
40. Dayan
42. Pica
45. Ally
47. Elstree
51. Sum
53. Our
54. Bowmen
55. Eloise
56. Ants
57. Side
58. Eel
60. Angus
61. Dog

Down
1. Pupa
2. Binders
3. Sothebys
5. Apollo
7. Gigolo
10. Pier
11. Punk
12. Hip
14. Poe
15. Dark
17. Urdu
19. Oxlips
20. Tendril
21. Opacity
22. Lismore
24. Luton
25. Alleys
26. Alias
27. Buy
28. Rem
29. Eli
32. Bad
33. Ivy
34. Don
38. Kris
41. Acer
43. Cub
44. Amos
45. Almond
46. Landsend
48. Lloyds
49. Tosh
50. Rue
52. Sea slug
59. Egon

142

Across
1. Probe
4. Reads
9. Boulder
11. Claimed
12. Toad
13. Smear
14. Stye
17. Bespattered
18. Hard and-fast
24. Imam
25. Stern
26. Hera
29. Watched
30. Split up
31. Unite
32. Leads

Down
2. Rhubarb
3. Beds
5. Edam
6. Demoted
7. Abate
8. Adieu
10. Rumba
11. Craft
15. Users
16. Croak
18. Hearten
19. Acted
20. Darts
21. Treated
22. Views
23. Lamps
27. Chit
28. Floe

143

D	E	S	I	S	T	S	■	F	O	P	S
A	■	O	■	A	■	U	■	I	■	L	■
N	Y	M	P	H	■	N	A	V	I	E	S
D	■	B	■	A	■	D	■	E	■	A	■
R	A	R	E	R	■	A	F	R	E	S	H
U	■	E	■	A	P	E	■	■	L	E	O
F	U	R	■	■	A	S	P	■	E	■	A
F	R	O	W	Z	Y	■	I	N	C	U	R
■	C	■	I	■	S	■	C	■	T	■	D
S	H	O	V	E	L	■	K	N	I	F	E
■	I	■	E	■	I	■	E	■	O	■	R
O	N	U	S	■	P	A	T	E	N	T	S

144

Across
6. Contralto
7. Acorn
8. Apple pie
9. Bus
11. Ice cream
13. Evergreen
14. Storage
18. Ale
20. Chrysanthemum
21. Perk
22. East
24. Hymn
25. Element
28. Toad-in-the-hole
30. Step
31. Nut
32. Beeswax

Down
1. Scrambled
2. Undo
3. Printing press
4. Bali
5. Godparent
10. Shelter
12. Emergency
15. Accents
16. Thunder
17. Emperor
19. Brother
23. Snake
26. Event
27. Miss
29. Tea
30. Sty

145

1. Genie
2. Ounce
3. Aisle
4. Lodge
5. Knife
6. Erase
7. Exile
8. Pixie
9. Elope
10. Rifle

The member is:
Goalkeeper

146
1. Blast
2. Remit
3. Idiot
4. Doubt
5. Erupt
6. Saint
7. Monet
8. Alert
9. Input
10. Daunt

The member is:
Bridesmaid

147
1. Canal
2. Angel
3. Level
4. Idyll
5. Feral
6. Oriel
7. Ravel
8. Novel
9. Impel
10. Atoll

The state is:
California

148
Tomato
3-letter examples:
Oat
Mat

149
Backbone
3-letter examples:
Cab
Con

150
Peanut
3-letter examples:
Pen
Tun

151
Footwear
3-letter examples:
Rot
War

152
Original copy
Living dead
Peace force
Working vacation
Accurate estimate
Bitter sweet
Cold sweat
Climb down
Never again
Good grief
Ill health
Sun shade
Loud whisper
Modern history
Nothing much

153
Organized chaos
Alone together
Open secret
Orderly confusion
Random order
Same difference
Student teacher
Live recording
Sweet tart
Unknown identity
Whole part
Virtual reality
Expected surprise
Front end
Definite maybe

154
Pleasant present
Float boat
Silly Billy
Staff laugh
State weight
Pretty ditty
Chew shoe
Fish dish
Lacking backing
Light bite
Meek Greek
Far star
Cool pool
Quiet riot
Clear cheer
Never ever

155
Preserve conserve
Slyer friar
Gory story
Forest florist
Stable table
Large charge
Stash cash
Crows doze
Steal meal
Horner's corners
Smugger mugger
Spryer buyer
Size thighs
Nearing clearing
Scary fairy
Soup scoop

156
Panorama
Eccentric
Dividend
Effervescence
Initiative
Keepsake
Appropriate

157
Absorb
Highlight
Skilfully
Momentum
Foolproof
Involve
Dynasty
Dazzle

158
Baffle
Aggregate
Adjust
Barrier
Statuette
Luxurious
Climax

159
Pennant
Clique
Dispossess
Kowtow

160
Succinct
Muddled
Stiff
Join
Mammoth
Monotonous
Horror
Puzzling

161
Invincibility
Back
Illegal
Inconvenient
Opaque
Intermittent
Unusual
Loyalty

162
Amalgamate
Hubbub
Hush-hush
Poppy cock
Senselessness
Revive

163
Deference
Dogged
Wayward
Affix

164
1. Mistletoe: mist, let, toe
2. Gallantry: gall, all, ant, try, Allan

165
1. Carpentry: entry, carp, car, pent, pen
2. Stallion: stall, tall, lion

166
Mix-up, stage-struck, pot-luck, rubber-stamp, feather-brain, hot-dog, duty-free, make-believe, secretary-general, middle-distance, museum-piece, mind-bending, thunder-clap, ticker-tape, moth-ball, low-key, round-table, rolling-pin, second-rate, role-playing.

167
Man-made, paper-weight, tip-off, pole-vaulter, carve-up, on-line, over-anxious, die-cast, drip-dry, clean-cut, large-scale, herring-bone, long-range, ice-cap, extra-terrestrial, zero-dividend, white-collar, bean-bag, perpetual-motion,giant-killer.

168
Hard-boiled, run-in, general-purpose, age-old, hero-worship, cop-out, fortune-teller, can-do, double-cross, laughing-stock, three-dimensional, hot-air, four-wheel, pop-up, fork-lift, felt-tipped, snare-drum, back-up, soap-opera, think-tank.

169
Home-stretch, fair-weather, second-guess, white-knuckle, red-hot, apple-cart, lift-off, cross-examine, swing-wing, kind-hearted, joint-stock, cost-effective, log-jam, never-never, spread-eagle, quick-change, cat-walk, solid-state, low-level, win-win.

170
Happiness

171
Tightrope

172
Halloween

173
Capricorn

174
METHASTY – AMETHYST
INUITMAT – TITANIUM
EARTHPIG – GRAPHITE
SNUGTENT – TUNGSTEN
MSAMIEUGN – MAGNESIUM

175
COOKCOAT – COCKATOO
GIRLTANS – STARLING
JANRIGHT – NIGHTJAR
TIMEOUTS – TITMOUSE
CAORNTRMO – CORMORANT

176
LARGEBED – BELGRADE
SADMUSCA – DAMASCUS
MOUTHARK – KHARTOUM
NEARCRAB – CANBERRA
BRASUHTCE – BUCHAREST

177
LOSECARS – LACROSSE
HINDGURL – HURDLING
LOFTALOB – FOOTBALL
WINGMIMS – SWIMMING
SERNTLWIG – WRESTLING

178
HOESCORN – SCHOONER
RUBSWEAT – WATERBUS
BITELOAF – LIFEBOAT
ARMTRAIN – TRIMARAN
CNARATMAA – CATAMARAN

179
MILDCURE – DULCIMER
SCANTTEA – CASTANET
TORNSHOP – POSTHORN
BENTROOM – TROMBONE
CIMAAHNRO – HARMONICA

180
DONFAGAN – FANDANGO
INHOPPER – HORNPIPE
GLADLAIR – GALLIARD
POLARICE – CAPRIOLE
FNOREADAL – FARANDOLE

181
HARE / REST
RICH / CHAT
DEAR / ARIA
PAGE / GENE
RECHARGE

182
MOTH / THIS
CARE / REEL
FEAT / ATOM
SEEN / ENVY
THREATEN

183
LOBE / BELL
FEAR / ARID
MASK / SKIN
COIN / INCH
BEARSKIN

184
CUSP / SPOT
ACHE / HEED
HERO / ROAR
PAID / IDLE
SPHEROID

185
ARCH / CHIP
LEAP / APEX
PIER / ERGO
NEON / ONUS
CHAPERON

186
LOAN / ANEW
GOAT / ATOP
OCHE / HEAD
COMA / MAIL
ANATHEMA

187
FAME / MEAN
SUCH / CHEW
SWAN / ANON
EPIC / ICON
REAL / ALAS
MECHANICAL

188
JAPE / PERK
CODE / DEEP
EAST / STEM
SARI / RIOT
LOAN / ANTE
PEDESTRIAN

189
Bemuse: all the others form a sequence where the first and last letters are consecutive letters of the alphabet:
aplomb
command
engulf
garnish.

190
Restore: all of the others can be paired so that the last four letters of the first word reversed are the first four letters of the second word:
mus**ical** / **laci**est
fr**amed** / **dema**nd
con**tort** / **trot**ter.

191
Magnum: it has the name of an animal embedded in it (ma**gnu**m) The rest have names of birds embedded in them:
b**emu**se
al**tit**ude
hyp**hen**ate
narr**owl**y.

192
Freighter: it has a number embedded in it reading forwards (fr**eigh**ter). The rest all have numbers embedded in them reading backwards:
gard**enin**g
d**eno**unce
undergr**owt**h
e**xis**ting
bru**net**te.

193
Basic: the first and last letters are consecutive letters of the alphabet – b : c. In all the others the first and last letters are consecutive letters of the alphabet, but in reverse.

194
Peripheral: in all the others one of the five letter words is an anagram of the last five letters of one of the ten letter words.
abori**ginal** / **align**
magis**trate** / **treat**
prose**cutor** / **court**
concer**tina** / **train**
snapd**ragon** / **organ**
enthu**siasm** / **amiss.**

195
Logical

196
Soft

197
Mean

198
Dynamic

199
Encouragement (one cute German).

200
Underneath (hunted near).

201
Consternation (tennis cartoon).

202
Procrastinate (Satanic report).

203
The theme is trees: lime, fir, plane, oak, elm, ash.

I considered myself fortunate to have obtained a comp**lime**ntary ticket to the **fir**st night opening of the new **Plane**t of the Apes movie. When the spotlight fell on the parade of celebrities, I remarked to the cl**oak**room attendant just how overwh**elm**ed I felt by the display of high f**ash**ion on show on the red carpet outside the theatre.

204
Making hay while the sun shines.

205
Sailing close to the wind.

206
Looking before I leap.

207
Keeping a straight face.

208
1. Like two peas in a pod.
2. Do a bunk.

209
1. Red in the face.
2. As far as one can tell.

210
1. Break of day.
2. Day in day out.

211
1. Is that so.
2. Pick up the bill.

212
1. At ease.
2. Get on with it.

213
Characteristic

214
Impressionable

215
Disciplinarian

216
Circumnavigate

217
Superstructure

218
Existentialism

219
1. See / sea
2. Foul / fowl

220
1. Missed / mist
2. Minor / miner

221
1. Lessen / lesson
2. Bored / board

222
1. Great / grate
2. Czech / cheque

223
1. Sweet / suite
2. Rough / ruff

224
1. Rues / ruse
2. Dire / dyer

225
You cannot be serious.

226
History repeats itself.

227
Tomorrow is another day.

228
We're such things as dreams are made of.

229
One Flew Over the Cuckoo's Nest.

230
Many things are lost for want of asking.

231
Drop in for dinner, would you like wine. What is your poison?

232
Error is always in a hurry.

233
To ask is no sin and to be refused is no calamity.

234
If you are patient in one moment of anger you will escape a hundred days of sorrow.

235
Along – lengthwise
Leapfrog – vault
Lapdog – canine
Oblong – rectangular
Pang – twinge
Endearing – adorable
Rung – crosspiece
Slang – jargon

236
Among – amidst
Loving – affectionate
Log – chronology
Overhang – projection
Pettifog – quibble
Evensong – vespers
Relaxing – peaceful
Soothing – pacifying

237
Agog – excited
Lapwing – peewit
Lambasting – reprimanding
Opening – opportunity
Prolong – lengthen
Earwig – insect
Railing – barrier
Strong – robust

238

239

240

241

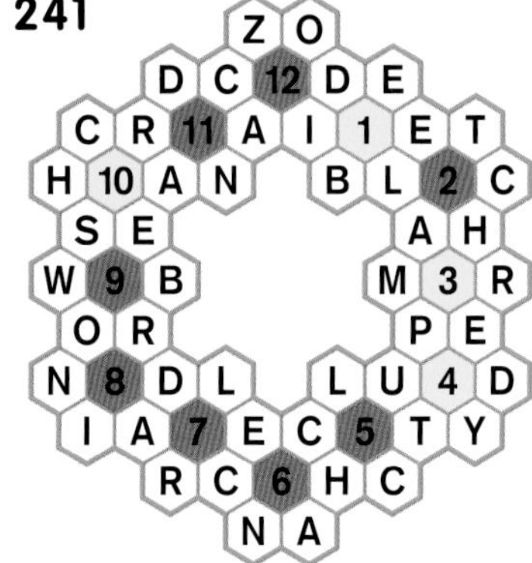

242
Spain: luminou**s** **paint**.

243
A train
t-rain: t (tea) before rain.

244
Volume Seven

245
They were swimming races. In swimming the winner is the first to touch the finishing line, but does not pass it.

246
David: DAVID less VI = DAD

247
Because you do not go on looking for it once you have found it.

248
Aegean Sea

249
March:
Mix me up for a magic spell,
(charm)
A piece of music that sounds swell,
(a march)
An animal that's a little mad,
(March hare)
Or a long walk when feeling glad,
(to march)
Maybe it's the time of year,
Look, and you will find me here.
(the month of March)

250
6**3** or 4**2** or 8**4**

251
Daughter

252
8: Literally 'slice' the roman numerals in half (IX XII XIII) and use the top halves of the figures, so, iv = 4 vii = 7 and viii = 8.

253
Herring (her ring)

254
Professionalism

255
Extraordinarily

256
Instrumentalist

257
Congratulations

258

A	B
short-lived, transitory	ephemeral
intermittent or occasional	sporadic
laughable or ridiculous	risible
acclaim, glory	kudos
give or promise	vouchsafe
ice-cream of Italian origin	cassata
disease, desperate condition	malady
pang, turmoil	throe
blunt, rude	brusque
sealed, airtight	hermetic

259

A	B
occurring during the day	diurnal
coarse or bawdy behaviour	ribaldry
small round piece of meat	noisette
the description of a coat of arms	blazon
diamond-like mineral used as a gemstone	zircon
way out	egress
to show or reveal clearly	evince
heron or other variety of wading bird	egret
a werewolf	lycanthrope
record, recount	chronicle

260

A	B
shaped like a snail shell	cochleate
to improve or to make better	ameliorate
room just under a pitched roof	garret
discoloured, as from a bruise	livid
decoration around an opening	architrave
stand for supporting a book or notes	lectern
carnation, pink or related flower	dianthus
foam or froth on the sea	spume
still in existence	extant
gum or resin used as varnish	mastic

261

A	B
bric-a-brac	curio
to question on a point of government	interpellate
hole in a fortification	embrasure
insert in conversation or change a manuscript	interpolate
resembling an eagle	aquiline
preferring to use force	hawkish
remedy for all diseases or ills	panacea
type of aquatic mammal	cetacean
back or side gate	postern
milk protein	casein

1

B: It is the only one in which the dot can be placed in both square and triangle only.

2

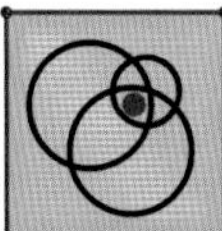

D: The dot can be placed so that it appears in all three circles.

3

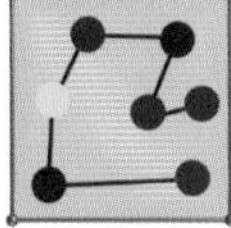

B: It contains a string of seven circles: red/blue/yellow/red/blue/red/red.

4

C: The dot can be placed in two circles and a triangle.

5

D: The square is coloured grey, the triangle is coloured orange, the circle is pink, the overlap between circle and square is yellow, the overlap between circle and triangle is green, the overlap between triangle and square is red and the overlap between square, triangle and circle is purple.

6

A: Imagine the dividing line in each square as a mirror. The only correct mirror image that has yellow/blue reversed is shown in A.

7 The golf ball.

8

9

10

11
B: Each shape has an extra line.

12
F: Each row and column contain two blue and one green flower, each a different size.

13
D: Turn it upside down to get an exact match.

14
1 and 8
2 and 9
3 and 6
4 and 7
5 and 10

15
C: All the other drawings have one white square in a horizontal line and one black square in a vertical line.

16

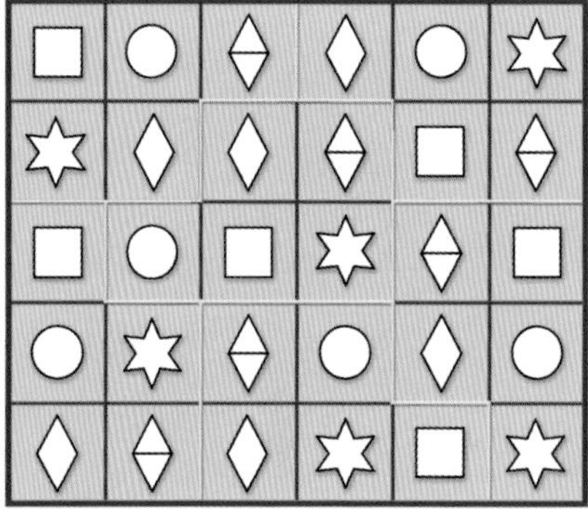

17
Black circle = 1
Diamond = 2
White triangle = 3
Black triangle = 4
Black star = 5
Black square = 6
White circle = 7
White square = 9

18

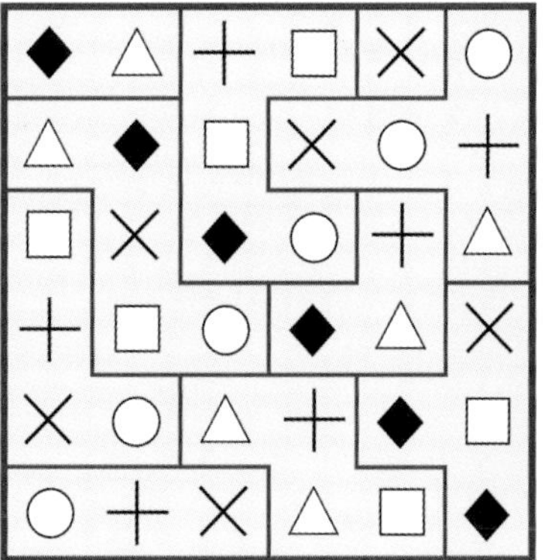

19
Close encounters 1
1. Fire extinguisher
2. Shell
3. C-clamp
4. Hair band

20
Close encounters 2
1. Light bulb
2. Pencil sharpener
3. Hair roller
4. Can opener

21
Close encounters 3
1. Safety pins
2. Threader (sewing)
3. Dummy
4. Hairbrush

22
Close encounters 4
1. Pine cone
2. Starfish
3. Hair clip
4. Cowboy boot

23

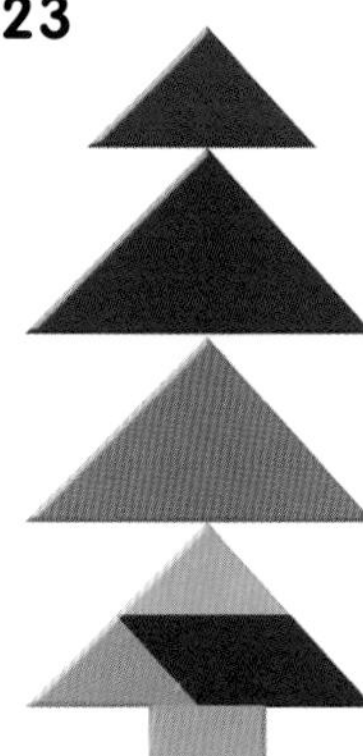

24

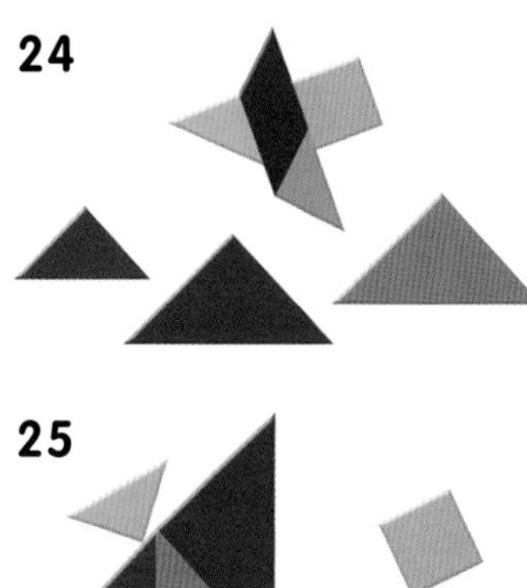

25

26

27

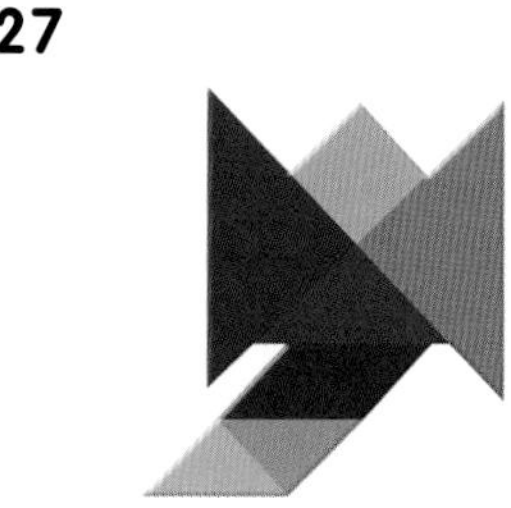

28

29

30

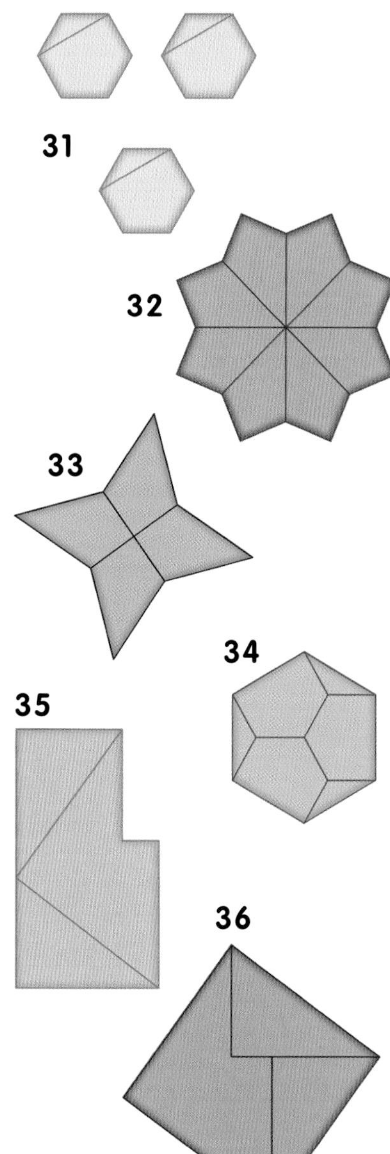

37

38

39

40

41

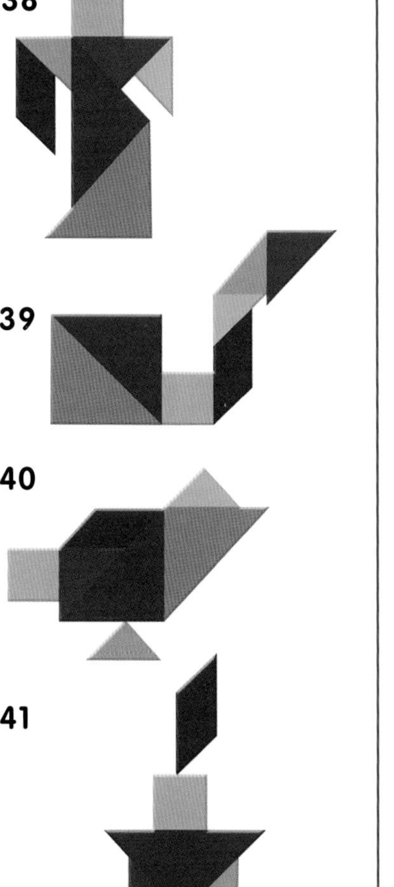

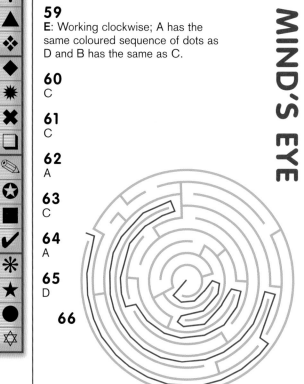

42
4

43
8

44
20

45
15

46
28

47
32

48
80

49
84

50
39

51
26

52
49

53
33

54
Single - A
Pair - C and D
Pair - G and F
Pair - J and E
Triple B and H and I

55
1 - B
2 - K
3 - L
4 - J
5 - C
6 - N
7 - F
8 - M

56
E: in all the others the section common to square and triangle is red and the section common to circle and triangle is yellow. In E it is the other way round.

57
C: in all the others dark blue is opposite black, green is opposite red, yellow is opposite light blue, purple is opposite light brown. In C, black is opposite light blue and yellow is opposite dark blue.

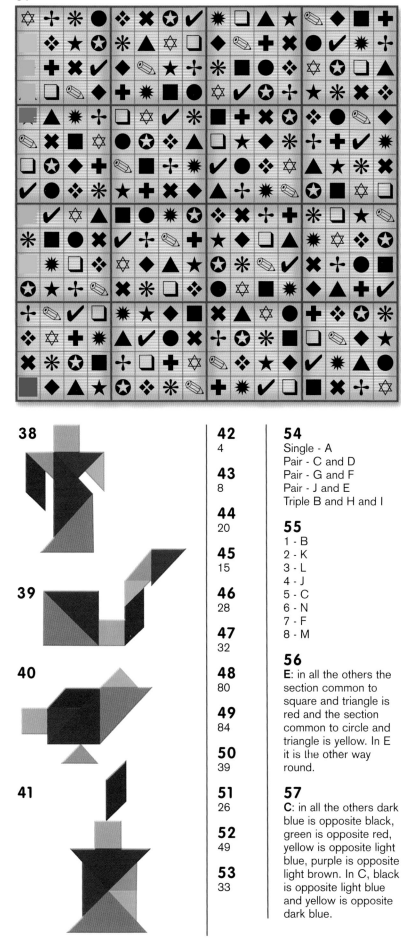

58
B: The rest are all the same figure rotated. B is a reflection of the other figures, not a rotation.

59
E: Working clockwise; A has the same coloured sequence of dots as D and B has the same as C.

60
C

61
C

62
A

63
C

64
A

65
D

66

67

68

69

70

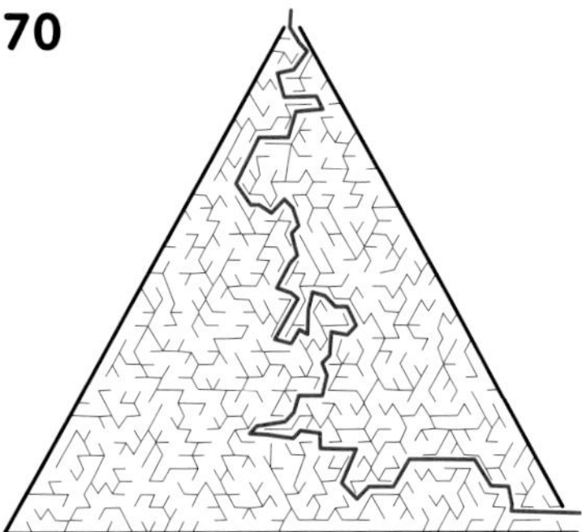

71

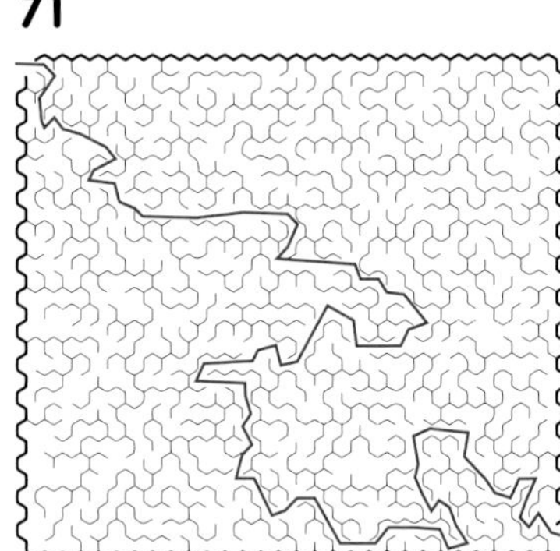

72

73
D, E

74

75
Crocodile tears.

76
Over the moon.

77
Under the weather.

78
Sick as a parrot.

79
Shoulder to cry on.

80
Stubborn as a mule.

81
Once bitten twice shy.

82
Some where over the rainbow.

84

85
1.

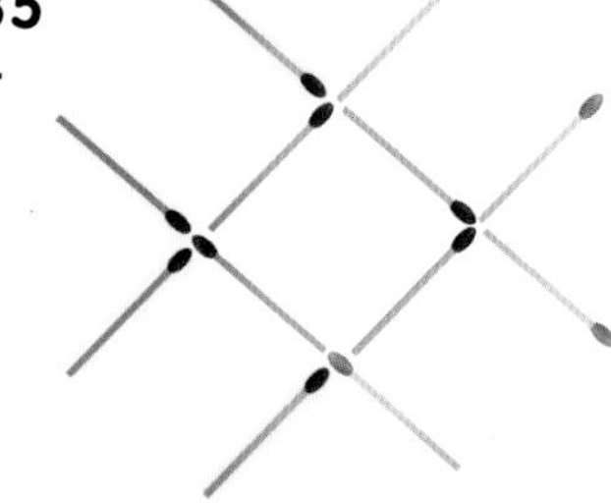

83

85 cont'd

2.

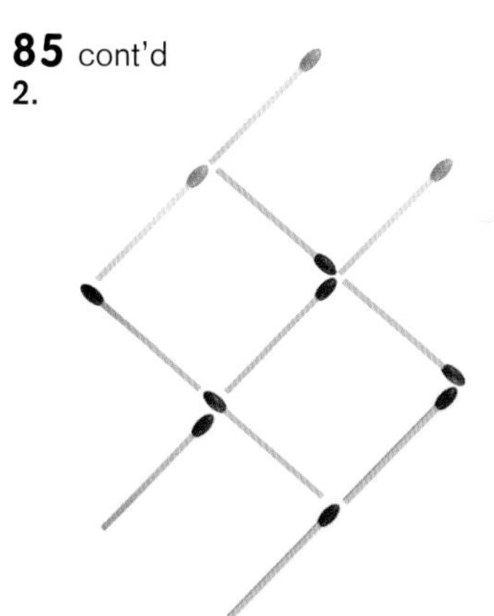

3.

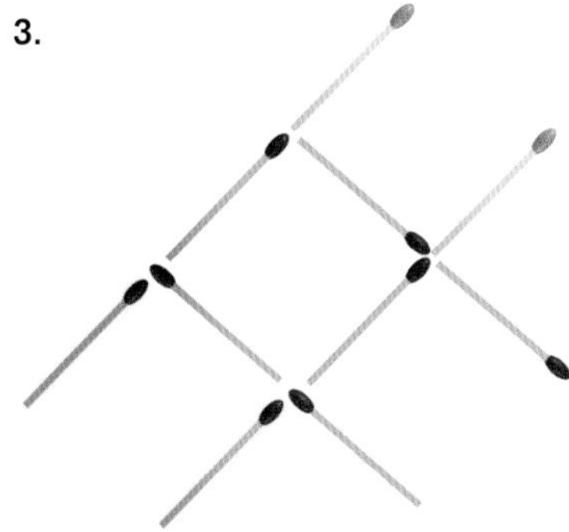

86

The wine glass is tilted forward and you are seeing it from underneath. Try it!

87

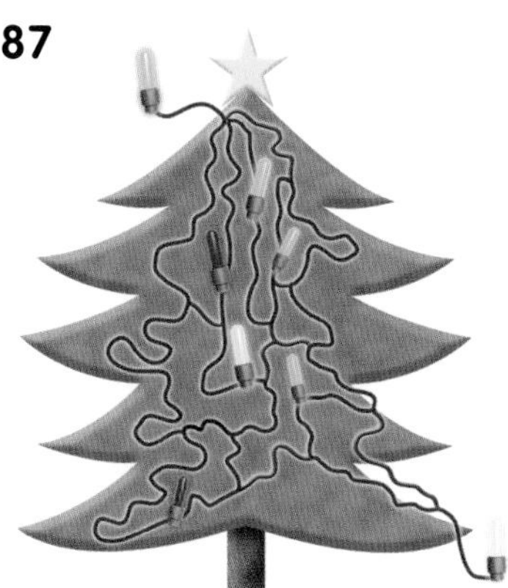

88

12 slices

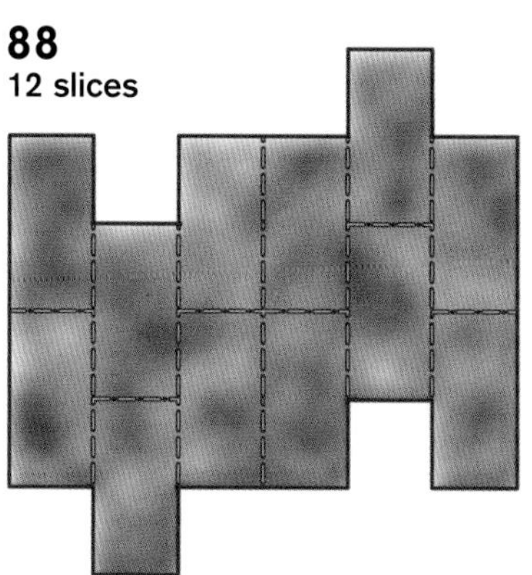

8 slices

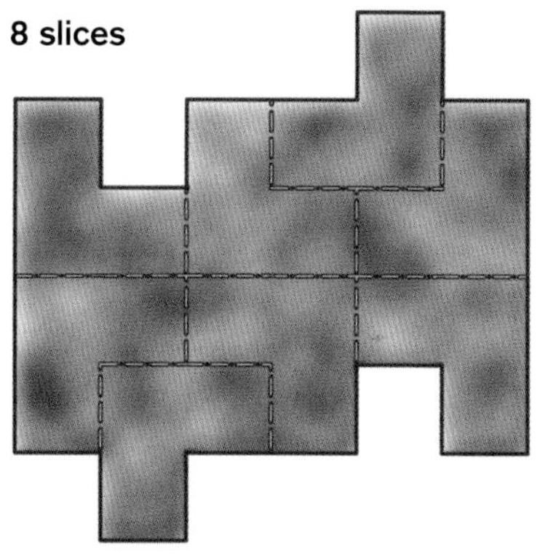

6 slices

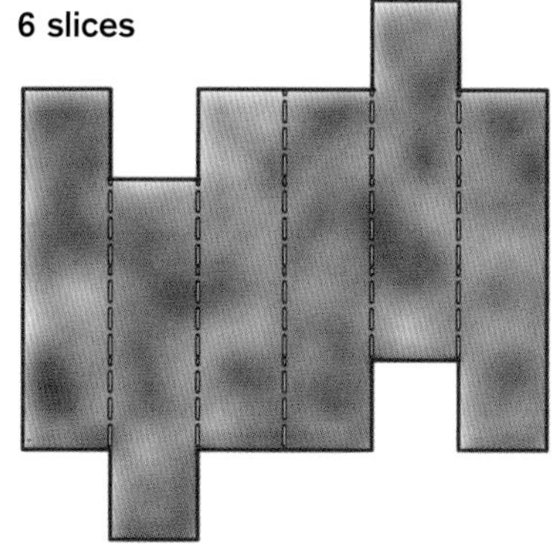

4 slices

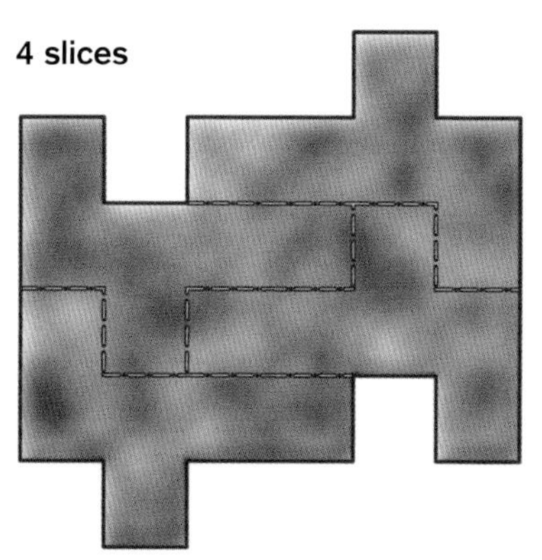

89

The left- and right-facing birds alternate as shown below.

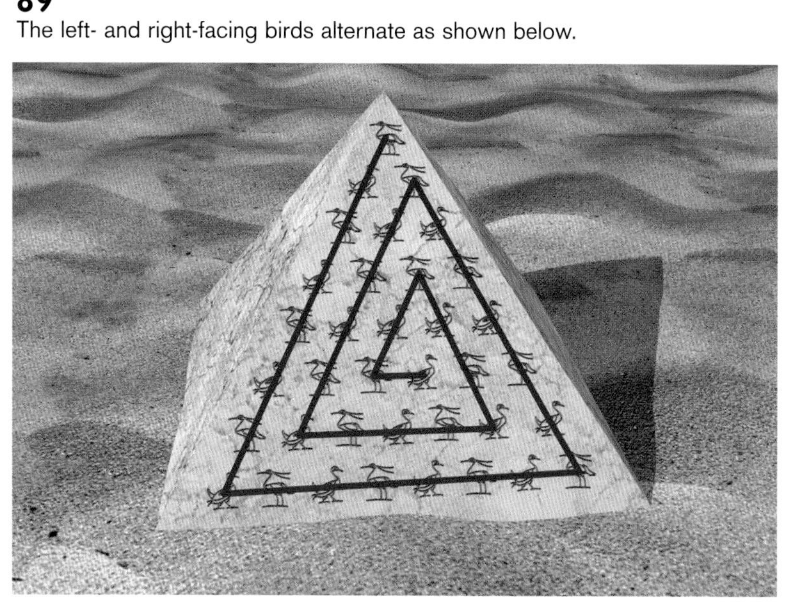

90

Jumping Jim should move in the following direction sequence to get to the ladder:
E, S, S, N, S, W, E, S, N, S, W, E, E, W, S, E, N, W, S, E.

91

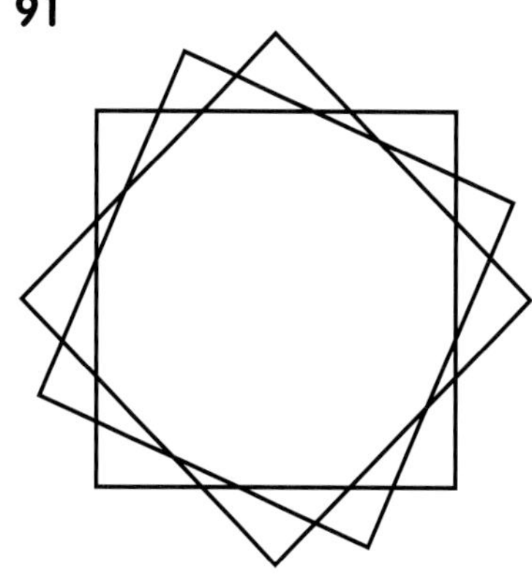

92

Row 1: JH JS 4S JC JD
Row 2: 5H 9D 5S 9C 5D
Row 3: AH KH 8S 8C AD
Row 4: 6H 10D 6C 10C 6D
Row 5: 7H QS 7S QC 7D

93

Row 1: KS 8C KH KC KD
Row 2: 6S JS JH JC 6D
Row 3: 8S QC QH QD 8D
Row 4: 4S 10S 10H 10D 4D
Row 5: AS 9C 9H AC AD

94

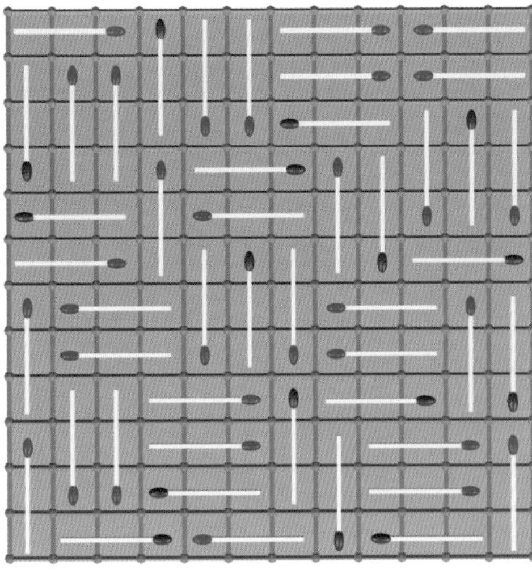

95

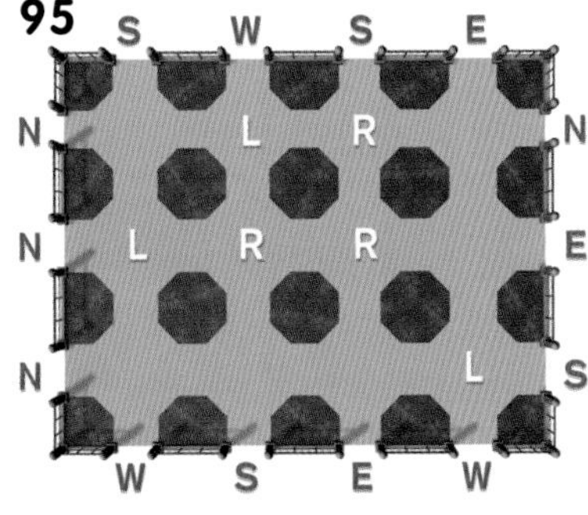

96

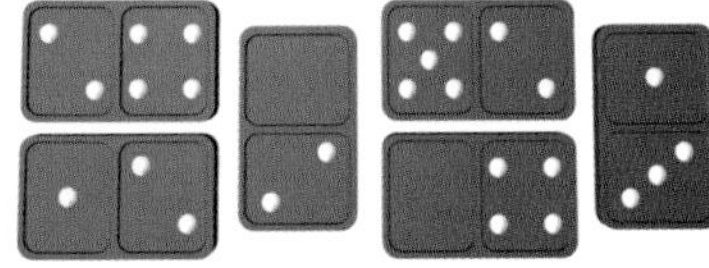

Think of the dominoes as two-digit numbers:
12 x 3 = 36
22 x 4 = 44
The bottom puzzle uses division:
24 / 12 = 2
52 / 4 = 13

97

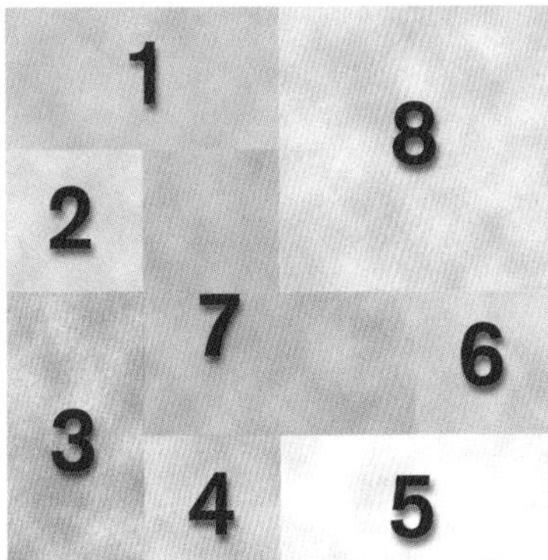

98

There is no single correct solution to this puzzle – there are several routes you can take, but here is one example.

Each move is shown as a number (the number on top of the die at the start of the move) and a letter (the compass direction of the move.). 2S–1E–4S–5S–3E–6E–4E–1N–5E–3S–1E–2N–3W–1W–4N–5N–3N.

The next twelve moves are: 2W–6N–4N–1E–2N–3E–6E–4S–2S–3W–6S–5W.

The next twelve moves are: 4W–2N–6N–5E–4N–1E–2E–6S–4S–1W–2S–3W.

The next eight moves are: 6W–4N–2N-3E–6N–5E–4E–2S.

The final moves to take you back home are: 6E–3S–5S–4S–2S–3W–6W–4W–1S–5S–6W–3W–1W–4N–5N–3W–6N. It is necessary to go around the loop three times in order to orientate the die to the letters on the grid.

99

H

I

A

C

F

G

D

B

E

100

Counting the five ID cards from left to right:
Card 1, name change.
Card 2, hat and wig added, earrings and scarf removed.
Card 3, birthday changed.
Cards 4 and 5, no change

101

1 = A
2 = D
3 = C
4 = B

102

1 = B
2 = D
3 = A
4 = C

103

1 = D
2 = A
3 = B
4 = C

1
64: Deduct 1,3,5,7,9,11.

2
a: Looking across each line numbers progress +3, –1, +3. Looking down each column they progress +1, –3, +1.

3
4 and 129: There are two interwoven sequences. In the first, starting at 1, add 32 each time. In the second, starting at 100, deduct 32 each time.

4
73542: Reverse the previous number each time, but deduct 1 from the middle digit.

5
182: The numbers 2, 4, 6, 8, 10, 12, 14, 16, 18, 2(0) are appearing with alteration of boundaries, in groups of three digits.

6
496: The digits 7496832 are being repeated in the same order.

7
7: Start at 1 and work clockwise to alternate segments adding 1, 2, 3, 4, 5, 6 in turn.

8
48: Multiply the digits in each number to obtain the next number in the sequence, for example; 2 x 3 x 9 x 7 = 378 and 3 x 7 x 8 = 168.

9
0: In the diagrams below, the numbers shown by the brown segments progress in the sequence 6, 5, 4. The numbers shown by the blue segments decrease in increments of four; 8, 4, 0. The numbers shown by the green segments progress 2, 5, 8 and the numbers shown by the grey segments progress 9, 6, 3.

6	8
2	9

5	4
5	6

4	0
8	3

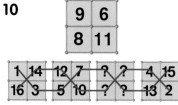

10

9	6
8	11

1	14
16	3

12	7
5	10

?	?
?	?

4	15
13	2

The numbers indicated by the red line are in the sequence 1, 3, 5, 7, 9, 11, 13, 15. The numbers indicated by the blue line are in the sequence 16, 14, 12, 10, 8, 6, 4, 2.

11
530: The numbers are all times with the dot missing and 45 minutes is added each time i.e. 1.45, 2.30, 3.15, 4.00, 4.45, 5.30.

12
c: Start at the bottom left-hand corner and work up the first column, then back down the second column etc, repeating the numbers 25683.

13
WITH + THE = QUEEN
E = 2 H = 4 I = 3 N = 6 Q=1
T= 8 U = 0 W = 9

14
HARRY + HARRY = POTTER
A = 3 E = 6 H = 5 O = 0 P = 1
R = 8 T = 7 Y = 4

15
AND + STILL + GOING = STRONG
A = 5 D = 7 G = 9 I = 8 L = 3
N = 6 O = 2 R = 4 S = 1 T = 0

16
ECHOED + LADY = AGATHA
A = 5 C = 9 D = 3 E = 4 G = 0
H = 7 L = 8 O = 1 T = 6 Y = 2

17
YOU + WOULD = NEVER
D = 4 E = 0 L =1 N = 6 O = 9
R = 7 U = 3 V = 2 W = 5 Y = 8

18
NO + PHONE + CALLS = PLEASE
A = 4 C = 9 E = 6 H = 2 L = 0
N = 8 O = 3 P = 1 S = 7

19
SWALLOW + MOOSE + EMU = ANIMALS
A = 8 E = 2 I = 3 L = 4 M = 5
N = 0 O = 1 S = 7 U = 6 W = 9

20
THESE + TWENTY = NOBLES
B = 1 E = 6 H = 4 L = 5 N = 8
O = 0 S = 9 T = 7 W = 2 Y = 3

21
PENGUIN + SEAGULL + GNU = ANIMALS
A = 5 E = 6 G = 4 I = 7 L = 9
M = 8 N = 2 P = 3 S = 1 U = 0

22
SALMON + MARLIN + BISON = ANIMALS
A = 1 B = 2 I = 5 L = 7 M = 4
N = 3 O = 6 R = 0 S = 9

23

3	1	2	5	6	8	7	9	4
4	8	7	2	9	3	6	5	1
5	6	9	4	7	1	2	3	8
7	9	3	6	8	4	1	2	5
1	5	8	7	2	9	4	6	3
2	4	6	3	1	5	8	7	9
8	7	1	9	3	2	5	4	6
6	3	5	8	4	7	9	1	2
9	2	4	1	5	6	3	8	7

24

8	7	4	1	9	6	3	2	5
1	9	3	5	2	7	8	4	6
2	6	5	3	4	8	1	7	9
4	5	6	7	8	3	2	9	1
3	2	7	9	5	1	6	8	4
9	8	1	4	6	2	7	5	3
5	1	2	8	3	9	4	6	7
7	4	8	6	1	5	9	3	2
6	3	9	2	7	4	5	1	8

25

8	4	9	7	3	5	2	6	1
1	6	3	4	2	8	9	7	5
7	2	5	9	6	1	8	4	3
9	5	6	2	7	3	1	8	4
2	3	1	8	4	6	5	9	7
4	8	7	1	5	9	3	2	6
3	7	4	5	9	2	6	1	8
5	1	2	6	8	7	4	3	9
6	9	8	3	1	4	7	5	2

26

6	4	3	1	8	7	5	2	9
2	5	9	6	4	3	8	1	7
7	1	8	2	5	9	4	6	3
4	2	6	8	3	5	7	9	1
9	8	5	7	1	2	6	3	4
3	7	1	9	6	4	2	5	8
8	3	2	4	9	6	1	7	5
5	6	4	3	7	1	9	8	2
1	9	7	5	2	8	3	4	6

27

1	3	9	7	8	5	2	4	6
4	5	2	1	6	3	7	8	9
6	7	8	9	4	2	3	5	1
9	6	3	4	1	7	8	2	5
7	2	4	6	5	8	1	9	3
8	1	5	2	3	9	4	6	7
3	4	6	8	9	1	5	7	2
2	9	1	5	7	4	6	3	8
5	8	7	3	2	6	9	1	4

28

9	5	4	1	6	8	2	3	7
2	3	6	5	4	7	1	9	8
8	7	1	2	9	3	5	6	4
6	1	3	8	7	9	4	2	5
5	8	2	6	1	4	3	7	9
4	9	7	3	5	2	8	1	6
7	4	5	9	3	1	6	8	2
3	2	9	4	8	6	7	5	1
1	6	8	7	2	5	9	4	3

29

1	9	8	3	2	4	5	7	6
5	7	4	6	9	8	3	2	1
2	3	6	5	1	7	4	8	9
8	5	7	9	6	3	1	4	2
6	4	3	1	8	2	7	9	5
9	2	1	4	7	5	8	6	3
7	8	5	2	3	6	9	1	4
3	6	9	8	4	1	2	5	7
4	1	2	7	5	9	6	3	8

30

1	4	3	8	7	6	9	2	5
5	8	9	2	4	3	1	7	6
2	6	7	1	9	5	4	8	3
7	1	4	5	6	2	8	3	9
9	2	8	7	3	4	5	6	1
3	5	6	9	1	8	2	4	7
4	9	5	6	8	7	3	1	2
8	7	1	3	2	9	6	5	4
6	3	2	4	5	1	7	9	8

31

3	9	1	6	8	2	5	7	4
5	6	4	1	3	7	8	9	2
2	8	7	5	4	9	3	1	6
9	5	6	3	7	8	4	2	1
1	7	2	9	5	4	6	3	8
8	4	3	2	1	6	9	5	7
6	2	8	7	9	5	1	4	3
7	1	5	4	6	3	2	8	9
4	3	9	8	2	1	7	6	5

32

4	1	3	2	9	5	6	7	8
7	6	2	1	8	3	5	4	9
5	9	8	7	6	4	3	2	1
2	3	6	4	1	9	7	8	5
9	5	4	6	7	8	1	3	2
8	7	1	3	5	2	4	9	6
3	4	9	5	2	1	8	6	7
1	8	7	9	4	6	2	5	3
6	2	5	8	3	7	9	1	4

33

9	8	4	6	7	3	2	5	1
1	5	6	9	2	8	7	4	3
3	2	7	4	1	5	9	6	8
5	7	8	1	9	6	3	2	4
2	9	1	3	8	4	6	7	5
4	6	3	7	5	2	1	8	9
8	1	9	2	4	7	5	3	6
7	3	5	8	6	9	4	1	2
6	4	2	5	3	1	8	9	7

34

8	7	6	3	5	4	2	9	1
2	9	3	1	8	6	7	5	4
5	1	4	9	2	7	8	3	6
9	5	2	8	4	1	3	6	7
4	3	7	6	9	2	5	1	8
6	8	1	5	7	3	9	4	2
1	4	8	7	3	9	6	2	5
7	2	9	4	6	5	1	8	3
3	6	5	2	1	8	4	7	9

35

3	9	7	5	2	8	6	1	4
8	6	1	3	7	4	9	2	5
4	5	2	1	9	6	7	8	3
5	3	6	4	8	7	1	9	2
7	2	4	9	3	1	8	5	6
9	1	8	6	5	2	4	3	7
6	4	5	8	1	3	2	7	9
2	8	9	7	6	5	3	4	1
1	7	3	2	4	9	5	6	8

36

3	2	5	6	9	1	4	7	8
6	4	7	2	8	5	1	9	3
1	9	8	4	3	7	6	2	5
4	6	2	3	7	8	5	1	9
5	8	9	1	2	4	3	6	7
7	1	3	9	5	6	8	4	2
9	5	6	7	4	3	2	8	1
8	7	1	5	6	2	9	3	4
2	3	4	8	1	9	7	5	6

37

5	8	7	9	6	3	2	4	1
9	3	2	1	7	4	6	8	5
1	6	4	8	5	2	9	3	7
7	9	5	4	8	6	1	2	3
8	4	1	2	3	9	5	7	6
6	2	3	7	1	5	8	9	4
3	1	9	5	2	7	4	6	8
4	5	6	3	9	8	7	1	2
2	7	8	6	4	1	3	5	9

38

5	8	2	3	1	4	9	7	6
6	3	7	8	2	9	4	5	1
1	9	4	6	7	5	2	3	8
7	6	1	4	8	3	5	9	2
9	2	8	5	6	7	3	1	4
3	4	5	2	9	1	6	8	7
8	7	6	9	3	2	1	4	5
4	1	9	7	5	6	8	2	3
2	5	3	1	4	8	7	6	9

39

5	6	1	8	2	3	7	4	9
2	7	3	6	4	9	1	5	8
8	4	9	1	5	7	6	3	2
9	3	6	2	8	5	4	1	7
1	5	8	7	9	4	2	6	3
4	2	7	3	6	1	8	9	5
7	9	2	4	3	6	5	8	1
6	1	5	9	7	8	3	2	4
3	8	4	5	1	2	9	7	6

40

6	3	5	8	4	9	1	7	2
4	2	8	3	7	1	5	9	6
1	7	9	6	5	2	4	3	8
5	9	6	7	2	4	3	8	1
2	4	3	1	9	8	6	5	7
7	8	1	5	3	6	2	4	9
3	1	2	9	8	5	7	6	4
8	6	7	4	1	3	9	2	5
9	5	4	2	6	7	8	1	3

41

3	1	7	6	5	9	4	8	2
5	4	6	8	2	3	7	9	1
8	9	2	7	1	4	6	3	5
1	5	4	2	9	8	3	6	7
9	6	3	5	7	1	2	4	8
7	2	8	3	4	6	5	1	9
2	8	1	4	6	5	9	7	3
4	3	5	9	8	7	1	2	6
6	7	9	1	3	2	8	5	4

42

1	6	7	4	5	3	2	8	9
5	4	2	8	9	1	7	3	6
3	9	8	2	6	7	4	1	5
8	1	4	6	3	9	5	7	2
6	2	5	7	1	4	8	9	3
9	7	3	5	2	8	6	4	1
2	8	9	1	7	5	3	6	4
7	5	1	3	4	6	9	2	8
4	3	6	9	8	2	1	5	7

43

6	9	5	7	8	4	1	3	2
8	7	1	9	3	2	4	6	5
4	3	2	1	6	5	7	9	8
2	5	9	3	7	1	8	4	6
7	8	3	6	4	9	5	2	1
1	4	6	5	2	8	3	7	9
9	2	4	8	5	7	6	1	3
3	1	8	4	9	6	2	5	7
5	6	7	2	1	3	9	8	4

44

6	7	1	5	4	8	9	3	2
5	9	4	7	3	2	8	6	1
2	3	8	9	6	1	4	7	5
4	8	6	2	7	5	1	9	3
1	2	9	3	8	6	7	5	4
3	5	7	1	9	4	6	2	8
8	1	3	6	2	7	5	4	9
7	4	2	8	5	9	3	1	6
9	6	5	4	1	3	2	8	7

45

1	8	9	6	5	4	7	2	3
3	5	2	7	8	1	6	9	4
6	7	4	3	2	9	5	1	8
9	3	8	1	6	7	2	4	5
5	4	1	2	3	8	9	6	7
2	6	7	9	4	5	8	3	1
7	9	3	5	1	6	4	8	2
8	1	6	4	7	2	3	5	9
4	2	5	8	9	3	1	7	6

46

$10: You spent $2 on the taxi tip, and have $2 change – so you spent $16 on the meal, the tip, and the taxi fare. As the meal was twice the taxi, then the meal was $10, the tip $1, and the taxi fare $5.

47

$5.84: Dinner plates must be one sixth of $3.18 – 53 cents each, so four will cost $2.12. Six soup bowls must be $5.76 minus $3.18 – 43 cents each, so four will cost $1.72. You're told that four plates, cups, and saucers cost $2, so there's no need to work anything else out: four complete place settings cost $2.12 + $1.72 + $2 = $5.84.

48

$8: Linda has one share, Eric two, and Sally four. That makes seven shares in all. $28 ÷ 7 = $4.
So, Linda has $4, Sally $16, and Eric $8.

49

$5.90: After allowing for postage, the buyer paid $19 for the guitar. 10% of this was commission ($1.90), and Tony had to pay the listing fee ($3), so he actually made $14.10. As he originally paid $20, he had lost $5.90.

50

$30: If a goat is worth a quarter of a cow, then 3 cows earned the farmer the same as 12 goats. Similarly, 5 sheep earned the same as 10 goats, and 11 chickens earned the same as 3 and two-thirds of a goat. Thus, he sold the equivalent of 7 + 12 + 10 + 3⅔, or 32⅔ goats. $980 divided by 32⅔ is $30 – the price of one goat.

51

£1.50: For 90p to be able to reverse their positions, the difference between the amount they each hold must be 90p. For each additional coin held, Rob has 15p (20p minus 5p) more than Mary. There are 6 x 15p in 90p – so they had 6 coins each: £1.50 in total.

52

$20: First, put the dwarfs in order:

Dozy > Sleepy
Sneezy > Snow White
Happy > Sneezy
Sleepy > Happy

So: Dozy – Sleepy – Happy – Sneezy – Snow White.
Happy is in the middle, so gets the average, which must be $100 divided by five = $20.

53

$9.54: The money can be written with just three digits – so must be between $1.01 and $9.99. Trial and error shows that there is only one set of numbers that fits this question: **$9.54 = $4.59 + $4.95**

54

$12,000: One half plus one quarter plus one sixth equals eleven twelfths (1/2 = 6/12; 1/4 = 3/12; 1/6 = 2/12). So, the remainder, $1,000, is one twelfth of the whole, which must have been $12,000.

55

16: Each nephew and niece got $5,500 plus a number of extra $100s depending upon the number of younger recipients.

Try an example: if there were 10 recipients then the amount of money in the bequest would be (5500 x 10) + (0 + 1 + 2 + 3 + 4 + 5 + 6 + 7 + 8 + 9) x 100.
This equals $59,500.00. Trial and error will lead you to 16.

That gives: (5500 x 16) + (100 x 120) which equals $88,000.00 + $12,000.00 or $100,000.00.
Therefore, there are 16 nephews and nieces.

56

36 cents: If the difference between double Sally's money and half Sally's money is 30 cents, then Sally must have 20 cents. So, Tom has 10 cents and Alice 5 cents, a total of 35 cents. With the penny they found, the total fare must be 36 cents, 12 cents each.

57

$25.20: This is the smallest amount that can be divided without remainder by all of 2, 3, 4, 5, 6, 7, 8, 9 and 10 (it's the least common multiple).

58

Across	Down
1. 108	**1.** 125
4. 754	**2.** 836
6. 30,668	**3.** 1,684
7. 516	**4.** 789
9. 923	**5.** 473
11. 445	**8.** 17,677
13. 1,696	**10.** 25,345
14. 7,030	**11.** 461
15. 120	**12.** 570
17. 273	**16.** 2,842
19. 856	**17.** 253
21. 46,422	**18.** 345
22. 375	**19.** 824
23. 400	**20.** 640

59

Across	Down
1. 144	**1.** 183
4. 375	**2.** 480
6. 85,609	**3.** 1,616
7. 360	**4.** 396
9. 688	**5.** 508
11. 862	**8.** 60,500
13. 1,525	**10.** 88,660
14. 1,266	**11.** 859
15. 980	**12.** 210
17. 709	**16.** 8,197
19. 807	**17.** 729
21. 60,995	**18.** 960
22. 900	**19.** 851
23. 168	**20.** 788

60

Across

1. 121
4. 617
6. 61,500
7. 259
9. 585
11. 407
13. 8,432
14. 2,496
15. 311
17. 965
19. 802
21. 10,000
22. 492
23. 776

Down

1. 142
2. 169
3. 4,550
4. 605
5. 5,725
8. 55,446
10. 87,990
11. 423
12. 721
16. 1,809
17. 934
18. 512
19. 807
20. 256

61

Across

1. 2,035
4. 1,336
6. 601
7. 1,824
10. 2,855
12. 325
14. 99,752
16. 2,122
18. 297
20. 2,866
23. 23,610
26. 243
27. 3,214
28. 2,606
31. 381
32. 8,790
33. 4,225

Down

1. 271
2. 362
3. 1,675
4. 11,212
5. 695
8. 869
9. 435
11. 552
13. 222
15. 776
17. 126
19. 724
21. 812
22. 65,430
24. 332
25. 150
26. 2,110
27. 338
29. 682
30. 615

62

Across

1. 8,135
4. 1,957
6. 474
7. 2,191
10. 5,066
12. 730
14. 18,563
16. 8,900
18. 112
20. 4,723
23. 16,920
26. 313
27. 6,034
28. 3,443
31. 271
32. 5,810
33. 1,515

Down

1. 862
2. 329
3. 4,420
4. 14,598
5. 776
8. 168
9. 176
11. 620
13. 331
15. 542
17. 999
19. 211
21. 750
22. 34,420
24. 633
25. 284
26. 3,018
27. 655
29. 405
30. 355

63

Across

1. 1,941
4. 1,961
6. 20,000
7. 12:32
9. 948
10. 80
11. 2,008
13. 1,547
14. 10
15. 699
16. 1,901
18. 48,240
20. 2,010
21. 1,966

Down

1. 1,971
2. 1,212
3. 50
4. 100,881
5. 1,600
8. 29,000
9. 99,999
10. 86,400
12. 826,140
14. 1,912
16. 1,801
17. 1,666
19. 24

Mystery Number = **31**

64

Across

1. 12
5. 13
6. 07:50
7. 6,824
8. 756
10. 9/11
12. 321
14. 1,070,110
17. 912
18. 113
19. 3,173,200
21. 926
23. 711
25. 196
27. 2,012
28. 1,918
29. 10
30. 48

Down

2. 2,001
3. 007
4. 666
5. 1,412
9. 500
11.11,236
12. 30107
13. 143
15. 747
16. 102
17. 999
20. 399
22. 20/20
24. 1,984
25. 121
26. 612

Mystery Number = **43**

65

Across

1. 1,225
3. 262,829
7. 1,008,569
8. 97,639
9. 2,723,230
13. 6,318,055
15. 38,766
16. 3,594,825
17. 655,565
18. 8,000

Down

1. 121,121
2. 58,873
4. 63,990
5. 8,836,210
6. 9,999
10. 2,157,755
11. 343
12. 151,590
13. 66,336
14. 88,448
15. 3,636

66

Across

1. 3,375
3. 168,448
7. 5,795,750
8. 26,450
9. 2,195,375
13. 2,972,067
15. 56,924
16. 4,543,227
17. 260,307
18. 2,197

Down

1. 305,125
2. 55,575
4. 61,025
5. 4,204,200
6. 8,910
10. 9,999,950
11. 729
12. 777,777
13. 24,480
14. 22,322
15. 5,572

67

15	4	20	16	10
2	19	18	23	3
21	25	1	7	11
5	9	14	13	24
22	8	12	6	17

68

14	3	11	13	24
19	23	7	10	6
20	15	1	17	12
4	22	25	9	5
8	2	21	16	18

69

16	7	10	1
2	9	8	15
3	12	5	14
13	6	11	4

70

12	7	9	6
13	2	16	3
8	11	5	10
1	14	4	15

71

5	3	7	21	29	23	3	4	5
12	8	10	27	25	28	2	8	6
11	6	9	26	22	24	7	4	9
8	14	12	21	29	23	3	10	5
10	7	13	2	5	14	7	12	6
7	5	3	4	7	9	11	13	9
2	9	6	8	6	10	15	8	4
10	4	8	3	2	13	9	12	5
7	3	5	1	5	16	14	11	7

72

46	1	2	3	42	41	40
45	31	16	33	30	15	5
44	32	24	23	28	18	6
7	14	29	25	21	36	43
11	13	22	27	26	37	39
12	35	34	17	20	19	38
10	49	48	47	8	9	4

73

17	6	24	4	14
16	9	7	22	11
12	19	1	13	20
2	10	25	23	5
18	21	8	3	15

74

1	15	14	4
12	6	7	9
8	10	11	5
13	3	2	16

75

13	8	12	1
2	11	7	14
3	10	6	15
16	5	9	4

76

7	25	24	4	5
8	12	17	10	18
6	11	13	15	20
23	16	9	14	3
21	1	2	22	19

77

0	11	10	-3
5	2	3	8
1	6	7	4
12	-1	-2	9

78

47	58	69	80	1	12	23	34	45
57	68	79	9	11	22	33	44	46
67	78	8	10	21	32	43	54	56
77	7	18	20	31	42	53	55	66
6	17	19	30	41	52	63	65	76
16	27	29	40	51	62	64	75	5
26	28	39	50	61	72	74	4	15
36	38	49	60	71	73	3	14	25
37	48	59	70	81	2	13	24	35

79

$4\frac{1}{2}$	8	$2\frac{1}{2}$
3	5	7
$7\frac{1}{2}$	2	$5\frac{1}{2}$

80

8	-7	-6	5
-4	3	2	-1
1	-2	-3	4
-5	6	7	-8

81

31	2	34	3	5	36
12	26	10	9	29	25
13	17	21	22	20	18
24	23	15	16	14	19
30	8	27	28	11	7
1	35	4	33	32	6

82
♣ = 2, ♦ = 5, ♥ = 9

83
11: (▲ = 4, ■ = 6, ● = 7)

84
7: (✔ = 1, ✖ = 3, ✪ = 8)

85
13: (❑ **= 3,** ○ = 4, ✢ = 6, ▽ = 7)

86
12: (♥ = 5, ♦ = 4, ♣ = 3, ♠ = 1)

87
15: (Σ = 3, Δ **= 5,** Φ = 7)

88
20: (A = 6, E = 4, I = 3, O = 8, U = 2)

89
17: (▼ = 1, ● = 3, ♦ = 5, ■ = 7, ▲ = 9)

90
It is possible, but only by rotating the 6 and converting it into 9. Whenever the sum of the digits of a number are divisible by 9 exactly, then that number is also divisible by 9 exactly. As the above digits total 18, which is divisible by 9 exactly, then any combination of the three digits will also be exactly divisible by 9.

91
23 1213 11121113
Each number in each line describes the number before it. Thus 12 is described as 1112 (1 x 1, 1 x 2) and 1112 is described as 3112 (3 x 1, 1 x 2).

92
3: Each number represents the amount of numbers that are immediately adjacent to it either horizontally, vertically or diagonally.

93
486 spots: Since 27 is one third of 81, each fish has the equivalent of 27 spots after two thirds of the male fish have been removed. The answer, therefore, is 18 x 27 = 486.

94
84 and **42**, respectively.
Multiply the numbers in the first and third columns. The number in the middle column is the product of these two numbers reversed. So 8 x 6 = 48 (reversed = 84), and 72 ÷ 3 = 24 (reversed = 42).

95
204: Each number in the block of nine numbers at the bottom right is the sum of the number directly above it, directly to the left of it and diagonally upwards to the left of it.

96
60

97
By trial and error, **73 people,** who each paid $39.

98
Because the different weights are not the correct distance from the apex to balance:
Left hand side
2 lengths x 6kg = 12.
Right hand side
4 lengths x 4kg = 16.
To balance, the 4kg weight must be three lengths from the apex.

99
5: (121) = square of 11 and (169) = square of 13.

100
Joan is 16 years old, Barbara is 60, Matilda is 80.

101
23 sacks: 29 apples in each sack.

102
47 minutes approximately (46.76 actual).
In one hour:
Man A can mow 0.5 of a field
Man B can mow 0.333 of a field
Man C can mow 0.25 of a field
Man D can mow 0.2 of a field
Therefore, working together for one hour they can mow 1.283 fields.
So to mow one field takes 60 minutes ÷ 1.283 = 46.76 minutes.

103
D: reading across, the numbers progress -2, +1, -2. Reading down, the numbers progress +2, -1, +2.

104
B: Reading across, the numbers progress +2, -4. Reading down, the numbers progress +3, -4.

105
A: Reading across, the numbers progress +2, +3, +2. Reading down, the numbers progress +4, +2, +4.

106
D: Reading across ,the numbers progress +1, +3, +1, +3. Reading down, the numbers progress +3, +1, +3, +1.

107
A: So that each line across and down contains the numbers 1–5 once each only.

108
C: Looking at the lines across and down, the third and fourth numbers are the sum of the previous two numbers.

109
B: Looking at lines across and down, the second three digits are all three times the value of the first three digits.

110
A: Reading across, the numbers progress -1, -2, -3, -4. Reading down, the numbers progress +1, +2, +3, +4.

111
B: The numbers across progress +2. +3, +4, +5 in turn. Reading down, the numbers in the first column progress +8, +12, +16; in the second column they progress +9, +13, +17; in the third column they progress +10, +14, +18; and in the fourth column they progress +11, +15, +19.

112
D: Starting at the bottom left-hand corner square and working up the first column, then back down the second column, and so on, the number sequence 75291 repeats.

113
It makes no difference. An order has a total of 31.6% whatever the choice.

114
27

115
The man is 64 years old and has 56 grandsons.

116
$2

117
.955 (63 saves divided by 66 shots)

118
120/1024

119
2,519

120
38,760

121
48

122
171

123

2	+	5	x	3	–	6	=	15
x	12	–	15	x	18	+		
4	x	1	+	6	–	3	=	7
+	21	x	24	–	27	x		
12	x	4	–	13	+	5	=	40
–	30	+	33	+	36	–		
2	+	12	–	4	x	14	=	140
=		=		=		=		
18		28		9		31		

124

2	+	4	x	6	–	5	=	31
–	10	x	18	+	30	–		
1	x	3	–	5	+	14	=	12
+	20	+	36	x	50	+		
9	x	7	–	21	+	10	=	52
x	30	–	48	–	70	x		
6	+	8	x	12	–	27	=	141
=		=		=		=		
60		11		219		27		

125

5	+	9	x	2	–	6	=	22
–		–		x		x		
4	x	2	+	20	–	5	=	23
+		x		+		–		
7	x	3	–	5	+	9	=	25
x		+		–		+		
3	x	9	–	16	+	10	=	21
=		=		=		=		
24		30		29		31		

126

5	+	23	–	21	x	2	=	14
–		–		+		+		
2	x	17	+	3	–	21	=	16
+		x		–		–		
3	x	3	+	20	–	18	=	11
x		+		x		x		
3	+	1	x	5	–	3	=	17
=		=		=		=		
18		19		20		15		

127

12	x	5	–	32	+	5	=	33
–		+		–		+		
4	+	3	x	9	–	5	=	58
+		–		x		–		
3	–	2	+	3	x	7	=	28
x		x		+		x		
4	x	11	–	9	+	7	=	42
=		=		=		=		
44		66		78		21		

128

23	–	14	+	6	x	5	=	75
+		–		+		x		
8	+	12	–	5	x	4	=	60
–		x		x		–		
17	x	6	+	8	–	14	=	96
x		+		–		+		
5	x	11	+	14	–	21	=	48
=		=		=		=		
70		23		74		27		

129

15	+	9	−	8	x	3	=	48
−		x		+		x		
7	−	4	x	6	+	14	=	32
+		+		−		+		
11	x	2	−	13	+	5	=	14
x		−		x		−		
1	x	12	−	10	+	16	=	18
=		=		=		=		
19		26		10		31		

130

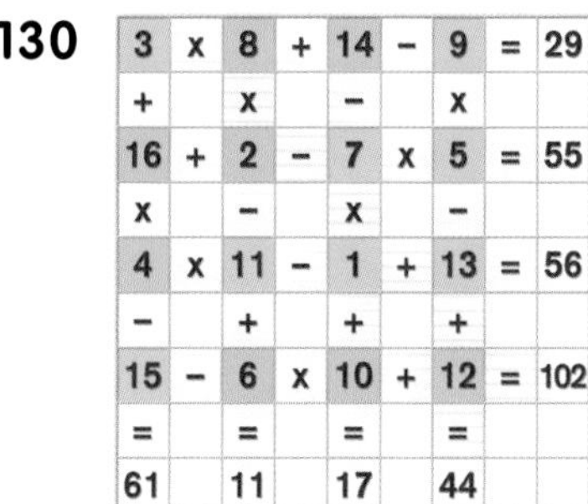

3	x	8	+	14	−	9	=	29
+		x		−		x		
16	+	2	−	7	x	5	=	55
x		−		x		−		
4	x	11	−	1	+	13	=	56
−		+		+		+		
15	−	6	x	10	+	12	=	102
=		=		=		=		
61		11		17		44		

131

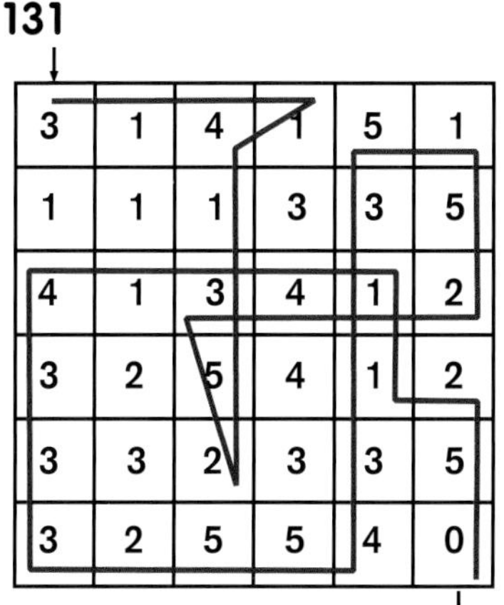

132

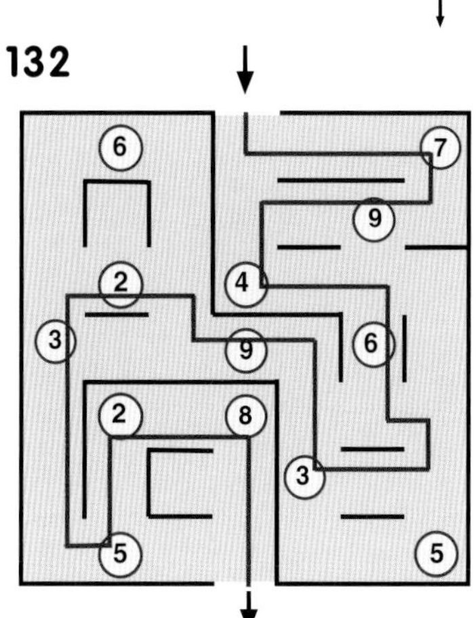

133

1

2	4	2	9	7	2	4	4	2
8	5	1	2	3	2	5	6	1
2	9	2	4	3	3	1	4	6
8	6	9	2	6	2	2	1	2
3	1	1	2	5	3	2	7	3
4	4	1	2	2	2	2	1	2
1	5	7	4	4	9	5	4	4
8	7	1	2	3	3	9	4	3
7	4	5	2	6	7	1	4	2

134

99 cents: $1 increased by 10% is 110 cents. A decrease of 10% of this total is a decrease of 11 cents. So 110 cents – 11 cents = 99 cents.

135

To find its worth after a number of years, multiply its cost by 0.9 for each year. As 0.9 x 0.9 x 0.9 x 0.9 x 0.9 x 0.9 = 0.53, about 53%, and 0.9 x 0.9 x 0.9 x 0.9 x 0.9 x 0.9 x 0.9 = 0.478, about 47%, the car must have been bought **7 years ago**.

136

8%: A profit of 20% means that for every dollar spent the shopkeeper makes $1.20. A reduction in price of 10% means he gets only $1.08 for every dollar he spent. That means 8 cents on the dollar, or 8%.

137

88%: Add up marks out of 100; he's earned 340 so far. If he attains 100 on the final paper that will give 440 over 5 papers, giving an average of 88%.

138

390: 25% + 64% = 89% who didn't vote for Twit, so 11% did. The majority is 64% – 11% = 53% (1,881). So the electorate is (100 ÷ 53) x 1,881 = 3,549. 11% of this is 390.

139

Imagine the other 26 cards go to a second player. If one player has all the hearts, the other has none. So the chances of getting all must be the same as getting none.

140

B W W W W W: There is no difference in the first 5 throws. So the difference in probability comes from the last throw. But W is twice as likely as B, so B W W W W W must be more probable than B W W W W B.

141

There are 15 minutes after the 10-past and before the 25-past buses, but 45 minutes after the 25-past bus and before the next 10-past bus. So you are **four times as likely** to catch the 10-past bus.

142

5 black socks and one white: The chances that the white sock turns up in the first 6, as opposed to being left in the half dozen in the drawer, is clearly 50/50.

143

Your friend: The odds are 3 to 1 in your friend's favour. Consider the first two tosses only. The results HH, HT, TH and TT are all equiprobable. You win if TT occurs in the first two tosses. In all the three other cases either he wins straight away with HT or, in the cases HH and TH, he wins eventually as an HT must occur before you have a chance to get a TT. So, only if you get TT in the first two tosses (with a probability of 25%) can you win at all.

144

You should swap. The chances of your choosing the one with the key in is **1/3**. What the jailer effectively does is to merge the other two boxes into one. So the chances of it being in the remaining box are 2/3, and you have a better chance of finding the key by swapping.

145

100%: A number is divisible (without remainder) by 9 if the sum of its digits is divisible by 9. So the number obtained by reversing the order of the digits in a number divisible by 9, is also divisible by 9. A number is divisible without remainder by 11 if the sum of the digits in the odd-numbered places differs from the sum of the digits in the even-numbered places by a multiple of 11. So reversing a number divisible by 11 gives another number divisible by 11. A number divisible by 9 and 11 is divisible by 99.

146

One-quarter or 25%: For each occasion 'DeeDum' in which Tweedledum (call him Dum) goes to town with Tweedledee (call him by Dee) there need to be two occasions when Tweedledee goes alone. For each occasion when Tweedledum goes to town with Tweedledee, there needs to be one when Tweedledum goes alone. So we therefore have the distribution:

DeeDum   Dee   Dee   Dum.

This means that for every occasion when Dee and Dum go together, there are two occasions when Dee goes alone, and one when Dum goes alone. From this we see that the chances that they both go are a quarter.

147

The chances of not seeing a shooting star in the hour are 100% – 36% = 64%. If the chances of not seeing a shooting star in any given half hour is Y, then the chances of not seeing a shooting star in two successive half hours are Y x Y. Clearly Y squared = 64/100, so Y = 8/10, which is 80/100 = 80%.

Therefore, the chances of seeing at least one star in half an hour are **20%**.

148

A	B	E	6	D	7	4	0	2	1	5	9	F	C	3	8
C	2	8	5	B	9	1	F	3	0	7	4	D	A	E	6
F	1	0	9	5	C	6	3	8	E	D	A	B	7	2	4
3	7	D	4	8	E	A	2	B	F	C	6	1	9	5	0
8	E	F	2	0	1	C	5	D	B	9	7	A	6	4	3
1	9	6	A	3	D	2	8	E	4	0	5	C	F	B	7
0	5	7	C	4	B	E	6	F	A	2	3	8	1	9	D
B	D	4	3	F	A	7	9	C	6	1	8	2	E	0	5
5	A	C	7	1	4	9	B	0	2	E	D	6	3	8	F
D	F	1	E	7	2	8	C	4	3	6	B	0	5	A	9
6	0	9	8	E	5	3	D	7	C	A	F	4	2	1	B
2	4	3	B	6	F	0	A	5	9	8	1	7	D	C	E
9	8	2	1	A	3	5	4	6	D	F	0	E	B	7	C
E	6	A	F	2	8	B	7	9	5	4	C	3	0	D	1
7	C	B	D	9	0	F	1	A	8	3	E	5	4	6	2
4	3	5	0	C	6	D	E	1	7	B	2	9	8	F	A

149

3	A	7	B	5	8	9	6	4	0	2	1	E	D	F	C
E	F	4	2	B	D	0	7	9	C	6	A	1	3	8	5
9	C	D	8	3	4	1	2	5	E	F	7	A	0	B	6
0	6	1	5	E	F	A	C	8	3	B	D	9	2	4	7
2	4	3	9	6	A	5	E	C	D	7	F	B	1	0	8
7	8	6	1	4	C	D	F	2	B	9	0	5	A	E	3
D	0	A	F	8	7	B	1	E	5	3	6	2	4	C	9
5	E	B	C	0	9	2	3	A	8	1	4	6	F	7	D
F	1	E	7	A	2	C	5	B	6	4	3	D	8	9	0
8	D	9	0	7	E	6	4	1	F	C	2	3	B	5	A
6	3	5	A	9	B	F	0	D	7	8	E	4	C	1	2
B	2	C	4	D	1	3	8	0	A	5	9	F	7	6	E
C	5	0	6	1	3	7	A	F	9	D	B	8	E	2	4
4	7	F	E	2	6	8	9	3	1	A	C	0	5	D	B
A	9	8	D	F	0	4	B	7	2	E	5	C	6	3	1
1	B	2	3	C	5	E	D	6	4	0	8	7	9	A	F

150

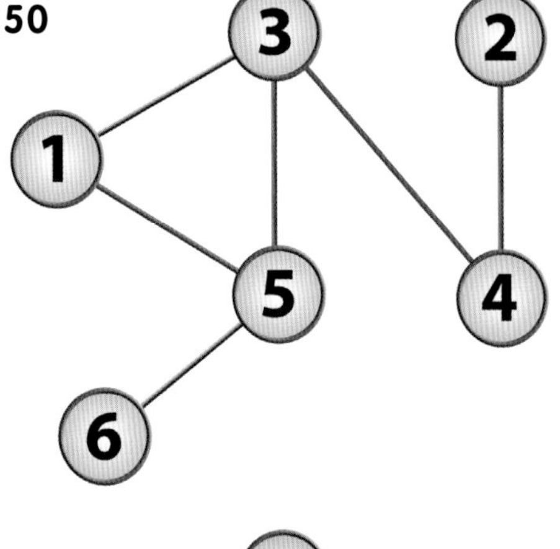

151

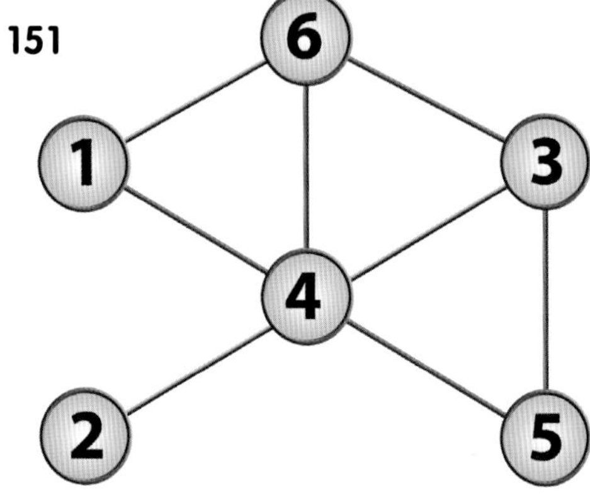

152

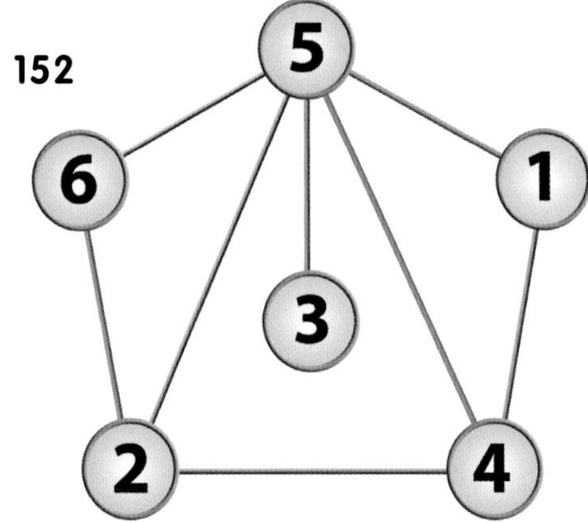

153

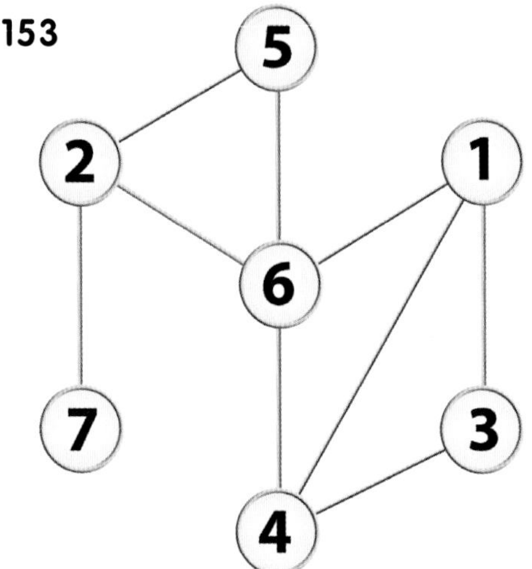

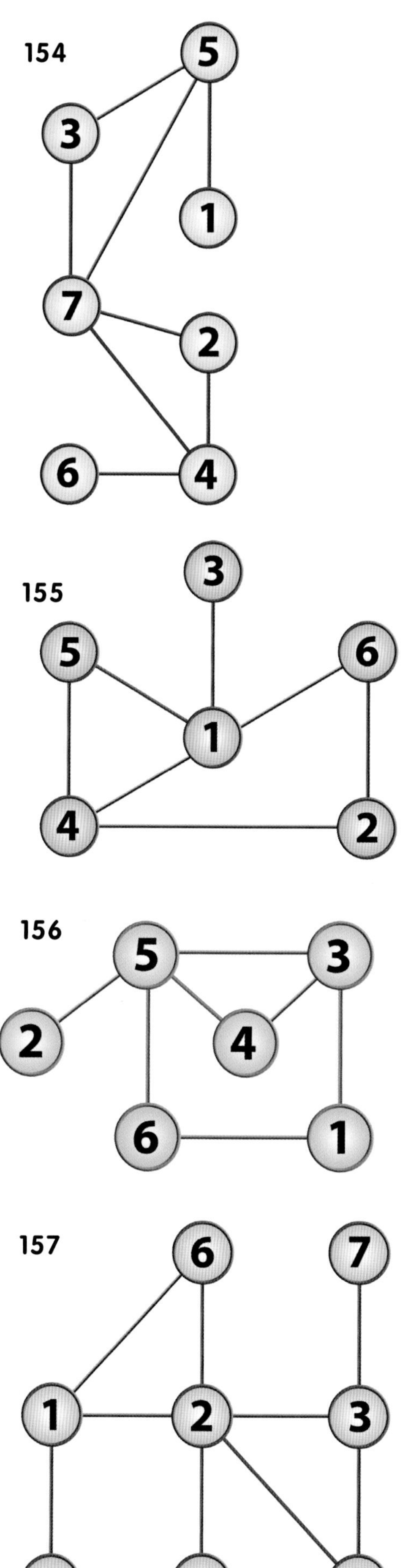
154
155
156
157

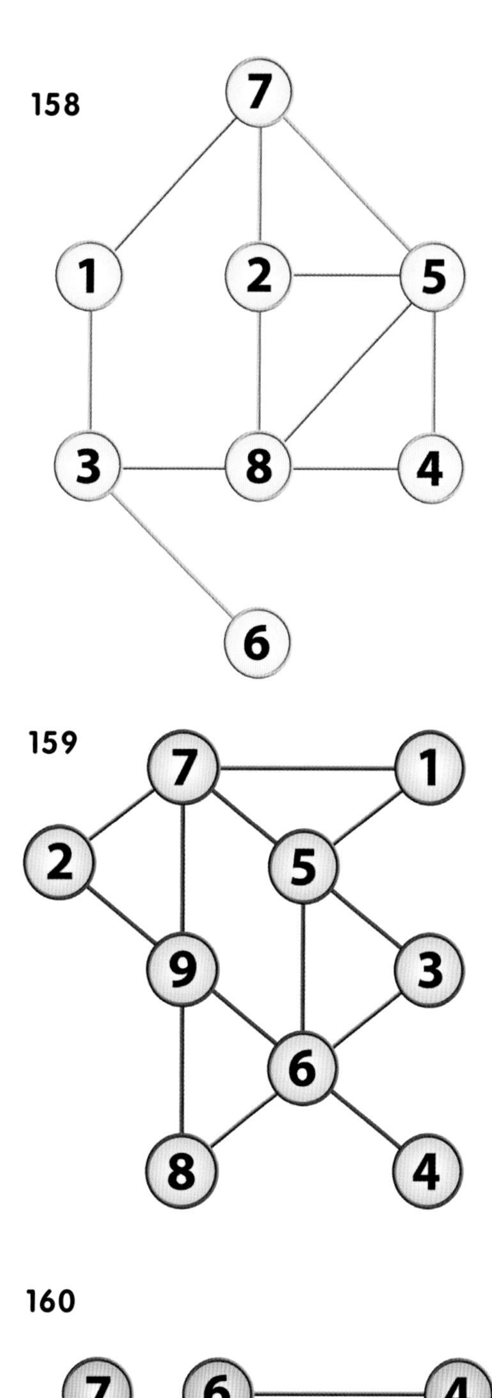
158
159

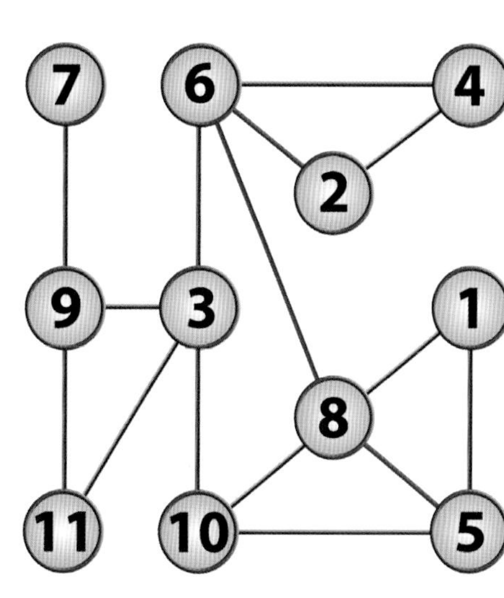
160

161

4	1	9	8	3	6	7	2	5				1	6	5	4	2	8	9	3	7
3	7	8	5	2	4	1	9	6				2	9	8	3	7	5	6	4	1
6	5	2	1	9	7	3	8	4				4	7	3	6	9	1	5	8	2
9	8	6	3	4	1	2	5	7				6	4	7	5	1	2	8	9	3
5	3	4	7	8	2	6	1	9				8	3	1	9	6	7	4	2	5
7	2	1	6	5	9	4	3	8				9	5	2	8	3	4	7	1	6
8	6	7	9	1	3	5	4	2	3	1	6	7	8	9	1	5	3	2	6	4
1	4	5	2	7	8	9	6	3	8	2	7	5	1	4	2	8	6	3	7	9
2	9	3	4	6	5	8	7	1	4	9	5	3	2	6	7	4	9	1	5	8
						1	9	6	7	3	2	4	5	8						
						7	5	8	9	4	1	2	6	3						
						3	2	4	5	6	8	1	9	7						
5	3	4	6	9	8	2	1	7	6	8	3	9	4	5	6	7	1	2	8	3
2	9	6	3	1	7	4	8	5	2	7	9	6	3	1	8	9	2	5	7	4
1	8	7	5	2	4	6	3	9	1	5	4	8	7	2	3	5	4	1	6	9
7	1	3	2	8	5	9	6	4				1	2	3	7	8	9	6	4	5
6	5	2	4	3	9	1	7	8				5	6	8	1	4	3	9	2	7
9	4	8	1	7	6	5	2	3				4	9	7	5	2	6	3	1	8
3	6	9	7	4	1	8	5	2				7	1	6	4	3	5	8	9	2
8	2	1	9	5	3	7	4	6				3	8	9	2	1	7	4	5	6
4	7	5	8	6	2	3	9	1				2	5	4	9	6	8	7	3	1

162

6	1	9	8	2	4	5	7	3				3	5	9	7	8	4	1	2	6
4	3	5	6	7	1	2	9	8				4	7	6	2	1	9	5	8	3
2	8	7	5	9	3	6	1	4				1	8	2	3	6	5	7	4	9
3	4	1	9	8	5	7	6	2				6	1	4	8	2	3	9	7	5
8	5	2	7	1	6	3	4	9				9	2	8	1	5	7	6	3	4
9	7	6	4	3	2	8	5	1				7	3	5	9	4	6	2	1	8
1	6	8	3	5	9	4	2	7	5	3	6	8	9	1	5	3	2	4	6	7
5	2	3	1	4	7	9	8	6	1	2	7	5	4	3	6	7	1	8	9	2
7	9	4	2	6	8	1	3	5	9	8	4	2	6	7	4	9	8	3	5	1
						3	9	4	7	5	8	1	2	6						
						7	1	8	4	6	2	9	3	5						
						6	5	2	3	1	9	4	7	8						
2	1	3	4	7	5	8	6	9	2	7	1	3	5	4	6	1	7	2	8	9
5	9	4	8	6	1	2	7	3	8	4	5	6	1	9	8	2	5	7	3	4
6	8	7	2	9	3	5	4	1	6	9	3	7	8	2	9	4	3	1	6	5
7	4	5	1	8	2	9	3	6				5	7	8	4	6	2	3	9	1
8	3	6	9	4	7	1	2	5				2	9	6	3	8	1	4	5	7
9	2	1	3	5	6	7	8	4				1	4	3	5	7	9	6	2	8
4	5	8	6	2	9	3	1	7				8	3	7	1	9	6	5	4	2
3	6	9	7	1	8	4	5	2				9	6	1	2	5	4	8	7	3
1	7	2	5	3	4	6	9	8				4	2	5	7	3	8	9	1	6

163

6	8	5	4	3	7	9	2	1				5	9	4	6	2	8	1	3	7
4	1	2	9	5	6	3	7	8				2	8	1	5	7	3	9	4	6
9	7	3	1	2	8	6	4	5				6	7	3	4	1	9	5	2	8
8	2	6	7	1	4	5	9	3				7	3	8	9	5	1	2	6	4
7	9	1	5	8	3	4	6	2				1	4	5	3	6	2	7	8	9
3	5	4	2	6	9	1	8	7				9	6	2	8	4	7	3	5	1
1	4	9	8	7	5	2	3	6	4	5	7	8	1	9	2	3	6	4	7	5
2	3	8	6	4	1	7	5	9	3	8	1	4	2	6	7	9	5	8	1	3
5	6	7	3	9	2	8	1	4	6	2	9	3	5	7	1	8	4	6	9	2
						3	2	5	9	1	8	6	7	4						
						4	9	7	2	6	5	1	3	8						
						1	6	8	7	4	3	2	9	5						
4	2	3	5	9	7	6	8	1	5	9	2	7	4	3	5	6	8	1	9	2
8	5	7	2	1	6	9	4	3	1	7	6	5	8	2	1	9	7	6	4	3
9	1	6	4	3	8	5	7	2	8	3	4	9	6	1	3	4	2	8	5	7
2	7	9	8	4	3	1	6	5				8	1	5	4	2	6	7	3	9
5	8	4	6	2	1	7	3	9				4	9	7	8	3	5	2	6	1
3	6	1	7	5	9	8	2	4				3	2	6	7	1	9	4	8	5
1	4	8	9	7	2	3	5	6				2	7	9	6	8	3	5	1	4
7	9	5	3	6	4	2	1	8				6	5	4	9	7	1	3	2	8
6	3	2	1	8	5	4	9	7				1	3	8	2	5	4	9	7	6

164

	14\		17\	18\	
\9	9	21\8	5	3	
\24	5	7	4	8	
	\23	9	2	7	5
	\11	5	6	\2	2

165

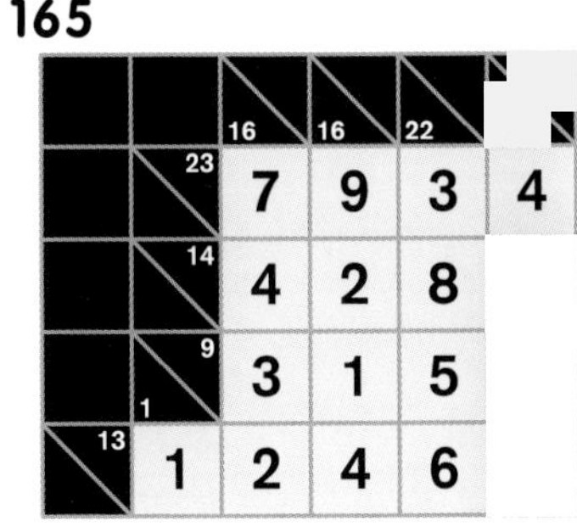

166

167

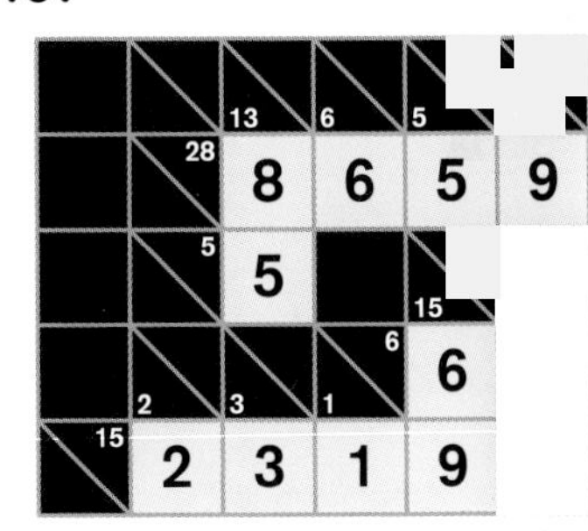

168

	24\	9\	18\	7\	20\
\35	6	9	8	7	5
\9	9	\1	1		8
\2	2	2\4	4	1\	1
\21	7	2	5	1	6

169

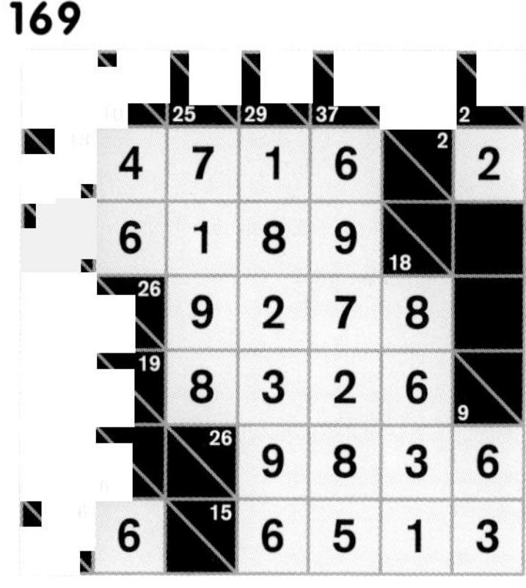

170

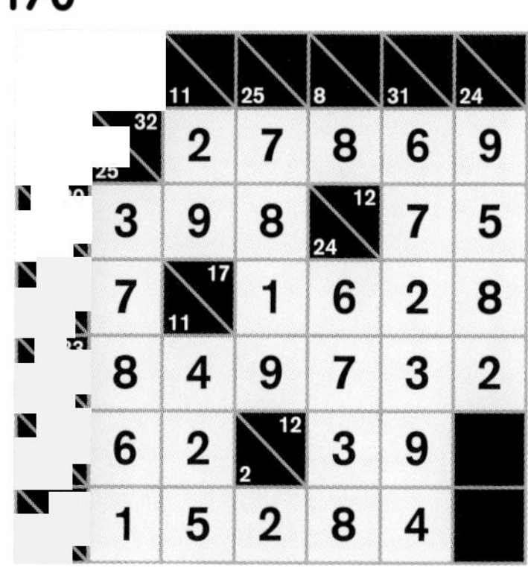

171

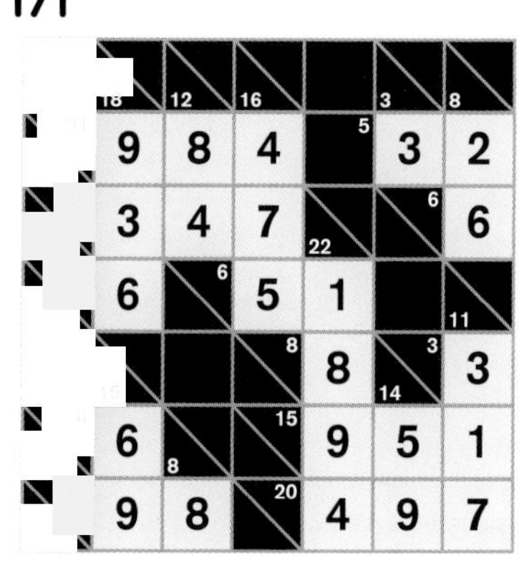

172

2		2	1	9	
3		1	2	3	7
1	2	3	5	7	6
6	3	9	7	2	1
4	9	6	3		3
	6	4	8		5

173

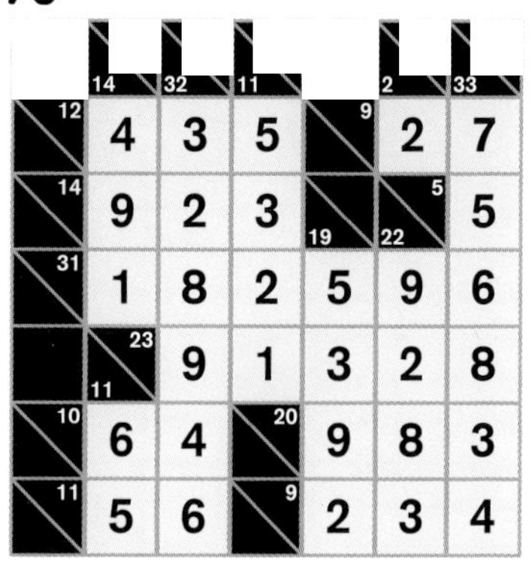

174

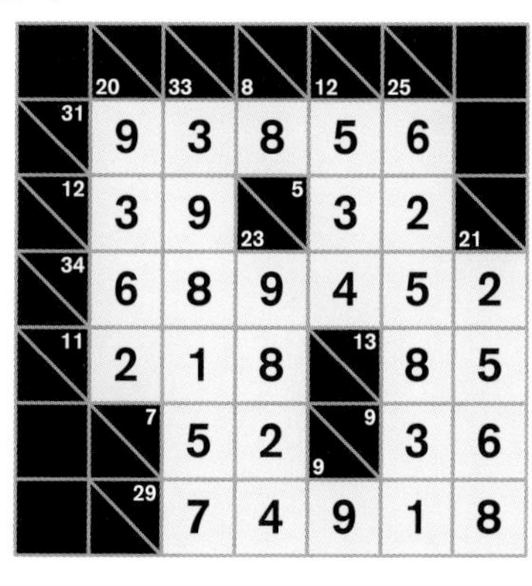

175

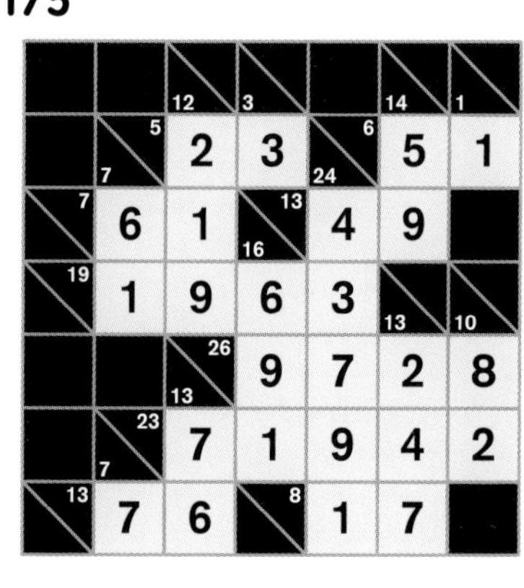

176

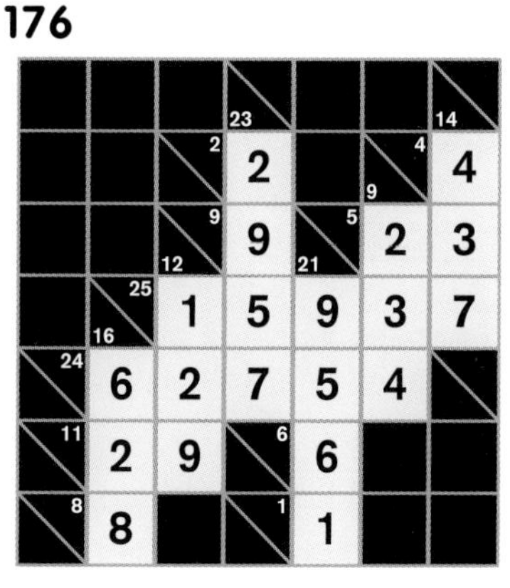

177

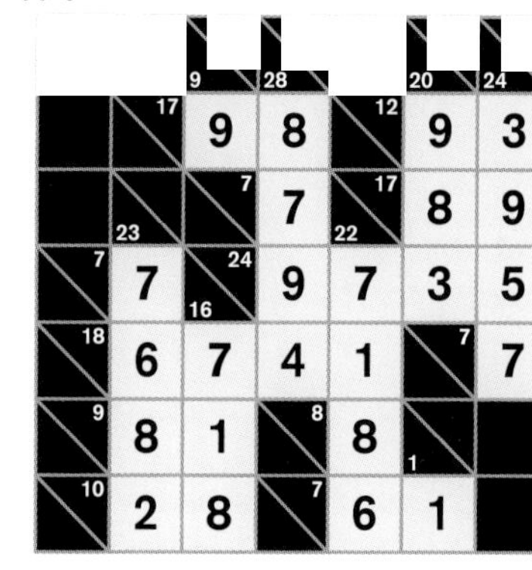

178

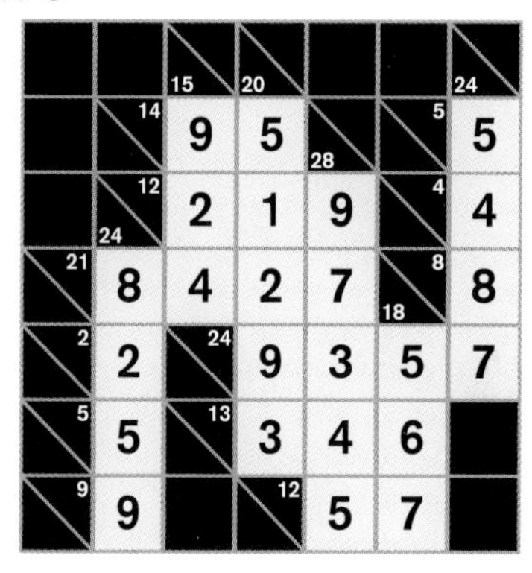

179

9	4		4	5	
8	5	1	7	4	
6	3	8	1	7	9
3	6	2	5	1	8
	9	5	8	2	3
	1	9		3	5

180

6	8	9	2		6
2		5	3	8	2
8	4	1	6	7	9
5	6	4	9		8
9	3	6	8		7
3		2	1	8	4

181

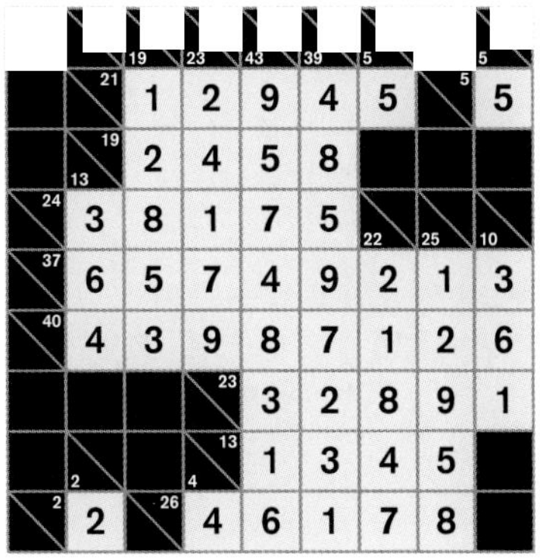

	1	2	9	4	5		5
	2	4	5	8			
3	8	1	7	5			
6	5	7	4	9	2	1	3
4	3	9	8	7	1	2	6
			3	2	8	9	1
			1	3	4	5	
2		4	6	1	7	8	

182

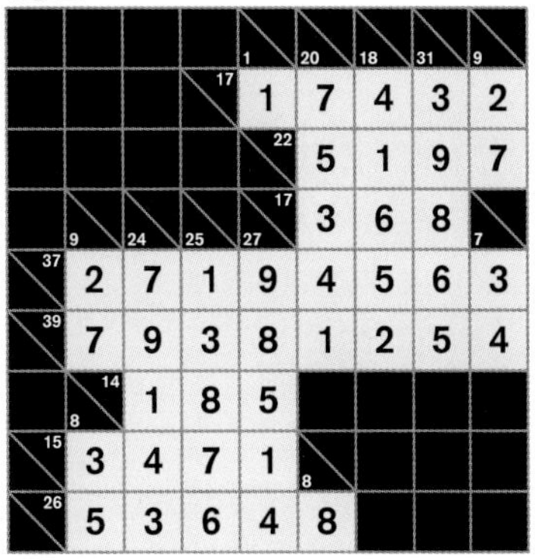

			1	7	4	3	2
				5	1	9	7
				3	6	8	
2	7	1	9	4	5	6	3
7	9	3	8	1	2	5	4
	1	8	5				
3	4	7	1				
5	3	6	4	8			

183

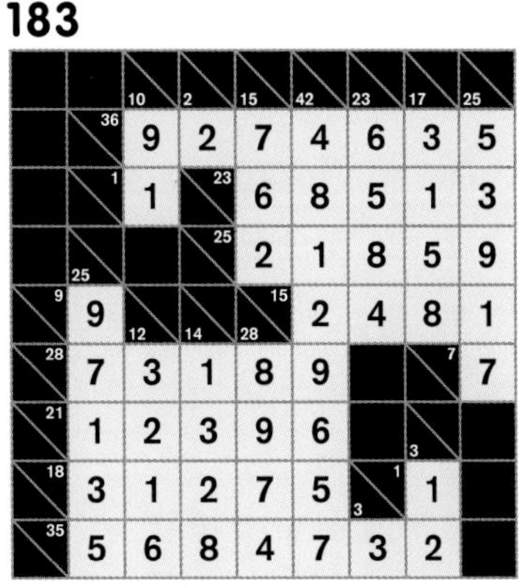

184

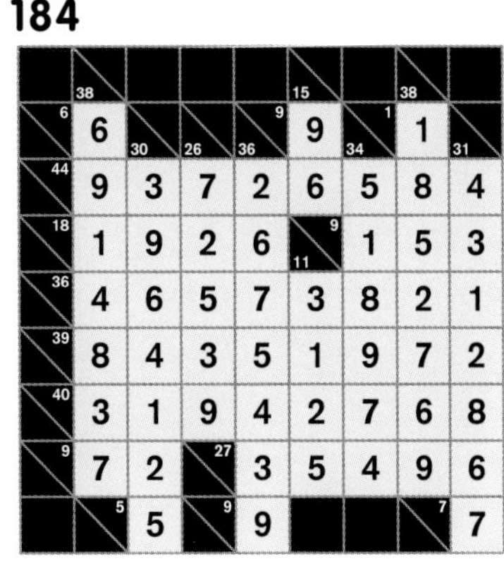

185

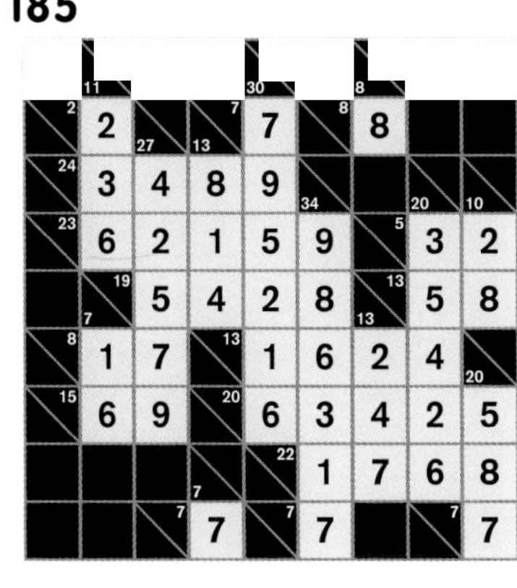

186

	1	4			1	2	
4	6	5	3		5	7	
3	5		6	4	3	8	7
			7	8	2		2
8		4	5	1			
6	2	9	1	3		4	1
	8	6		2	1	7	5
	1	8			8	2	

187

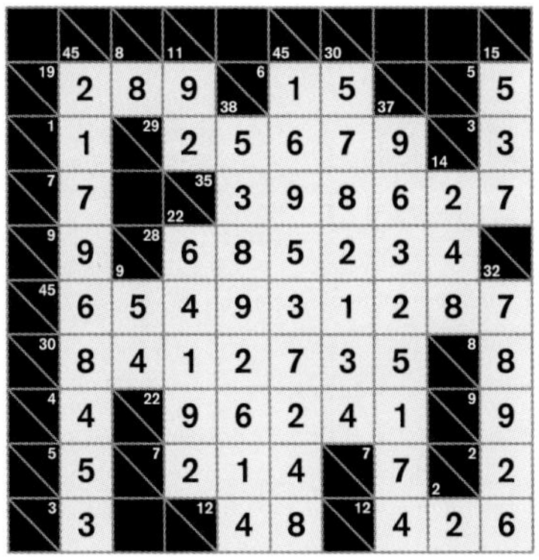

2	8	9		1	5			5
1		2	5	6	7	9		3
7			3	9	8	6	2	7
9		6	8	5	2	3	4	
6	5	4	9	3	1	2	8	7
8	4	1	2	7	3	5		8
4		9	6	2	4	1		9
5		2	1	4		7		2
3			4	8		4	2	6

188

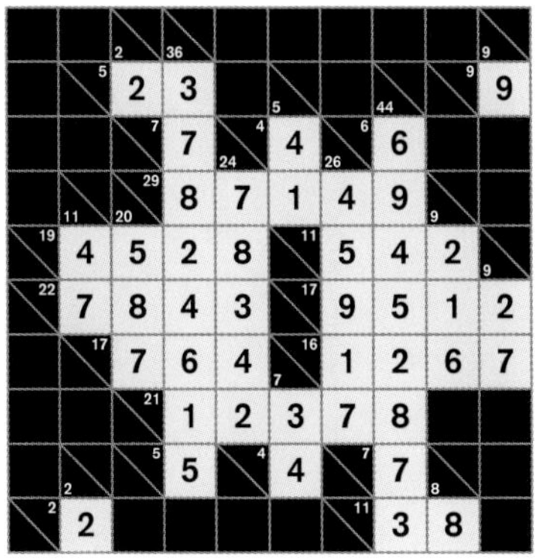

	2	3						9
		7		4		6		
		8	7	1	4	9		
4	5	2	8		5	4	2	
7	8	4	3		9	5	1	2
	7	6	4		1	2	6	7
		1	2	3	7	8		
		5		4		7		
2						3	8	

189

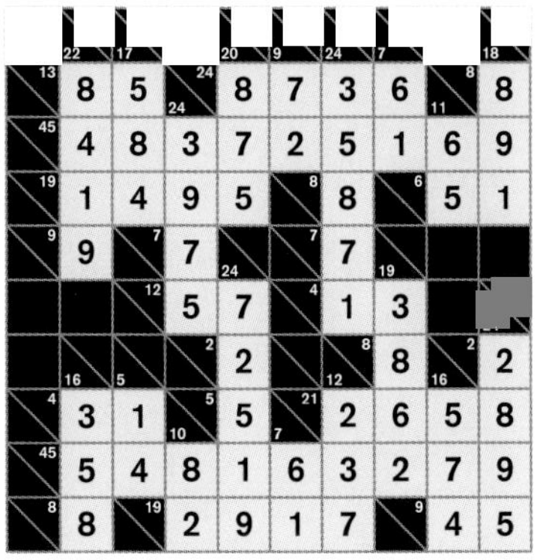

8	5		8	7	3	6		8
4	8	3	7	2	5	1	6	9
1	4	9	5		8		5	1
9		7			7			
		5	7		1	3		
			2			8		2
3	1		5		2	6	5	8
5	4	8	1	6	3	2	7	9
8		2	9	1	7		4	5

190

1	2	3		5	7		7	5
8		1	6	4	9		8	
6			7	2	8	3	9	
7	5		8	7	4	5	2	6
9	2	6	4	1	3	7	5	8
4	7	5	1	3	6		6	1
	9	7	2	6	5			7
	1		3	8	1	5		9
4	6		5	9		7	2	3

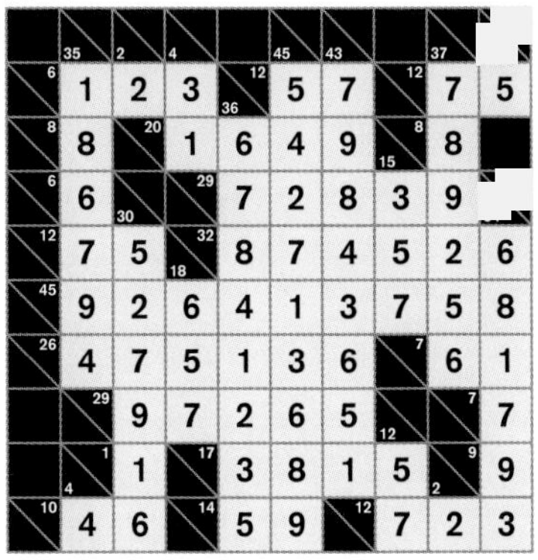

191

4	x	6	−	5	+	11	=	30
−	15	−	27	x	39	−		
3	+	2	x	14	−	9	=	61
+	30	x	42	+	56	x		
8	x	17	+	9	−	24	=	121
x	45	+	57	−	69	+		
9	+	11	x	20	−	16	=	384
=		=		=		=		
81		79		59		64		

192

9	x	4	−	14	+	8	=	30
−	28	+	36	−	45	−		
8	−	7	x	11	+	12	=	23
x	54	x	63	+	72	+		
21	−	17	x	28	+	21	=	133
+	81	−	90	x	99	x		
19	−	24	+	21	x	29	=	464
=		=		=		=		
40		163		651		493		

193

7	x	5	+	3	–	12	=	26
–		x		–		x		
4	+	6	x	3	–	2	=	28
x		–		+		+		
8	–	9	+	10	x	3	=	27
+		+		x		–		
5	x	4	–	3	+	4	=	21
=		=		=		=		
29		25		30		23		

194

18	+	21	–	30	x	5	=	45
–		+		–		x		
12	x	5	–	27	+	9	=	42
x		–		x		–		
7	+	10	x	3	–	8	=	43
+		x		+		+		
4	x	3	+	41	–	4	=	49
=		=		=		=		
46		48		50		41		

195

23	6	19	2	15
4	12	25	8	16
10	18	1	14	22
11	24	7	20	3
17	5	13	21	9

17	5	10	20	13
16	23	14	8	4
11	7	1	25	21
2	24	18	9	12
19	6	22	3	15

196

C: Allocate a value of 2 to each red circle and a value of 1 to each blue circle. A Magic 15 is thus produced in which the number 1–9 are arranged so that each row, column and each diagonal line totals 15.

197

1	63	62	4	5	59	58	8
56	15	49	48	19	44	20	9
55	47	25	39	38	28	18	10
11	22	36	30	31	33	43	54
53	42	32	34	35	29	23	12
13	24	37	27	26	40	41	52
14	45	16	17	46	21	50	51
57	2	3	61	60	6	7	64

198

1	35	4	33	32	6
30	8	27	28	11	7
24	23	15	16	14	19
13	17	21	22	20	18
12	26	10	9	29	25
31	2	34	3	5	36

199

64	3	61	2	48	19	45	18
57	6	60	7	41	22	44	23
4	63	1	62	20	47	17	46
5	58	8	59	21	42	24	43
56	11	53	10	40	27	37	26
49	14	52	15	33	30	36	31
12	55	9	54	28	39	25	38
13	50	16	51	29	34	32	35

200

	8		8		1				1		4	
6	4	4	1	7	8	8		2	7	0	3	4
	1		2		1		3		1		2	
1	0	3	4	2	8		3	2	6	6	6	6
	8		6				3		1		4	
		5	2	3	6	9	3		7	6	8	0
	1				0		3				6	
7	0	2	9		2	2	3	2	3	8		
	1		8		0				2		1	
1	0	5	6	3	3		7	5	4	3	5	9
	1		3		0		0		9		6	
5	0	8	8	6		1	2	3	5	2	2	8
	0		9				8		6		5	

1

2

3

35 - 16 = 19

4

5

6

7

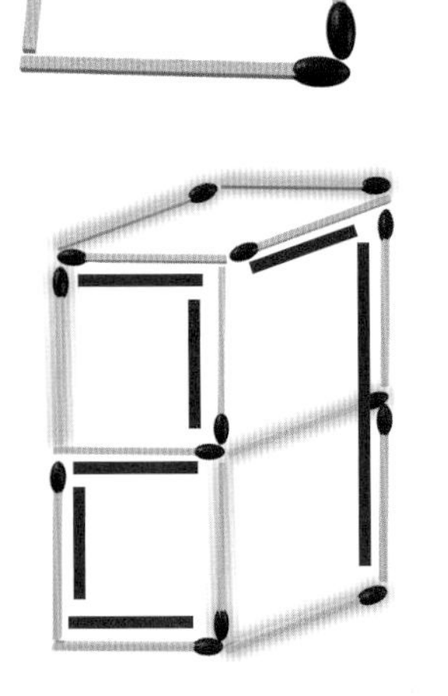

8

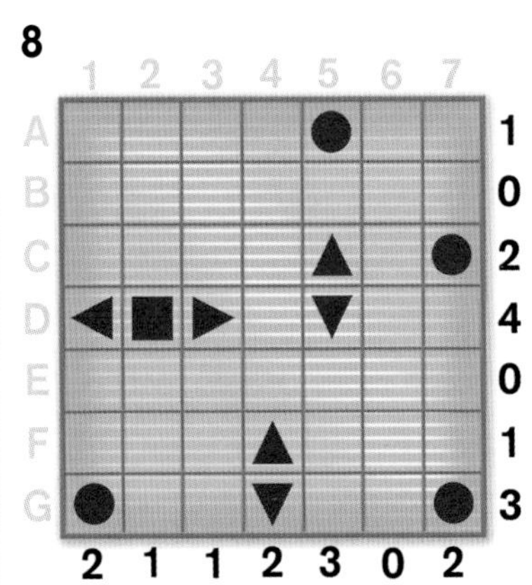

9

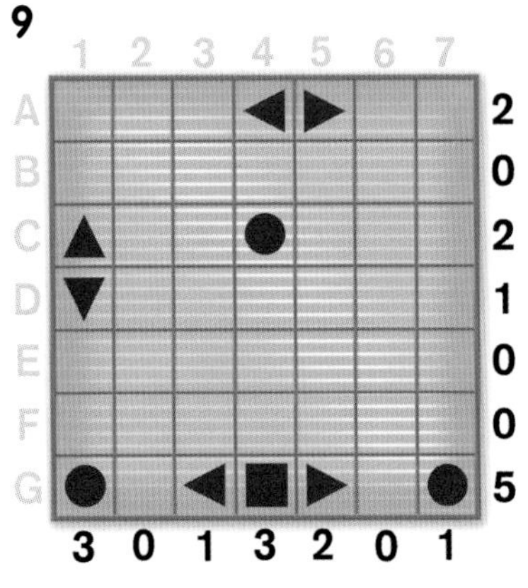

10

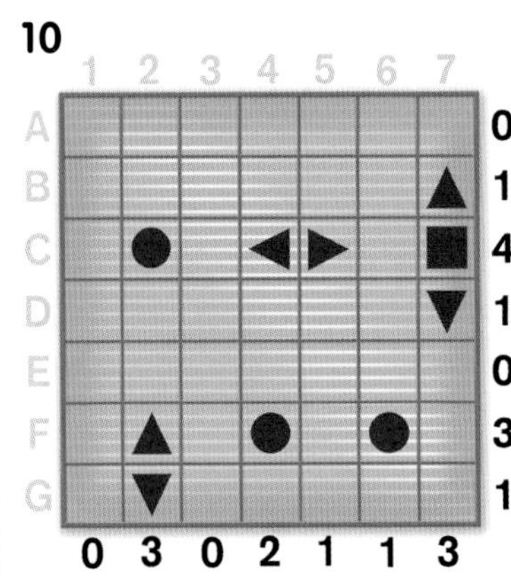

11

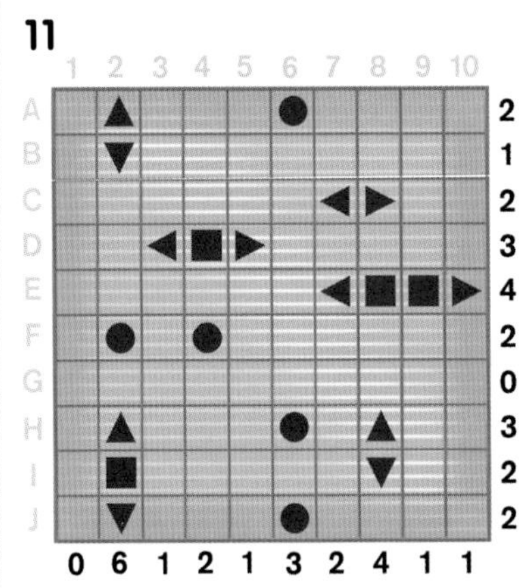

12

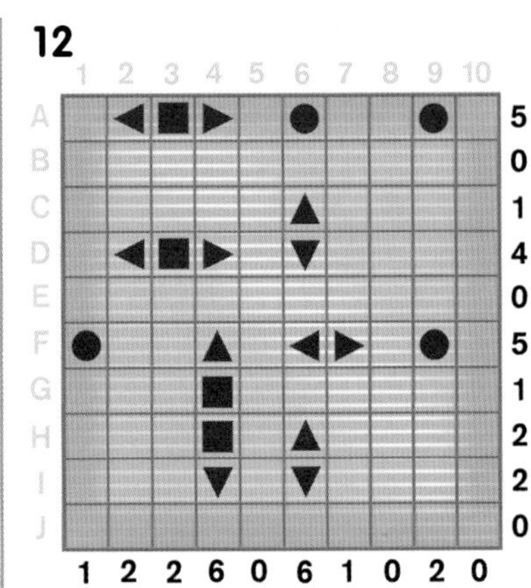

13

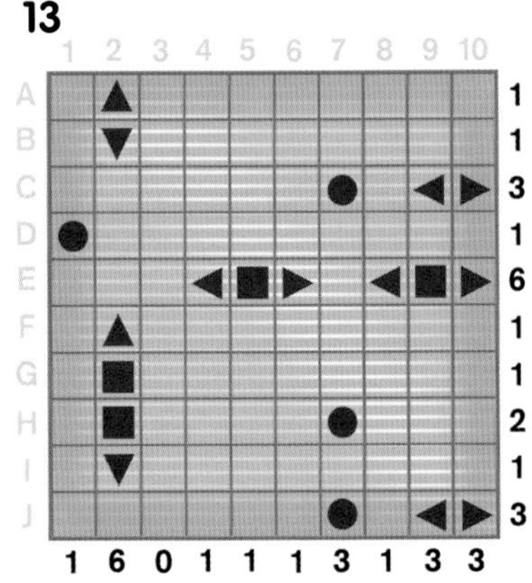

14

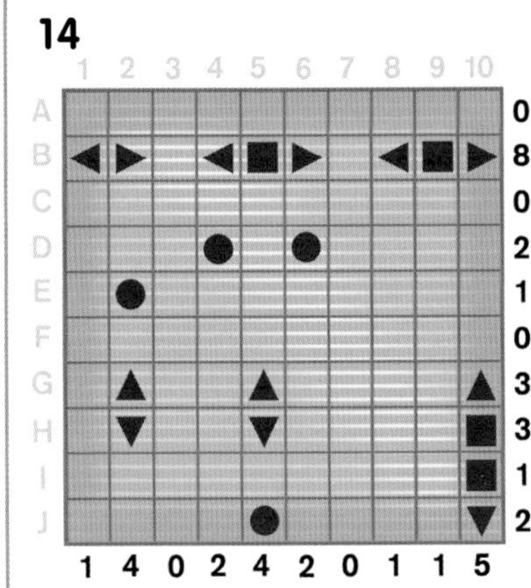

15

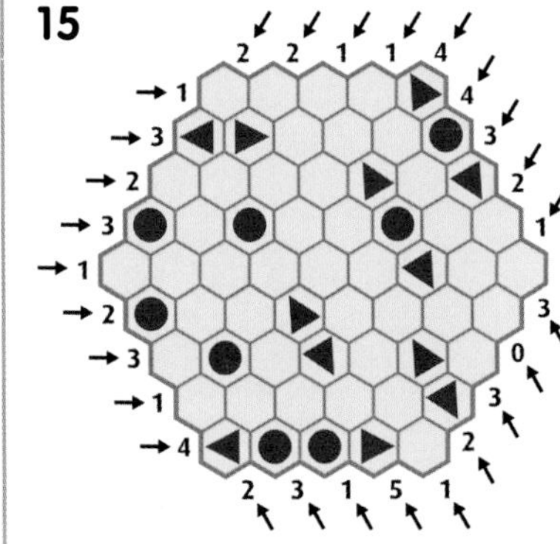

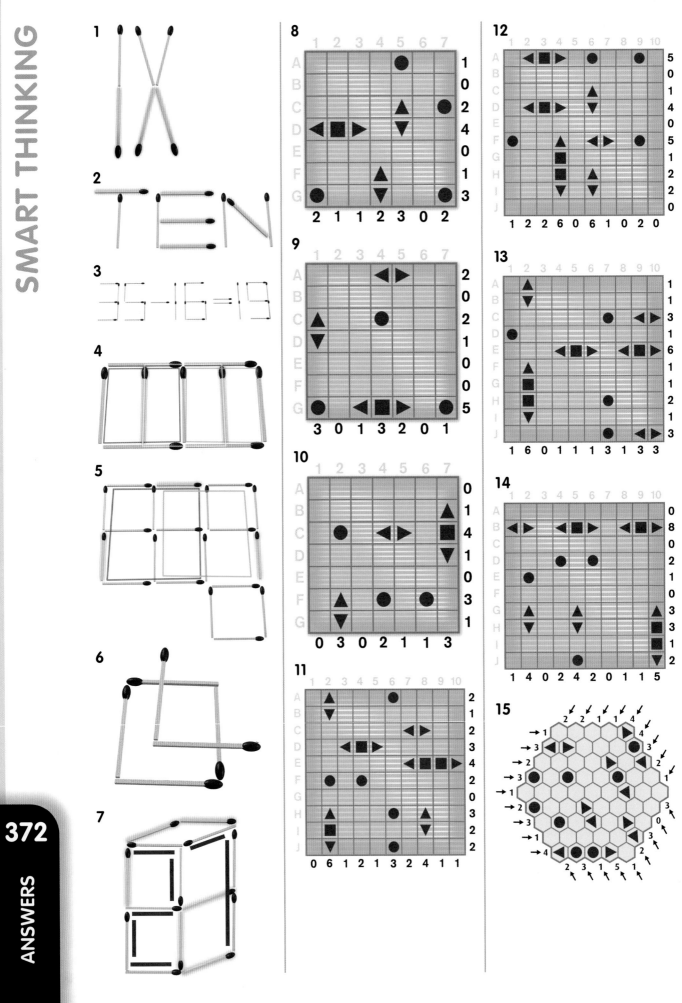

16

17

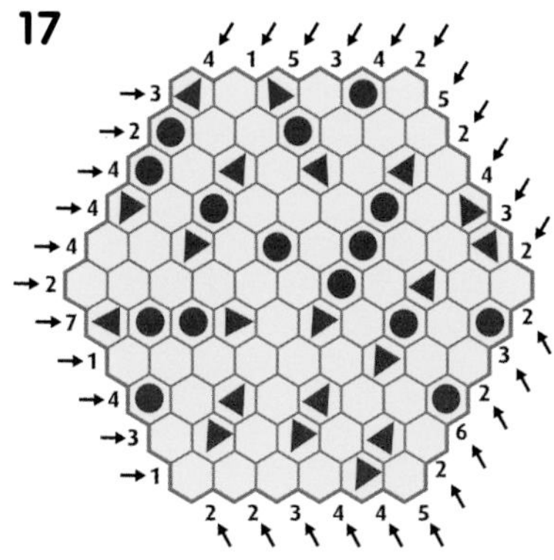

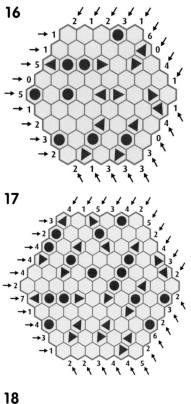

18
Party
arty; par; pry; pay; part.

19
Chart
hart; cart; chat; char; cat.

20
The passengers pick one clasp and one buckle randomly, so we consider the probability of the five passengers belting up correctly according to which passenger starts. From left to right, call the passengers A, B, C, D and E.

a. C starts; he has a 50% chance of choosing the correct buckle and clasp. If he chooses correctly, the other passengers are forced to choose the right pair. Probability of success = 1/2.

b. A starts; she is certain to choose the correct pair; if then:
- **i.** B or E chooses next; they must be correct unless the middle one of the remaining passengers then chooses and picks wrong. Probability of success = 5/6.
- **ii.** C or D chooses next; if they choose correctly, all passengers must belt up correctly, so probability of success = 1/2.

So the probability of success when A starts is the average of (bi) and (bii), which is 1/2 (5/6 +1/2) or 2/3.

c. B starts; if he chooses correctly, then A must be right; and the passengers will belt up correctly unless D chooses before C and E and gets it wrong. Probability of success is 1/2 x 5/6 = 5/12.

d. When D starts the probability of success is 5/12

e. When E starts the probability of success is 2/3.

The overall probability of success is therefore the average of **a** through **e** = 1/5 (2/1 + 2/3+ 5/12 + 5/12 +2/3) = 32/60 = 8/15.
This answer can also be expressed as 8 to 7, or 53.5%.

21
There are several ways of approaching this problem. Here is one. Weigh four balls, call them A, B, C and D, against four balls, E, F, G and H.

a. If they balance, then the rogue ball is I, J, K or L. So weigh I, J and K against A, B, C.
- **i.** If they again balance, weigh L (the faulty ball) against any other ball to find out whether it is heavier or lighter.
- **ii.** If they do not balance, you know whether the odd ball is heavier or lighter. Weigh J against K to identify which of I, J or K is the odd ball.

b. If A, B, C and D go down, then weigh A, B, E against C, D, F.
- **i.** If they now balance, G or H must be lighter. Weigh them against one another, or either one against a true ball, will establish which.
- **ii.** If they still go down, then A or B must be heavy or F is light. Weigh A against B to establish which.
- **iii.** If they now go up, then C or D must be heavy or E is light. Weigh C against D to establish which.

c. If A, B, C and D go up, the identical tests (with reverse conclusions) will again establish the odd ball.

22
Tea towel

23
Don Quixote

24
Bulldozer

25
Dead ringer

26
Shooting the breeze.

27
Generation gap

28
A bird in the hand.

29
Back soon.

30
Ill in bed.

31
Split screen.

32
Wunderkind

33
Shin bone.

34
Parting shot.

35
Eyeliner

36
Bacon and eggs.

37
Apartheid

38
Timeshare

39
Horse

40
Yacht

41
A sponge.

42
The third: Lions that haven't eaten in three years are dead.

43
Ankle

44
A towel.

45
He put a hole in the barrel.

46
Genesis

47
Dickens (Charles)

48
Around the table are a woman and her brother, her daughter and his son (or his daughter and her son).

49
A pack of cards.

50
Four: Take out three socks and they might be all different. Take out a fourth and you're bound to have a pair.

51
Peace

52
They are two of three triplets.

53
A window.

54
Orange: One, ear, ogre, rage, organ.

55
Anemone

56
A postage stamp.

57
When the rich man reached the phone booth he found a carrier pigeon in a cage. It had a message attached, telling him to put the diamond in a small bag which was around the pigeon's neck and to release the bird. The man did this and the police watched the bird as it returned across the city to its owner.

58
Four, arranged like this:

● ●

● ●

59
Gambler

60
'Language' is the third word in 'the English language'.

61
Under the carpet in the study. Ignore the spaces and read the message backwards.

62
Taking the initial letter of every word, Simon Simple read: 'Take the night flight to Rome.'

63
Live and let die: Each letter is substituted with another that is two further along in the alphabet. So L becomes N, I becomes K and so on.

64
Congratulations, code-breaker: Take the first letter of the first word and the last letter of the second – C and O. Then do the same with the next pair – the N of never and the G of spring. Continue to the end and you get the message above.

65
The message is **'We will attack at sunset tomorrow'**: The sentence is split into groups of four letters and a dummy letter inserted in the middle of each group.

66
Many hands make light work: All the consonants in the original proverb have been moved forward one place in the alphabet, so M becomes L, N becomes M and so on. But the vowels (including Y) remain the same.

67
This is really easy: Write the two 'words' one above the other, like this:

T	I	I	R
A	L	E	S
H	S	S	E
L	Y	A	Y

Now take the first letter of the top line, the first of the bottom line, the second of the top, the second of the bottom, and so on.

68
Look at the keypad on your telephone: number 2 can represent A, B or C, 3 is D, E or F and so on. Using the only combination of letters that make sense, you get: 'Anyone who has never made a mistake has never tried anything new.'

69
Answer B.

70
U2: arrange the letters in order of the number that is paired with them to spell out the phrase 'pure logic'.

71
3 minutes:
1. Pop in the first slices 1 and 2 and toast = 1 minute.
2. Take out slice 1 from the toaster and turn slice 2 round. Replace slice 1 with slice 3, and toast = 1 minute (slice 2 is now toasted on both sides; slices 1 and 3 are toasted on one side only).
3. Toast the remaining sides of slices 1 and 3 = 1 minute.

72

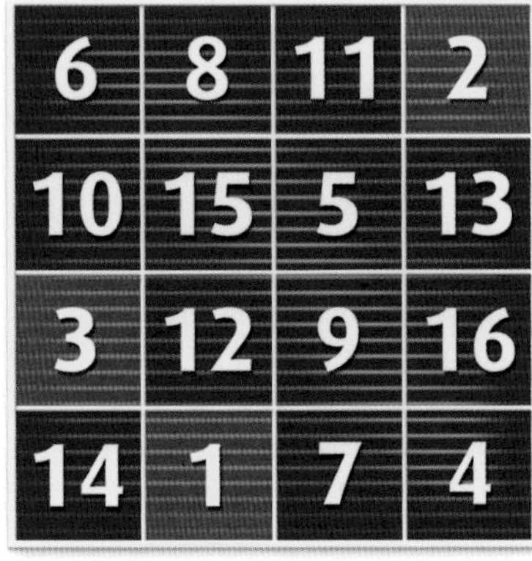

6	8	11	2
10	15	5	13
3	12	9	16
14	1	7	4

Rule 1 No two consecutive numbers appear in adjacent horizontal, vertical or diagonal lines.

Rule 2 No two consecutive numbers appear in adjacent horizontal, vertical or diagonal squares.

73
Number the discs 1, 2, 3, 4 so that 1 is the smallest disk, and proceed as follows:
1 to Peg C (1C), 2B, 1B, 3C, 1A, 2C, 1C, 4B, 1B, 2A, 1A, 3B, 1C, 2B, 1B.

74
In the following sequence:

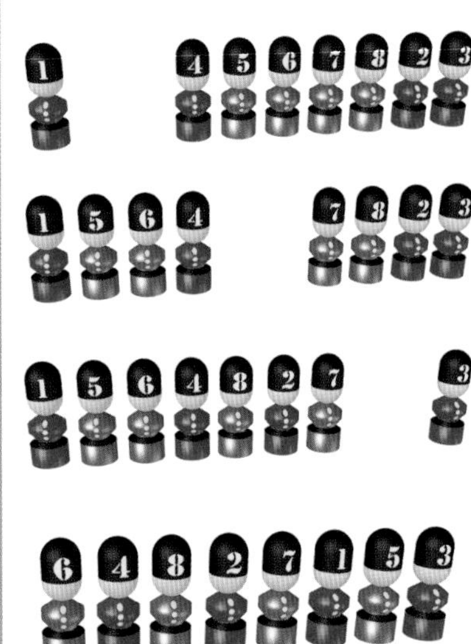

75

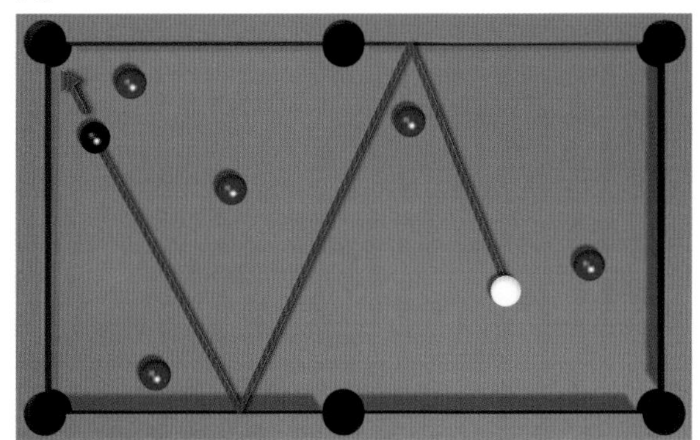

76

77

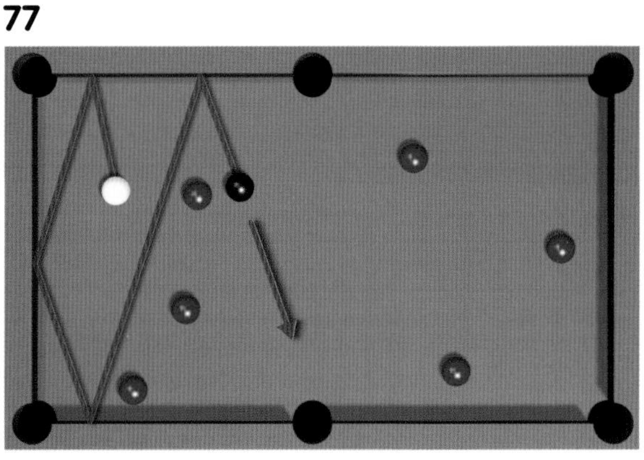

78

79

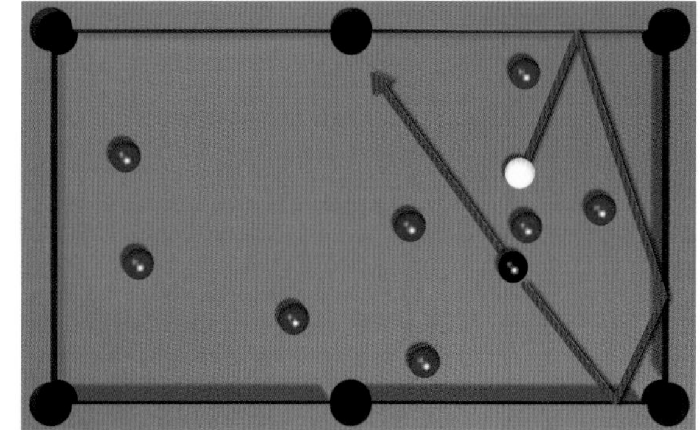

80

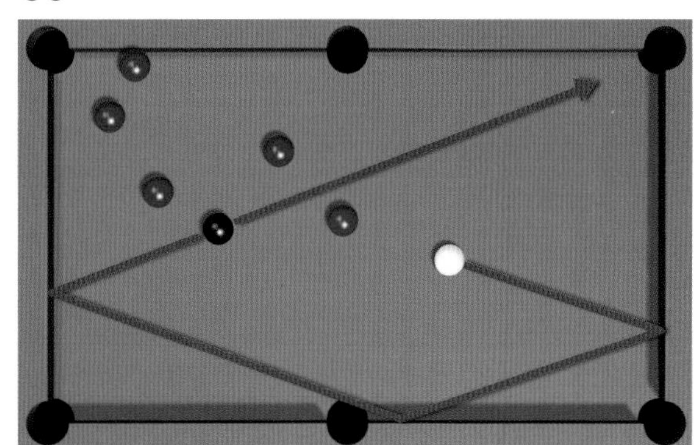

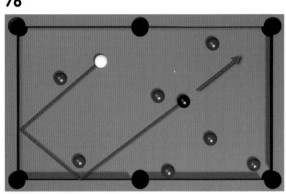

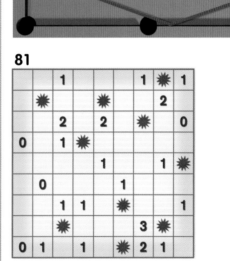

81

		1				1	✹	1
	✹			✹			2	
		2		2		✹		0
0		1	✹					
				1			1	✹
	0				1			
		1	1		✹			1
		✹				3	✹	
0	1		1		✹	2	1	

82

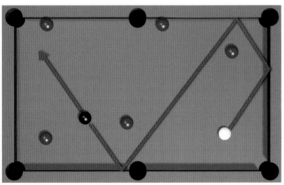

0				✹				
		✹	2		2	✹		
	2		2					
0		✹			2			0
	1			✹		✹		
		0			3	2	1	
✹				2	✹			
	2		✹				0	
1	✹							

83

				0				
	0				1		✷	1
				✷				1
1	✷		2	3			0	
			✷		✷			
0				4		2		0
			✷		✷			
	1	2		3		3	✷	
	✷	1			✷		1	

84

	0			0				
							0	
	✷		✷		✷			
		3	3	3		2		
0		✷		✷			✷	
					2			1
	✷	2	1		✷			
	1	2	✷	3		2	0	
					✷			

85

				0				
	0					✷	2	
			✷			2		✷
	✷	2		2	✷	1		1
	2				2			
1	✷			1		✷	2	✷
		3	✷					1
	✷	2			0			
1			0				0	

86

1	✷				✷			1
			1				✷	
✷	1			✷		1		2
1			2		2		1	✷
		1		✷				
✷	2	✷			3	✷	1	
2				✷				1
✷		1	2				✷	
		✷	1	1	✷	2		

87

1			1	1		1	1	
	✷	2	✷			✷		1
2								✷
1	✷		✷		✷	1	1	
	1		1					1
1		1		1		✷		✷
✷	1		✷			3		
2			2		✷		✷	
✷	1	1	✷					

88

				1	✷			
	✷	2		3		3	1	
	1		✷		✷		✷	
			2					2
	✷	2	✷	2	✷	1		✷
	2		2				2	
✷	1		✷		1	✷		
		2			2			✷
1	✷			1	✷	1		1

89

✷	2		1				1	
1		✷				✷		
			3	✷	3			✷
1	2	✷				✷		1
✷			2		3		2	
		1		✷		✷		
	2	✷			3	3		
✷	2		2		✷		✷	
1			✷	2				

90

1			✷				✷	1
✷		1		1			3	✷
	2	1	1		1	✷		
✷			✷	2			2	
	2		1		✷		1	✷
	✷			2		2	2	1
1		2	✷			✷		
	1	1		1	2		3	✷
✷	1					✷		1

91

The 16-year resident lives at Rose Cottage (clue 4). The 8-year resident's home isn't White Gates (clue 3), so must be Meadow View, and he is therefore Walter Young (clue 1). He isn't from Islington (clue 1), and can't be from Paddington (clue 2), so must be from Battersea. Alan Bradley can't be from Paddington (clue 2), so must come from Islington, leaving Mavis Norton as the person from Paddington, who must have lived in the village for 16 years (clue 2), at Rose Cottage. By elimination, Alan Bradley must have lived in the village for 11 years, at White Gates.
Alan Bradley, Islington, 11 years, White Gates.
Mavis Norton, Paddington, 16 years, Rose Cottage.
Walter Young, Battersea, 8 years, Meadow View.

92

Elder moved in in 1995 (clue 4), so, from clue 1, Senior must have arrived in 1990 and Grey in 1985. Grey is Margaret (clue 3), so Elder, who isn't Daisy (clue 4), must be Henry, leaving Daisy's surname as Senior. From clue 1, Margaret Grey must have come from Mulbury, and, from clue 2, Henry Elder lived in Wishingwell. By elimination, Daisy Senior's former home was in Plighwood.
Daisy Senior, Plighwood, 1990.
Henry Elder, Wishingwell, 1995.
Margaret Grey, Mulbury, 1985.

93

Bill Cobb lives in Rockett Road (clue 3), so Mick North, who doesn't live in Pinwheel Gardens (clue 1), must be the man from Squibb Street who provided a barbecue (clue 2), and Steve Tibbs must live in Pinwheel Gardens. Mick North's display can't have begun at 7.30pm (clue 1), and the one that began at 7.00pm finished with fish and chips (clue 4), so Mick North's party must have begun at 7.15pm, and the one that began at 7.30pm must have ended with curry. From clue 1, this must have been Steve Tibbs's party in Pinwheel Gardens. So, by elimination, Bill Cobb's party in Rockett Road must have been the one which began at 7.00pm and ended with fish and chips.
Bill Cobb, Rockett Road, 7.00pm, fish and chips.
Mick North, Squibb Street, 7.15pm, barbecue.
Steve Tibbs, Pinwheel Gardens, 7.30pm, curry.

94

'Red Biddy' was tried in 1649 (clue 4), so the witch tried in 1648, who wasn't 'Mother Bluenose' (clue 3), must have been 'Granny Noggs', and her real name was therefore Alice Noggs (clue 1). By elimination, 'Mother Bluenose' must have been tried in 1647, and came from Gammonham (clue 2). Edith Rudge, therefore, can't have been tried in 1648 (clue 4), so her trial must have been in 1649, and so her nickname was 'Red Biddy'. Therefore, Alice Noggs must have lived in Hillside (clue 4). Clara Pinch didn't come from Lychgate (clue 3), so she must have come from Gammonham, and was 'Mother Bluenose', tried in 1647. By elimination it must have been Edith Rudge who lived in Lychgate.

Alice Noggs, 'Granny Noggs', Hillside, 1648.
Clara Pinch, 'Mother Bluenose', Gammonham, 1647.
Edith Rudge, 'Red Biddy', Lychgate, 1649.

95

Ringwell 4, the number for Holly Farm (clue 3), wasn't the number for Reginald Haughton or Mr Sloman (clue 1), or Mr Digby (clue 4), so it must have been for Mr Morley. The subscriber on Ringwell 1 can't have been Mr Sloman (clue 1), or Mr Digby (clue 4), so must have been Reginald Haughton, and, from clue 1, Mr Sloman must have been on Ringwell 2, leaving Mr Digby as Ringwell 3, and he was therefore Lionel (clue 2). Now, from clue 4, Ringwell 4 must have been Frederick's number, and Mr Sloman, on Ringwell 2, must have been at the King's Head. By elimination, Mr Sloman on Ringwell 2 must have been Alfred. Finally, Ringwell 3 wasn't the number for the Manor House (clue 2), so must have been the Post Office Stores, leaving the Manor House's number as Ringwell 1, and thus Reginald Haughton's home.

Ringwell 1, Reginald Haughton, Manor House.
Ringwell 2, Alfred Sloman, King's Head.
Ringwell 3, Lionel Digby, Post Office Stores.
Ringwell 4, Frederick Morley, Holly Farm.

96

Agent AX34 wasn't Algy Blake (clue 1), Mark Niles (clue 2) or Jack Keane (clue 5), so must have been Paul Rouse, alias 'Anibal Gomes' (clue 4). The agent who posed as 'Jose Braga', the juggler, can't have been AX31 (clue 2) or AX33, who posed as a clown (clue 3), so must have been AX32. So, from clue 2, Mark Niles must have been AX31. We now know the cover occupations of AX32 and AX33, so, from clue 5, the trick rider must have been AX34, and Jack Keane must have been AX33, who posed as a clown. By elimination, Algy Blake must have been AX32, who posed as 'Jose Braga' the juggler, and Mark Niles, agent AX31, must have posed as a strongman. Therefore, from clue 1, Jack Keane, agent AX33, must have used the name 'Manuel Silva', and, by elimination, Mark Niles, agent AX31, must have called himself 'Teofilo Mendes'.

Algy Blake, AX32, 'Jose Braga', juggler.
Jack Keane, AX33, 'Manuel Silva', clown.
Mark Niles, AX31, Teofilo Mendes, strongman.
Paul Rouse, AX34, Anibal Gomes, trick rider.

97

Greybeard was reviewed on the 28th (clue 3), so the play reviewed on the 7th, which can't have been **The Tempest** (clue 1) or **The Hollow** (clue 5), must have been **Under Milk Wood**, by NADS (clue 2). The play reviewed on the 21st wasn't the CTC performance deemed 'terrible' (clue 4) and, from clue 1, it can't have been performed by WRTC, so it must have been performed by the City Players. Now, from clue 1, **The Tempest** can't have been reviewed on the 14th and must have been reviewed on the 21st, leaving **The Hollow** as the play reviewed on the 14th. Therefore NADS' production of **Under Milk Wood** reviewed on the 7th was described as 'a curate's egg' (clue 5), and, from clue 1, WRTC performed **The Hollow**, reviewed on the 14th, leaving **Greybeard**, reviewed on the 28th, as the CTC production described as 'terrible'. **The Hollow** was performed by WRTC, so it wasn't described as 'workmanlike' (clue 1), so it must have been called 'very good', leaving 'workmanlike' as the opinion given on the 21st in the review of **The Tempest** by the City Players.

7th, Under Milk Wood, NADS, 'a curate's egg'.
14th, The Hollow, WRTC, 'very good'.
21st, The Tempest, City Players, 'workmanlike'.
28th, Greybeard, CTC, 'terrible'.

98

Badger's boss is Hafnium (clue 2), and Porcupine's objective is Petunia (clue 4), so, from clue 5, the codename of the operation in which Lambda and its boss are aiming at Orchid, which ends in the same letter as that of Thorium's operation, must be either Badger or Gazelle. Muskdeer's objective isn't Cowslip (clue 1), so, by elimination, it must be Lavender. Therefore, from clue 3, Mercury and his Omicron taskforce must be undertaking Gazelle, and therefore Lambda is pursuing Orchid in Badger, under Hafnium. So, from clue 5, Thorium must be running Muskdeer. By elimination, Gazelle's objective must be Cowslip, and Astatine must be in charge of Porcupine, the object of which is Petunia. The taskforce involved isn't Gamma (clue 1), so must be Theta, leaving Gamma as the taskforce assigned to Muskdeer.

Badger, Hafnium, Lambda, Orchid.
Gazelle, Mercury, Omicron, Cowslip.
Muskdeer, Thorium, Gamma, Lavender.
Porcupine, Astatine, Theta, Petunia.

99

The final clue completing the Daily Express crossword was 7 across (clue 4). Clue 3 across was not the final one in the Independent or the Guardian (clue 1), or the Times (clue 3), so it must have been the Daily Telegraph, so the solver must have been Vic Tourier (clue 6), with the answer 'BAGATELLE' (clue 1). Therefore, 'MOTLEY' must have been the answer to either 4 down or 5 down (clue 3), but as 7 across was the last clue in the Daily Express, 6 across must have been in the Times and 'MOTLEY' must have been the answer to 4 down (also clue 3). The latter was not the final clue in the Independent (clue 1), so it must have been the Guardian. So, Mary Lebone must have completed her crossword with 5 down in the Independent. The answer was not 'EXPONENT' (clue 1) or 'PEDESTAL', which was the final answer in Lou Waters' crossword (clue 3), so it must have been 'RELISH'. As Paddy Tunn was not doing the Times crossword (clue 2), his final clue was not 4 down, and as his final clue number was lower than that of Lou Waters (also clue 2), it was not 7 across, so must have been 6 across, and therefore Paddy must read the Times. Therefore, Lou Waters must have solved 7 across 'PEDESTAL' (clue 2), and must therefore have been solving the Daily Express crossword. By elimination, the Guardian reader must have been Canon Street, and Paddy Tunn must have completed his Times crossword with 6 across 'EXPONENT'.

Mary Lebone, Independent, 5 down, 'RELISH'.
Canon Street, Guardian, 4 down, 'MOTLEY'.
Vic Tourier, Daily Telegraph, 3 across, 'BAGATELLE'.
Paddy Tunn, Times, 6 across, 'EXPONENT'.
Lou Waters, Daily Express, 7 across, 'PEDESTAL'.

100

The person in seat 4, who bought lot 6, didn't hold paddle 161, or paddle 114, which was held by the occupant of seat 3 (clue 7). Clue 5 rules out lot 6 for the owner of paddle 193, and the owner of paddle 128 bought lot 60 (clue 6). Since lot 17 went to Philip (clue 3), clue 1 rules out the holder of paddle 130 for lot 6, which had to go to the owner of paddle 149. So, from clue 2, Edward had seat 6. Bidder 4 is not Edward or Philip, while Connor had seat 5 (clue 6); clue 1 rules out lot 6 for Marvin, and clue 2 rules out Alistair, so, by elimination, Tarquin had to be in seat 4. So, from clue 4, lot 53 was bought by the holder of paddle 161. Neither Connor, Edward nor Tarquin were in seat 1. Clue 2 rules out Alistair, and clue 1, Marvin. So, it must be Philip's seat. His even-numbered paddle (clue 3), is not 114 or 128, so it must be 130. Clue 1 tells us Marvin bought lot 21. We've matched four lot numbers with paddles. Marvin can't have held up paddle 193 after buying lot 21 (clue 5), so he must have had paddle 114, and so sat in seat 3, which leaves the holder of paddle 193 as the buyer of lot 44. Alistair must have had seat 2. From clue 8, he must have bought lot 53, and had paddle 161. Connor didn't buy lot 60 (clue 6), so must have bought lot 44, so lot 60 was Edward's.

1, Philip, lot 17, paddle 130.
2, Alistair, lot 53, paddle 161.
3, Marvin, lot 21, paddle 114.
4, Tarquin, lot 6, paddle 149.
5, Connor, lot 44, paddle 193.
6, Edward, lot 60, paddle 128.

101

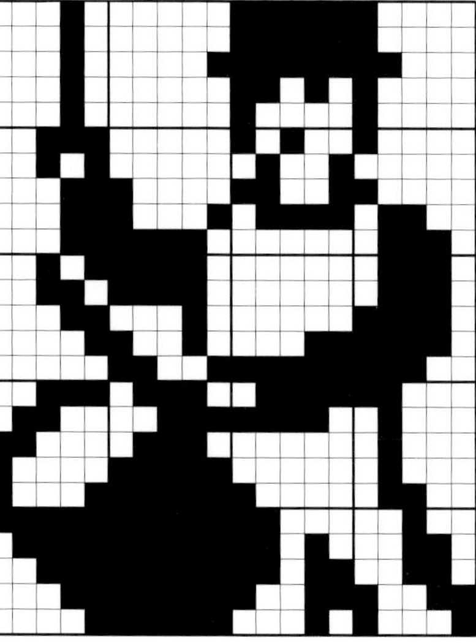

102

103

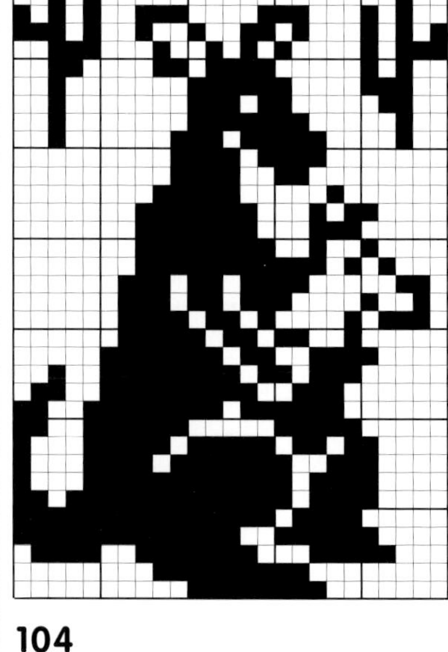

104

105

106

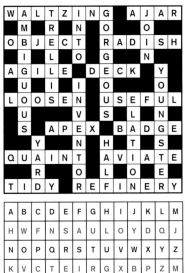

A	B	C	D	E	F	G	H	I	J	K	L	M
H	W	F	N	S	A	U	L	O	Y	D	Q	J
N	O	P	Q	R	S	T	U	V	W	X	Y	Z
K	V	C	T	E	I	R	G	X	B	P	Z	M

107

They will both be the same distance from Hull when they meet, as they will be the same distance from anywhere else for that matter!

108

Six ties: one striped, one plain brown, one plain red, one plain green, one polka dot and one plain black.

109

N: the letters can be rearranged to spell out the word TRIANGLE.

110

They all have an aquatic creature hidden within them:

Duk(e El)lington	**eel**
The (New T)estament	**newt**
A (car p)ark	**carp**
The game of S(crab)ble	**crab**
A cro(cod)ile	**cod**

111

This is true every year. In the example given, Christmas Day 2002 was on a Wednesday. One week later New Year's Day was also on a Wednesday, but in the year 2003. New Year's Day in 2002 was on a Tuesday.

112

b. VER: so that when read backwards the phrase REVERSE SEQUENCE appears.

113

One word only (which is an anagram of no wry noodle).

114

B: so that when the figures are read sideways the letters K L M N appear.

115

Looking across each line, the first number represents the number of empty squares to the left and the second number those to the right, before the next number or the end of the line is reached.

			33			
		21		12		
	15					
					51	
		24				
	12					
		22	33			

116

A: read the initial letters of the words working from left to right across each row in turn to spell out CHOOSE ONE.

117

CAPTAIN'S CHAIRS: fourteen letters less nine letters = A PAIR.

118

Puzzle: Rotate the N blocks 90° clockwise.

119 C	**123** A	**127** B
120 B	**124** C	**128** C
121 A	**125** C	**129** B
122 C	**126** B	**130** A

131

1. Cocker spaniel
2. Pomeranian
3. Chihuahua
4. Siamese
5. Dachshund

Siamese is the odd one out as it is a breed of cat. The rest are all breeds of dog.

132

Meet me tonight: this is what is known as a book cipher. Each number in the question represents the number of the letter in the question i.e.
'Pay careful attention to the instructions when decoding the following message'
where p = 1, a =2, y = 3, c = 4 and so on.

133

1277 73353 73512
BEST THING SINCE
743122 16212
SLICED BREAD

134

1673231314
ARTIFICIAL
357244332512
INTELLIGENCE

135

6651617735173 55 37
PROCRASTINATION IS
732 73322 52 7352
THE THIEF OF TIME

136

The decoded message reads: 'A considerate person is someone who can play the bagpipes but doesn't.'

Each letter represents its position in the grid as follows:

1	2	3	4	5	
A	B	C	D	E	1
F	G	H	I	J	2
K	L	M	N	O	3
P	Q	R	S	T	4
U	V	W	X	Y	5

So, for example, B is represented by the number 12 because it is in the first row, second column, and the letter R is represented by the number 43 because it is in the fourth row, third column.

137

1. 485 8121478
THE PARADOX
13 1 5134521753
IS A MYSTERIOUS
25134
BEAST.

2. 485 78415134
THE OPTIMIST
827341153 4814 75
PROCLAIMS THAT WE
4165 16 485 2534
LIVE IN THE BEST
76 144 87331245
OF ALL POSSIBLE
772443, 164 485
WORLDS, AND THE
853315134 65123
PESSIMIST FEARS
4813 13 4255
THIS IS TRUE
126167 315312
IRVING CAESAR

138

X marks the spot: add up each group of three numbers and take the corresponding letter in the alphabet to reveal the message.

139

Q	U	I	Z		M	U	L	T	I	P	L	E
U		D		B		S		H		R		W
A	V	E	R	A	G	E		O	Z	O	N	E
D		A		R		F		S		J		R
R	U	L	E	R		U	N	E	V	E	N	
A				E		L				C		C
N	I	B	B	L	E		K	E	T	T	L	E
T		E				E		X				M
	A	S	Y	L	U	M		C	Y	C	L	E
S		I		E		P		E		H		T
W	E	D	G	E		I	M	P	R	O	V	E
I		E		C		R		T		K		R
M	I	S	C	H	I	E	F		D	E	F	Y

140

O	B	L	I	Q	U	E		M	A	C	A	W
V		U		U		X		O		O		O
E	X	P	I	A	T	E		L	U	N	A	R
R		I		R		M		A		J		S
T	E	N	O	R		P	A	R	Q	U	E	T
				E		T				R		E
D	A	Z	Z	L	E		S	H	R	E	W	D
E		E				S		O				
F	E	A	R	F	U	L		L	U	C	K	Y
L		L		I		E		D		H		I
A	B	O	V	E		E	P	I	S	O	D	E
T		U		R		V		N		K		L
E	S	S	A	Y		E	G	G	H	E	A	D

141

	E		W		D		U		B		B	
S	N	E	E	Z	E		S	E	E	S	A	W
	O		E		L		H		E		F	
J	U	M	P		I	D	E	N	T	I	F	Y
	G				V		R		R		L	
C	H	I	C	K	E	N		J	O	K	E	R
			O		R		R		O			
S	P	E	N	D		T	E	X	T	I	L	E
	R		Q		A		V				I	
S	E	Q	U	E	N	C	E		M	A	Z	E
	F		E		G		R		I		A	
V	E	S	S	E	L		S	E	N	T	R	Y
	R		T		E		E		X		D	

142

H	I	G	H		R	E	V	E	R	S	A	L
O		A		J		M		X		P		E
S	Q	U	E	E	Z	E		E	X	I	L	E
P		Z		S		R		R		N		K
I	N	E	R	T		G	A	T	E	A	U	
T				E		E				C		E
A	D	V	E	R	B		A	N	T	H	E	M
L		E				Z		E				P
	C	H	E	Q	U	E		A	W	F	U	L
E		I		U		A		R		L		O
C	O	C	O	A		L	I	B	R	A	R	Y
H		L		K		O		Y		K		E
O	M	E	L	E	T	T	E		J	E	E	R

143

F	O	L	D	E	R		S	Y	M	B	O	L
A		U		M		D		I		L		E
C	A	P	A	B	L	E		E	X	A	L	T
A		I		A		T		L		T		T
D	O	N	O	R		R	A	D	I	A	T	E
E				G		I				N		R
	A	C	C	O	M	M	O	D	A	T	E	
B		H				E		O				O
A	B	A	N	D	O	N		L	A	G	E	R
M		L		O		T		P		L		D
B	U	I	L	D		A	C	H	I	E	V	E
O		C		G		L		I		A		A
O	P	E	N	E	R		A	N	I	M	A	L

144

E	X	A	C	T		P	R	O	B	A	T	I	O	N
X		R		A		L		V		R		N		I
P	E	G		C	H	A	S	E		B	I	N	G	E
E		U		T		S		R		I				C
C	H	E	M	I	S	T		L	A	T	T	I	C	E
T				L		E	R	A		E		M		
A	M	A	T	E	U	R		P	E	R	H	A	P	S
N		D			S				E			G		U
T	R	A	P	P	E	R		N	U	C	L	E	A	R
		G		R		A	X	E		I				R
E	M	E	R	A	L	D		M	E	S	S	A	G	E
T				T		I		E		T		V		N
H	A	B	I	T		A	I	S	L	E		O	D	D
O		A		L		T		I		R		I		E
S	E	N	S	E	L	E	S	S		N	A	D	I	R

145

C	H	A	O	S		P	O	D		R	O	B	I	N
R		R		P	A	L		I	C	E		A		E
A	N	G	E	L		A	R	T		P	A	P	E	R
M		U		I	N	N		T	I	E				V
P	L	E	A	T		T	R	Y		L	E	A	F	Y
	E		D				O					L		
M	A	N	O	R		S	E	E		S	E	D	A	N
A		U		A	S	P		V	A	A		E		O
R	U	D	D	Y		A	C	E		W	O	R	L	D
		G					O				D		I	
F	L	E	E	T		S	O	B		B	E	R	E	T
L				E	A	T		A	G	E		E		A
A	S	P	E	N		O	P	T		A	L	I	E	N
S		A		S	U	N		H	E	R		G		G
H	E	D	G	E		E	W	E		D	I	N	G	O

146

6	5	7		8	5	2		7	8	8
4	1	3		7	4	2		5	2	3
7	2	6	5	6	7	8		2	1	3
			4	5	8	4	8	5		
8	6	2	3	1	4		6	1	3	4
4	7	3	2	0		8	7	8	7	9
3	5	7	5		8	9	3	2	9	1
		5	4	1	0	3	2			
8	6	1		7	2	2	5	1	2	9
2	5	9		5	8	8		4	0	5
4	1	2		9	7	5		1	7	2

147

Kin: All the words in Column A can be prefixed with CAT and all the words in Column B can be prefixed with DOG.

148

The old school chum she had just bumped into was named **Peter**.

149

7: The numbers in all the same coloured segments in the four heptagons always total 30, ie. all the yellow triangles add up to 30 when added together, as do all the green ones and so on.

150

4 kilograms: As half of Tinkerbell's weight is added to 2 kilograms, then 2 kilograms must be half of the total.

151

26 minutes: The secret is to ensure that the slowest people make the fewest crossings and the fastest people the most crossings.
In total 5 journeys need to be made, but by sending them across together the two slowest people only have to make one crossing:

a. Jane and Gordon cross	3 mins
b. Jane returns	2 mins
c. Paul and Colonel cross	15 mins
d. Gordon returns	3 mins
e. Jane and Gordon cross	3 mins
Total 26 minutes	

152

Instead of pulling out the cork, push it into the bottle.

153

8642139: Rearrange the digits so that all the even numbers in descending order are followed by all the odd numbers in ascending order.

154

M and U: They are the alternate letters in The United States of America, starting with T and H respectively.

155

Leonatus: None of the names repeat a letter.

156

10: Each number represents the number of other numbers with which it shares the same line across, followed by the number of other numbers with which it shares the same line down.

157

A: Take the first letter from the first day of the week (Sunday), then the second letter from the second day of the week, and so on.

Sunday, M**o**nday, Tu**e**sday, Wed**n**esday, Thur**s**day, Frida**y**, Saturd**a**y.

158

C: They are the digitally displayed numbers 0, 2, 4, 6, 8, complete with their right-hand mirror image.

159

The only fair way is to cut the cake from the centre. That way each person gets an equal amount of cake, cream and marzipan. The way to do this is to calculate that the total length of the four sides is 90cm (4 x 22.5). Then divide 90 by 5 = 18. Starting at one of the corners, measure 18cm lengths right round the edge of the cake. Then cut from the centre to where you have marked off each 18cm length. Although each portion will be a different shape, each will contain exactly the same amount of cake, cream and marzipan.

160

Make both ends meet.

Take the first letter of each word in the top row, the second letter from each word in the second row, the third letter from each word in the third row and the last letter from each letter in the bottom row.

161

eu: They are the vowels extracted from the question in the same order in which they appear, and split into groups of two letters.

162

20: Looking at diagonal lines as indicated the totals are 2, 4, 6, 8, 10, 12, 14, 16, 18, 20.

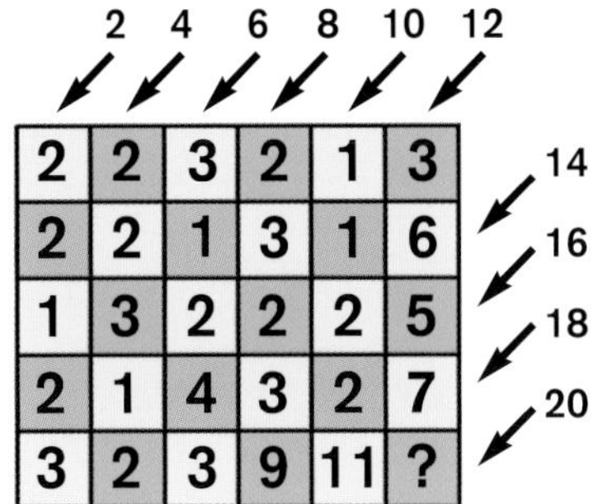

163

Sandwich.

The letters ABCDEFGH appear in the words in turn in the same position as they appear in the alphabet:

Aqueduct, o**B**stacle, in**C**ubate, hea**D**long, outw**E**igh, boast**F**ul, shorta**G**e, sandwic**H**.

164

Leg: So that the beginnings and ends of the words spell out 'straight down the middle'.

agha**st** **rai**sin
kni**ght** **dow**ager
spi**n** **th**is
tot**em** **id**ea
en**d** **le**g

165

Brisbane: The words end and start alternately with the last and first two letters of the numbers one, two, three, four, five, six, seven, eight, nine and ten.

Alkali**ne**, **tw**ilight, carefr**ee**, **fo**restry, positi**ve**, **si**ngular, tungst**en**, **Ei**nstein, Brisba**ne**, **te**merity.

166

Car: Take the first letter from the first word, the second letter from the second word, the third letter from the third word, and repeat until you reach the bottom of the list to spell out LEFT RIGHT CENTRE.

LOG
P**E**T
EL**F**
TRY
A**R**M
SK**I**
GAP
S**H**E
CA**T**
CAR
P**E**N
TI**N**
TOP
O**R**B
ON**E**

167

The woman had hiccups and asked her husband to give her a shock. A little later he jumped out at her wearing a Halloween mask. She died from a heart attack. They had not known that she had a weak heart.

168

One gravedigger was a woman and she dug four graves.

169

The man is carrying a sponge.

170

The word is 'queue'.

171

He suspected that one of the servants was stealing from him. He told them all that the black hen had magic powers and if they stroked it, it could then tell him which one of them was the thief. He secretly put soot on the hen. The honest servants stroked the hen and got soot on their hands. The thief did not stroke the hen and came out with clean hands. This gave him away.

172

Fire had broken out at the man's home. The sprinkler system had been activated and the downpour ruined his watercolour paintings but saved the house and all his other belongings from destruction.

173

He sent the left boots to one port of entry and the right boots to another port of entry. It was unlikely that any official would steal a consignment of left boots as he would be unable to use or sell them.

174

A small plane was inside a transporter plane.

175

Mary was a new born baby and the nurse cut her umbilical cord.

176

The woman was married but was acting in a play where she played a single woman. She did this six nights a week and twice on Saturdays because of the matinee performances.

177

If you said 50 miles, then you are an experienced puzzler who has seen this problem before. After all, the trains are approaching from 100 miles apart at a combined speed of 100mph, so they will collide in just one hour, during which time the fly has flown 50 miles...

Unfortunately, this is the wrong answer! Since the first train is going at 60mph and the poor fly can only do 50mph, he remains stuck fast on the front of the first locomotive, totally unable to do anything except stare at the oncoming disaster and mutter, 'It's a helluva way to run a railroad'.

178
The only order satisfying the four conditions is yellow, red, red.

179
Smith, where Jones had had 'had had', had had 'had'. 'Had had' had had the teacher's approval.

180
The roll of two dice. The chances of getting double-one, double-six or any combination that equals seven in the throw of two dice is 1 in 72, and, of course, you can never throw just a one.

181
Alice's lie means that she doesn't know who did it, so it cannot be her. Benny's lie means that it was not him. Carol's lie now means that it must be her or Donald; Donald's lie, therefore, means it must be Carol.

182
Each farmer should pay for the length of road that he traverses. So Able should pay one unit, Baker two units, Charlie 3 units and Dog 4 units. There are 10 units altogether, so a unit will be 10% of the total cost.

183
The blue box:
On the yellow box one statement is true and one is false.
True: 'The presents are not in this box'.
False: 'They are in the red box'.

On the red box both statements are true: 'The presents are not in the yellow box' and 'They are in the blue box'.

On the blue box, both statements are false: 'The presents are not in this box' and 'They are in the yellow box'.

184
All but two: Let's start off with a few letters and envelopes to explore the situation. When there is only one letter, Mrs. Flubbit can't make a mistake and there is no problem. When there are two letters, there is only one way she can make a mistake, and so there is no need to open any envelopes to deduce what is in each! With three letters, a, b and c, Mrs. Flubbit could have put them into envelopes A, B and C in just two possible orders: b, c, a or c, a, b. Let's open envelope A. It must contain letter b or c, and immediately determines the contents of all three envelopes. From this case it is clear that we can never deduce the contents when there are three envelopes still unopened. Can we conclude that we must open all the envelopes except two to establish the contents of all envelopes? Yes, but only by adopting a strategy. Instead of opening all but two of the envelopes at random, we open, say, envelope A, which contains letter c, then we open envelope C and find that it contains, for example, letter e. We then open envelope E, and so on. When we get down to two envelopes we will have at most one opened letter and one opened envelope which are not paired off. So we can determine the contents of all the envelopes once we have opened all but two.

185
The treasure was distributed as follows:
3,000 Gold
4,000 Silver
5,000 Bronze

Thickplank was thus the only guard who was telling the truth.

186
Uncle Omar solves the problem by loaning the estate his oil well. There are then 42 wells. The first son gets 21, the second gets 14 and the third gets 6, leaving one oil well, which they gratefully return to Omar.

187
A is wearing label B
B is wearing label A
C is wearing label D
D is wearing label C

As A and C could swap labels without improving matters, we know that A is not wearing C's label and vice versa. And because A speaks to the man wearing D, A has to be wearing B. This means that C is wearing neither A nor B, so must be wearing D. As D speaks to the man wearing A, we know that this was neither A nor C, so he must have been B. Leaving D to wear C.

188
Key.

189
Koala.

190
Call the three barrels A, B and C. The three operations are:
1. Transfer 1 litre from C to B,
2. Transfer 2 litres from B to A, and
3. Transfer 3 litres from C to A.

191
The correct order of the books is **After-Dinner Insults**, **Evenings in the Bath**, **Faking a Heart Attack**, **Desert Pub Crawl**, **Cruel Cake Recipes**, **Baking a Brick** and **Grandma the Polevaulter**.

The best way to solve it is to try all the combinations in which **Grandma the Polevaulter** is three places to the right of **Desert Pub Crawl.**Then try arranging the other five books in the vacant places. You will find that only one arrangement works.

192
There are 28 steps needed to end up with exactly 8 glasses-worth of wine in one of the containers.
1. Fill the 15-glass container.
2. Pour the contents of the 15-glass container into the 16-glass container.
3. Fill the 15-glass container again.
4. Pour one glass worth of wine from the 15-glass container into the 16-glass container, thus filling it.
5. Empty the contents of the 16-glass container back into the barrel.
6. Pour the contents of the 15-glass container (14 glasses-worth of wine) into the 16-glass container.
7. Fill the 15-glass container again.
8. Fill the 16-glass container from the 15-glass container (2 glasses-worth).
9. Empty the 16-glass container back into the barrel.

If you now repeat steps 6 to 9 over and over you will find that you have 8 glasses-worth of wine in the 15-glass container.

193
2 girls = 50%.
1 boy and 1 girl = 50%.
When the little girl answers the door, this eliminates the possibility that the family has two boys. If there are two girls, a girl has to answer the door; if they have a girl and a boy, the boy might have answered the door. So the combinations with a boy in them must be halved. This gives a new percentage of 50% girl, 50% boy for the unknown child.

To explain further: say you repeated the experience 100 times. Then a girl from a girl–girl family would answer the door 25 times (25 such families), a girl from a girl–boy family would also answer the door 25 times (50 such families, but a girl only answers the door in half of the cases) while a girl would never answer the door if the family had two boys.

194
When the short candle has burnt away 3 cm, the long one will have burnt away 6 cm and they will both be 2 cm long. When the long one has burnt completely out the short one will be 1 cm long. The long candle burns twice as much as the short candle. 'Short is the long one when it is as long as the short one' means when they are the same length, and 'when the long one is no longer' means that it no longer exists.

195
Let us suppose that the price in Padua is higher than the price in Venice; the other case simply reverses the numbers. The youngest son must have sold more pearls at the higher price in Padua than the second youngest, who must have sold more at Padua than the third youngest... The most that the youngest can have sold at Padua is nine, and this means that the most the eldest can have sold at Padua is one. But he sold at least one at Padua, so we see that the youngest must have sold nine in Padua and one in Venice. Let us say for convenience that the total number of units earned by each son is 100. Then the value of one sold at Padua must be the same as the value of 11 sold in Venice. So now we can see that the Padua price is 11 and the Venice price is 1.

196
There are 3 possible solutions:

1. Mr. White gave a black shirt to Mr. Brown.
   Mr. Black gave a green shirt to Mr. White.
   Mr. Brown gave a white shirt to Mr. Green.
   Mr. Green gave a brown shirt to Mr. Black.

2. Mr. Black gave a brown shirt to Mr. Green.
   Mr. White gave a black shirt to Mr. Brown.
   Mr. Brown gave a green shirt to Mr. White.
   Mr. Green gave a white shirt to Mr. Black.

3. Mr. White gave a black shirt to Mr. Brown.
   Mr. Black gave a green shirt to Mr. White.
   Mr. Brown gave a white shirt to Mr. Green.
   Mr. Green gave a brown shirt to Mr. Black.

197
The numbers of the three pairs of carols I sang at the carol service were, in no particular order, 49 and 98, 19 and 95, 16 and 64. Removing the common digit in each pair retained the original ratio, viz: 4:8, 1:5 and 1:4, respectively.

198
There are several ways to approach this. The simplest is to observe that the baker's wife cannot be Mrs. Brewer (unless she talks to herself). She also cannot be Mrs. Baker, since the baker is not Mr. Baker. So she must be Mrs. Butcher. Now the Brewer cannot be Mr. Brewer and we have just seen that he cannot be Mr. Butcher, so he must be Mr. Baker and the butcher must be Mr. Brewer. Mr. Brewer, the butcher, did not marry his sister Miss Brewer, nor did he marry Miss Butcher, so he must have married Miss Baker.

199
Quigley = E. The full classification of knaves is: Truthful Knaves – G; Lying Knaves – B, E; Conformists – C; Dissidents – A, D, F. Knaves with no letters are Zombies. You know what the instruction from the DOI is for each knave.

The only solution that satisfies all the conditions is: A is a Dissident who is told to lie and so gives the true shortest route. B is a Lying Knave and so gives a false shortest route. C is a Conformist and so gives a false shortest route. D is a Dissident who is told to tell the truth, so he gives a false shortest route. E, Quigley, is a Lying Knave, and so points away from himself. F is a Dissident who was told to lie, so he tells the truth and gives the shortest route. Finally, G is a Truthful Knave so he shows the shortest route.

200
34: Now the only possibility to total 66 for the other four darts is 8, 6, 19 and 33.

201
As each girl had three sandwiches, Jessica gave Samantha one and Amy gave her two. So Jessica should get $1, and Amy $2.

202
There are several ways of approaching this problem. Here is one:

First, weigh four balls and call them A, B, C and D, against four balls, E, F, G and H.

a. If they balance, then the rogue ball is I, J, K or L. So weigh I, J and K against A, B and C.
   i. If they again balance, weigh L (the faulty ball) against any other ball to find out whether it is heavier or lighter.
   ii. If they do not balance, you know whether the odd ball is heavier or lighter. Now weigh J against K to identify which of I, J or K is the odd ball.
b. If A, B, C and D, go down, weigh A, B and E against C, D and F.
   i. If they now balance, then G or H must be lighter, and weighing them against one another, or either one against a true ball, will establish which.
   ii. If they still go down, then A or B must be heavy or F is light. Weigh A against B to establish which.
   iii. If they now go up, then C or D must be heavy or E is light. Weigh C against D to find which.
c. If A, B, C and D go up, identical tests will again find the odd ball.

203
Dad is going to Yemen. On the dial that is 93636, which is 306 squared.

204
4, 19   3, 15   10, 18   6, 11   2, 17
The numbers on each balloon add up to 42.

205
Since the cauldron spilled over once the last ingredient was put in and the total of all the ingredients is 145%, the dishwater must have been put in last or the cauldron would have spilled over earlier.

Label the ingredients: sheep droppings = A, crushed pig's ear = B, snow = C, brandy = D and dishwater = E. As the snow was added two places after the sheep droppings and the brandy was added later than the crushed pig's ear, but before the snow, the only possible arrangement is B, A, D, C, E. So the correct order is: crushed pig's ear, sheep droppings, brandy, snow and dishwater.

206
The answers to **a.** and **b.** are shown in bold.

Vanilla	Banana	Strawberry	Lemon	Lime
John	Julie	Sandy	Leslie	Andy
Chick	**Chocolates**	Bunny	Egg	Bonnet
Train	Tank	Bus	**Plane**	Boat
Solitaire	Tiddlywinks	Parcheesi	Snakes	Chess

1
TART
CART
CAST
CASH
DASH
DISH

2
FOOL
POOL
POLL
POLE
SOLE
SALE
SAGE

3
FREE
FRED
BRED
BRAD
BRAY
TRAY
TRAP

4
FRESH
FLESH
FLASH
SLASH
SLOSH
SLOTH
SLOTS
SLATS
SLATE
STATE
STALE

8
Velocity
Voyager
Verbatim
Vertical
Voracity
Vocalist
Virulent

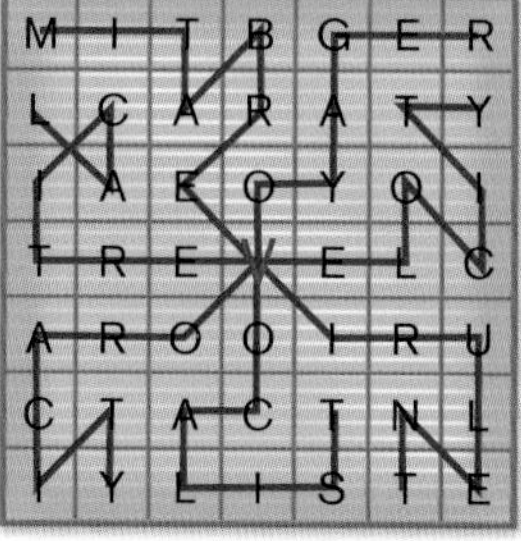

9

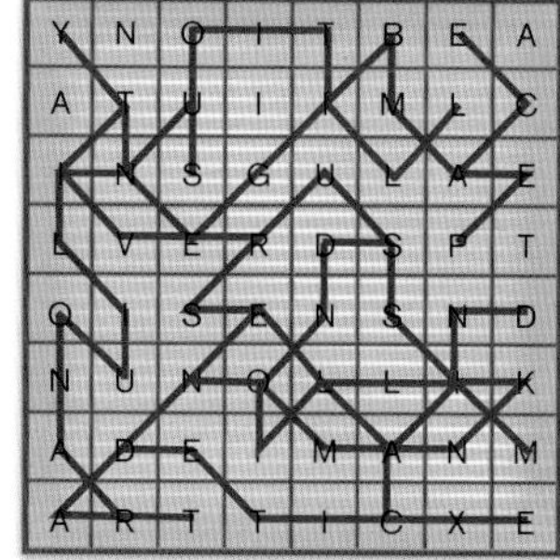

1. Excited
2. Ambitious
3. Universe
4. Tranquility
5. Russia
6. Diamonds
7. Million
8. Intelligent
9. Calendar
10. Mankind
11. Peace

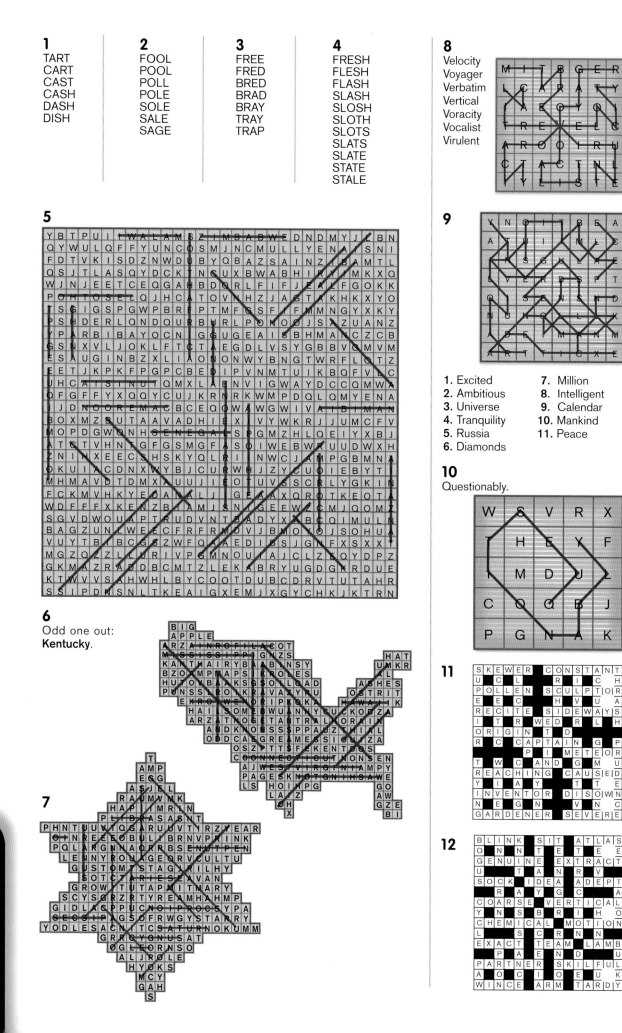

5

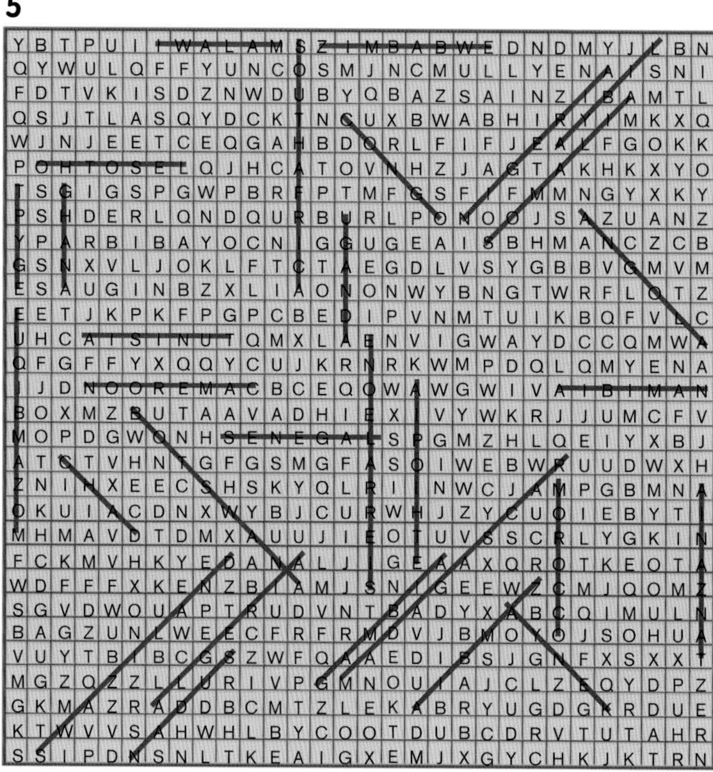

6
Odd one out:
Kentucky.

7

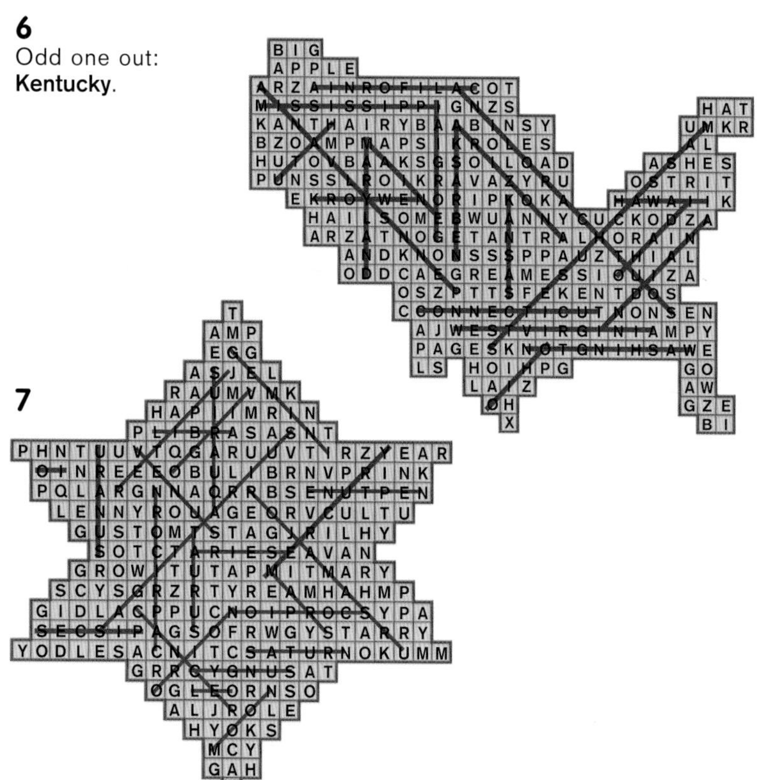

10
Questionably.

11

S	K	E	W	E	R	■	C	O	N	S	T	A	N	T
U	■	C	■	L	■	■	■	R	■	I	■	C		H
P	O	L	L	E	N	■	S	C	U	L	P	T	O	R
E	■	E	■	C	■	■	■	H	■	V	■	U		A
R	E	C	I	T	E	■	S	I	D	E	W	A	Y	S
I	■	T	■	R	■	W	E	D	■	R	■	L	■	H
O	R	I	G	I	N	■	T	■	D	■	■	■	■	■
R	■	C	■	C	A	P	T	A	I	N	■	G	■	P
■	■	■	■	■	P	■	I	■	M	E	T	E	O	R
T	■	W	■	C	■	A	N	D	■	G	■	M		U
R	E	A	C	H	I	N	G	■	C	A	U	S	E	D
Y	■	I	■	A	■	Y	■	■	■	T	■	T		E
I	N	V	E	N	T	O	R	■	D	I	S	O	W	N
N	■	E	■	G	■	N	■	■	■	V	■	N		C
G	A	R	D	E	N	E	R	■	S	E	V	E	R	E

12

13

Across
1. Resign
4. Wrap
8. Lug
9. Filters
10. Clear
11. Pawed
13. Hasty
15. Bytes
17. Prompts
19. Inn
20. Sake
21. Entrée

Down
1. Relic
2. Signets
3. Go far
5. Rye
6. Posed
7. Clap
12. Wittier
13. Hopes
14. Yaps
15. Bosun
16. Sense
18. Oak

14

Across
7. Gibbon
8. Slang
9. Aaron Copland
13. Amadeus
17. Red flag
21. Absolute zero
24. Gourd
25. Unreal

Down
1. Iguana
2. Iberia
3. Lounge
4. RSVP
5. Lava
6. Aged
10. Ouse
11. Leaf
12. Nova
14. Moab
15. Dido
16. Urdu
18. Duenna
19. Lieder
20. Googly
21. Argo
22. Stud
23. Lido

15

Across
1. Material
5. Plus
8. Panic
11. Apple
15. *All Quiet on the Western Front*
16. Dance
17. Trade
18. Freed
19. Ugliest
20. Rheas
22. Dream
24. Attract
26. Morse
27. Impi
28. History
29. Reindeer
34. April
35. Liner
36. Allowed
38. Error
40. General Theory of Relativity
44. Rufus
46. Atlases
48. Burma
50. Issue
51. Brighton
52. Contact
53. Axle
57. Trout
59. Winslow
60. Sabre
62. Spode
63. Evening
65. Pluto
67. Jumbo
69. Lasso
70. Seasonal Affective Disorder
71. Dress
72. Steel
73. Ritz
74. Preserve

Down
1. Meanders
2. Talented
3. Route
4. Agent
6. Litre
7. Shelf
8. Presently
9. Noted
10. Circuit
11. Awful
12. Pioneer
13. Entitled
14. Horace
21. Sampler
22. Drill
23. Mushrooms
24. *Apocalypse Now*
25. Arrow
26. Midge
28. Hunch
30. India
31. Earliest
32. Langur
33. Transfer
37. Lifeboats
39. Rhymes
41. Least
42. Egret
43. Icicles
45. Sight
47. Linen
49. Amaze
52. Colourful
54. Stressed
55. Consider
56. Resource
58. Operate
59. Wigwams
61. Bumper
64. Irons
65. Phase
66. Oscar
67. Joist
68. Osier
69. Lions

16

Across
1. Workstation
7. Roughcast
13. Hyenas
14. Samoa
15. Kangaroo
16. Spectator
17. Toledo
18. Epic
20. Scuba
21. Emperor
23. Strings
27. Straight-cut
29. Giant toad
31. Ridley
33. Drum pad
34. Strike
35. Firethorn
37. Field events
40. Hyphens
41. Britpop
42. Stuff
46. Dumb
48. Beachy
49. Bagatelle
52. Advocaat
53. Visor
54. *I, Robot*
55. Synthesis
56. Wisdom teeth

Down
2. Olympic
3. King cobra
4. Tuscan
5. Tasso
6. Ohms
8. Orkney
9. Guncotton
10. Clare
11. Smoking jacket
12. Nabokov
19. Regulus
22. Matadors
24. Inter
25. Iggy
26. Vindaloo
28. Trinity Sunday
30. Splints
32. Leech
34. Suez
36. Handbrake
38. Entrecote
39. Archive
43. Fallout
44. Mai tai
45. Valium
47. Blott
50. Acrid
51. Asti

17

Across
4. War cry
7. Squeeze
8. Bemuse
9. Arrests
10. Tennis
11. Suzette
15. Ariadne
19. Pineal
20. Leather
21. Hobnob
22. Opinion
23. Smelly

Down
1. Essays
2. Quartz
3. Jetset
4. Webster
5. Romania
6. Russian
12. Uniform
13. Eternal
14. Tallboy
16. Italic
17. Dahlia
18. Errant

18

Across
1. Bacchus
5. Nehru
8. Arachno-phobia
9. Cher
10. Nematode
12. Equity
13. Plisse
16. Farouche
17. Whit
19. Francis Xavier
20. Radon
21. Cistern

Down
1. Blanche
2. Chateau-briand
3. Haha
4. Stoker
5. Nahuatls
6. Hobson's Choice
7. Ukase
11. Etruscan
14. Enteron
15. Physic
16. Fifer
18. Hans

19

Across
1. Adventure
8. Mess
9. Immediate
10. Opal
13. Plaid
15. Impure
16. Notion
17. Cellos
19. Agreed
20. Flesh
21. Edge
24. Admission
25. Nose
26. Centurion

Down
2. Dame
3. Even
4. Trifle
5. Retain
6. Despaired
7. Esplanade
11. Miscreant
12. Apologise
13. Proof
14. Dough
18. Sledge
19. Assist
22. User
23. Dodo

20

Across
1. Drawer
4. Swap
8. Ill
9. Rarebit
10. Envoy
11. March
13. First
15. Cache
17. Bloater
19. Tag
20. Eden
21. Goalie

Down
1. Drive
2. All over
3. Early
5. Web
6. Pitch
7. Drum
12. Recital
13. Fibre
14. Tate
15. Cargo
16. Eagle
18. Ore

21

Across
1. Rapport
5. Pilot
8. Sprat
9. Narrate
10. Operator
11. Fare
13. Deputy
15. Lament
18. Cage
19. Serenade
22. Dead end
23. Exist
24. Tutor
25. Mislead

Down
1. Respond
2. Purse
3. Outcasts
4. Tannoy
5. Park
6. Leakage
7. Theme
12. Careless
14. Pageant
16. Treated
17. Seldom
18. Cadet
20. Agile
21. Pear

22

Across
1. Chancer
5. Focus
8. Yeast
9. Sultana
10. Turn a blind eye
11. Summer
12. Icecap
15. Flesh and blood
18. Bugbear
19. Nudge
20. Dirge
21. Extinct

Down
1. Crypt
2. Anagram
3. Cottage cheese
4. Rustle
5. Filing cabinet
6. Craze
7. Shake up
11. Sofa bed
13. Croydon
14. Untrue
16. Edgar
17. Dwelt

23

Across
6. Thermometer
7. Engage
8. Pots
9. Frogs
11. Order
13. Stem
14. Notice
16. Transparent

Down
1. Chin
2. Arrangement
3. Cones
4. Temperature
5. Beetle
10. Return
12. Snaps
15. Cane

The ocean is therefore INDIAN

24

Across
1. Clockwise
8. Photographs
9. Tier
10. Hairdo
12. Inhale
13. Yarn
15. Honeysuckle
16. Hey presto

Down
2. Loose change
3. Crop
4. Warsaw
5. Supermarket
6. Spotlight
7. Astounded
11. Play up
14. Cube

25

Across
1. Require
5. Italy
8. Feast
9. Protégé
10. Allergic
11. Maid
13. Nudist
15. Recent
18. Crew
19. Portable
22. Onerous
23. Night
24. Ditch
25. Elector

Down
1. Refrain
2. Quail
3. Interest
4. Esprit
5. Idol
6. Average
7. Yield
12. Sentence
14. Deepest
16. Tweeter
17. Mousse
18. Cloud
20. Bigot
21. Posh

26

Across
7. Top brass
9. Cuckoo
10. Dane
11. Cover notes
12. Fat cat
14. Normandy
15. Pre-Raphaelite
17. Brisbane
19. In situ
21. Maiden over
22. Knox
23. Let fly
24. No matter

Down
1. Sonata
2. Oboe
3. Calcutta
4. Scorer
5. Acrobatics
6. Bone idle
8. Seventh heaven
13. Cheesed off
15. Partakes
16. Epigrams
18. Annoys
20. Trowel
22. Kate

27

Row 1: Junior • Undo
Row 2: Order • Droop
Row 3: Heist • Style
Row 4: Need • Attend
Row 5: Wrench • Tall
Row 6: Also • Greasy
Row 7: Young • Beach
Row 8: Nick • Damage
Row 9: Enough • Weak

Column A Author:
John Wayne
Quote: Courage is being scared to death and saddling up anyway.

28

Row 1: Moving • Rich
Row 2: Abhor • Might
Row 3: Countryside
Row 4: Minnow • Gush
Row 5: Investigate
Row 6: Latch • Uncut
Row 7: Lull • Bronze
Row 8: Affix • On air
Row 9: Niche • Sinew

Column A Author:
(Harold) Macmillan
Quote: The wind of change is blowing through this continent.

29

Row 1: Allay • Mogul
Row 2: Rotund • Hark
Row 3: Mean • Sheikh
Row 4: Switchblade
Row 5: Trace • Blase
Row 6: Rank • Sleuth
Row 7: Opaque • Tome
Row 8: Next • Innate
Row 9: Grasshopper

Column A Author:
(Neil) Armstrong
Quote: Houston, Tranquillity Base here.The Eagle has landed.

30

Row 1: Gall bladder
Row 2: Earthenware
Row 3: Off-the-shelf
Row 4: Reservation
Row 5: Gastronomic
Row 6: Extravagant
Row 7: Watercourse
Row 8: Bureaucracy
Row 9: Unfortunate
Row 10: Showjumping
Row 11: Hospitality

Column A Author:
George W. Bush
Quote: Everywhere that freedom stirs, let tyrants fear.

31

1. Elizabeth Taylor
2. Michael Douglas
3. Meryl Streep
4. Jason Robards
5. Halle Berry

32

1. Nicole Kidman
2. Cate Blanchett
3. Kevin Spacey
4. Robert Redford
5. Clint Eastwood

33

1. Desolate
2. Satisfactory
3. Compensation
4. Merchandise

34

1. Differentiated
2. Straightforward
3. Educational
4. Opportunity

35

1. Argentina
2. Thailand
3. Romania
4. Mongolia

36

1. Macedonia
2. Slovenia
3. Bangladesh
4. Senegal

37

1. b
2. a
3. d
4. b
5. a
6. a
7. c
8. d
9. b
10. a
11. a
12. b
13. c
14. c
15. b

38

1. b
2. a
3. c
4. b
5. c
6. d
7. a
8. c
9. a
10. d
11. b
12. a
13. c
14. b
15. d

39

1. Calibre
2. Breathe
3. Atheist
4. Isthmus
5. Mussel
6. Seller
7. Erase
8. Sever
9. Vertical

40

1. Dearer
2. Error
3. Orange
4. Gentle
5. Leather
6. Hermit
7. Mitten
8. Tender
9. Deride

41

1. Escape
2. Aperture
3. Tureen
4. Entrap
5. Rapid
6. Ideal
7. Alien
8. Enable
9. Bleach
10. Aches

42

1. Denis Law
2. Eric Cantona
3. Osvaldo Ardiles
4. Diego Maradona

43

1. David Seaman
2. Jimmy Floyd Hasselbaink
3. Steven Gerrard
4. Patrick Vieira

44

1. Crab Nebula
2. Jodrell Bank
3. Yuri Gagarin
4. Alpha Centauri

45

1. Solar System
2. International Space Station
3. Rocket launcher
4. Moon walk

46

Simplicity
Defeated
Persevere
Exhibitionist
Barbarian

47

Artificial
Luxurious
Dolorous
Reverence
Manageable

48

4 Horsemen of the Apocalypse.
5 sides of a pentagon.
8 legs on a spider.
6 wives of King Henry the Eighth.
7 deadly sins.

49

2001: A Space Odyssey
101 Dalmatians
The 39 Steps
Twelve Angry Men
Seven Brides for Seven Brothers

50

10 events in the decathlon.
20 fluid ounces in a pint.
40 days in Lent.
60 years diamond wedding anniversary.
90 degrees in a right angle.

51

1. Cross	FIRE	Place
2. Street	LIGHT	Relief
3. Real	ESTATE	Tax
4. Life	LONG	Boat
5. Swimming	POOL	Table
6. Break	DANCE	Hall
7. Chair	LEG	Room
8. Water	TIGHT	Rope
9. Film	CREW	Cut
10. Power	STATION	Master

52

1. Roaring	TRADE	Winds
2. High	BROW	Beaten
3. Saw	TOOTH	Ache
4. Turn	PIKE	Staff
5. Cartridge	PAPER	Chain
6. Stone	DEAD	Reckoning
7. Slow	MOTION	Sickness
8. Turning	POINT	Blank
9. Rear	GUARD	Rail
10. Push	BUTTON	Hole

53

1. Berlin
2. Abrupt
3. Nearly
4. Kimono
5. Retina
6. Utopia
7. Pepper
8. Trophy
9. Cavity
10. Yearly

First column: Bankruptcy

54

1. Twelve
2. Ocelot
3. Record
4. Carrot
5. Hector
6. Lentil
7. Indigo
8. Gannet
9. Havana
10. Tarzan

First column: Torchlight

55

1. Barrel
2. Ambush
3. Russet
4. Gravel
5. Easter
6. Butter
7. Orient
8. Azalea
9. Riches
10. Dodgem

First column: Bargeboard

56

Dear Chris
My congratulations on **you're** graduation. **You're** mum tells me **thatt your** now a **Batchelor** of English. I hope you won't be **embarassed**, but I know how hard you have worked for the **preceeding** three years and how **conciencious** you have been. It can be a hard **existance** being a student, but it is **definately** worth the effort. You've learned **indispensible** skills and are now in a **priviliged** position in the job market. **Me and your uncle** would like to take you for a meal to show you how proud we are.
With lots of love **Ant** Karen

Correct spellings
your; Your; that; you are (or you're); bachelor; embarrassed; preceding; conscientious; existence; definitely; indispensable; privileged; Your uncle and I; Aunt

57

A weary night had become the first day of the new **milennium**. The **Inspecter** reached across the table and snatched the **notbook** from her hands. It was full of notes written in miniscule handwriting – did it contain evidence of a dangerous **liason**? The suspect was a large bulky woman and the chair was **scarcly** large enough to **acomodate** her. At first it was hard to **guauge** her reaction. He studied the picture from the **moniter.** He thought she fits the **identafication** perfectly. And in that moment he glimpsed the **wierd** and amazing truth. **'You are witholding** the truth from me' he said. **Hed** made the **conection** at last. '**Your harassing** me,' she said. She became rigid all over, so much so that she **didnt** turn her head at the **rythmic** clanging of the bell.

Correct spellings
millennium; Inspector; notebook; liaison; scarcely; accommodate; gauge; monitor; identification; weird; 'You are withholding; He'd; connection; 'You're harassing; didn't; rhythmic

58

After a long week of **dischord** at work, marked only by ever more **bizare** demands from the boss, what could be nicer than that **quintesentially** British pastime of a quick escape to the **tranquillity** of the countryside. The **affect** of drawing the first few **breathes** of rural air into your lungs is enough to calm even the most **comitted** city dweller. But we **shouldnt** be **decieved** about the reality of the rural **idyl**. Sadly**,** as the roads try to cope with the **haemorhage** of urban types heading towards greener pastures, **alluding** the crowds is becoming even harder. In **todays** countryside, even if you get to sip a **daquiri** on your **verrandah**, to the **ernest** strains of **cooeing** doves, **your** almost certain to be **acompanied** by the **incesant** drone of four-by-fours on the nearby **moterway**.

Correct spellings
discord; bizarre; quintessentially; tranquility; effect; breaths; committed; shouldn't; deceived; idyll; haemorrhage; eluding; today's; daiquiri; your veranda; earnest; cooing; you're; accompanied; incessant; motorway

59

Nodding acquaintance.

60

Tortoiseshell butterfly.

61

1. Sundry / sun-dry
2. Draw back / drawback
3. Notable / not able
4. Convict
5. Moderate
6. Console
7. Permit

62

Mount St Helens / mounts the lens.

63

1. Star comedy by Democrats.
2. A man, a plan a canal, Panama.
3. Won't lovers revolt now
4. Damn! I. Agassi, miss again! Mad!

64

1. No, slang is a signal, son.
2. I'm a lasagna hog; go hang a salami.
3. Marge lets Norah see Sharon's telegram.
4. Revered now, I live on. O did I do no evil, I wonder, ever?

65

1. Chasten
2. Bravery
3. Pestilent
4. Insolvent
5. Compression
6. Discourtesy

66

1. Excitement
2. Friendship
3. Irreverent
4. Despondent
5. Combustion
6. Miscellany
7. Pilgrimage
8. Profundity

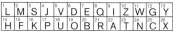

67

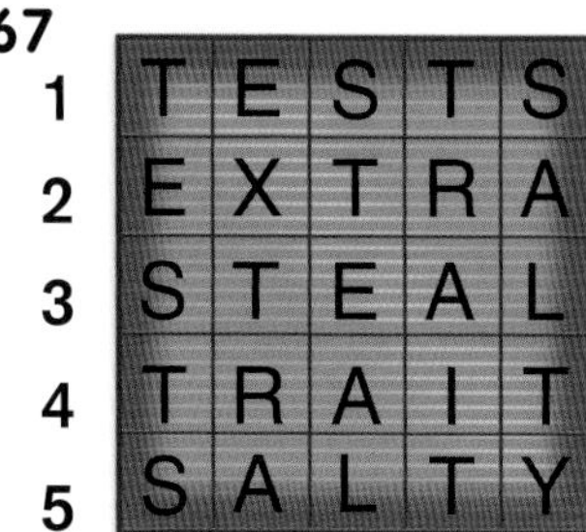

68

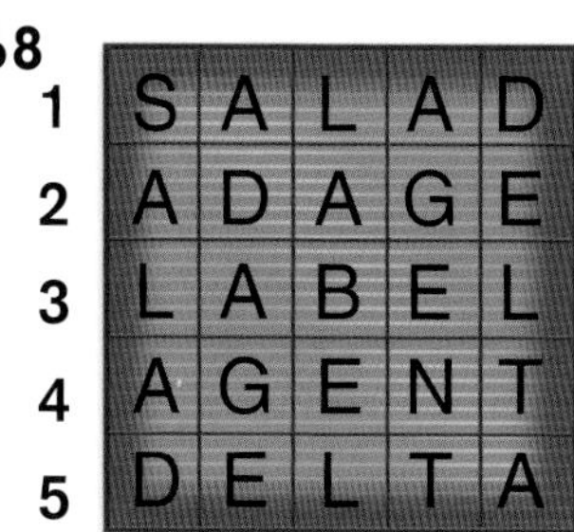

69

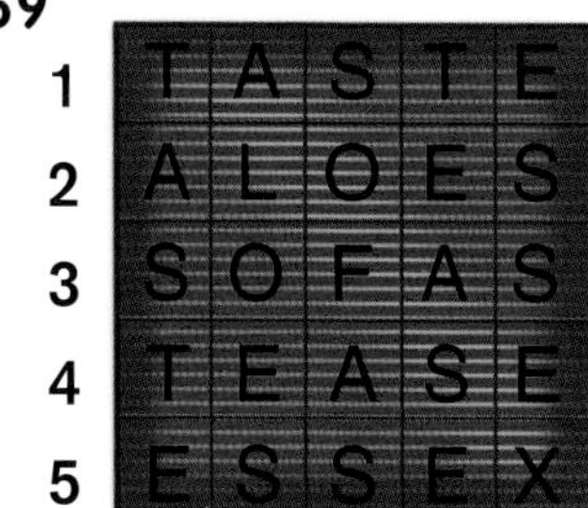

70

1	2	3	4	5	6	7	8	9	10	11	12	13
X	A	Z	B	W	J	H	P	N	D	V	R	E
14	**15**	**16**	**17**	**18**	**19**	**20**	**21**	**22**	**23**	**24**	**25**	**26**
O	U	L	T	C	M	Q	F	I	G	Y	S	K

71

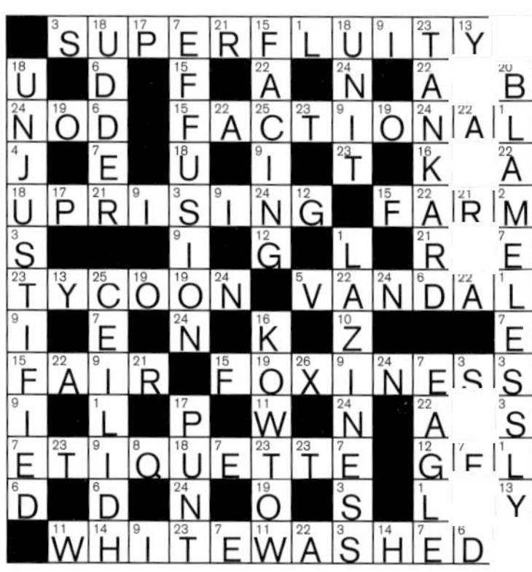

1	2	3	4	5	6	7	8	9	10	11	12	13
L	M	S	J	V	D	E	Q	I	Z	W	G	Y
14	**15**	**16**	**17**	**18**	**19**	**20**	**21**	**22**	**23**	**24**	**25**	**26**
H	F	K	P	U	O	B	R	A	T	N	C	X

72

Across
7. Lamp
8. Calendar
9. Identity
10. Rest
11. Pigeon
13. Runner
15. Thread
17. Sketch
18. Flat
20. Nautical
22. Engineer
23. Cage

Down
1. Sandwich
2. Open
3. Action
4. Player
5. Entrance
6. Bass
12. Electric
14. Exchange
16. Dancer
17. Square
19. Long
21. Inch

73

Across
1. Pop
3. Rowan
4. Rebus
7. Alabaster
9. Takings
12. Body-builder
18. Kangaroo court
19. Sesame
22. Sonant
27. Bargain basement
28. Skier
29. Angle

Down
1. Proverb
2. Peanuts
5. Blot
6. Mews
8. Adieu
10. Any
11. Gel
12. Brace
13. Dogma
14. Barge
15. Irons
16. Drown
17. Rerun
19. Sham
20. Sign
21. Mainstay
23. Observer
24. Army
25. Tune
26. Abridge

74

	M		S		E		B		T		G
	O	C	C	U	R		A	C	U	T	E
C	O	L	A		A	C	R	O	B	A	T
	D	A	R	E		I	G	U	A	N	A
G	Y	M		A	S	T	E	R			W
		M	U	S	T	Y		T	U	N	A
G	E	Y	S	E	R		E		N	A	Y
	G		A	L	E		W	A	T	T	
T	O	P			S	P	E	C	I	A	L
		A	B	U	S	E		R	E	L	Y
A	T	L	A	S		C	U	E			E
	U		S		G	A	P		A	T	
U	N	I	T	E		N	O	R	M	A	L
	D	R	E	A	M		N	O	B	L	E
P	R	O		T	A	B		B	L	O	W
	A	N	T		P	E	T		E	N	D

75

	P		O		L		G		L		T
	R	E	V	U	E		O	B	E	S	E
C	O	D	E		N	O	R		F	U	R
	S	I	R		T	W	I	S	T	E	R
M	Y	T	H		I	L	L			D	O
			E	E	L		L	A	G	E	R
M	E	D	A	L		Y	A	R	N		
	R	I	D	D	L	E		M	A	S	H
G	A	S		E	A	S	T		S	U	E
	S	T	O	R	M		U	S	H	E	R
F	E	U	D		P	A	G	E		T	O
		R	E	D		B	O	W	L		
E	B	B		R	O	O	F		U	S	E
	I		B	Y	L	A	W		C	O	D
L	A	N	E		D	R	A	W	I	N	G
	S	O	D	A		D	R	E	D	G	E

76

1. Edit – condense (once, send).
2. Plot – subterfuge (stub, refuge).

77

1. Spin – pirouette (tie, troupe).
2. Vary – fluctuate (cute, fault).
3. Mix – intermingle (grim, lenient).

78

1. Comma
2. Agora
3. Mania
4. Osaka
5. Ultra
6. Flora
7. Llama
8. Aroma
9. Gamma
10. Erica

The disguise is: **Camouflage**

79

Budgerigar

80

Misjudgement

81

Kingfisher

82

Orchestrator

83

Across
1. Offer
4. Flaps
10. Lax
11. Scowl
12. Top deck
13. Peak
14. Decipher
16. Eclair
17. Pollen count
20. Disaster
22. Taxi
24. Sag
25. Norma
26. Iceberg
27. Paint
28. Dingy
29. Amusement park
32. Explosive
35. Ire
36. Larva
37. Yawing
39. Lance
40. Keg
42. Mousse
44. Tennis racket
47. Sleepy
49. Dwells
51. Faint-hearted
55. Poetry
59. Eye
61. Nylon
62. Caviar
64. Erode
65. Ask
66. Sooner or later
67. Attorneys

Down
2. Foxtail
3. Easy
5. Lollipop
6. Pitch
7. Slipped disc
8. Cover
9. Apprentices
15. Pins and needles
18. Leading lady
19. Beard
21. Signature
23. Magistrate
29. Axiom
30. Euro
31. Kiwis
33. Pulse
34. Ideal
38. Niagara
41. Exports
43. Use
45. Nun
46. Kit
48. Ewe
49. Dress
50. Lintel
52. Arnold
53. Hover
54. Eject
56. Obese
57. Alto
58. Board
60. Eros
62. Cute
63. Read
65. Apse

84

Begonia = big + aeon
Primrose = rise + romp
Clematis = last + mice
Edelweiss = lies + weeds
Daffodil = did + offal

85

Kestrel = rest + elk
Flamingo = main + golf
Starling = ant + girls
Albatross = atlas + robs
Blackbird = bald + brick
Budgerigar = brigade + rug
Wagtail = wit + gala

86

87

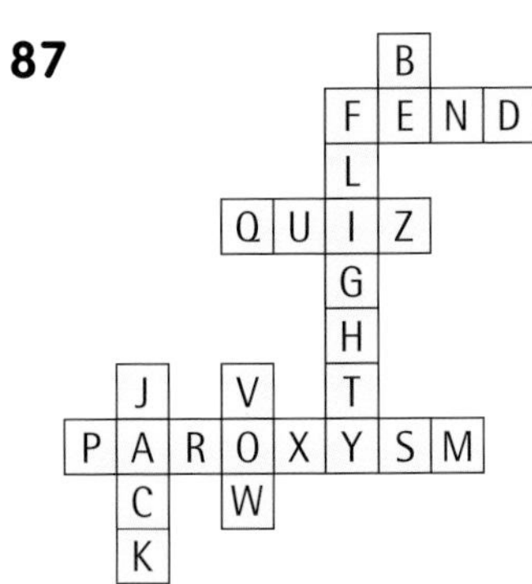

88

Solutions to puzzles 88-92 are clockwise from the top

Knickers, Cardigan, Bloomers, Camisole
Key: Lingerie

89

Dormouse, Mongoose, Kangaroo, Antelope
Key: Marmoset

90

Daffodil, Camomile, Lavender, Hyacinth
Key: Oleander

91

Golf course, Grandstand, Strokeplay, Triple jump
Key: Putting green

92

Credit card, Investment, Paper money, Cheque book
Key: Caveat emptor

93

Transcendental

94
Phosphorescent

95
Aristocratical

96
1. Tripping the light fantastic.
2. Adding fuel to the fire.

97
1. Pulling the wool over somone's eyes.
2. Turning over a new leaf.

98
Impresario

99
Balderdash

100
Embarrassment

101
Intergalactic

102
Ambassador, pilchard, malinger, insolence, fortunate.

103
Thankless, orchestra, bilateral, immediate, dishonest.

104
1. **Pentagon**: the others are all solid figures.
2. **Retriever**: the others all spell a word backwards.
3. **Rhine**: the others all flow through a capital city.

105
1. **Hydrogen**: all the others are Noble, inert gases.
2. **Container**: the others all have alternate vowels.
3. **Pisco**: the other drinks are all aniseed based.

106
1. **Balaclava**: the others are all named after people.
2. **Seal**: the others are all homophones, words that sound the same but are spelled differently, while seal merely has different meanings.
3. **Brassiere**: they have all become generic terms, but brassiere has never been trademarked.

107
1. **Paten**: all the others are appointments in the church hierarchy. The paten is a dish used for the Eucharist.
2. **Sweater**: the others are verbs as well as nouns, while the word sweater is formed from a verb.
3. **Hephaestus**: all the others were fathered by Zeus.

108
1. Student
2. Search
3. Talisman
4. Terse
5. Cleaver

109
1. Pedant
2. Cede
3. Shirk
4. Detour
5. Thinking

110
black–mail–bag–pipe–line–out–lay–off–white

111
night–club–house–hold–up–right–hand–some–day

112
letter–head–line–up–set–back–water–bed–post

113
money–box–car–pool–side–show–man–made–up–river–bank

114
pen–knife–edge–wise–crack–down–fall–out–house–fly–paper

115
foot–hill–side–show–down–under–world–wide–open–air–bubble–gum–boot

116

Fall	BACK	Hand
Bird	BRAIN	Storm
Dog	TOOTH	Paste
Scout	CAMP	Follower

117

Beach	BALL	Cock
Kerb	APPEAL	Fund
Wheel	CHAIR	Person
White	FLAG	Staff

118
1. Season
2. Sadden
3. Tally
4. Dirty
5. Forget

119
1. Reluctance
2. Earliest
3. Illuminate
4. Lubricate
5. Pitcher

120
1. Generous
2. Surprise
3. Begin
4. Spent
5. Mellow

121
1. Musters
2. Deleted
3. Cut
4. Release
5. Persevere

122
Bear witness
Calf love
Chicken wire
Church mouse
Copycat
Cowslip
Dog rose
Foxglove
Horsepower
Jack rabbit
Lionheart
March hare
Pelican crossing
Spread eagle
White elephant

Flowers: Cowslip, Dog rose, Foxglove.

123
Blood bank
Brainchild
Chestnut
Earwig
Faint heart
Footnote
Funny bone
Handbell
Hawkeye
Head office
Lip service
Mouth organ
Muscle bound
Nerve centre
Nose flute
Paperback
Rock face
Spare rib
Tongue twister
Tooth fairy

Harmony: Handbell, Mouth organ, Nose flute.

124
Bandwagon
Bicycle chain
Boob tube
Bus conductor
Cartridge
Coach party
Donkey jacket
Fellowship
Ghost train
Inkjet
Panda car
Rocket salad
Sledgehammer
Tank top
Vanguard

Clothes: Boob tube, Donkey jacket, Tank top.

125
Enid and Edna dine.

126
No lemons, no melon.

127
No, it is opposition.

128
Nurse, I spy gypsies run.

129
Marge lets Norah see Sharon's telegram.

130
A dog! A panic in a pagoda.

131
Murder for a jar of red rum.

132
Was it Eliot's toilet I saw?

133
Was it a car or a cat I saw?

134
Golf? No sir, prefer prison flog.

135
Rats live on no evil star.

136
Anne, I vote more cars race Rome to Vienna.

137

H	E	I	S	T				B	A	C	O	N
E	I	G	E	R				A	G	A	V	E
I	G	L	O	O				C	A	N	O	E
S	E	O	U	L				O	V	O	I	D
T	R	O	L	L	I	N	E	N	E	E	D	Y
				I	V	O	R	Y				
				N	O	D	A	L				
				E	R	A	T	O				
O	C	E	A	N	Y	L	O	N	A	D	I	R
C	O	P	R	A				A	W	A	R	E
E	P	S	O	M				D	A	Y	A	N
A	R	O	S	E				I	R	A	T	E
N	A	M	E	D				R	E	N	E	W

138

C	R	A	W	L				M	E	R	I	T
R	A	D	I	O				E	T	U	D	E
A	D	D	E	R				R	U	L	E	R
W	I	E	L	D				I	D	E	A	S
L	O	R	D	S	A	B	O	T	E	R	S	E
				A	P	A	C	E				
				B	A	S	T	E				
				O	C	T	E	T				
A	D	A	P	T	E	E	T	H	E	R	O	D
D	E	F	E	R				E	L	O	P	E
A	F	I	R	E				R	O	W	E	L
P	E	R	O	N				O	P	E	R	A
T	R	E	N	D				D	E	L	A	Y

139
Star – Tubs
Sheer – Tiffs
Steeds – Tuffet

2
1. Babylon
2. Through a crack in the wall
3. The Tomb of Ninus
4. Mulberry
5. White
6. Thisbe
7. Thisbe's cloak
8. With his sword
9. Not quite
10. Purple

3
1. Shamrock
2. Wilson
3. Tweed jackets
4. India
5. East London
6. Mrs. Higson
7. Winchester
8. Train
9. Marylebone
10. Laundry

4
1. St. Stephen's Tower
2. 96.3 metres (316 feet)
3. 1858
4. 13.8 tons
5. Sir Benjamin Hall
6. Ben Caunt
7. 1962
8. Metal fatigue
9. 1 May
10. 90 minutes

5
1. Scarlet Ribbons
2. Eight
3. Swingleton Down
4. Six
5. Ornamental Arch
6. 40
7. Antagonist
8. 23
9. Ornamental Arch
10. 44.

9
1. e7 – g8+; h6 x h5
2. f2 – h2 mate

10
1. f5 – e6; e8 – f8
2. d5 – d8 mate

11
1. f8 – h8; e7 – f6
2. g7 – g8 = knight mate

12
1. e2 x e6+; f7 x f6
2. d3 – g6 mate

NB: Black's only other reply to White's first move would be to block the check by moving his bishop from f8 – e7. White would simply have taken Black's bishop, in this instance e6 x e7 forcing checkmate.

13
Key move: g8-g7

Alternative checkmates:
1. **Move 1** f6 – e6;
   Move 2 d1 – d5 mate
2. **Move 1** f6 x d6;
   Move 2 d1 – e1 mate
3. **Move 1** f6 – g6+;
   Move 2 g7 x g6 mate
4. **Move 1** f6 – h6;
   Move 2 g7 x h6 mate
5. **Move 1** f6 – f7;
   Move 2 g7 x f7 mate
6. **Move 1** f6 – f8;
   Move 2 g7 x f8 mate
7. **Move 1** f6 – f5;
   Move 2 h4 – g6 mate
8. **Move 1** f6 – f4;
   Move 2 c4 – d5 mate

14
1. f2 – f3; e7 – e6
2. g2 – g4; d8 – h4 mate

16
C

22
Sun

23
Star

24
Day

25
Night

26
Gold

27
End

32
3

33
9

34
7

35
4

36
3

37
1

38
Recall, memory
forget, mislay

39
Think – from **t**ake, **h**ear, **i**con, **n**ews, **k**iln

40
Invent, create, design
brainy, clever, sharp

41
Mull – from leap, dune, file, from

42
Hamlet

43
Juliet

44
Othello

45
Antony and Cleopatra

46
Shakespeare

47
LEAR – when G, O, B, T, H, E, T and E are removed.

48
Row 1, female 2nd from right = Row 2, female 4th from right.

49
1. Ant
2. Ostrich
3. Fox
4. 1 (Lion)
5. 2 (Fox)
6. Foal
7. Loaf

50
1. Spring
2. Box
3. Camera
4. Rage
5. 2 (Car)
6. 3 (Kite)
7. Gear

51
1. Light
2. Jar
3. Dress
4. 3 (Nurse)
5. 1 (Jar)
6. Rest
7. Night

52
1. Pure
2. 2 (Russia)
3. Poland
4. Egypt
5. Uruguay
6. Egypt
7. Peru

53
1. Top centre (Clint Eastwood)
2. Centre (Madonna)
3. Bottom left (Oliver Hardy)
4. Top left (Neil Armstrong)
5. Michael Jackson
6. Marilyn Monroe
7. Nero

54
1. Led
2. Oar
3. Try
4. Lot
5. Ear
6. Dry
7. Lay

55
1. Stonehenge
2. Top centre and top right (Eiffel Tower, Louvre)
3. Middle left (Great Wall of China)
4. Centre (Stonehenge) on top of bottom middle (Tower Bridge)
5. Bottom left (White House)
6. London Bridge
7. Wall

56
1. Top left (Head) above middle left (Face)
2. Letter and Light
3. Top centre (Hot)
4. Bottom centre (Currant) and Bottom right (Meat)
5. Army
6. Red
7. Eye

57
1. Hand
2. Some
3. On and Off
4. Washbag
5. 3 (Bill)
6. Ball
7. Set

58
1. 4 and 13
2. 8 (Kite) and 12 (Arrow)
3. 3 (Triangle)
4. Right
5. Star
6. 10 (Pentagon)
7. 6 (Square)

59
1. Screwdriver, hammer, saw, wrench
2. 6 (Knife) and 11 (Fork)
3. 20 (Scissors)
4. 5 (Hammer)
5. Bed
6. Vacuum cleaner, computer, TV, radio, lamp, fridge, washing machine, kettle, toaster
7. 2 (Bucket: fire bucket, bucket seat)

60
1. Paris
2. 13 (Eve)
3. Tag
4. Anna and Bob
5. Ringo
6. May and Amy
7. September

61-65

Assessment
5 – 6 Exceptional
3 – 4 Good
1 – 2 Average

61
1. b
2. a
3. c
4. b
5. c
6. a

62
1. c
2. c
3. b
4. c
5. a
6. b

63
1. c
2. c
3. a
4. c
5. c
6. a

64
1. c
2. a
3. c
4. b
5. a
6. b

65
1. c
2. a
3. a
4. b
5. c
6. a

66-68

Assessment
9 – 10 Exceptional
6 – 8 Good
3 – 5 Average

66
1. Diamond
2. Triangle
3. 2
4. JWK
5. 5
6. LPA
7. Diamond
8. Black circle
9. 2, 9
10. 16

67
1. 2
2. Blue
3. Circle
4. P
5. Purple
6. Blue
7. Triangle
8. 5
9. Blue
10. Bue

68
1. West
2. F
3. South
4. Yellow circle
5. Red
6. Circle
7. Star, circle
8. South-west
9. T
10. Red star

69
1. Uganda
2. Guernsey
3. Gibraltar
4. Republic of Congo
5. The Gambia
6. 5
7. Libya
8. Tonga
9. Norfolk Island
10. Red, blue and green
11. Virgin Islands
12. 5
13. Ivory Coast

70
INOC = Coin
SEAT = East
CILE = Lice
PYSE = Espy
NABE = Bean
SURT = Rust
MEAN = Amen
RYET = Tyre
WREE = Ewer
ODET = Dote

Solution: Celebrated

71

TRAPIVE = Private
REUSUN = Unsure
BELTOT = Bottle
SAILIE = Liaise
FINEUS = Infuse
MATRES = Stream
KREACH = Hacker
MENIMU = Immune
LESTEN = Nestle
SERAGE = Grease

Solution: Publishing

72

REECE SIX = Exercise
NOT QUIET = Quotient
FATE N SUN = Unfasten
GOOEY LID = Ideology
ER CAVITY = Veracity
SODA REST = Assorted
LEND RAVE = Lavender
GENE REIN = Engineer
GENIE GEL = Negligée
WROTE MAP = Tapeworm

Solution: Equivalent

73

HONOUR AIMS = Harmonious
SAUNA TRIAL = Australian
PAINT ROUTE = Reputation
STRAIT DIME = Dermatitis
ISSUE ROBOT = Boisterous
SHOVE A WORD = Overshadow
ELITE TRIAL = Illiterate
I STUN MY OIL = Luminosity
GET ICE CORN = Egocentric
GUARD MARTY = Dramaturgy

Solution: Hard-boiled

INDEX OF PUZZLES

PUZZLE CONTRIBUTORS

Contributors are listed with the numbers of the puzzles they created. Any puzzles not listed were created by Planet Three Publishing Network Ltd.

A WORD A DAY

Brainwarp: 7–12, 22-26, 28-31, 43-44, 49-50, 88–93, 130-137, 144-151
Philip Carter: 13–21, 100–103, 106-110, 152-259
Aleric Linden / Puzzle House: 32-34, 51-56, 138-140
Puzzler Media Limited: 37-40, 45-48, 141-143
Don Manley: 35-36, 41-42
Jeffery Pike: 57-87, 104-105, 111-129

THE MIND'S EYE

Philip Carter: 1-6, 56-59
Puzzler Media Limited: 11-18, 29-30
Chris Maslanka: 24-28, 31-36, 38-41, 88, 91
Brainwarp: 37
Anthony Williams: 74, 99
Steve Ryan: 84, 94
Angus Lavery: 85-86, 89, 97
Clare Brooks: 87
Robert Abbot: 90, 98
Paul Lamford: 92-93
Jim Winslow: 95
Roger Myers: 96

THINK OF A NUMBER

Philip Carter: 1-12, 67-81, 90-95, 103-112, 150-160, 195-199
Truman Collins: 3-22
Brainwarp: 23-57, 131-133, 148-149
Aleric Linden: 58-66, 200
Jeffery Pike: 82-89
Ken Russell: 96-102, 113-122
Puzzler Media Limited: 123-130, 191-194
Chris Maslanka: 134-147
Predrag Stanojevic: 161-163.
MyKakuroThing.com: 164-190

SMART THINKING

Philip Carter: 1-7, 69-80, 106-118, 131-138, 147-166
Brainwarp: 8-17
Stefanie Rohan: 18-19
Paul Lamford: 20-21, 193, 197, 202
Chris Maslanka: 23-38, 187, 194
Jeffery Pike: 39-68.
Puzzler Media Limited: 81-105
Aleric Linden: 119-130
Phil Austin: 139-146
Paul Sloane: 167-176
David Singmaster: 177, 181-182, 184, 186, 195, 198, 201
Barry Clarke: 178, 185, 190-191, 190-191, 205
Angus Lavery: 180, 183, 192, 196, 206
David J. Bodycombe: 188-189
Erik Solomon: 199
Roger Myers: 200, 203
Steve Ryan: 204

WORD CHALLENGES

Brainwarp: 1–4, 6-7, 22–24, 26, 42-45, 53-55, 67-69, 74-75, 78-83
Philip Carter: 8–10, 59-60, 76-77, 84-87, 93-101, 110-115, 125-139
Aleric Linden: 11–12, 27–30, 72-73
Puzzler Media Limited: 13, 16, 19–21, 25, 70-71
Don Manley: 14–15, 17–18
Jeffery Pike: 31–41, 46-52, 61-66
Phil Austin: 88-92, 102-109, 118-124

MEMORY

Jeffery Pike: 2-5
Aleric Linden: 9-14
Philip Carter: 15-21, 61-68
Jonathan Hancock: 22-60

PICTURE CREDITS

Photographs

16: **Photodisc**
332: **NHPA**
333: **Alamy; Empics; Getty Images; NASA; The Kobal Collection; Rex Features; Ronald Reagan Library; Topham**

Illustrations

133, 144: **Anthony Williams,** 202: **graphics factory** (cow); **Getty Images** (sunny landscape)

All other images Reader's Digest / Planet Three Publishing Network Ltd.